D1195684

Radiation Effects on Organic Materials

Radiation Effects on Organic Materials

Edited by

Robert O. Bolt and **James G. Carroll**

Supervising Research Chemist *Research Engineer*

California Research Corporation
Richmond, California

Prepared under the auspices
of the Division of Technical Information
United States Atomic Energy Commission

ACADEMIC PRESS · 1963
NEW YORK AND LONDON

ACADEMIC PRESS INC.
111 FIFTH AVENUE, NEW YORK 3, NEW YORK

United Kingdom Edition published by
ACADEMIC PRESS INC. (LONDON) LTD.
BERKELEY SQUARE HOUSE, LONDON W.1

Library of Congress Catalog Card Number 62–21141

PRINTED IN THE UNITED STATES OF AMERICA

List of Contributors

RAYMOND S. ALGER, *U. S. Naval Radiological Defense Laboratory, San Francisco, California*

ROBERT O. BOLT, *California Research Corporation, Richmond, California*

C. DANIEL BOPP, *Oak Ridge National Laboratory, Oak Ridge, Tennessee*

JOHN W. BORN, *B. F. Goodrich Company, Brecksville, Ohio*

IRVING A. BREGER, *U. S. Geological Survey, Washington, D. C.*

JAMES G. CARROLL, *California Research Corporation, Richmond, California*

K. LYNN HALL, *California Research Corporation, Richmond, California*

ROBERT Y. MIXER, *Richfield Oil Corporation, Anaheim, California*

AMOS S. NEWTON, *Lawrence Radiation Laboratory, University of California, Berkeley, California*

WILLIAM W. PARKINSON, *Oak Ridge National Laboratory, Oak Ridge, Tennessee*

HENRY A. RUTHERFORD, *North Carolina State College, Raleigh, North Carolina*

OSCAR SISMAN, *Oak Ridge National Laboratory, Oak Ridge, Tennessee*

CHARLES A. TRILLING, *Atomics International, Canoga Park, California*

Preface

This book is concerned with nuclear radiation and its effects on the properties of organic liquids, solids, and gases. Radiation-induced changes in properties are of real importance to engineers and scientists who have the task of selecting materials for use in the presence of radiation. These research and development people, for whom the book is written, are conversant with the fundamentals of physics, chemistry, and engineering. Thus the text presents a minimum of such fundamentals. Background and recent information on radiation effects are emphasized. In addition, principles are evolved to aid the reader in understanding future developments in this fast growing field.

A vital first step in writing the book was to select the organic materials to be covered. From the point of view of the scientist-engineer, there are many organic substances on which radiation effects are only of fringe interest. Thus certain areas are not covered in the book; e.g., foods, drugs, and aqueous solutions of organic materials (except as water is an environmental factor). Coal is included to round out the fuel picture, but the extensive work on graphite and other forms of carbon was excluded. The large and exciting fields of radiation chemistry and radiation-induced polymerization are presented only briefly as background information.

Generally the individual chapters were written by experts who are involved in current research in a given area. This allowed very new items to be included as well as past work. In most cases published literature and research in progress well into 1961 received coverage. In several chapters involving fast moving research, work in 1962 is cited.

We recognize that there are many workers of note who are not included in the roster of contributing authors; however, their research received recognition, and the reference sections are replete with their names.

The preparation of the book was sponsored by the Scientific Publications Branch, Division of Technical Information, U. S. Atomic Energy Commission.

November, 1962
ROBERT O. BOLT
JAMES G. CARROLL

Acknowledgments

The Editors are happy for this opportunity to thank the numerous people who lent a helping hand with the book. Many specialists in their own right were involved, experts in the mechanics of various scientific disciplines, experts in word mechanics, etc., and even experts in holding the Authors' and Editors' hands. Special mention goes to the reviewers, often unnamed, whose painstaking work was much appreciated.

Joseph G. Gratton, U. S. Atomic Energy Commission, Washington, D. C., handled administrative details, including contacts with these reviewers, with great facility. Miss Marian C. Fox, AEC, Oak Ridge, Tennessee, did an outstanding job as superreviewer and supereditor. Wert J. Pearson, AEC, Oak Ridge, assisted in preparing the final copy for the illustrations.

Special mention is also made of two of the Editors' colleagues at California Research: Robert L. Haynor and Fred A. Bell. Mr. Haynor's knowledge of scientific information resources, handling, and retrieval was used effectively in the initial literature survey, outline, and writing phases of the book. The Editors are grateful for his help. Mr. Bell's specialty is art work for scientific literature, and he has developed a discerning eye in his 35 years of experience. He either drew or redrew every illustration in the book. The Editors feel that he did a splendid job.

Contents

CHAPTER ONE

Introduction

JAMES G. CARROLL and ROBERT O. BOLT

CHAPTER TWO

Interaction of Radiation with Matter

AMOS S. NEWTON

CHAPTER THREE

Mechanisms of Chemical Effects of Ionizing Radiation

AMOS S. NEWTON

CHAPTER FOUR

Radiation Chemistry of Pure Compounds

K. LYNN HALL, ROBERT O. BOLT, and JAMES G. CARROLL

CHAPTER FIVE

Polymers

OSCAR SISMAN, WILLIAM W. PARKINSON, and C. DANIEL BOPP

CHAPTER SIX

Plastics

C. DANIEL BOPP, WILLIAM W. PARKINSON, and OSCAR SISMAN

CHAPTER SEVEN

Elastomeric Materials

JOHN W. BORN

CHAPTER EIGHT
Coolants
JAMES G. CARROLL, ROBERT O. BOLT, and CHARLES A. TRILLING

CHAPTER NINE
Lubricants
JAMES G. CARROLL and ROBERT O. BOLT

CHAPTER TEN
Adhesives
ROBERT Y. MIXER

CHAPTER ELEVEN
Textiles
HENRY A. RUTHERFORD

CHAPTER TWELVE
Coatings and Films
JAMES G. CARROLL and ROBERT O. BOLT

CHAPTER THIRTEEN
Dielectric Fluids
RAYMOND S. ALGER

CHAPTER FOURTEEN
Fuels and Fluid Shield Materials
JAMES G. CARROLL and ROBERT O. BOLT

CHAPTER FIFTEEN
Coal, Wood, and Explosives
IRVING A. BREGER, JAMES G. CARROLL, and ROBERT O. BOLT

CHAPTER SIXTEEN

Potential Benefits

JAMES G. CARROLL and ROBERT O. BOLT

CHAPTER 1

Introduction

BY JAMES G. CARROLL AND ROBERT O. BOLT

1-1 Objectives

Organic materials are sensitive to high-energy radiation. Neutrons affect the nuclei of atoms making up these materials; other energetic radiations affect primarily the electrons. The subsequent alterations in molecular structure govern changes in physical and chemical properties. These changes in properties, radiation effects,† are the subject of this book.

The radiolysis‡ of organic materials has long been of interest to scientists. Radiation effects, however, have only recently become important to engineers. The first successful chain-reacting pile in 1942 created this engineering interest. The reactor at the University of Chicago was the precursor of the many reactors and other radiation sources in the research and power fields for which materials of construction are required. Such materials include many organic plastics, elastomers, coolants, lubricants, etc.

Early studies of materials for use in and around reactors or other radiation sources showed organic products to be among the least resistant to radiolysis. Organic materials have characteristic properties imparted by distinctive molecular arrangements, which radiation effectively alters. This is illustrated[6] by Fig. 1.1. Much of the literature published during the last 10 years has been devoted to organic compounds. In general, the literature covers such aspects as (1) the resistance of various types of compounds, (2) the variation of resistance among classes, and (3) means of improving stability, etc. The objective of this book is to summarize this literature and its background and to provide a guide for interpreting future data on radiation effects.

1-2 Organization

An organic material is chosen for a particular application because of a unique property or characteristic that it possesses. The degree to which

---

† Sometimes called "radiation damage;" the thought being that any change in properties is undesirable. Some radiolytic changes are beneficial, hence the use of "radiation effects."

‡ Chemical decomposition by the action of high-energy radiation.

this characteristic is retained over the period of use is important. The three agents that commonly degrade organic compounds are heat, oxygen, and mechanical stress. Radiation is the fourth agent that must be considered when organic materials are used in its presence.

The chapters in this book, following the four introductory chapters, are arranged according to a particular type of material and its use. This

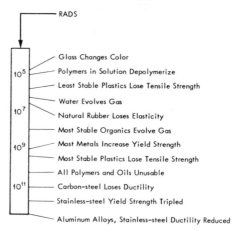

FIG. 1.1 Relative effects of radiation on various materials.

organization permits some overlap. For example, silicones appear in several chapters because they are considered as polymers, plastics, coatings, and oil lubricants. In each case a different treatment is involved, depending upon the applications being discussed.

1-3 Sources of Data

Studies of radiation effects have been conducted by universities, government laboratories, and industrial research organizations. Most of the work has been sponsored by the Atomic Energy Commission and by the U. S. Air Force as part of systems-development programs. Since the 1955 International Conference on the Peaceful Uses of Atomic Energy in Geneva, the general subject of radiation effects is no longer under security classification. Some information is still unavailable, but most has been published in unclassified technical reports; and since 1955 articles have appeared freely in technical journals.

Journals and available reports were reviewed for the book. *Chemical Abstracts* and *Nuclear Science Abstracts* were also consulted to assure complete coverage. In addition, use was made of the Radiation Effects Information Center accession lists published by Battelle Memorial Institute. Literature references are given at the end of each chapter.

1-4 Radiation Units

Most of the chapters to follow deal primarily with variations in the properties of organic materials which result from radiolysis. Such variations are caused mostly by ionization and free-radical formation.† For a given radiation type, the changes in properties are proportional to energy absorption. Therefore absorbed dose is the parameter of most importance and usefulness.

Throughout the book the unit chosen to express absorbed dose is the rad, which is defined by the International Commission on Radiological Units[5] as 100 ergs (absorbed)/g of material. The single unit is sufficient for all types of radiation. The rad is increasing in favor with various working committees of the American Society for Testing Materials and of the American Institute of Electrical Engineers. Many of the other units available, e.g., roentgens and ergs per gram referred to carbon, describe a radiation field. They express energy that a standard would have received instead of energy a sample actually received. These units serve merely as a basis for calculating absorbed dose.

The Editors are fully aware of the vital and vexing role of dosimetry in reporting radiation-effects data. This is a subject of some complexity and is beyond the scope of the present work. It has received treatment elsewhere.[1,3] The measurement of incident and absorbed energy depends on

Table 1.1—ENERGY CONVERSION UNITS

$$1 \text{ rad} \equiv 100 \text{ ergs (absorbed)/g of material}$$
$$\equiv 6.24 \times 10^{13} \text{ ev/g}$$
$$= 1.14 \text{ r (of dry air)}$$
$$= 1.08 \text{ reps (of tissue)}$$
$$= 1.83 \times 10^{12} \text{ ion pair/g of air}$$
$$(\text{gamma and X rays, W} = 34 \text{ ev per ion pair})$$
$$= 10^{-5} \text{ watt-sec/g}$$
$$= 2.78 \times 10^{-9} \text{ watt-hr/g}$$
$$= 1.16 \times 10^{-10} \text{ watt-days/g}$$
$$= 4.30 \times 10^{-6} \text{ Btu/lb}$$
$$= 10^{-6} \text{ megarad}$$

many variables. Each author was confronted with the problem of dosimetry in conducting his own research. Thus he became familiar with the uncertainties applicable to his field of endeavor. With this experience each author converted primary radiation measurements to rads using the best means available to him. Because the authors have already made the comparison for him, the reader is spared the agonizing appraisal and comparison of dosimetric methods.

† With certain crystalline materials neutron capture by nuclei to form "impurity" atoms can be important.[4]

Table 1.1 lists many of the relationships used in converting primary data to rad values. Other relationships of interest are also included. It must be remembered that the radiation effect caused by a rad is not independent of the type of radiation involved.† Thus the radiation source used is specified throughout the book.

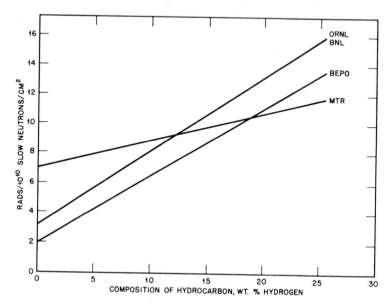

Fig. 1.2 Relationship of rads and reactor radiation in hydrocarbons. Reactor slow neutrons are subcadmium values monitored with cobalt; gamma rays and higher energy neutrons were also present. Oak Ridge Graphite Reactor hole 19, Brookhaven Research Reactor hole 25, and a British Experimental Pile hole (unknown) are holes in graphite-moderated air-cooled reactors fueled with natural uranium. Materials Testing Reactor hole VH-3 is in a water-moderated and -cooled reactor fueled with enriched uranium.

Conversions involving reactor-exposure data are particularly difficult. Figure 1.2 presents relationships[2,7] for several reactor facilities as applied to hydrocarbons.

References

1. Cheek, C. H., and Linnenbom, V. J., *Calculation of Absorbed Dose,* Report NRL-5448, Naval Research Laboratory, February 1960.
2. David, V. W., and Irving, R., Effects of Nuclear Radiation on Hydrocarbon Oils, Greases, and Some Synthetic Fluids, *Conference on Lubrication and Wear Proceedings,* Institution of Mechanical Engineers, London, 1957.
3. Hine, G. J., and Brownell, G. L., *Radiation Dosimetry,* Academic Press, Inc., New York, 1956.

† See Ch. 3, Sect. 3-3.2, for further discussion.

4. Hotten, B. W., and Carroll, J. G., Radiation Damage in Lubricating Greases, *Ind. Eng. Chem.*, *50*(2): 217 (February 1958).

5. National Bureau of Standards, Report of the International Commission on Radiological Units and Measurements (ICRU) 1956, *NBS Handbook 62*, April 1957.

6. Sisman, O., and Wilson, J. C., Engineering Use of Damage Data, *Nucleonics, 14* (9): 58 (September 1956).

7. Smith, H. P., (Ed.), *Compilation of Organic Moderator and Coolant Technology*, USAEC Report TID-7007 [Pt. 2 (Del.)], p. 361, January 1957.

CHAPTER 2

Interaction of Radiation with Matter

By Amos S. Newton

2-1 Introduction

An understanding of the nature of the interactions of ionizing radiation with matter is basic to considerations of the chemical and physical effects produced in matter by such radiation. The processes by which radiation loses energy and their significance in radiation-effects work are reviewed in this chapter.

Two concepts are of prime importance: (1) The passage of even heavy particles, such as alpha particles, through matter does not generally result in violent molecular disruptions. The energy loss by these particles is in a series of small increments. If a comparatively large energy increment is dissipated in a single collision, this energy results in a fast secondary electron and a residual ion in a comparatively low energy state. (2) The process of absorption of energy from ionizing radiation results initially in a nonhomogeneous distribution of ions, radicals, and various excited species in the material. The degree of nonhomogeneity varies with the type and intensity of radiation involved and the density of the absorber. If only the radiation type is varied in a given absorber, differences in nonhomogeneity are the result of differences in the rates of energy loss of the various types of radiation. The rates of energy loss are, in turn, a function of differences in the mechanisms of energy loss.†

Bohr, Bethe, and others have developed the theory of energy loss so that it is possible to calculate with reasonable accuracy the LET and the range of any simple radiation in any absorber.[2,3,14,32] Unfortunately, little is known of the mathematical treatment of the residual energy states of the molecules or atoms of the absorbing material. This information would be very valuable in the interpretation of the chemical effects of radiation. Knowledge of the primary energy states of the absorber has been largely deduced by inference from the resultant chemical or physical effects produced by irradiation.

---

† The linear energy transfer (LET) is the rate of energy loss of an ionizing radiation per unit length of its track. It is a differential quantity characteristic of the radiation, its energy, and the absorber.

7

2-2 Interaction of Swiftly Moving Charged Particles with Matter

A high-energy charged particle loses energy by electric interactions with electrons in the absorbing material. These interactions result in a net transfer of energy to the electrons, raising them to excited levels in the atoms or molecules concerned. If these levels are above the ionization potential of the atom or molecule, ionization results. If they are below the ionization potential (in a bound state), an excited atom or molecule results. The nuclear dimensions and nuclear forces are of such short radius that energy loss by collisions with nuclei is much less probable than that by interactions with electrons. Thus nuclear collisions can be neglected in calculations of the LET of ionizing particles in organic materials.

When a charged particle, such as a proton, passes near an electron, the amount of energy transferred depends on the velocity of the proton and its distance of closest approach, the "impact parameter." The coulombic force between the proton and the electron is determined by the familiar electrostatic formula, i.e., the product of the charges divided by the square of the distance between them. This force is multiplied by the time duration of the interaction to obtain the impulse. The impulse is an inverse function of the velocity of the proton. The resultant impulse is perpendicular to the path of the particle. Forces parallel to the path as the electron is approached are canceled by those that occur as the proton moves away from the electron. At a given impact parameter, a fast proton transfers less energy to an electron than a slow one.

A particle moving at less than the orbital velocity of an electron in the absorber can capture an electron from the absorber. The electron can later be stripped after further passage through the absorber, and charge exchanges can occur between the absorber and the particle. This process is of some importance near the end of the range of an alpha particle and along the whole range of fission fragments. Considerable straggling results, i.e., variation in ranges among particles of the same initial energy.

For ionizing particles heavier than electrons, the nonrelativistic equation for energy loss per unit length of path x by a particle of mass M, charge z, energy E, and velocity v in an absorber of atomic number Z with N atoms per cubic centimeter is

$$-\frac{dE}{dx} = \frac{4\pi e^4 z^2 N Z}{mv^2} \ln \frac{2mv^2}{\bar{I}} \tag{2.1}$$

Here e is the charge on the electron, m is the mass of the electron, and $\bar{I}$ is an average excitation potential of the absorber atom considering all electrons in the absorber as participating. Two features are significant about this equation: (1) the ionizing particle is characterized only by its charge and velocity, i.e., its mass is not in the equation; and (2) NZ simply represents the electron density of the material. Differences characteristic of absorber materials occur only in the logarithmic term.

The excitation potential, $\bar{I}$, is not equal to the spectroscopic ionization potential since it includes the number-average effects of all electrons in the material, whether they be in inner K or L shells or in higher valence shells. An approximate formula for $\bar{I}$ for elements at atomic number Z is

$$\bar{I} = aZ \qquad (2.2)$$

where a is a constant of about 16 electron volts (ev) for hydrogen, about 12 ev for elements from carbon to aluminum, and about 9.5 ev for heavier elements. The exact values of $\bar{I}$ for various elements must be determined experimentally.

For compounds or mixtures of materials as absorbing media, Bragg's rule states that the range (in mass/unit area) or rate of energy loss (in energy/mass/unit area) of an ionizing particle is independent of the chemical or physical state of the absorbing medium and is an additive function of its elemental composition. Work by Thompson in 1952 shows this to be true to about 1% accuracy for fast protons in organic compounds.[43] The range of an ionizing particle in matter is defined in terms of the thickness of material required to reduce the particle to zero kinetic energy. This range is usually expressed in centimeters of path length for gases and in milligrams or grams per square centimeter of path length in liquids or solids.

2-2.1 ELECTRONS

The electron is the fundamental negatively charged particle. It has a rest mass 1/1837 of that of the proton and carries a charge of 4.803×10^{-10} electrostatic unit (esu). It is the only negatively charged ionizing particle of direct interest in the study of radiation effects. The positron has the same mass as the electron, but it carries a positive charge and may be considered an antielectron. The positron is of only secondary practical importance, even though it is emitted by some artificially radioactive nuclei and is formed from the interaction of very high energy gamma rays with matter by the pair-production process. High-energy electrons that are accelerated in machines such as Van de Graaff generators have beam characteristics that depend on the type of accelerator used. Some beam characteristics of various accelerators are shown in Table 2.1.

Beta rays are high-energy electrons resulting from a disintegration in which an electron is emitted from the nucleus. From a given disintegration beta rays show a continuous distribution of energies from zero to the maximum energy of the disintegration. Conservation of energy in beta decay is accomplished by emission of a neutrino with the beta ray. Neutrinos, with zero charge and essentially zero mass, show almost no interactions with matter. The average energy of beta rays is about one-third the maximum energy of the disintegration. Beta rays have been used in studying radiation effects by incorporating the radioactive material (especially C^{14} or tritium) in the material under study. In this way the irradiation is symmetrically distributed throughout the specimen except for some wall effects for which corrections can be made.

Table 2.1—CHARACTERISTICS OF SOME ELECTRON ACCELERATORS

Accelerator	Energy range, Mev	Beam-current range	Beam characteristics
Van de Graaff	1–6	0–4 ma	Continuous mono-energetic beam
Resonant transformer	1–3.5	0–7 ma	Pulsed polyenergetic beam
Betatron	6–30	0–1 μa (external)	Pulsed nearly mono-energetic beam
Linear accelerator	3–25 (and higher)	0–300 μa	Pulsed polyenergetic beam

Cathode rays are electrons emitted by a heated filament (cathode). They can be accelerated to any given potential. Basically all high-energy electrons from machines are cathode rays, but the term is usually applied only to relatively low voltage electrons. Mass-spectrometer appearance potentials and fragmentation studies are examples of studies utilizing cathode rays.

Compton electrons result from the interaction of a gamma ray or an X ray with electrons in an absorber. They exhibit a spread in energy from zero to nearly that of the incident high-energy ray. They are of primary importance in the radiation effects produced by gamma rays.

Delta rays (δ *rays*) are energetic secondary electrons formed in the track of an ionizing particle. They are oriented around the track of the particle and exhibit a spread in energy from a few volts to the maximum energy transfer, satisfying the requirements of energy and momentum conservation.

Photoelectrons result from the interaction of X rays or low-energy gamma rays with bound electrons in the absorber by the photoelectric process. Photoelectrons possess the full energy of the gamma ray or X ray minus the binding energy of the atomic level from which they were ejected. They are nearly monoenergetic when produced by monoenergetic gamma or X rays.

Conversion electrons are formed by the interaction of a gamma ray emitted in a nuclear transformation with a low-lying electron (K, L, or M shell) in the same atom. This interaction may be considered as an internal photoelectric process. Conversion electrons are of little importance in radiation effects.

2-2.1.1 Physical Aspects of the Interaction of Electrons with Matter

Electrons of energy below 1 Mev lose energy until they reach a low-energy level mainly by a series of inelastic collisions with the electrons in the absorber. The equation for energy loss by electrons through collisions is a modification of the general equation (Eq. 2.1) for energy loss by ionization and excitation. The treatment of electrons differs from that of heavier charged particles in that the heavier particles are assumed to suffer essentially no deflection in a collision with a bound electron; an impinging electron suffers considerable deflection. Also, after the collision of two electrons, it is impossible to distinguish which was the impinger (identity criterion). If the electron of higher resultant energy is designated as the impinger, the calculated maximum energy loss is $\frac{1}{4} mv^2$, where m and v are the mass and velocity of the electron. It would be $\frac{1}{2} mv^2$ if the initial electron were stopped and the struck electron received all the energy. This, by definition, would result in no loss of energy.

The energy loss in the nonrelativistic case, for electrons of velocity well below the velocity of light, is given by

$$-\frac{dE}{dx} = \frac{4\pi e^4 N Z}{mv^2} \ln \left[\frac{mv^2}{2\bar{I}} (\epsilon/2)^{1/2} \right] \qquad (2.3)$$

where $-dE/dx$ is the rate of energy loss by an electron of charge e and mass m in an absorber with N atoms per cubic centimeter, Z electrons per atom, and a mean excitation potential $\bar{I}$. The natural logarithm base is ϵ. Equation 2.3 differs from Eq. 2.1 in the lack of the z^2 term and in the addition of the $(\epsilon/2)^{1/2}$ term in the logarithm to satisfy the identity criterion.

For electron energies higher than 0.5 Mev $(E > m_0 c^2)$ a relativistic formula must be used.[4] The mean excitation potential $\bar{I}$ is the same as that defined by Eq. 2.2. In general, electrons and protons of the same velocity exhibit quite comparable rates of energy loss, though electrons and protons of the same velocity have vastly different energies.

Electrons also lose energy by producing electromagnetic radiation as they are slowed in passing through the electromagnetic field of the nucleus. This process is known as "bremsstrahlung production" and is a significant fraction of the energy dissipation when the electrons have a velocity near that of light. The ratio of radiative-energy loss to collision-energy loss is approximated in Eq. 2.4, where E is the electron energy in million electron volts and Z is the atomic number of the absorber,

$$\frac{\left(-\dfrac{dE}{dx}\right)_{\text{radiation}}}{\left(-\dfrac{dE}{dx}\right)_{\text{collision}}} \cong \frac{EZ}{800} \tag{2.4}$$

For carbon ($Z = 6$) the radiant energy loss is 10% of the collision energy loss for about 13-Mev electrons. Thus, for most work in radiation effects, the radiation losses by electrons will represent a correction to the total energy loss when electrons of energy greater than a few million electron volts are used. If heavy elements are present, the correction can become quite large. Figure 2.1 shows the collision and bremsstrahlung losses in

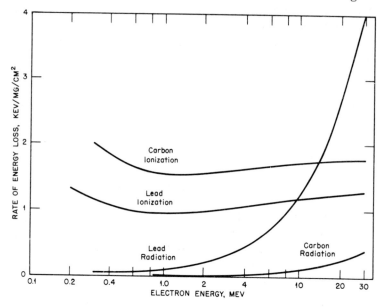

FIG. 2.1 Electron energy loss by ionization (collision) and radiation (bremsstrahlung) in carbon and lead. (From O. Halpern and H. Hall, *Physical Review*, Ref. 23.)

carbon and lead, respectively, at various electron energies. The radiation loss must be considered in very precise work on organic systems when electron sources of energy greater than about 1 Mev are used. The bremsstrahlung, being similar to gamma rays, may escape the target; consequently, this energy would not always be available for chemical reactions.

Owing to the possible large deflections suffered by electrons in their passage through matter, the range of electrons is a less precise concept than that of heavier particles such as protons or alpha particles. Large differences in the ranges of monoenergetic electrons are common. The range is important for estimating the maximum depth of penetration of electrons when they are used to study radiation effects. Electron energies are characterized by the maximum range that electrons exhibit in aluminum. Since the range does not change drastically with small changes in atomic number, the range in aluminum can be used as a first approximation for the range in most carbon compounds. The range–energy relations given by Glendenin[18,19] fit the experimental data well in the applicable energy regions:

$$R_{(g/cm^2 \, Al)} = 0.542E - 0.133 \qquad \text{for } E > 0.8 \text{ Mev} \qquad (2.5)$$

$$R_{(g/cm^2 \, Al)} = 0.407E^{1.38} \qquad \text{for } 0.8 \text{ Mev} > E > 0.15 \text{ Mev} \qquad (2.6)$$

2-2.1.2 Dosimetry of Electrons

The accurate measurement of radiation dosage, i.e., the total energy absorbed by a system, is important in evaluating radiation effects. The following methods are applicable to electron irradiations.

1. *Ionization measurements:* Knowledge of the current generated in a suitable gaseous ionization chamber and of the energy required to form an ion pair (electron plus a positive ion) in the gas[31] allows a calculation of the energy absorbed by the gas. This system is directly useful for electron dosimetry only if the chamber is designed so the Bragg-Gray cavity principle applies, i.e., if there is no change in electron flux or dose to the sample when the ionization chamber is introduced.

2. *Beam-current and beam-energy measurements:* Data on the electron current collected in the target during an irradiation and knowledge of the electron energy from the source can be used to calculate the energy input to the system.[41] If the electrons are energetic (> 1 Mev), correction must be made for energy loss by bremsstrahlung in precise work. Secondary-electron emission from the target must also be prevented since the loss of such electrons subtracts from the true beam. The target must also be thick to ensure complete absorption of the electron beam impingent upon it.

3. *Calorimetric measurements:* Energy from an electron source absorbed in a calorimeter containing a material having radiation absorption characteristics similar to those of the target material will yield the dose rate to a target material irradiated with the same beam characteristics (energy and current). Correction must be made to the energy input calculated from the temperature rise for any chemical action or physical change produced in the calorimeter; usually this correction is small.

4. *Chemical dosimeters:* The chemical change produced in the dosimeter is a measure of the energy input. The chemical change is compared with standards, and the source is then calibrated. The two chemical dosimeters in common use are the ferrous sulfate dosimeter (Fricke dosimeter) and the ceric sulfate dosimeter. The ferrous sulfate dosimeter[41] is limited to low electron currents (10^{-7} to 10^{-10} amp) owing to rapid oxygen deple-

tion in the system. The ceric sulfate dosimeter does not depend on the presence of oxygen and can be used for higher dose rates and higher total energy inputs than can the ferrous sulfate dosimeter. For monitoring the electron irradiation of gaseous systems, the polymerization of acetylene has been used as a dosimeter.[35]

5. *Phenomenological changes:* The coloration of plastics such as Mylar, methyl methacrylate, and polystyrene has been used as a monitor.[5] The darkening of silver-activated phosphate glass has also been used. Dependence of calibration on dose rate and a nonlinear calibration curve is usual with such monitors. Their convenience makes them useful for many studies where absolute accuracy is not essential.

2-2.2 PROTONS, DEUTERONS, ALPHA PARTICLES, AND OTHER HEAVY IONS

Positively charged ions that have been used in the study of radiation effects include protons, deuterons, alpha particles, helium ions, and fission fragments. Other particles, such as high-energy multiply charged carbon, nitrogen, oxygen, and neon ions, have not been studied for their radiation effects; but with the development of heavy-ion linear accelerators, it is expected that they will be so utilized. The physical properties of some par-

Table 2.2—PHYSICAL PROPERTIES OF IONIZING PARTICLES

Particle	Symbol	Rest mass, amu[a]	Charge, electron charge units[b]	Spin
Proton	H^+	1.00757	+1	½
Deuteron	D^+	2.01416	+1	1
Alpha particle	α	4.0280	+2	0
Helium ion	He^{++}			
Electron	e^-	0.0005486	−1	½
Positron	e^+	0.0005486	+1	½
Neutron	n	1.00893	0	½

[a] One atomic mass unit is ¹⁄₁₆ the mass of the oxygen isotope of mass 16.
[b] One electron charge is 4.803×10^{-10} esu.

ticles that are in common use for studying radiation effects are listed in Table 2.2. Sources of these particles are given in Table 2.3.

The early work on radiation effects on chemical systems was done with alpha particles and beta rays from naturally radioactive substances.[37] The use of radioactive material has now been largely superseded by the use of accelerated particles. Particle accelerators, such as cyclotrons and linear accelerators, have made high-energy protons, deuterons, and helium ions available in large beam currents; and studies using these particles are a valuable adjunct to studies with gamma rays, electrons, and reactor radiations. The use of one or another of these positive ions is dictated by convenience; but with organic materials helium ions are sometimes preferred because their use induces less radioactivity in the target materials than does the use of protons or deuterons. This is an advantage when the mate-

Table 2.3—SOURCES OF HIGH-ENERGY POSITIVE IONS

Accelerator	Ions	Energy range, Mev	External beam current, μa	Beam characteristics
Cyclotron	H$^+$	6–20	0–100	Beam pulsed at ~11 Mc,
	D$^+$	12–40		nearly monoenergetic
	He^{++}	24–80		
Synchro-cyclotron	H$^+$	100–800	0–1	Pulsed beam, nearly
	D$^+$			monoenergetic
	He^{++}			
Van de Graaff	H$^+$	1–6	0–100	Continuous monoenergetic
	D$^+$			beam
Linear accelerator	H$^+$	32	0–1	Pulsed monoenergetic beam
Heavy-ion linear accelerator	C^{+5}, N^{+6}, etc.	10 Mev/nuclear particle (120 Mev C^{+5}, etc.)	0–1	Pulsed monoenergetic beam

rial is to be studied soon after irradiation. Fission fragments can be used for irradiation by incorporating uranium in the material under investigation and irradiating the mixture with thermal neutrons.

2-2.2.1 *Stopping of Heavy Ions in Matter*

The general theory of the stopping of charged particles was outlined in Sect. 2-2. For positive ions the rate of energy loss is independent of the mass of the particle and dependent only on the velocity and the charge (Eq. 2.1). The following correlations can be made in terms of the rate of energy loss by protons at a given energy: (1) Helium ions have four times the rate of energy loss of protons of the same velocity, i.e., one-fourth the energy.

$$4\left[\left(-\frac{dE}{dx}\right)_{(H^+,E)}\right] = \left(-\frac{dE}{dx}\right)_{(He^{++},4E)} \tag{2.7}$$

(2) Deuterons have the same rate of energy loss as protons of half the deuteron energy. Protons and deuterons show the same rate of energy loss at the same velocity.

$$\left(-\frac{dE}{dx}\right)_{(H^+,E)} = \left(-\frac{dE}{dx}\right)_{(D_+,2E)} \tag{2.8}$$

For fission fragments the situation is more complicated, but Bohr[10] gives the range of a fission fragment of initial charge Z_1^{eff} and mass A_1 in terms of the range of an alpha particle of the same velocity:

$$\frac{R_F(v)}{R_\alpha(v)} = \frac{7A_1}{(Z_1^{eff})^2} \tag{2.9}$$

The initial charge of the fragments[36] is about 16 to 20. Fission fragments do not exhibit a high ionization at the end of the tracks; they show a continuous decrease in density of ionization as they are slowed down because the fragments continually pick up charges as they slow down, reducing the Z_1^{eff}.

Range–energy curves and rate of energy loss vs. energy curves for protons, deuterons, and helium ions have been compiled by Aron, Hoffman, and Williams.[2] A maximum rate of energy loss is shown by positive ions (H^+, D^+, or He^{++}) at energies somewhere below 100 kev, depending on the

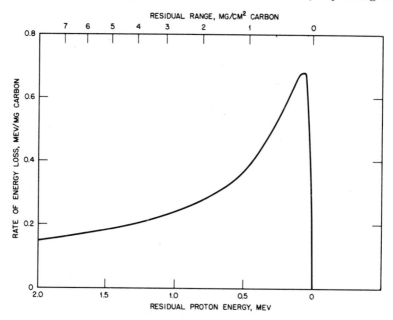

FIG. 2.2   Energy-loss curve (Bragg) for stopping protons in carbon.

particle and the absorber. The well-known Bragg curve (Fig. 2.2) illustrates this point for protons stopping in a carbon absorber. For radiation effects, energy loss rate is important since the density of ionization at the end of the track may be several times the mean density along the track.

2-2.2.2 *Delta Rays (δ Rays)*

Much of the ionization and excitation produced by heavy ions is caused by delta rays (secondary electrons). The maximum energy of delta rays of electron mass m produced by a heavy particle of mass M and energy E is given by the relation

$$E_\delta(\text{max.}) = 4E \frac{mM}{(M + m)^2} \cong \frac{4Em}{M} \qquad (2.10)$$

For a 10-Mev helium ion, this maximum energy of delta rays is only about 5.4 kev. Since the maximum energy of delta rays is inversely proportional to the mass of the ionizing particle, heavier particles such as fission fragments exhibit more compact and intense tracks of ionization than do lighter particles such as protons.

2-2.2.3 *Dosimetry of Heavy Ions*

The ferrous sulfate dosimeter can be used with heavy ions as well as electrons. Beams of heavy ions from an accelerator are best measured by the ion current collected and the energy of the impingent beam. The beam energy is usually determined from the range in aluminum, and corrections are made for energy loss in the accelerator and target windows and any air space or other absorber not present during the range measurement. Escape of secondary electrons must be prevented as this leads to a high ion current. In fission-fragment irradiations the energy input can be calculated from a measurement of the neutron flux used to induce fission, the fissionable isotope content of the system, and the cross section for fission of that isotope.

2-3 Neutrons

Neutrons differ from the ionizing radiations used in the study of radiation effects in that they are electrically neutral and exhibit no electric interactions with electrons or nuclei. Because they themselves are not ionizing particles, they transfer energy to their environment largely by elastic collisions with nuclei of the absorber. Thus the actual ionization and excitation from energetic neutrons are caused by recoil of charged particles. Neutrons are radioactive, decaying by beta emission to a proton and an electron with a half life of 13 min.

Even though neutrons are uncharged, their energies are expressed in electron volts, this being a convenient measure of their kinetic energy. Neutrons have been classified into groups according to their energy. These classifications are not rigorously defined, and different authors use them in various ways. For radiation-effects work the following classification is reasonable.

Thermal neutrons are those whose mean kinetic energy is that of a particle of 1 amu at the temperature of the environment. At room temperature (78°F), this corresponds to an energy of 0.025 ev and a velocity of 2200 meters/sec. The term "slow neutrons" is loosely used as a synonym for thermal neutrons. Thermal neutrons have a Boltzmann distribution of energies about the mean energy.

Epithermal neutrons are those having energies above the thermal region and below the intermediate region. This is a region in which many elements exhibit high resonance-capture cross sections.

Intermediate neutrons are those having energies from 100 ev to about 100 kev. These neutrons are important to radiation-effects work in that the recoil protons produced by them cannot in themselves promote secondary ionizations. The lower energy limit for recoil protons capable of producing secondary ionization has been set by Rossi[40] at about 20 kev in biological tissue.

Fast neutrons are those of energy above 100 kev. Some authors use the term "fast neutrons" to include only those above a given threshold in which they are interested. According to Rossi's definition, a fast neutron is one that produces a recoil proton capable of secondary ionizations, i.e., a recoil proton of energy greater than about 20 kev.

The number of neutrons passing through a given area in unit time is called the "neutron flux." This may be a random flux comprised of neutrons going in all directions as in a reactor, or it may be a directed beam of neutrons as from a cyclotron target. If in the system under consideration there are, on the average, n neutrons per cubic centimeter, each with a velocity v in centimeters per second, then the neutron flux is nv (neutrons/cm²/sec). This is the number of neutrons per second entering an imaginary sphere of 1 cm² cross-sectional area.[27] The total number of neutrons per square centimeter to which a system is subjected, i.e., the neutron exposure, is found by multiplying the flux by the time of the exposure; thus, nvt (neutrons/cm²) is the exposure (also called the "neutron dose").

2-3.1 Neutron Sources

Since neutrons do not occur in the free state in nature, the only sources are those involving nuclear reactions. The neutron source of prime interest is the nuclear reactor. The neutron flux in a reactor depends on the reactor type and size and on the power level of operation. In addition, the flux varies with location within a given reactor. Although the fission reaction produces neutrons with energies to 15 Mev and higher, with an average energy of about 2 Mev, the mean energy of the neutrons inside a reactor is much less than this, the major portion being near thermal. If an increased flux of fast neutrons is desired, a converter can be used in which the material to be irradiated is surrounded by fissionable material. The resultant flux is a mixture of slow and fast neutrons.

The classical source of neutrons is the Ra–Be (radium–beryllium) source in which alpha particles from radium yield neutrons by the reaction

$$_4Be^9 + \alpha \rightarrow {_6}C^{12} + {_0}n^1$$

Such reactions are usually written $Be^9(\alpha,n)C^{12}$. These neutrons have a maximum energy of up to 13 Mev, with an average energy of about 4 Mev. A 1-g Ra–Be source has a yield of about 1.7×10^7 neutrons/sec distributed in all directions from the source, giving a flux of some 1.5×10^4 neutrons/cm²/sec at 10 cm from the source.

Other laboratory sources of neutrons, which produce higher fluxes, are accelerators, e.g., cyclotrons or Van de Graaff generators, with suitable target materials. The yields from these depend on the energy of the particles and the target reaction. High-current accelerators can be the most prolific sources of neutrons of energy greater than 1 Mev.

A convenient source of fast neutrons is the deuteron–neutron reaction, $H^2(d,n)He^3$. Deuterons accelerated from a Van de Graaff generator or a cyclotron are allowed to impinge on a target of heavy ice, D_2O. The yield of neutrons using 1-Mev D^+ is about 5×10^9 neutrons/sec/μa of deuteron current. Since 1 ma of deuteron current is possible, yields of 10^{12} to 10^{13} fast neutrons/sec can be obtained. The usable flux is lower than this and depends on placement of the sample with respect to the target. The neutrons are close to monoenergetic if thin targets are used in the accelerator. The use of 2-Mev or higher energy electrons on a beryllium target utilizing the reaction $Be^9(\gamma,n)Be^8$ can yield neutron intensities equivalent to several grams of radium. The use of deuterons on lithium, $Li^7(d,n)Be^8$, yields higher energy neutrons for a given accelerator energy.

2-3.2 Nuclear Properties of Neutrons

The slowing down of charged particles is largely due to interactions with electrons. No interactions between neutrons and electrons occur, and most degradation results from elastic collisions with atoms of the absorber. In many materials inelastic collisions with nuclei are also important and may contribute to the energy dissipation in the system, especially for neutrons in the intermediate energy range.

2-3.2.1 Cross Sections

With regard to the properties of neutron interactions, the concept of cross sections is used in much the same manner as it is used for molecular collisions in the kinetic theory of gases. An atom is said to have a cross section for a given type of interaction with a neutron (or other particle). This is another way of expressing the probability of the reaction, which is proportional to a calculated cross-sectional area presented by the nucleus to the impingent particle. The cross section for an activation process is defined by the equation

$$A^* = nvtN_A V\sigma \tag{2.11}$$

where A^* is the number of atoms of A activated in a time t by a flux of particles nv, using a target material with a volume V and N_A atoms of A per cubic centimeter. The cross section for the process is σ. This equation does not distinguish whether the impingent particle has an area and the nucleus is point size or whether the particle is point size and the nucleus is of a given area.

Cross sections are usually measured in barns, a barn being equal to 10^{-24} cm^2. Processes with low probability of occurrence are measured in millibarns. The cross section need bear no relation to the geometric cross section of the atomic nucleus concerned. For high-energy particles the total cross section of all the nuclear reactions approximates nuclear dimensions, but for slow neutrons the variation is much greater; and cross sections for radiative capture of neutrons by nuclei are sometimes many times greater than nuclear dimensions.

2-3.2.2 *Radiative Capture of Neutrons*

When a neutron strikes and enters a nucleus, a compound nucleus is formed. With thermal neutrons, in most cases, the excitation energy of the compound nucleus is too low for the emission of a charged particle; therefore the nucleus is stabilized by the emission of a gamma ray. Hence, the process is called "radiative capture."

For neutron energies in the thermal and epithermal regions, the probabilities of neutron capture vary with the nuclear species. The cross section for capture in helium is zero, whereas in Xe^{135} it is 3.5×10^6 barns. Reactor construction materials are chosen for their low cross sections for radiative capture as well as their engineering properties. In general, cross sections for radiative capture are an inverse function of the neutron velocity (the $1/v$ law). At energies slightly above the thermal region, however, a process known as "resonance capture" becomes important. In the energy region from 0.1 to 1000 ev, many elements exhibit high peaks in a plot of neutron-absorption cross section vs. energy. Cadmium, for example, exhibits a single very high peak at 0.176 ev. The half-width of such resonance peaks may be only 0.1 to 0.2 ev. The explanation is found in the Breit-Wigner theory. If the neutron has just the amount of energy necessary to form a compound nucleus at an exact nuclear energy level, then the probability for such neutron capture will be high.

In hydrogenous materials many thermal neutrons are captured by hydrogen, $H^1(n,\gamma)H^2$. This reaction contributes to the gamma-ray flux in such systems. It also contributes some direct ionization by the recoil deuterons.

2-3.2.3 *Ejection of Charged Particles*

A nucleus can capture a fast neutron and eject a charged particle. Each reaction of this type is characterized by a neutron-energy threshold. In a few isolated cases, this threshold may be zero. At energies somewhat higher than the threshold, the cross section reaches a plateau. The ejection of a positively charged particle, a proton, deuteron, or alpha particle, from a nucleus requires that the ejected particle be given sufficient energy to overcome the binding energy in the nucleus and to pass through the nuclear charge barrier. If the charge on a nucleus is considered as residing on the shell, there is a potential barrier to passage of a charged particle in either direction through this shell. Thus the threshold energy for proton ejection increases with the atomic number of the irradiated nucleus, i.e., with increasing charge on the shell. For a given nucleus the threshold for ejection of an alpha particle is higher than that for a proton or a deuteron because the former is doubly charged and the latter two are singly charged.

A similar process not involving charged particles is the $(n,2n)$ reaction in which a neutron forms a compound nucleus with a nuclide and two neutrons are ejected. Since no charge barrier exists for neutrons, the threshold is determined by the binding energy of the neutron in the nucleus. Inelastic scattering, the $(n,n\gamma)$ process, occurs in the neutron-energy region where the neutrons have insufficient energy to eject a particle but merely raise the nucleus to an excited level.

An example of a charged-particle ejection reaction that is of importance in the study of radiation effects is $N^{14}(n,p)C^{14}$. This reaction has an unusually low threshold and occurs with thermal neutrons. The ejected protons have an energy of over 0.6 Mev. This reaction may contribute significantly to the total energy dissipation in reactor irradiations of materials containing nitrogen.

2-3.2.4 *Fission*

When a neutron enters the nucleus of certain heavy nuclides (U^{235}, U^{233}, Pu^{239}), instead of becoming stable by gamma emission, the nucleus breaks into two fragments of approximately equal mass. This splitting process is accompanied by the simultaneous emission of gamma rays and some excess neutrons. The neutron-proton ratios are lower for stable nuclides in the center of the periodic table than for the heavy elements, and the binding energies of nuclides are greater in the middle region. The fission process is accompanied by the release of tremendous amounts of energy owing to this difference in binding energies. Several free neutrons are ejected because of the differences in the neutron-proton ratios involved. U^{235} yields two fission fragments, a light and a heavy, the light being centered about mass 95 and the heavy about mass 138. These have average kinetic energies of 97 and 65 Mev, respectively. In addition, about 2.5 prompt neutrons are ejected. The neutron-energy spectrum is a continuous distribution; the yield is maximum at 1 Mev and decreases exponentially to about 14 Mev. Since the neutron-proton ratios in the two fragments are on the average above that for stable nuclei, many of the products are radioactive. Decay occurs by beta emission through a decay chain to stable nuclei, the average product undergoing about three successive beta decays in reaching a stable nucleus. Gamma rays are emitted in the fission process itself and in the decay of the resulting radioactive fission products.

2-3.3 MODERATION OF NEUTRONS

The principal mode of slowing down neutrons in a reactor is by elastic scattering, which is accomplished by the moderator. The slowing down or moderating process is the familiar billiard-ball problem in which both momentum and energy are conserved. In radiation effects the interest is centered on the energy transferred to the struck particle rather than on the energy lost by the neutron. In the collision of a neutron of energy E with a nucleus of mass M, the recoil energy, E_r, can vary from zero to the maximum energy given by the relation

$$E_r(\text{max}) = \frac{4M}{(M + 1)^2} E \qquad (2.12)$$

The average energy of recoil is approximately half the maximum energy; so for scattering of neutrons by protons $(M = 1)$, the average energy of the recoil proton is half that of the incident neutron. The cross section for scatterings by protons is large, and the energy transfer per collision is also large. Thus in hydrogenous materials, i.e., most organic substances, neutrons are rapidly reduced to thermal velocities; and most of the energy will appear as energy of recoil protons.

Since thermal neutrons do not have sufficient energy to cause an elastic recoil that will break a chemical bond (3 to 5 ev necessary), they have no chemical effect except for such (n,γ) reactions as occur with hydrogen or other elements, (n,p) reactions with nitrogen, and (n,α) reactions with boron or lithium which may occur. The particle and recoil nucleus from such reactions can cause ionization. Elastic collisions of epithermal and low intermediate energy neutrons in organic compounds can break bonds and give recoil protons, but these produce no further ionizations. Fast neutrons give higher energy recoil protons, which can cause clusters of ionization and excitation along their tracks. These recoil protons are stopped by the processes described in Sect. 2-2. Since the average energy of the recoil protons is low (< 1 Mev average for pile neutrons), the tracks are short and the density of ionization and excitation is high.

A special effect in solids called the "Wigner effect" is caused by the displacement of atoms in the solid material by fast-neutron collisions. In graphite moderators carbon atoms can be displaced from their sites by a neutron collision when the recoil energy of the struck carbon atom is greater than the lattice binding energy. The carbon atom is displaced in the lattice, forming a vacant lattice site and an interstitial atom. On continued irradiation these defects in the lattice change the electrical, thermal, and mechanical properties of the graphite. In organic materials such displacements are not as important as excitation and ionization in their effects on the properties of the material.

2-3.4 MEASUREMENT OF NEUTRON FLUX

The low flux levels of interest to health physicists and biologists[40] are generally below those at which radiation effects to chemical systems appear. Sensitive devices, such as plastic-wall ionization chambers and fission

Table 2.4—SOME THRESHOLD DETECTORS[a] FOR NEUTRONS[43]

Element	Reaction	Effective threshold energy, Mev	Effective cross section, barns	Half life of product
Phosphorous	$P^{31}(n,p)Si^{31}$	2.4	0.075	2.62 hr
Sulfur	$S^{32}(n,p)P^{32}$	2.8	0.300	14.3 days
Aluminum	$Al^{27}(n,p)Mg^{27}$	4.6	0.039	9.8 min
Nickel	$Ni^{58}(n,p)Co^{58}$	5.0	1.23	72 days
Silicon	$Si^{28}(n,p)Al^{28}$	5.5	0.080	2.3 min
Magnesium	$Mg^{24}(n,p)Na^{24}$	6.3	0.048	14.9 hr
Aluminum	$Al^{27}(n,\alpha)Na^{24}$	8.1	0.111	14.9 hr
Np^{237}	$Np^{237}(n,fission)$	0.76	1.5	
U^{238}	$U^{238}(n,fission)$	1.43	0.54	
Th^{232}	$Th^{232}(n,fission)$	2.00	0.0598	

[a] Choice of cross sections and thresholds are arbitrary and interrelated. They have been adopted for consistency.

chambers coupled with suitable electronic systems, are used directly for neutron-flux monitoring in reactors. Fission counters, i.e., a thin foil of fissionable material in a proportional counting tube, are useful for the measurement of neutron fluxes as high as 10^{12} neutrons/cm^2/sec. Thorium or U^{238} can be used in fission counters for fast neutrons.

For monitoring the integrated flux of neutrons to which a sample is exposed, the most direct method is the activation of thin foils of various elements located at various positions around the sample.[20,44,45] Thin-foil detectors of gold, indium, cobalt, or antimony exposed with and without cadmium covers measure the total low-energy components. Fast neutrons are measured with a series of threshold detectors; these do not yield a complete neutron-energy distribution curve, but the measurements are sufficient for many purposes. Some threshold detectors that have been used and the effective energy of their activation are listed in Table 2.4. The flux is evaluated by removing these foils after the irradiation and measuring the induced radioactivity to determine the number of atoms of the element activated. These detectors measure only the integrated flux over the duration of an experiment and do not measure fluctuations during the experiment. Phenomenological detectors such as graphite[38] or germanium[8] have been used, the change in resistance being calibrated against the fast-neutron exposure.

2-3.5 DOSIMETRY OF MIXED RADIATION FIELDS

The monitoring of mixed radiation fields such as occur in a reactor is quite difficult. The neutron-energy distribution and the ratio of neutrons to gamma rays vary from point to point in the reactor and at a given point with changes of an experiment in a neighboring test hole. In addition, the neutron spectrum and gamma-ray intensity measured in a bare hole differ from those with a sample or with monitors in the hole. With large samples of organic materials, the moderation of neutrons by the sample itself may cause a variation in neutron-energy distribution through the sample; whether or not this self-moderation is serious depends on the initial neutron distribution as determined by the reactor environment.

The total energy input in a system under investigation can theoretically be best measured with a calorimeter, though use of such instruments is difficult in practice. This instrument should be similar in composition to the system under investigation, and the calorimetric values should be corrected for any chemical or physical changes that occur. A calorimetric system was used by Richardson, Allen, and Boyle[39] to estimate the energy absorbed in water, heavy water, carbon, and bismuth; and from these results they estimated the relative energy contribution of neutrons and gamma rays. Other methods such as the independent determination of neutron spectrum and the gamma flux by proportional counting techniques are also used. Chemical dosimeters, such as nitric oxide for gaseous systems[12] and boric acid solutions for water systems,[22] have also been suggested.

2-4 Electromagnetic Radiations

Gamma rays, X rays, and bremsstrahlung are electromagnetic radiations of interest in the study of radiation effects. Gamma rays originate in nuclear processes, e.g., the decay of an excited nucleus after neutron absorption or after beta decay. Those arising from nuclear disintegration are monoenergetic, although from a given nucleus the gamma rays may be emitted from a series of levels and the observed radiation may be a mixture of several energies of gamma rays. In the well-known Co^{60} radiation source, the gamma rays are emitted after the beta decay (0.36-Mev β^-) and consist of two energy groups of 1.173- and 1.332-Mev gamma rays. Since these are in equal yield, the energy of the gamma rays from the Co^{60} source is usually given as 1.25 Mev, the average of these values.

X rays are always formed by the interaction of an energetic charged particle with matter. They result from two effects. The first is the disruption of the target atom by an electron being knocked out of a low-lying shell. When this shell is filled from an outer shell, X rays are emitted. These X rays have discrete energies corresponding to the energy spacing of the levels in the element irradiated. The energies of such X rays are well known for various types of target materials. Accompanying the discrete X rays are bremsstrahlung, which result from energy loss by electrons in a nuclear field. These have a continuous energy distribution. Most commercial X-ray machines emit a continuous spectrum of radiation which is nearly all bremsstrahlung, with the characteristic X rays of the target material superimposed on this continuous distribution.

2-4.1 Sources of Electromagnetic Radiation

Many types of sources have been used in the study of radiation effects. The simplest source is an X-ray tube, and many studies at low intensity have been made with machines having energies in the 50- to 200-kv range. Electron accelerators, e.g., Van de Graaff machines and resonant transformers, yield high fluxes of bremsstrahlung when suitable targets are used. The radiation from such sources is not isotropically distributed, and most of it is in the forward direction. The dose rate to a sample is thus a function of the geometry of the target and sample system.

The Co^{60} source, presently in widespread use, consists of cobalt slugs that have been irradiated in a reactor to form Co^{60} by the (n,γ) process on Co^{59}. Sources of 1000 curies will give a gamma-ray intensity of over 10^6 rads/hr for 10 to 20 ml of organic materials. If larger samples are to be irradiated, the Co^{60} must be arranged to accommodate the larger volume, and the geometry is such that the intensity is lowered. The calibration of the source slowly changes with time because Co^{60} has a 5.3-year half life. Such changes are readily calculated.

Cesium-137 with a 33-year half life has been proposed as a radiation source. The pure isotope can be separated from reactor fission-product residues in which it is found in high yield. The decay through a meta-stable state in Ba^{137m} to stable Ba^{137} is accompanied by a 0.663-Mev gamma ray. High specific activity sources are possible.

Spent fuel rods from high-flux reactors are also used as gamma-ray sources. These emit gamma rays with a wide energy distribution. Because of the presence of fission products with various half lives, both the intensity of the gamma rays emitted and the energy distribution change with time.

A high-intensity source has been proposed which would consist of a reactor in which an indium sulfate solution is circulated through the reactor and then around a gamma-ray test facility for irradiation experiments.[6] The capture of neutrons by indium and the subsequent decay of the active indium would provide gamma rays without the presence of neutron effects.

2-4.2 ABSORPTION OF ELECTROMAGNETIC RADIATION

In marked contrast to charged particles, electromagnetic radiation does not have a definite range in matter. This difference results from different types of absorption processes in the two cases. Charged particles lose their energy in a series of small steps, whereas, in general, electromagnetic radiation is either completely removed from a beam by absorption or scattering or continues on at the same energy. The latter radiation resembles the absorption of light in this respect. Thus an absorption curve follows the same form equation as the Lambert-Beer law for light absorption:

$$I = I_0 e^{-\mu x} \qquad (2.13)$$

where I_0 is the initial intensity of radiation, μ is the absorption coefficient of the absorber, and I is the intensity of the radiation after passing through a thickness x of absorber.

The energy of gamma rays is characterized by the absorption coefficient, μ, in a given absorber. Because a plot of log intensity vs. thickness yields a straight line, it has become customary to characterize the energy of gamma rays in terms of the half-thickness, i.e., the thickness of the absorber required to reduce the intensity to one-half its value. This is related to the absorption coefficient, μ, by the relation

$$x_{1/2} = \frac{0.693}{\mu} \qquad (2.14)$$

The thickness can be expressed in many different units, e.g., centimeters, grams per square centimeter, and electrons per square centimeter. The values of μ and $x_{1/2}$ must be expressed in the same units. In radiochemistry the thickness of absorber is generally given in grams per square centimeter, in which case the absorption coefficient has the units square centimeter per gram. The latter is called the "mass absorption coefficient" for energy absorption.

2-4.3 INTERACTION WITH MATTER

The absorption of X rays and low-energy gamma rays occurs almost entirely by interaction with electrons. With absorbers containing elements of low atomic number and with gamma rays of energy below 20 Mev, the contribution of nuclear interactions is a negligible fraction of the total absorption.

2-4.3.1 *Photoelectric Absorption*

With low-energy X rays and gamma rays, the principal contribution to the absorption is made by the photoelectric process. Here the radiation interacts with a bound electron, ejecting it from the atom. The process is most efficient when the energy of the X rays is equal to, or only slightly higher than, the binding energy of the electron ejected. The kinetic energy of the ejected electron is the difference between the energy of the radiation $h\nu$, and the binding energy of the electron in the atom, E_B,

$$E_{e^-} = h\nu - E_B \tag{2.15}$$

With high-energy X rays or gamma rays, all electrons take part in the absorption, but the cross section for interaction decreases rapidly with increase of X-ray energy above that of the K-electron energy in the absorber. The theoretical treatment of the photoelectric effect is quite difficult, but an approximate correlation of the interaction cross section with energy and type of absorber is as follows:

$$\sigma_A \simeq k \frac{Z^4}{(h\nu)^3} \tag{2.16}$$

where σ_A is the photoelectric cross section per atom of absorber, k is an empirical constant, Z is the atomic number of the absorber, and $h\nu$ is the energy of the photon. Thus photoelectric interaction is most efficient for heavy elements and for low-energy photons. This dependence is illustrated in Fig. 2.3.

Below 100-kev energy the photon energy becomes equal to the K-electron energy for heavy absorbers. When the photon energy becomes less than the binding energy of an electron in a given level, that electron can no longer participate in photoelectric absorption, and the absorption coefficient suddenly drops. In a plot of absorption coefficient vs. photon energy, these sudden drops where the various electron levels become inactive are called "absorption edges." These are characteristic physical constants of the absorber. In Fig. 2.3 the sudden change in absorption of electromagnetic radiation in lead at about 0.09 Mev illustrates the absorption edge caused by the K electrons in lead. The absorption edges of light elements are all below 10 kev, and this effect does not enter into direct consideration in the irradiation of organic materials.

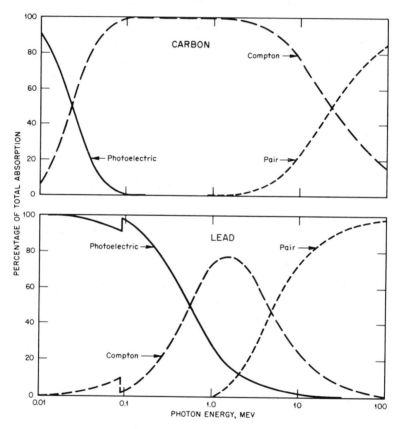

FIG. 2.3 Relative probabilities for photoelectric absorption, Compton scattering, and pair production by gamma rays in carbon and lead. [From U. Fano, *Radiation Biology*, A. Hollaender (Ed.), McGraw-Hill Book Company, Inc., Ref. 14.]

When a photon ejects an electron from a K, L, M, or higher atomic level in the absorber, an electron vacancy results. When this vacancy is filled by an electron from a higher level, electromagnetic radiation characteristic of the transition is emitted. This is called "fluorescent X radiation." In irradiated samples of appreciable volume, the fluorescent X rays will be almost totally reabsorbed by photoelectric interaction with electrons in higher atomic levels.

2-4.3.2 Compton Scattering[13]

This process is responsible for the bulk of the effects in organic materials with 0.1- to 2-Mev gamma rays. The gamma ray interacts with an electron and imparts a fraction of its energy to that electron. The gamma ray suffers an energy loss and a change in wave length in the process. The

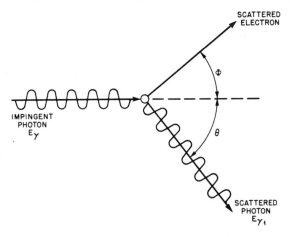

FIG. 2.4 Schematic representation of the Compton scattering process.

absorber also emits fluorescent X rays as a result of transitions to fill the electron vacancy as described for photoelectric absorption. Since momentum and energy must be conserved, the direction and energy of the electron are related to the direction and energy of the scattered gamma ray, as shown in Fig. 2.4. The relevant equations concerning the energy relationships in this system can be summarized as follows:

$$E_{\gamma_1} = h\nu' = \frac{m_0 C^2}{(1 - \cos\theta) + 1/\alpha} \qquad (2.17)$$

$$E_{e^-} = h\nu_0 \frac{\alpha(1 - \cos\theta)}{1 + \alpha(1 - \cos\theta)} \qquad (2.18)$$

where $m_0 C^2$ is the rest energy of the electron, α equals $h\nu_0/m_0 C^2$, and θ is the photon scattering angle. Thus the energy of the electron is determined by the angle of scatter of the photon and its resultant energy. The angle of electron scatter, Φ in Fig. 2.4, is related to that of the photon by considerations of momentum conservation. The maximum energy that can be given an electron by Compton scattering is

$$E_{e^-}(\max) = h\nu_0 \frac{2\alpha}{1 + 2\alpha} \simeq \frac{4E\gamma^2}{1 + 4E_\gamma} \qquad (2.19)$$

The maximum fraction of the energy that can be given a free (unbound) electron is thus a function of photon energy as shown in Fig. 2.5. Note that low-energy photons suffer only small changes in energy, whereas high-energy photons can lose almost all their energy in a Compton scattering

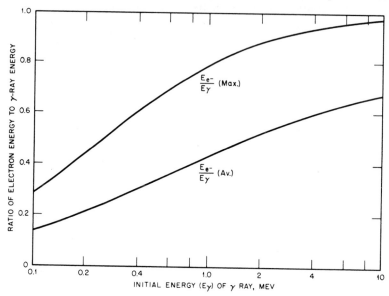

Fig. 2.5 Maximum and average energy of Compton electrons as fractions of initial gamma-ray energy.

process. Bethe[4] has described the more complicated calculation of the average energy of the Compton electron as shown in Fig. 2.5. This average energy is close to 50% of the maximum energy in the 0.1- to 0.5-Mev region and increases slowly with photon energy until it is 70% of the maximum energy of 10 Mev.

2-4.3.3 Pair Production

When a photon of energy greater than 1.02 Mev $(2m_0C^2)$ interacts with the field of a nucleus, an electron–positron pair can be created. These particles have energies divided approximately equally, although near the threshold energy for production the positron is the more energetic since it is repelled by the nucleus whereas the electron is attracted. Momentum and energy are conserved in the process by recoil of the nucleus. The probability of pair production increases with energy; and with gamma rays of energy above about 9 Mev, it is proportional to the logarithm of the gamma-ray energy. Since the probability of pair production also increases with Z^2 of the absorber, it is greatest in materials containing heavy elements. Pair production also occurs in the field of electrons, but it is a less probable process than in the field of the nucleus. When it occurs near electrons, it is called triplet production because of the recoil electron.

The subsequent action of the positron in traversing matter is quite similar to that of a fast electron with the difference that the positron is annihilated before or shortly after stopping. Positrons produce ionization, secondary electrons, and excitation along their tracks in the same manner as electrons. They are removed from the scene by annihilation with an electron, creating two gamma rays, each having an energy of 0.51 Mev. Thus the net effect is the degrading of an energetic gamma ray into two lower energy gamma rays with the energy difference being used for ionization and excitation in the absorbing material.

2-4.3.4 *Total Absorption Process of Gamma Rays*

The total process of gamma-ray absorption is the sum of each of the three effects: the photoelectric effect, dominant with low-energy gamma rays and X rays; the Compton effect, dominant for intermediate-energy gamma rays; and pair production, dominant with very high energy gamma rays. The relative importance of these effects in carbon and lead is shown in Fig. 2.3. In the carbon (organic) system Compton scattering is by far the most important process for all irradiations except those in which low or very high energy radiation makes an important contribution to the total intensity.

2-4.4 DOSIMETRY OF ELECTROMAGNETIC RADIATION

Four of the five methods of electron dosimetry given in Sect. 2-2.1.2 can be applied to gamma rays.

1. *Ionization measurements.* The principle was described before. Such measurements are used[24] as a primary standardization method for aqueous dosimeters. It has been suggested[7] that the standard gamma dosimeter for organic materials be an ion chamber made of graphite and that carbon dioxide be used for the gas. The dose can then be measured in carbon and expressed in ergs per gram of carbon. Conversion to dose received by an organic sample (of only slightly different electron density) involves only a small correction.

2. *Calorimetric measurements.* As with electrons, this method gives directly the energy absorbed from a radiation field. Calorimetry is also a primary standard used to calibrate chemical dosimeters.

3. *Chemical dosimeters.* The most common and practical means of measuring gamma dose rates is to use either the ferrous sulfate or ceric sulfate dosimeter. The $FeSO_4$ dosimeter has been carefully calibrated by calorimetric measurements of gamma-ray absorption in water and is quite reproducible within its limits of intensity and total dose.[24,46] The ceric

sulfate dosimeter has been compared to the ferrous sulfate dosimeter and is useful at higher gamma-ray intensities than the ferrous sulfate system.[25,47] The principal mode of energy loss of gamma rays is Compton scattering. This is directly proportional to the electron density in the system. Thus the dose rate found with the chemical dosimeters must be corrected for the relative electron densities in the dosimeter and in the test system to obtain the dose rate for the latter. Such a procedure neglects the contributions of Compton electrons from the container walls. These may be significant for small volume samples.

An alternate procedure is to use for the chemical dosimeter a material such as cyclohexane or benzene for which the yield of a readily measured product (H_2 in this case) is known. Purity of the reagents is a problem for such dosimeters.

Other chemical changes have been used for dosimeters, e.g., the production of HCl in chlorinated hydrocarbon–water systems, in which the pH change on irradiation is measured with suitable indicators,[42] and the production of phenols in benzoic acid–water[11] solutions.

4. *Phenomenological changes.* As with electrons, various property changes in monitoring materials have been correlated with gamma dose, e.g., darkening of silver-activated phosphate glass. Remarks made previously apply to gamma dosimetry as well.

References

Several of the following were cited in the text as authority for statements made. Others were not quoted but are included because they contain pertinent information. All were consulted in the preparation of this chapter.

1. Adair, R. K., Neutron Cross Sections, *Revs. Modern Phys., 22*(3): 249 (July 1950).
2. Aron, W. A., Hoffman, B. G., and Williams, F. C., *Range Energy Curves,* USAEC Report AECU-663, University of California Radiation Laboratory, May 1951.
3. Barschall, H. H., Rosen, L., Taschek, R. F., and Williams, J. H., Measurement of Fast Neutron Flux, *Revs. Modern Phys., 24*(1): 1 (January 1952).
4. Bethe, H. A., and Ashkin, J., Passage of Radiations Through Matter, in *Experimental Nuclear Physics,* Vol. I, p. 166, Segrè, E., (Ed.), John Wiley & Sons, Inc., New York, 1953.
5. Boag, J. W., Dolphin, G. W., and Rotblatt, J., Radiation Dosimetry by Transparent Plastics, *Radiation Research, 9*(6): 589 (December 1958).
6. Bray, D. T., and Leyse, C. F., Food Irradiation Reactor, *Nucleonics, 15*(7): 76 (July 1957).
7. Burrus, W. R., *Standard Instrumentation Techniques for Nuclear Environmental Testing,* Report WADC-TN-57-207, Wright Air Development Center, May 1957.
8. Cassen, B., A Gamma Ray Insensitive Semiconductor Fast Neutron Dosimeter Using Single Crystal Germanium, in *Proceedings of the First International Conference on the Peaceful Uses of Atomic Energy, Geneva, 1955,* Vol. 14, p. 218, United Nations, New York, 1956.
9. Cowan, F. P., and O'Brien, J. F., Methods of Measurement of Neutron Flux at Low Levels, in *Proceedings of the First International Conference on the Peaceful*

Uses of Atomic Energy, Geneva, 1955, Vol. 14, p. 213, United Nations, New York, 1956.

10. Davisson, C. M., and Evans, R. D., Gamma Ray Absorption Coefficients, *Revs. Modern Phys., 24*(2): 79 (April 1952).

11. Day, M. J., and Stein, G., Chemical Dosimetry of Ionizing Radiations, *Nucleonics, 8*(2): 34 (February 1951).

12. Dondes, S., A High Level Dosimeter for Detection of Beta and Gamma Radiations and Thermal Neutrons, in *Proceedings of the First International Conference on the Peaceful Uses of Atomic Energy, Geneva, 1955,* Vol. 14, p. 176, United Nations, New York, 1956.

13. Evans, R. D., *The Atomic Nucleus,* pp. 567–745, McGraw-Hill Book Company, Inc., New York, 1955.

14. Fano, U., Principles of Radiological Physics, in *Radiation Biology,* Vol. I, Pt. I, p. 1, Hollaender, A. (Ed.), McGraw-Hill Book Company, Inc., New York, 1954.

15. Fermi, E., Ionization Loss of Energy in Gases and Condensed Materials, *Phys. Rev., 57*(6): 485 (March 15, 1940).

16. Fowler, J. F., and Day, M. J., High Dose Measurements by Optical Absorption, *Nucleonics, 13*(12): 52 (December 1955).

17. Friedlander, G., and Kennedy, J. W., *Nuclear and Radiochemistry,* John Wiley & Sons, Inc., New York, 1955.

18. Glendenin, L. E., Determination of Energy of Beta Particles and Photons by Absorption, *Nucleonics, 2*(1): 12 (January 1948).

19. Glendenin, L. E., and Coryell, C. D., Relation Between Range and Energy of Beta Particles, Paper 11, p. 129, in *Radiochemical Studies: The Fission Products,* National Nuclear Energy Series, Div. IV, Vol. 9, McGraw-Hill Book Company, Inc., New York, 1951.

20. Greenfield, M. A., Koontz, R. L., Jarrett, A. A., and Taylor, J. K., Measuring Flux Absolutely with In Foils, *Nucleonics, 15*(3): 57 (March 1957).

21. Halliday, D., *Introductory Nuclear Physics,* 2nd ed., John Wiley & Sons, Inc., New York, 1955.

22. Hart, E. J., and Gordon, S., Gas Evolution for Dosimetry of High Gamma and Neutron Fluxes, *Nucleonics, 12*(4): 40 (April 1954).

23. Halpern, O., and Hall, H., The Ionization Loss of Energy of Fast Charged Particles in Gases and Condensed Media, *Phys. Rev., 73*(5): 477 (March 1, 1948).

24. Hochanadel, C. J., and Ghormley, J. A., A Calibration of Gamma Ray Actinometers, *J. Chem. Phys., 21*(5): 880 (May 1953).

25. Hummel, R. W., Van Cleave, A. B., and Spinks, J. W. T., Betatron Irradiations of Aqueous Ceric Sulfate Solutions, *Can. J. Chem., 31*(12): 1203 (December 1953).

26. Hughes, D. J., and Schwartz, R. B., *Neutron Cross Sections,* USAEC Report BNL-325, 2nd ed., Brookhaven National Laboratory, July 1958.

27. Hughes, D. J., *Pile Neutron Research,* Addison-Wesley Publishing Company, Inc., Cambridge, Mass., 1953.

28. Hughes, D. J., *Neutron Cross Sections,* Pergamon Press, New York, 1957.

29. Hurst, G. S., Techniques of Measuring Neutron Spectra with Threshold Detectors, *Rev. Sci. Instr., 27*(3): 153 (March 1956).

30. Hurst, G. S., Ritchie, R. H., and Mills, W. A., Fast Neutron Dosimetry, in *Proceedings of the First International Conference on the Peaceful Uses of Atomic Energy, Geneva, 1955,* Vol. 14, p. 220, United Nations, New York, 1956.

31. Jesse, W. P., and Sadauskis, J., Alpha-Particle Ionization in Pure Gases and the Average Energy to Make an Ion Pair, *Phys. Rev., 90*(6): 1120 (June 15, 1953).

32. Johns, H. E., and Laughlin, J. S., Interaction of Radiation with Matter, in *Radia-*

tion Dosimetry, p. 49, Hine, G. J., and Brownell, G. L., (Eds.), Academic Press, Inc., New York, 1956.

33. Jones, H. E., Till, J. E., and Cormack, D. V., Electron Energy Distributions Produced by Gamma Rays, *Nucleonics, 12*(10): 40 (October 1954).

34. Knipp, J., and Teller, E., On the Energy Loss of Heavy Ions, *Phys. Rev., 59*(8): 659 (April 15, 1941).

35. Lampe, F. W., High Energy Electron Irradiation of Neopentane, *J. Phys. Chem., 61*(7): 1015 (July 1957).

36. Lassen, N. O., Energy Loss and Total Charges of Fission Fragments Passing Through Matter, in *Proceedings of the First International Conference on the Peaceful Uses of Atomic Energy, Geneva, 1955.* Vol. 2, p. 214, United Nations, New York, 1956.

37. Lind, S. C., *The Chemical Effects of Alpha Particles and Electrons,* Chemical Catalog Company, Inc., New York, 1928.

38. Primak, W., Fast Neutron Damaging in Nuclear Reactors. I Radiation Damage Monitoring with the Electrical Conductivity of Graphite, *Nuclear Sci. Eng., 2*(1): 49 (January 1957).

39. Richardson, D. M., Allen, A. O., and Boyle, J. W., Dosimetry of Reactor Radiations by Calorimetric Measurement, in *Proceedings of the First International Conference on the Peaceful Uses of Atomic Energy, Geneva, 1955,* Vol. 14, p. 209, United Nations, New York, 1956.

40. Rossi, H. H., Neutrons and Mixed Radiations, in *Radiation Dosimetry,* p. 667, Hine, G. H., and Brownell, G. L., (Eds.), Academic Press, Inc., New York, 1956.

41. Schuler, R. H., and Allen, A. O., Yield of the Ferrous Radiation Dosimeter: An Improved Cathode Ray Determination, *J. Chem. Phys., 24*(1): 56 (January 1956).

42. Taplin, G. V., Chemical and Colorimetric Dosimeters, in *Radiation Dosimetry,* p. 357, Hine, G. J., and Brownell, G. L., (Ed.), Academic Press. Inc., New York, 1956.

43. Thompson, T. J., *Effects of Chemical Structure on Stopping Powers for High Energy Protons.* USAEC Report UCRL-1910, University of California Radiation Laboratory, August 1952.

44. Trice, J. B., *A Series of Thermal, Epithermal, and Fast Neutron Measurements in the MTR,* USAEC Report CF-55-10-140, Oak Ridge National Laboratory, October 1955.

45. Uthe, P. M., Jr., *Attainment of Neutron Flux Spectra from Foil Activation,* Report USAFIT-TR-57-3, Wright-Patterson Air Force Base, March 1957.

46. Weiss, J., Allen, A. O., and Schwartz, H. A., Use of the Fricke Ferrous Sulfate Dosimeter for Gamma-Ray Doses in the Range 4 to 40 kr, in *Proceedings of the First International Conference on the Peaceful Uses of Atomic Energy, Geneva, 1955,* Vol. 14, p. 179, United Nations, New York, 1956.

47. Weiss, J., Chemical Dosimetry Using Ferrous and Ceric Sulphates, *Nucleonics, 10*(7): 28 (July 1952).

CHAPTER 3

Mechanisms of Chemical Effects of Ionizing Radiation

By Amos S. Newton

3-1 Fundamental Considerations

The theoretical treatment of the physical aspects of the absorption of ionizing radiation in matter is comparatively well understood except for very slow particles. Similar treatment of the chemical aspects, however, is in a much less satisfactory state. Many of the proposed mechanisms of chemical action are the results of deductive reasoning based on the chemical products produced in various systems, and many fundamental mechanisms involve adaption or extrapolation of processes from photochemical studies.

There are some basic differences between photochemistry and radiation chemistry. (1) In photochemical studies the absorption of a single photon results in the primary excitation of only a single molecule. On the other hand, ionizing radiation produces excitation in many molecules before its total energy is absorbed. (2) In photochemistry the excited species are randomly distributed throughout the volume (a concentration gradient may exist in a highly absorbing system). In radiation chemistry the species are distributed in clusters along the path of the radiation. (3) A third difference is that light may excite a molecule to only one of a few of its possible excited states, whereas passage of ionizing radiation can, in principle, produce all possible excited states of the molecules and the molecule ion. Thus the initial situation resulting from an ionizing particle is much more complicated than that resulting from the absorption of light.

3-1.1 Nature of Ionizing-radiation Tracks

Ionizing radiations produce a series of randomly distributed primary events along the path of the particle or ray. Secondary events are clustered about the sites of these primary interactions. Gamma rays act primarily to produce Compton electrons, and these primary ionizations are far apart. For example, a 1-Mev gamma ray has a mean distance of penetration into aluminum of about 6.2 cm before it produces a Compton electron. The average energy of this electron will be 0.45 Mev, and a scattered gamma average energy of 0.55 Mev will be formed. The mean thickness of aluminum penetrated before a second Compton electron is formed by this scattered gamma ray will be another 4.75 cm. Thus for all practical purposes gamma rays can be considered as producing Compton electrons randomly in the absorber.

In light elements the fluorescent X rays resulting from the Compton scattering process or from the photoelectric absorption of gamma rays are of low energy. They cause low-energy photoelectrons to be formed near the site of the initial event but still remote as far as direct interaction with any excited species formed by the initial electron is concerned. These Compton electrons and photoelectrons result in the formation of excited ions of the molecules concerned. In gamma-ray irradiations, however, the bulk of the ionization and excitation comes from further interactions by the Compton electrons.

A fast electron interacts to form secondary electrons. These secondaries are called "delta rays" when they have sufficient energy to produce further secondaries. This division between delta rays and other low-energy secondary electrons is at about 75 to 100 ev. Only about 5% of the primary fast-electron interactions result in delta rays. Thus these rays are the exception rather than the rule. Delta rays, however, cause about half the total ionization from fast electrons because some of them carry considerable energy and produce further low-energy secondaries along their own tracks. The electrons of energies less than 100 ev result in a cluster of ionizations and excitations of less than 10 A (angstroms) $(1A = 10^{-8}$ cm) radius.[15,35] Such a cluster is generally referred to as a "spur." This cluster will contain an average of 1 to 5 ions, 2 to 10 excited molecules, and less than about 20 unexcited molecules based on the energy dissipation per ion pair in the gas phase (about 25 to 32 ev per ion pair for most substances).[25] The delta rays dissipate their energy in the same manner as the faster electrons except that the spurs they produce are closer together since the delta rays are less energetic than the primary electrons.

From this description a fast-electron track may be pictured as a string of small randomly spaced spurs. Each of these spurs is essentially independent of its neighbors. Branching off from this primary track are other strings of such spurs. These are the delta rays, which also are formed in a random fashion along the track. This picture applies whether the primary radiation is gamma rays or high-energy electrons.† Table 3.1 shows this equivalence for Co[60] gamma rays and 2-Mev electrons. For these two radiations there was no difference in the yield of the ferrous sulfate dosimeter, which is sensitive to differences in linear energy transfer (LET).

---

† A high-intensity electron beam can effectively saturate a target, and the concept of independent tracks would not apply. The saturation current depends on the nature of the beam and the lifetime of the spurs. For some processes electron beams of about 100 ma and 3 Mev have been interpreted as producing overlapping of tracks in a 2-μsec pulse.[32] This is a dose rate of about 10^{10} rads/sec.

Table 3.1—YIELDS OF THE FERROUS SULFATE DOSIMETER
WITH VARIOUS RADIATIONS

Radiation	Source	Energy, Mev	Yield of ferric ions/100 ev ($G_{Fe^{+3}}$)
Electrons[38]	Van de Graaff	2	15.45 ± 0.11
Gamma rays[24]	Co^{60}	1.25 gamma ray	15.6 ± 0.3
		0.5 e^- (av.)	
Electrons[28]	Tritium	0.00569 (av.)	12.9
Deuterons[37]	Cyclotron	18	11.6
		10	10.7
Helium ions[27]	Cyclotron	35	9.0
		10	6.8
Alpha particles[28]	Po^{210}	5.30	6.2

The tracks of heavy positive ions, such as protons, alpha particles, and helium ions, are somewhat different in character but only because the primary ionizations are much closer together. They are so close together in alpha-particle tracks that they may be considered as one continuous

Table 3.2—AVERAGE DISTANCES BETWEEN DELTA RAYS AND BETWEEN
PRIMARY IONIZATIONS IN ELECTRON, PROTON, AND
HELIUM-ION TRACKS[a]

Particle	Particle energy, Mev	Average distance between delta rays (electrons >100 ev), A	Average distance between primary ionizations (spurs + delta ray), A
Electron	0.01	5,800	326
	0.1	44,000	2,170
	0.5	116,000	4,800
	1.0	132,000	5,700
Proton	1.0	328	25
	5.0	1,560	105
	10.0	3,130	191
Helium ion (alpha ray)	1.0	24	1.9
	5.0	102	7.7
	10.0	200	14.2

[a] Calculated from data of Lea[27] for biological tissue with a density of 1 and composition $C_1H_{10}O_{5.21}N_{0.29}$ (Ca, Mg, Na, Cl, etc.)$_{0.031}$. Data for most organic materials will show the same order of magnitude of values when corrected for density.

column of ionization and excitation, i.e., the distance between the primary ionizations, as shown in Table 3.2, is less than the diameter of a spur. Some delta rays branch off from this column, but most of these are of low energy. Hence alpha tracks are very compact. Proton tracks are more diffuse, but even here the primary ionizations, especially near the end of the tracks, show a density of about 400 times that of primary ionizations from an electron of comparable energy. Thus chemical differences resulting from differences in the density of ionization and excitation are less pronounced between protons and electrons than between helium ions and electrons.

As the ionizing particles are slowed down, the density of ionization increases and the spurs become more closely spaced. Near the ends of proton and alpha-particle tracks the density of ionization is very high owing to the Bragg effect. At very low energies protons and alpha particles capture electrons and become electrically neutral. A local increase in temperature results when these particles are finally reduced to thermal energies by molecular collisions with the absorber.

The fate of slow electrons with energies below the lowest electronic excitation potential of the absorber (about 3 to 5 ev for many organic materials) is less clearly understood. Because these electrons can no longer produce electronic excitations, their energy must be dissipated by collisions in which vibrational, rotational, and translational states in the absorber are excited.[34] In mixtures containing a material with many low-lying energy levels, the collisions may produce high excitation by successive low-excitation steps.[8] For the electron to recombine with a positive ion, its energy must be reduced to about 0.1 ev. Thus the slow electron must make many collisions before it is captured.

3-1.2 TIME SCALE OF EVENTS

The ultimate chemical effects produced by radiation are dependent upon the relative times required for various competitive physical processes to occur in the system. Although these times are very short by observational standards, they may be long by atomic standards. One microsecond is a short time on an observational scale, but a molecular bond goes through some 10^7 vibrational cycles in that time. In a gas at 1 atm, dissociation of an excited molecule may occur in a few vibrational cycles to the exclusion of a process such as fluorescence, which requires a time longer than 10^{-9} sec ($> 10^4$ vibrational cycles).

The times required for some processes of interest to radiation chemistry are shown[14] in Fig. 3.1. Those that occur in a time shorter than 10^{-14} sec all involve primary electronic processes in the molecule. The fastest molecular reaction is dissociation in a single vibrational cycle, which occurs in about 10^{-13} sec. Other molecular events require milliseconds. Some free radicals that are formed by secondary processes in the bulk solution may have lives measured in seconds; in some polymerization reactions radicals have been observed for days after irradiation.[12]

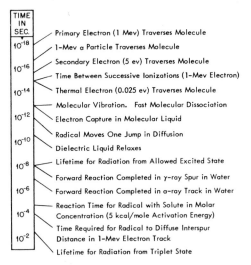

FIG. 3.1 Approximate time scale for some events in radiation chemistry. (From H. A. Dewhurst, A. H. Samuel, and J. L. Magee, *Radiation Research,* Ref. 14.)

3-1.3 PRIMARY PROCESSES IN RADIATION CHEMISTRY

The passage of radiation through matter causes primarily ions and electronically excited states of molecules. These primary reactions have been summarized in various ways by Burton and others.[4,5,10] In the reactions given below, the broken arrow designates the interaction of the molecule M with ionizing radiation. An excited singlet state of M is shown as M′, and an excited triplet state, as M‴. The further reactions of these ions and excited species are dependent on their properties and will be discussed in Sect. 3-1.4.

$$M \longrightarrow\!\!\!\text{-}\!\!\!\text{vw}\!\!\!\longrightarrow M^{+} + e^{-} \tag{3.1}$$

$$M \longrightarrow\!\!\!\text{-}\!\!\!\text{vw}\!\!\!\longrightarrow M^{++} + 2e^{-} \tag{3.2}$$

$$M \longrightarrow\!\!\!\text{-}\!\!\!\text{vw}\!\!\!\longrightarrow M' \tag{3.3}$$

$$M \longrightarrow\!\!\!\text{-}\!\!\!\text{vw}\!\!\!\longrightarrow M''' \tag{3.4}$$

The number of doubly charged ions initially formed from polyatomic molecules is unknown since most of them dissociate rapidly into two positive ions. In mass spectrometry monatomic gases (except helium) give about 10% of the total ionization current as doubly charged ions. With complicated molecules such doubly charged ions occur in much less abundance owing to their immediate fragmentation. In condensed phases two fates of doubly charged ions are possible. The first is the splitting of the ion into two positive-ion fragments because of the high repulsion of the two positive charges

$$M^{++} \rightarrow A^+ + B^+ \tag{3.5}$$

The second is a charge-exchange reaction in which two singly charged molecule ions are formed

$$M^{++} + M \rightarrow 2M^+ \tag{3.6}$$

The latter reaction requires that the ionization potential for M^{++} be more than twice that for M^+. Only a few ionization potentials of doubly charged ions of polyatomic molecules have been measured. In these cases the values for the doubly charged ions are from 2.5 to 3 times those for the singly charged ions.

3-1.4 Excited States of Molecules

The classification of the energy states of excited polyatomic molecules is quite complicated. Atoms have only electronically excited states to be considered. Polyatomic molecules, however, show electronic, vibrational, and rotational excitations, and every electronically excited state has an accompanying set of vibrational and rotation states. On an energy scale differences between rotational states are represented by about 0.01 ev, vibrational states by about 0.1 ev, and electronic states by the order of 3 ev. In absorption spectra rotational excitation shows as absorption in the microwave and far infrared regions; vibrational excitations absorb in the near infrared; and electronic excitations absorb in the ultraviolet.

For diatomic molecules the electronic and vibrational states can be represented on a potential-energy diagram, a curve representing the potential energy of the molecule as a function of the interatomic distance. More complicated molecules cannot be represented directly by two-dimensional figures. Even though the more complicated molecules are of greater interest, it is convenient to illustrate typical types of transitions between energy states by potential-energy diagrams for diatomic molecules. As a very rough approximation, such a curve may be considered as representing the potential energy of one bond between two groups in a polyatomic molecule. Since this curve would then be a slice through a polydimensional figure, it must be considered as a smeared line because of interactions with other bonds in the molecule.

In Fig. 3.2 curve E_G represents the electronic ground state of a diatomic molecule. The molecule has an equilibrium interatomic distance at the minimum in the curve. The horizontal lines on the curve represent a few of the vibrational levels in this lowest electronic state. These vibrational energy levels have energies defined by the vibrational quantum number, n, but the energy of the level is given by the term, $n + \frac{1}{2}$. Thus the lowest vibrational level, $n = 0$, still has vibrational energy. This lowest vibrational energy is known as the zero-point energy. At room temperature most molecules are in the lowest vibrational level.

Transitions to higher electronic states can occur from any point in the vibrational cycle, but the transition probability is higher from some points than from others. On a classical basis, considering the diatomic molecule as a harmonic oscillator, the probability of transition would be greatest from the ends of the cycle since the momentum of the atoms must be reversed at these points; and the time spent at the ends of the cycles would be greater than that spent in the center. On the basis of quantum mechanics, however, the transition probability from the lowest vibrational level is greatest at the center of the vibrational cycle, and such transitions have been so drawn in Figs. 3.2 through 3.5. Higher vibrational levels exhibit high transition probabilities near the ends of the cycles and also have high transition probabilities at certain intermediate points that are maxima in the wave function of the level.

3-1.4.1 *Singlet and Triplet States*

In the normal configuration of most molecules, the shared electrons in a given bond between atoms are paired with regard to electron spin, and the spin effects (resultant spin) cancel. The multiplicity† of a state in regard to the resultant spin, s, is $2s + 1$. Thus, when the electrons are paired, the resultant spin is zero, and the multiplicity of the state is one. This is the singlet state. In a triplet state the electrons are unpaired, the resultant spin is one, and the multiplicity is three. For every excited singlet state of a molecule, there is a corresponding triplet state. This is usually at a lower energy than the corresponding singlet state. For saturated molecules many of these triplet states may be dissociative, i.e., result in dissociation. The lowest triplet state in hydrogen is dissociative.

Transitions between singlet and triplet states are forbidden by the laws of quantum mechanics, i.e., the selection rules for all optical transitions (transitions excited by light) demand that there be no change in spin ($\Delta s = 0$). However, transitions between singlet and triplet states do occur; but, with molecules containing light elements, absorption of optical radiation corresponding to these transitions is very weak. On the other hand, in work with ionizing radiations, Burton[4,5] has estimated the number of primary excitations to singlet states by electron impact to be twice the number of ions, and the number of excitations to triplet states to be as much as 8% of the singlet excitations.

Molecules in the triplet state, containing unpaired electrons, are paramagnetic and may be considered as diradicals. The ground state of molecular oxygen is a triplet state, and this accounts for many of its reactions in radiation chemistry as well as in ordinary chemistry.

---

† A nonrigorous concept of multiplicity is that there are $2s + 1$ ways in which the resultant spin can couple with the orbital angular momentum along the molecular axis to yield the total angular momentum along this axis.

In principle, ionizing radiation can produce all possible excited states. The only theoretical calculations on the distribution of such states are those of Bethe.[31] He showed that, of the hydrogen atoms affected by high-energy-electron impact, about 50% are in the first excited state, 7.8% in the second excited state, 6.7% in higher states, and 32.5% are ionized. Such calculations are not feasible for molecules, but it is expected that the proportion in excited states higher than the first excited state will be greater for molecules than for atomic hydrogen.

The processes by which a molecule in an excited state can dissipate its energy are governed by two principles. First is the Franck-Condon principle: electronic transitions, because of their great speed, must occur without change in interatomic distances in the molecule. The second is the resonance principle: the more closely matched the energy levels of two states, the more probable the transfer of energy between them.

1. *Dissociation:* On excitation, a molecule will dissociate if it is excited to a repulsive state (no minimum in the potential-energy curve) or to a vibrational or rotational level above the dissociation limit for the state.

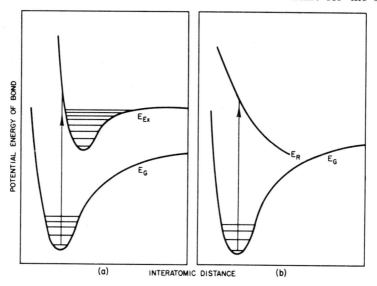

Fig. 3.2 Schematic representation of dissociation of a diatomic molecule by electronic excitation processes. (a) Excitation to a point in the electronic state, E_{Ex}, above the dissociation limit. (b) Excitation to an electronic state, E_R, which is repulsive, i.e., has no minimum in potential energy and is dissociative at all points.

These dissociations are illustrated in Fig. 3.2. They occur on the first vibrational cycle (about 10^{-13} sec) and result in formation of two radicals each with excess kinetic energy. In polyatomic molecules, even though the initial vibrational level of the excited state is below the dissociation limit, sufficient vibrational energy for dissociation may in time be transferred to one bond. This is a slower process than direct dissociation.

2. *Predissociation:* This is another process that can result in dissociation. In predissociation the potential-energy curve of an excited state of a molecule crosses that of another state that is dissociative, either because the crossing state is a repulsive state or because the vibrational level at the crossover point is above the dissociation limit of the crossing state. These two conditions are shown in Fig. 3.3. The molecule in vibration will at some

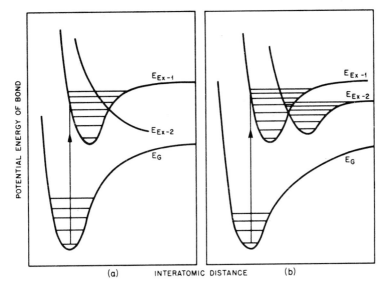

FIG. 3.3 Schematic representation of two types of predissociation processes for a diatomic molecule. (a) Excitation to a vibrational level in the electronic excited state, E_{Ex-1}, which is higher than the crossing point of a repulsive state, E_{Ex-2}. (b) Excitation to a vibrational level in the electronic excited state, E_{Ex-1}, which is above the dissociation limit of a crossing state, E_{Ex-2}.

point in the vibrational cycle be at the same interatomic distance as that of the dissociative state, and sooner or later the crossover will occur. Because the vibrational levels do not match exactly, the crossing over from one state to the other may be as slow as 10^{-9} sec. In complicated molecules, if the vibrational level of the electronic excited state is higher in energy than the dissociation energy of the weakest bond in the molecule, predissociation is a relatively probable process.

3. *Internal conversion:* This is a process by which electronic energy is converted to vibrational energy. If this is to occur, a vibrational level in the excited state must match a high-lying vibrational level in a lower electronic state. A crossover between the states can then occur, as shown in Fig. 3.4, leaving the molecule at an effective high vibrational energy that

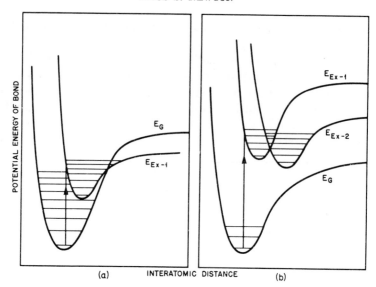

FIG. 3.4 Schematic representation of internal conversion processes with a diatomic molecule. (a) Excitation to a vibrational level in the electronic excited state, E_{Ex-1}, from which a crossover to a high-lying vibrational level in E_G can occur. From this level the energy can be dissipated by collisional deactivation of the vibrational levels. (b) Excitation to a high vibrational level in the electronic excited state, E_{Ex-1}, from which a crossover is possible to a vibrational level in E_{Ex-2}.

can be dissipated by collisions. This process is the principal one by which a singlet state is converted to the corresponding triplet state, which lies at a slightly lower energy. This latter process is called "intersystem crossing."

4. *Fluorescence (or luminescence):* This is the emission of light by a molecule in passing from an excited state to a lower state as shown in Fig. 3.5. The time requirement in the excited state is 10^{-9} sec or longer for an allowed transition. If the transition is a forbidden one, e.g., triplet state to singlet state, the time is usually longer than 10^{-6} sec; the process is called "phosphorescence." In polyatomic molecules the transition may occur to any one of several vibrational levels or to states intermediate with the ground state; thus the spectra of fluorescent radiation can be quite complicated. Deactivation of vibrational levels by radiationless transitions is common in polyatomic molecules because the vibrational energy in one bond can be dissipated in other bonds of the molecule.

5. *External conversion (or excitation transfer):* This can occur in a system containing two or more molecules if the excited state of molecule A is near some vibrational level in an excited state of molecule B

$$A^* + B \rightarrow B^* + A \tag{3.7}$$

This process is known as "quenching" because it was first observed in studies of fluorescence when such a transfer of energy quenched the fluorescence of molecule A. The excitation of B can result in dissociation, called "chemical quenching," or can simply result in molecule B being left with increased vibrational, rotational, and translational energy. The latter case is called "physical quenching." Chemical quenching of the 2537-A resonance line of excited mercury atoms is the basis of many photochemical studies, i.e., the mercury-sensitized decompositions. Here mercury vapor is added to the material under study and radiation is absorbed by the mercury atoms. The energy is transferred to the material, causing its decomposition. Physical quenching is also called "collisional deactivation."

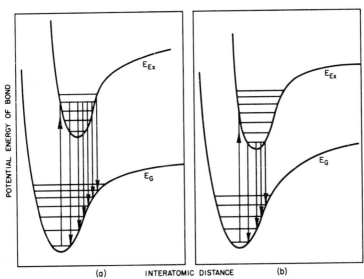

FIG. 3.5 Schematic representation of two excitation processes followed by deactivation of the excited state by fluorescence in a diatomic molecule. (a) Excitation to a high vibrational level in the electronic excited state, E_{Ex}, from which transitions occur to various vibrational levels in E_G with emission of light (fluorescent radiation). (b) Excitation to a high vibrational level in the electronic excited state, E_{Ex}, followed by a radiationless transition to the lowest vibrational level of E_{Ex}. From this level transitions occur to various levels in E_G with fluorescence.

This excitation transfer is probable in systems of polyatomic molecules owing to the availability of many degrees of vibrational freedom. This increases the probability of matching the energies of states in two molecules. Excitation transfer is of importance in scintillation counters where the process of sensitized fluorescence is used. The excitation energy of the solvent can be transferred to the sensitizer, which then dissipates the energy in fluorescence. The process is also important in radiation protection. If transfer of energy occurs between molecules with exactly matching energy states, it is known as "resonance transfer." Resonance transfer between like molecules is a highly effective and rapid method of spreading excited molecules away from their initial sites of formation in the spurs.

The previous discussion of the fate of excited states applies equally well to excited singlet and triplet states; however, transitions with the latter occur only to lower triplet states. Transitions from triplet to lower singlet states, including the ground state, are forbidden. Unless the state is dissociative, molecules will have a long life in the first excited triplet state before decay by a forbidden fluorescence to the singlet ground state. This time may be as long as milliseconds or even seconds; thus molecules in the first excited triplet state have many opportunities for reactions with radicals or molecules to produce chemical effects before they are deactivated.

3-1.4.2 *Positive Ions and Ion Neutralization*

The positive ions formed in the track and spurs must eventually be neutralized. The time for this process in the liquid state has been estimated by Samuel and Magee[35] to be of the order of 10^{-13} sec, about equal to one vibrational cycle. Platzman[34] suggests a much longer time. At present the lifetime of positive ions in liquids is indeterminate. In the gas phase there is no question that a long time cycle applies since the electron escapes from the vicinity of the positive ion immediately. The main difference in the effect of short or long time cycles is whether or not ion dissociations occur before neutralization and whether or not charge exchange with molecules of lower ionization potential can occur before neutralization. Ion reactions are probably not the predominant feature of the radiolysis mechanism in most liquid systems. The complexity of the over-all reactions is such that it has not been possible to isolate ionic mechanisms for proof experiments.

Mass-spectrometer studies, in which electrons of 50 to 100 ev are used to irradiate molecules in the gas phase, show that most molecule ions dissociate into fragments. Thus the molecule ion is formed in an excited state in a large number of cases. Highly symmetrical molecules, such as carbon tetrachloride, neopentane, and tertiary butyl alcohol, yield no parent molecule ions. This suggests that the ground state and all excited states of these molecule ions are dissociative. In the general case, however, the initial ionization leaves either an excited- or a ground-state molecule ion. If an excited state is formed, it can dissociate before recombination if the long time cycle is assumed

$$M^{+*} \rightarrow A^+ + B \tag{3.8}$$

where A^+ and B can be a radical ion and a radical, respectively. The dissociation can also proceed by molecular disproportionation to yield a molecule ion and a molecule

$$M^{+*} \rightarrow M_1^+ + M_2 \tag{3.9}$$

One of the molecules, M_1 or M_2, will be unsaturated; and the gain in energy from the formation of the double bond will make the process exothermic.

In both these processes the charge is generally carried by the fragment of lower ionization potential. The mass spectra of organic compounds are abundantly filled with examples of both types of ion fragmentation. The molecular dissociation requires an atom transfer (usually hydrogen); therefore Reaction 3.9 is a slower process than Reaction 3.8, which can occur in a single vibrational cycle. With many organic compounds, however, molecular fragmentation predominates. Lower molecular weight molecule ions result. These may be the largest peaks in the mass spectrum. For example, with butyric acid, mass 60, CH_3COOH^+ is the largest peak in the mass spectrum.

In a system containing two types of molecules, charge exchange can occur with the molecule of lower ionization potential

$$M^+ + A \rightarrow A^+ + M \tag{3.10}$$

Such an exchange in the liquid state demands a long life for the positive ions. This is a mechanism of possible importance in the "protection" of organic materials through the use of additives of low ionization potential. Resonance charge exchange with like molecules is also a mechanism by which ions can be rapidly diffused away from the spurs.

When an ion recombines with an electron, a highly excited state of the molecule is formed. Capture of the electron by the ion with simultaneous emission of radiation in a transition to the ground state is not a very probable process. The dissipation of the recombination energy by such excited states follows the mechanisms of dissociation, internal conversion, fluorescence, or external conversion, as outlined previously.

3-1.5 SECONDARY PROCESSES IN RADIATION CHEMISTRY

Secondary processes occur after the primary ionization and excitation and lead to final chemical effects. With such processes the principle of microscopic reversibility must not be violated, i.e., on the atomic or molecular scale, each individual step in a mechanism must be reversible even though the complete macroscopic process is irreversible. Thus a mechanism for dissociation of a molecule into two radicals by a unimolecular process cannot be formulated unless the radicals can recombine without the presence of a third body.

3-1.5.1 *Molecular and Radical Processes*

An excited molecule can dissociate into two radicals or into two molecules. Any excess energy can be partially converted into kinetic energy. Radicals formed with high kinetic energy are termed "hot" radicals. The excited molecule, M^*, can be the result of either an initial excitation or an ion recombination

$$M^* \rightarrow R_1 + R_2 \qquad (3.11)$$

$$M^* \rightarrow M_1 + M_2 \qquad (3.12)$$

When the molecular-dissociation process occurs, the molecules represent final products of the radiolysis. This is a slower process than Reaction 3.11 since it requires the shift of an atom (usually hydrogen). If the radical dissociation occurs, the free radicals formed may engage in the following types of reactions.[35]

1. *Radical–radical recombination reactions:* These occur primarily in the spurs where the concentration of radicals is high

$$R_1 + R_2 \rightarrow M \qquad (3.13)$$

$$R_x + R_y \rightarrow M_3 \qquad (3.14)$$

Reaction 3.13 represents a recombination of radicals to the original molecule and results in no net effect. Reaction 3.14 represents the reaction of two radicals that combine to form a new molecule, different from M. If the two radicals in Reaction 3.14 are hydrogen radicals, a third body must be present to conserve energy and momentum. The activation energy for such a radical–radical combination is generally quite low and may be zero for many radicals, but there are steric factors that may reduce the probability of recombination.

2. *Radical–radical disproportionation reactions:* These also occur, usually with transfer of a hydrogen atom. Thus two ethyl radicals may combine to form butane by Reaction 3.14 or disproportionate to form ethylene and ethane by Reaction 3.15

$$C_2H_5\cdot + C_2H_5\cdot \rightarrow C_2H_4 + C_2H_6 \qquad (3.15)$$

Such reactions have small activation energies and are highly exothermic because of the energy gained in forming the double bond. The two radicals need not be identical for disproportionation reactions to occur.

3. *Abstraction reactions.* Radicals in the spur or radicals that escape from the spur may react with molecules to abstract a hydrogen atom. Such reactions must be exothermic to occur. They have activation energies of 5 to 10 kcal/mole.

$$R\cdot + MH \rightarrow M\cdot + RH \qquad (3.16)$$

The radical $M\cdot$ cannot react with molecules MH by the mechanism in Reaction 3.16 since this would produce no net change. Therefore $M\cdot$ radicals have a long life in the bulk of the solution and disappear only by radical–radical combinations, radical dissociation, or by reaction with radical scavengers. In unsaturated compounds M· can disappear by addition to the double bond (Reaction 3.22). The reaction

$$M· + M· \rightarrow MM \tag{3.17}$$

can account in part for the apparent dimerization of many molecules under irradiation. If M· is a large radical, a decomposition into a smaller molecule and radical can occur

$$M· \rightarrow M_1 + R_1· \tag{3.18}$$

The activation energy of this process is high for hydrocarbon radicals (20 to 40 kcal/mole) but occurs with a low activation energy for large polyhalogen radicals, in which case $R_1·$ is usually the halide atom.

3-1.5.2 Radical Scavengers

Certain molecules possess a high affinity for radicals and may react with them on almost every collision. For example, an added stable free radical such as diphenylpicrylhydrazyl (DPPH), nitric oxide (NO), or an oxygen molecule, which has two unpaired electrons (a diradical), reacts readily with free radicals

$$R· + NO \rightarrow RNO \rightarrow Products \tag{3.19}$$
$$R· + O_2 \rightarrow RO_2· \tag{3.20}$$

Thus irradiations in which nitric oxide or oxygen is added yield less of some products but may yield more of others, this yield depending on how the products of Reactions 3.19 and 3.20 enter into the over-all reaction sequence. All halogen molecules are radical scavengers in organic systems owing to the weakness of the halogen–halogen bond compared with carbon–halogen bonds. The reaction

$$R· + I_2 \rightarrow RI + I· \tag{3.21}$$

is energetically favorable for practically all radicals, and iodine has been widely used to study the formation of radicals in various systems under irradiation. It also has the advantage that the amount of iodine consumed is easily determined by use of a spectrophotometer.[20,42]

The most general radical scavenger and the one most likely to influence radiation effects in organic systems is an unsaturated molecule. Radicals add to a double bond quite readily

$$R· + C_2H_4 \rightarrow RCH_2CH_2· \tag{3.22}$$

A reaction of this type is the first step in the radical catalyzed polymerization of unsaturated hydrocarbons and vinyl derivatives in general. The succeeding steps are additions of more olefin to the product radical. The chain is finally terminated by a radical–radical reaction. Activation energies of 0.2 to 10 kcal/mole have been found for the addition of hydrogen atoms to various olefins and aromatics.[39]

In the study of a chemical compound initially containing dissolved oxygen or an unsaturated impurity, the effect of the radical scavenger (or excitation scavenger if it has lower excited states than the system under study) is to reduce the yield of products until the scavenger is removed from the system. Similarly the production of an unsaturated compound as a product may produce a change in yields of various products with increased time of irradiation. Thus the true yields from a pure compound must be determined at near zero irradiation, usually by an extrapolation technique (see Sect. 3-4.6).

3-2 Effects of Physical State

The rate of energy absorption from an ionizing radiation per unit mass of absorber is dependent only on the type of matter present and is, to a first approximation, independent of the physical state. The density in space and the subsequent distribution of the ionized and excited species produced are markedly dependent on the physical state, and some of the processes by which products are formed are influenced by this distribution.

3-2.1 Gaseous State

Irradiations in the gaseous state are characterized by the physical freedom of the primary products of the exposure. Thus ions formed have long lifetimes because the electron and positive ion are immediately separated. Similarly excited states that dissociate into free radicals do so to leave the radicals widely spaced with little chance for primary recombination. This low chance of primary recombination results in a higher yield of products from most organic compounds when they are irradiated in the gaseous state than when irradiated in the liquid or solid state. In addition, the presence of long-lived ions in the gaseous state can result in reactions in which negative ions are formed by electron attachment to polar molecules and reactions between positive ions and molecules. Such reactions are not probable in the liquid state.

3-2.1.1 *Ion–Molecule Reactions*

From mass-spectrometer studies of the ionization patterns of mixtures of gases at high pressures, ions in the gas phase have been found to react with molecules to yield product ions heavier than the parent molecule. The collision cross section for such reactions is large (up to 10^{-14} cm^2), and the rate constants are also large, indicating reaction at every collision.[21] Some typical reactions that have been observed are the following.[17,26,40]

$$CH_4^+ + CH_4 \rightarrow CH_5^+ + CH_3\cdot \qquad (3.23)$$

$$CH_3^+ + CH_4 \rightarrow C_2H_5^+ + H_2 \qquad (3.24)$$

$$C_2H_4^+ + C_2H_4 \rightarrow C_3H_5^+ + CH_3\cdot \qquad (3.25)$$

$$\rightarrow C_4H_7^+ + H\cdot$$

$$C_2H_2^+ + C_2H_4 \rightarrow C_3H_3^+ + CH_3\cdot \qquad (3.26)$$

$$C_2H_2^+ + C_2H_2 \rightarrow C_4H_3^+ + H\cdot \qquad (3.27)$$

$$\rightarrow C_4H_2^+ + H_2$$

$$H_2O^+ + H_2O \rightarrow H_3O^+ + OH \qquad (3.28)$$

$$CH_3^+ + C_6H_{14} \rightarrow CH_4 + C_6H_{13}^+ \qquad (3.29)$$

Reactions such as Reactions 3.24 through 3.27 provide a mechanism by which high-molecular-weight hydrocarbons can be produced in the radiolysis of low-molecular-weight gases. Neutralization of the product ions leads to radicals that, on combination with other radicals of the same or a different type, yield products containing severalfold more carbon atoms than the original gas molecule.

Such reactions have high cross sections; and, therefore, their specific rate constants are high. These reactions can thus compete very favorably with other reactions in the radiation chemistry of gases. Their possible role in the radiation chemistry of liquids has not been determined. If ion recombination in the liquid state is fast ($<10^{-12}$ sec), then they probably are unimportant; but, if it is as long as 10^{-9} sec, then such reactions can compete with other processes. Schuler[36] suggests that they can occur in the radiolysis of liquid alkyl halides.

3-2.1.2 Radical Reactions

Radical reactions, as discussed in Sect. 3-1.5.1, are fairly well understood from the results of photochemistry.[39] Reactions of monatomic radicals require the presence of a third body for momentum and energy conservation. In the gaseous state, wall effects are common. Radical reactions are one of the principal paths by which final products are formed in the radiolysis of gases. However, molecule ion reactions and molecular decompositions are also important contributors to the yield of products. The temperature of the system exposed to ionizing radiations must be considered in the formulation of reaction mechanisms. Many of the radical chain reactions observed in high-temperature photolysis or in thermal-degradation studies will not occur at lower temperatures. The activation energy of such secondary processes must always be considered.

3-2.2 LIQUID STATE

The study of the liquid state is complicated by the existence of the Franck-Rabinowitch cage effect, which was first applied in the photochemistry of liquids. The radical and excited species formed in a spur are "caged" near their site of formation by collisions with the surrounding molecules of liquids. After the primary excitations the cage effect maintains for some time a high concentration of radicals and long-lived excited molecules formed in the spurs. This increases the probability of recombination or radical–radical reactions compared to the probability of such reactions in the gas phase. The effect is particularly noticed in the total yield of products, which, in general, is lower in the liquid phase than in the gas phase. Although other effects may enter, the major portion of this difference must be assigned to recombination of the primary fragments to re-form the original molecule. If fragmentation of a molecule occurs to give a hydrogen atom, that portion of the energy which results in kinetic energy will be almost all carried by the hydrogen atom

$$MH^* \rightarrow M\cdot + H\cdot \tag{3.30}$$

Owing to its small size, a hydrogen atom can escape from the cage more readily than can heavier radicals.

Another feature of the liquid state is the importance of the deactivation of excited states by processes similar to the quenching of fluorescence in the photochemistry of gases. Because the collision time between molecules in a liquid is of the same order as the time for one vibration, excited states that have lifetimes longer than a few vibrational cycles can be effectively quenched by collisional deactivation. This argument also applies to the ions formed in the liquid. Those formed in excited states with lifetimes greater than 10^{-12} sec will have a high probability of being deactivated, hence, a low probability of dissociation. Thus the consideration of ionic species in the liquid state is effectively limited to the molecule ion. One molecule-ion reaction of possible importance in the liquid and solid states has been postulated[4]

$$MH^+ + MH + e^- \rightarrow MM + H_2 \tag{3.31}$$

Here the neutralization of the molecule ion effectively occurs at the same time as collision with another molecule. Such a reaction has little probability of occurrence in the gas phase, where molecular collisions are less frequent, but it may occur in the liquid state where the molecule ion is in collision with some molecule almost continuously.

Solvent interactions, e.g., solvation, can affect the reactivity of excited species in the liquid state. Even a weak solvation greatly increases the probability of internal conversion of excited electronic states. A strong solvation in a polar liquid can change the character of the reactive species completely. In water a positive ion will always be solvated $[M^+(H_2O)_n]$ when it has only thermal kinetic energy owing to charge interactions with the water dipole.

3-2.3 SOLID STATE

Solids may be divided into (1) conductors in which there are free electrons in the conduction band and electron mobility is very high, (2) semiconductors in which only a small activation energy is necessary to raise an electron to the conduction band, and (3) dielectrics in which all electrons are bound. Most pure organic materials are dielectrics; therefore conductors and semiconductors will not be discussed here nor will displacement of heavy atoms in such materials be considered. These have been reviewed recently elsewhere.[23] Many studies have been made on the coloration of crystalline solids by radiation. This event is related to the absorption of light by displaced electrons and the resulting electron vacancies in the crystal lattice of such solids. Fewer studies have been made on the chemical effects of radiation in such crystalline solid materials.

With organic solids the yields of primary bond cleavages and free radicals do not appear to differ greatly from those observed in the liquid state. The final chemical results are influenced by the lack of mobility of the radicals and the excited species involved. These specific effects will be discussed in later chapters of the book.

3-3 Effects of Linear Energy Transfer

3-3.1 EFFECTS IN WATER SOLUTION

The radiolysis of materials in dilute aqueous solutions shows the effects of linear energy transfer (LET) (see Ch. 2, Sect. 2-1). For example, the yield of ferric ions formed in the ferrous sulfate dosimeter decreases rapidly with increase in LET, as shown in Table 3.1. The first attempt to correlate such effects with differences in ionization density in water solutions was made by Lea.[27] He assumed that radicals produced from excited molecules occur close together in tracks. In the primary excitation process, the following reactions were assumed to occur:

$$H_2O^* \rightarrow H\cdot + OH\cdot \tag{3.32}$$

$$H_2O \rightarrow H_2O^+ + e^- \tag{3.33}$$
$$\downarrow$$
$$H^+ + OH\cdot$$

Lea further assumed that the hydrogen atoms and electrons escaped from the primary track and that, at some distance away from the site of the initial ionization, the electron was captured either by water or by the hydrogen ion:

$$e^- + H_2O \rightarrow H_2O^- \rightarrow H\cdot + OH^- \tag{3.34}$$

$$H^+ + e^- + M \rightarrow H\cdot + M^* \tag{3.35}$$

Thus OH radicals are formed in the core of the track, and hydrogen radicals are formed at the periphery of the track. If such an initial distribution is assumed, the time required for the overlapping of the tracks from various types of radiation can be calculated from diffusion theory. Calculation would also yield the number of radicals remaining uncombined at various times after the initial passage of the radiation. This treatment predicts more radicals to remain uncombined from X rays than from alpha particles at the time the tracks overlap. The concentration of uncombined radicals at the time of overlapping is assumed to be a measure of the effectiveness of radicals for reaction with a solute.

The treatment of Samuel and Magee[35] differs in that the range of the electron in water before recapture is assumed to be very short and recapture is assumed to occur in less than 10^{-12} sec. The Coulomb field of the positive ion prevents escape of the electron. This treatment emphasizes the existence of spurs and the spacing of these spurs along the track. All radicals are initially confined to the spur. The recombination of the primary radicals takes only about 10^{-8} sec. After this time those that have not reacted have diffused out of the spurs and have little further probability of recombination. The spurs in electron tracks are treated independently since they do not merge until the distribution in a large volume of the solution is essentially homogeneous. In alpha-particle tracks the spurs are assumed to overlap immediately, and the diffusion is treated as the expansion of a cylinder. Samuel and Magee calculated the ratio of molecular products from water, i.e., H_2 and H_2O_2 for electron and alpha-particle tracks. This allowed a comparison of the products from direct radical reactions in the spurs with those products arising from radical reactions in the bulk of the solution. The latter are measured by radical reactions with scavengers. The agreement between theory and experiment was quite good.

At present neither theory has been extrapolated to organic systems in which the number of radical possibilities is high and other reactive species also occur.[30]

3-3.2 Effects in Organic Systems

In organic systems the products produced by radiation are quite complex and result from the competitive operation of several mechanisms. Thus the differences in yields of various products from radiations of different ionization density characteristics might be expected to vary in a complex fashion according to their mechanism of formation. Studies of the effect of LET on the yields of products bear directly on the mechanisms by which these products are formed. In general, the total yield of products is less with radiations of high LET than with gamma rays. For example, in the radiolysis of isopropyl ether, shown in Table 3.3, the yield of hydrogen is similar for both helium ions and gamma rays.

The yields of propylene and propane differ markedly, however, and the total gas production is higher when gamma rays are used than when helium ions are used for the irradiation. In this case the propane yield was the most sensitive to radiation type.

Sworski and Burton have observed similar effects in the comparison of electron and mixed pile irradiations of aromatic compounds.[41] The gas formed in the reactor irradiations was lower in methane but higher in hydrogen than that formed in electron irradiations. In a study of organic

Table 3.3—YIELDS OF SOME GASEOUS PRODUCTS FROM
ISOPROPYL ETHER PRODUCED ON IRRADIATION
WITH HELIUM IONS AND GAMMA RAYS[32]

Product	$G_{(product)}$, molecules/100 ev (from 42-Mev helium ions)	$G_{(product)}$, molecules/100 ev (from Co^{60} gamma rays)
Hydrogen	2.43	2.23
Carbon monoxide	0.075	0.047
Methane	0.87	1.47
Propylene	1.43	1.87
Propane	0.54	2.39
Total gas	5.75	8.37
Polymer	0.3	0.3

reactor coolants, de Halas[13] found reactor radiations to be more destructive than gamma rays. Charlesby has stated that the effects of X rays, electrons, and mixed pile radiations on polymers are dependent only on the energy absorbed and are independent of the radiation type.[11] In view of work with lower molecular weight compounds, this statement should probably be used only as a first approximation.

3-4 Chemical Results of Irradiation

3-4.1 GAS PRODUCTION FROM ORGANIC COMPOUNDS

All organic compounds yield low-molecular-weight gaseous products on irradiation. Because the gaseous products are easy to study experimentally, more information is available on them than on higher molecular weight products. The yield of gaseous products varies widely with compound type. Saturated materials yield the most gas and aromatics yield the least.

The composition of the gas produced is a function of the number and types of the groups making up the molecules. A statistical rule[6] is that, when special chemical effects are not significant, the composition of gaseous radiolysis products from organic compounds is determined by the number and frequency of occurrence of parent groups in the affected molecule from which these products are formed. This rule has limitations because very few types of compounds are free of special chemical effects. Normal saturated hydrocarbons yield principally hydrogen, methane being produced only from the end groups. The ratio of hydrogen to methane increases with increasing molecular weight. With branched-chain hydrocarbons relatively more methane is produced, and the yield of methane increases with the number of methyl groups on the hydrocarbon chain. The statistical rule works well for saturated hydrocarbons; but the presence of electronegative groups, e.g., oxygen, carbonyl, halogens, double bonds, or aromatic groups, drastically changes the composition of gas from that predicted on a purely statistical basis. As shown in Table 3.3, the yields of propane and propylene are higher than the yield of methane from isopropyl ether despite the fact that there are four methyl groups in the molecule and only two isopropyl groups. The nature of the bonding of every group must be considered as well as the total number of a given type group.

3-4.2 POLYMER FORMATION

In the irradiation of almost all organic compounds, products are formed which are generally grouped under the designation "polymers." In most cases these are not the true high-molecular-weight polymers that are obtained from vinyl compounds. They are high-boiling-point materials that have not been separated and identified. The total yield of such products is usually estimated by calculating the number of molecules of the original material that must have reacted to give the observed weight of polymer. This assumes the products to result from a combination of molecules of the original material. As with gas yields, the yields of high-boiling-point products vary widely. It is significant that a few compounds, such as benzene, which appear very radiation resistant to gas production, still produce appreciable amounts of polymer.[33]

3-4.3 POLYMERIZATION OF UNSATURATED COMPOUNDS

This is a very promising field for future utilization of radiation. Free-radical-induced polymerizations occur as well with radiation as with other radical sources. The rate of polymerization, in addition to the rate of the termination step, is limited by the intensity of the radiation. Under such conditions the rate of formation of polymer is proportional to the square root of the dose rate, I:

$$\frac{d(\text{polymer})}{dt} = kI^{1/2} \tag{3.36}$$

In systems where the polymer is not soluble in the monomer or solvent, e.g., in the polymerization of acrylonitrile in water solution, the termination step is inhibited by the precipitation of the growing polymer; and the rate law follows a higher power of intensity,

$$\frac{d(\text{polymer})}{dt} = kI^{0.7-0.8} \tag{3.37}$$

For a given dosage of radiation, the total number of individual molecules of polymer formed is approximately constant. If the dose is given at a slow rate, the molecules are of higher molecular weight, and the over-all weight yield of polymer is larger than if the radiation dose were given at a rapid rate. This limitation can be overcome by the use of emulsion polymerization techniques, where the termination step is inhibited by lack of diffusion of radicals between the emulsion micelles and the solution.

Polymerizations in the solid state have also been performed by radiation. If the same monomer is irradiated above and below the melting point, the yield of polymer is usually less for the solid state than for the liquid state.

3-4.4 Cross Linking and Degradation

The irradiation of high-molecular-weight polymers results in gas production and cross linking and degradation of the polymer. Whether cross linking or degradation is the dominant feature of the irradiation mechanism is a function of the structure of the polymer chain (see Chs. 5, 6, and 7). Cross linking is the formation of new bonds between adjacent high polymer molecules. It causes an increase in the average molecular weight of the polymer. Continued irradiation of polymers in which cross linking is highly dominant results in a three-dimensional network of molecules of great strength and stability. Degradation, the opposite of cross linking, is the breaking of primary polymer linkages. It causes a decrease in the average molecular weight of the polymer.

In cross linking a small side group, usually a hydrogen atom, is broken off the main chain, and the resulting free bond on the chain then forms a link to a bond on a neighboring molecule. Several mechanisms have been proposed whereby these free linkages occur at neighboring points so that joining is possible. The process is much too efficient to be explained by the joining of radicals formed as random radicals along the chain. The simplest mechanism is the reaction of the trapped hydrogen radical with a neighboring C–H group. If this reaction is with a neighboring molecule, the free bonds formed can combine to yield a cross link. If the hydrogen is abstracted from a neighboring atom on the same chain, a double bond is formed. Recently Burton[4] has suggested an ion–molecule–electron recombination mechanism similar to Reaction 3.31 and suggests it to explain the difference between cross linking and degrading reactions (Fig. 3.6).

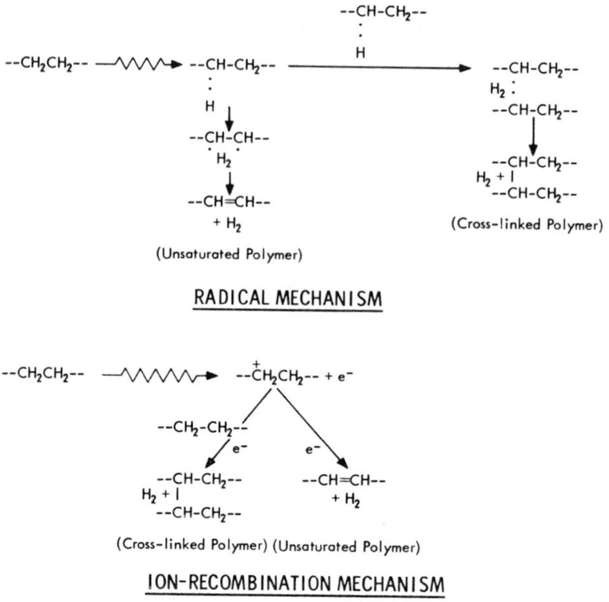

RADICAL MECHANISM

ION-RECOMBINATION MECHANISM

FIG. 3.6 Schematic representation of radical and ion recombination mechanism for production of cross-linked and unsaturated polymers.

3-4.5 PROTECTION AND SENSITIZATION

If the addition of small amounts of a compound B reduces the chemical or physical effects produced by radiation on a compound A, the process is called "protection." If the effects on A are increased, the process is called "sensitization." Protection is quite important in the formulation of radiation-resistant materials.

Protection can be divided into two general categories. The first is true protection in which the protective agent absorbs energy from the irradiated primary material and dissipates this energy as heat or light without itself being destroyed. Probably no case of true protection exists. Some chemical action on the protection agent always results, although in some cases such action may be quite small and the protective effect a real one. Aromatic hydrocarbons are good protective agents for a large number of chemicals because they have many low-lying excited states, have low ionization potentials, and are themselves radiation resistant. This transfer of energy from higher excited states or charge exchange with the ion of the primary compound results in the dissipation of the energy in the aromatic hydrocarbon. This is by fluorescence or by heat formation, with little decomposition of the aromatic material. Burton and Patrick[9] have shown that cyclohexane is protected from decomposition under radiation by small amounts of added benzene. Internal protective agents also can be built into molecules by adding aromatic groups. Alexander and Charlesby[1] reported that the cross linking of dodecane was inhibited by substituting aromatic groups for hydrogen in the molecule.

The second type of protection is known as "sacrificial protection." In this case the added component is preferentially destroyed. The total destruction in the system remains about the same as it would have been without the added protective agent. Iodine or other radical scavengers are examples of sacrificial protective agents. In this case secondary attack on the solvent molecules by radicals is prevented by the scavenger. Some of these radical scavengers may exhibit a protective action beyond that afforded by radical scavenging alone.[7]

Examples of sensitization are not numerous. The action of sensitizers appears to be that of changing the course of the reaction so that normal termination steps are eliminated. Oxygen acts as a sensitizer for degradation in the irradiation of polymers that normally cross link. Such polymers are degraded in the presence of oxygen. Another sensitization by oxygen has been reported by Bakh and Sorokin,[2] who found the yield of hydrogen from oxygenated ethanol to be twice that from deaerated ethanol. Sensitizers may also act by promotion of a chain reaction in the system to increase the decomposition of the original material. In irradiations of alkyl iodide–cyclohexane mixtures, alkyl iodides are reported to undergo a chain reaction with cyclohexane to increase its decomposition over that found in pure cyclohexane.[4]

3-4.6 CONSECUTIVE PROCESSES

These processes are most important when organic materials are used in high-intensity radiation fields. Here the data on pure compounds obtained by the radiation chemist in short irradiations are of little help to the engineer who is interested in the behavior of a material in long exposures.

Continued irradiation of almost any organic compound results in a tarlike residue and various gaseous products. The intermediate steps in such processes received little attention. The important factor in such long irradiations is that the rates of formation of products obtained from compounds at low levels of decomposition cannot be extrapolated linearly to very high levels of destruction. Owing to the formation and destruction of secondary, tertiary, and higher order products, an internal protective system will be formed which will influence the rate of decomposition of the original material. The presence of consecutive processes in an irradiation is indicated by a nonlinear function of product yield and dose or as a nonconstant value of product yield per unit energy input as the total energy input is increased.

Consecutive processes are difficult to interpret in terms of specific mechanisms since the presence of various products in solution presents a formidable mixture to interpret kinetically. This interpretation in specific cases for materials that must be subjected to high radiation doses will be an important step toward finding means to delay or prevent the development of undesired properties in such materials.

References

Several of the following were cited in the text as authority for statements made. Others were not quoted but are included because they contain pertinent information. All were consulted in the preparation of this chapter.

1. Alexander, P., and Charlesby, A., Energy Transfer in Macromolecules Exposed to Ionizing Radiations, *Nature, 173:* 578 (March 1954).
2. Bakh, N. A., and Sorokin, Yu. I., Oxidation of Organic Compounds with Molecular Oxygen by Action of Ionizing Radiations. III. Oxidative Radiolysis of Ethyl Alcohol, in *Sbornik Rabot Radiatsionnoi Khim., Akad. Nauk SSSR,* p. 163, 1955 [*Symposium on Radiation Chemistry, Academy of Science, USSR,* p. 135, Bakh, N. A., (Ed.), Moscow, 1955 (Consultants Bureau, New York, 1956)].
3. Bovey, F. A., *The Effects of Ionizing Radiation on Natural and Synthetic High Polymers,* p. 37, Interscience Publishers, Inc., New York, 1958.
4. Burton, M., Experimental Techniques and Current Concepts—Organic Substances, in *Effects of Radiation on Materials,* p. 243, Harwood, J. J., Hausner, H. H., Morse, J. G., and Rauch, W. G., (Eds.), Reinhold Publishing Corp., New York, 1958.
5. Burton, M., Radiolyse de Liquidee Organique, in *Actions Chimiques et Biologiques des Radiations,* p. 2, Hassinsky, M., (Ed.), Troisieme Serie, Paris, Masson et Cie, (in French), 1958.
6. Burton, M., Elementary Chemical Processes in Radiobiological Reactions, in *Symposium on Radiobiology,* p. 97, Nickson, J. J., (Ed.), John Wiley & Sons, Inc., New York, 1952.
7. Burton, M., and Lipsky, S., Mechanisms of Protection in Radiolysis of Organic Systems, *J. Phys. Chem., 61*(11): 1461 (November 1957).
8. Burton, M., and Magee, J. L., Successive Excitations by Low Energy Electrons: General Principle, *J. Chem. Phys., 23*(11): 2194 (November 1955).
9. Burton, M., and Patrick, W. N., Radiation Chemistry of Mixtures of Cyclohexane and Benzene-d$_6$, *J. Phys. Chem., 58*(5): 421 (May 1954).
10. Chapiro, A., Chemical Evidence of Track Effects in the Radiolysis of Liquids, *Radiation Research, 6*(1): 11 (January 1957).
11. Charlesby, A., Effect of Radiation on Behavior and Properties of Polymers, in *Effects of Radiation on Materials,* p. 262, Harwood. J. J., Hausner, H. H., Morse, J. G., and Rauch, W. G., (Eds.), Reinhold Publishing Corp., New York, 1958.
12. Collinson, E., Dainton, F. S., and McNaughton, C. S., The Polymerization of Acrylamide in Aqueous Solution. Part I. The X Ray and Gamma Ray Initiated Reaction, *Trans. Faraday Soc., 53*(4): 476 (April 1957).
13. de Halas, D. R., *Kinetics of the Decomposition of Organic Reactor Coolants,* USAEC Report HW-56769, Hanford Atomic Products Operation, July 1958.
14. Dewhurst, H. A., Samuel, A. H., and Magee, J. L., A Theoretical Survey of the Radiation Chemistry of Water and Aqueous Solutions, *Radiation Research, 1*(1): 62 (February 1954).

15. Fano, U., Principles of Radiological Physics, in *Radiation Biology,* Vol. I, Pt. I, p. 1, Hollaender, A., (Ed.), McGraw-Hill Book Company, Inc., New York, 1954.

16. Field, F. H., and Franklin, J. L., *Electron Impact Phenomena,* Academic Press, Inc., New York, 1957.

17. Field, F. H., Franklin, J. L., and Lampe, F. W., Reaction of Gaseous Ions. I. Methane and Ethylene, *J. Am. Chem. Soc.,* 79(10): 2419 (May 1957); and Reactions of Gaseous Ions. II. Acetylene, *J. Am. Chem. Soc.* 79(11): 2665 (June 1957).

18. Franck, J., and Platzman, R. L., Physical Principles Underlying Photochemical, Radiation Chemical, and Radiobiological Reactions, in *Radiation Biology,* Vol. I, Pt. I, p. 191, Hollaender, A., (Ed.), Mc-Graw-Hill Book Company, Inc., New York, 1954.

19. Ganguly, A. K., and Magee, J. L., Theory of Radiation Chemistry. III. Radical Reaction Mechanisms in the Tracks of Ionizing Particles, *J. Chem. Phys.,* 25(1): 129 (July 1956).

20. Gevantman, L. H., and Williams, R. R., Jr., Detection and Identification of Free Radicals in the Radiolysis of Alkanes and Alkyl Iodides, *J. Phys. Chem.,* 56(5): 569 (May 1952).

21. Gioumousis, G., and Stevenson, D. P., Reactions of Gaseous Molecule Ions with Gaseous Molecules. V. Theory, *J. Chem. Phys.,* 29(2): 294 (August 1958).

22. Gurnee, E. F., and Magee, J. L., Interchange of Charge Between Gaseous Molecules in Resonant and Near Resonant Processes, *J. Chem. Phys.,* 26(4): 1237 (April 1957); see also: Magee, J. L., Elementary Processes in Radiation Chemistry. III. Charge Transfer Mechanisms, *J. Phys. Chem.,* 56(5): 555 (May 1952).

23. Harwood, J. J., Hausner, H. H., Morse, J. G., and Rauch, W. G., (Eds.), *Effects of Radiation on Materials,* Reinhold Publishing Corp., New York, 1958.

24. Hochanadel, C. J., and Ghormley, J. A., A Calibration of Gamma Ray Actinometers, *J. Chem. Phys.,* 21(5): 880 (May 1953).

25. Jesse, W. P., and Sadauskis, J., Alpha Particle Ionization in Pure Gases and the Average Energy to Make an Ion Pair, *Phys. Rev.,* 90(6): 1120 (June 1953).

26. Lampe, F. W., Field, F. H., and Franklin, J. L., Reactions of Gaseous Ions. IV. Water, *J. Am. Chem. Soc.,* 79(23): 6132 (December 1957).

27. Lea, D. E., *Actions of Radiations on Living Cells,* p. 1, The Macmillan Co., New York, 1947.

28. McDonell, W. R., and Hart, E. J., Oxidation of Aqueous Ferrous Sulfate Solutions by Charged Particle Reactions, *J. Am. Chem. Soc.,* 76(8): 2121 (April 1954).

29. Magee, J. L., Theory of Radiation Chemistry. I. Some Effects of Variation in Ionization Density, *J. Am. Chem. Soc.,* 73(7): 3270 (July 1951).

30. Monchick, L., Magee, J. L., and Samuel, A. H., Theory of Radiation Chemistry. IV. Chemical Reactions in the General Track Composed of N Particles, *J. Chem. Phys.,* 26(4): 935 (April 1957).

31. Mott, N. F., and Massey, H. S. W., *Theory of Atomic Collisions,* p. 248, 2nd ed., Oxford Clarendon Press, London, 1949.

32. Newton, A. S., Some Aspects of the Radiolysis of Isopropyl Ether, *J. Phys. Chem.,* 61(11): 1490 (November 1957).

33. Patrick, W. N., and Burton, M., Polymer Production in Radiolysis of Benzene, *J. Am. Chem. Soc.,* 76(10): 2626 (May 1954).

34. Platzman, R. L., Subexcitation Electrons, *Radiation Research,* 2(1): 1 (February 1955).

35. Samuel, A. H., and Magee, J. L., Theory of Radiation Chemistry. II. Track Effects in the Radiolysis of Water, *J. Chem. Phys.,* 21(6): 1080 (June 1953).

36. Schuler, R. H., Comments on the Importance of Ion-Molecule Reactions in Liquid Phase Radiation Chemistry, *J. Chem. Phys.,* 26(2): 425 (February 1957).

37. Schuler, R. H., and Allen, A. O., Radiation Chemical Studies with Cyclotron Beams, *J. Am. Chem. Soc.,* 77(2): 507 (January 1955).

38. Schuler, R. H., and Allen, A. O., Yield of the Ferrous Radiation Dosimeter: An Improved Cathode Ray Determination. *J. Chem. Phys.,* 24(1): 56 (January 1956).

39. Steacie, E. W. R., *Atomic and Free Radical Reactions,* Vols. I and II, Reinhold Publishing Corp., New York, 1954.

40. Stevenson, D. P., and Schissler, D. O., Reactions of Gaseous Molecule Ions with Gaseous Molecules. IV. Experimental Methods and Results, *J. Chem. Phys.,* 29 (2): 282 (August 1958).

41. Sworski, T. J., and Burton, M., A Study of the Effect of Impingent-particle Velocity in Radiolysis of Some Aromatic Compounds, *J. Am. Chem. Soc.,* 73(8): 3790 (August 1951).

42. Weber, E. N., Forsyth, P. F., and Schuler, R. H., Radical Production in the Radiolysis of Hydrocarbons, *Radiation Research,* 3(1): 68 (September 1955).

CHAPTER 4

Radiation Chemistry of Pure Compounds

BY K. LYNN HALL, ROBERT O. BOLT, AND JAMES G. CARROLL

4-1 Introduction

Background information on the more important organic compounds is presented in this chapter. The coverage includes saturated and unsaturated aliphatic hydrocarbons, aromatic hydrocarbons, oxygen-containing compounds, and organic halides. A comprehensive treatment of polymers is taken up in Ch. 5. In the presentation of radiation effects on materials in chapters to follow, changes in physical properties are the major concern. Changes in composition, of prime importance to the radiation chemist, are of less interest to the average reader and are much more difficult to measure. However, knowledge of the individual behavior patterns of various pure materials is helpful to an understanding of radiation-induced changes in the gross properties of lubricants, plastics, etc., which are complex mixtures of pure compounds.

The objective of most work in radiation chemistry is a basic understanding of the chemical consequences of the interaction of radiation with matter. Pure compounds are irradiated and then analyzed for changes in composition and for yields of individual products. Product yields are explained in terms of reaction mechanisms involving intermediates such as radicals or ions. Low radiation doses ($<10^7$ rads) are used to prevent the build-up of large product concentrations and consequent multiple-order reactions (Ch. 3, Sect. 3-4.6). In contrast, relatively high doses are necessary to produce measurable physical-property changes.

4-1.1 DISCUSSION OF TERMS

Certain terms as they are used in this chapter are defined below.

Primary: Primary processes were treated in Ch. 3, Sect. 3-1.3. Such processes produce *primary species*, which are the excited molecules and ions that result from the passage of radiation through matter. Primary processes occur in the first 10^{-14} sec on the time scale for events in radiation chemistry (Ch. 3, Fig. 3.1). Although primary species include both ions and excited molecules found via several paths (Ch. 3, Eqs. 3.1 to 3.4), in this chapter all primary events are represented by a single reaction:

$$M \rightsquigarrow M^* \tag{4.1}$$

M^* includes ground and excited species of both singly (M^+) and doubly (M^{++}) charged ions and singlet (M') and triplet (M''') states. Reaction 4.1 is shown schematically in Fig. 4.1 together with the secondary processes of more direct concern.

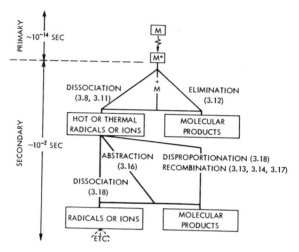

Fig. 4.1 Primary and secondary processes in radiolysis. Numbers refer to reactions in Ch. 3; "hot" radicals are those possessing very high kinetic energy.

Secondary: Chapter 3, Sect. 3-1.5, discusses the secondary processes. These are the various reactions of the primary species which result in ultimate molecular products. These processes are over in approximately 10^{-2} sec on the time scale of Fig. 3.1.

Multiple Order: Multiple-order processes were covered in Ch. 3, Sect. 3-4.6. They give rise to secondary, tertiary, and higher order products.

Products: Radiolysis products are stable molecular species, as distinguished from reactive intermediates such as free radicals and ions. Some of these molecular species are more reactive (less stable) than others, and their lifetimes can depend markedly upon the environment in which they exist.

Initial Products: These are the products first formed; they are not always observable. Very reactive first products may disappear at relatively low doses. For instance, olefins were only recently observed in the radiolysis of saturated hydrocarbons[5] at very low doses. The amount of initial products present at a given time thus depends upon the stability or lifetime of the initial product in the radiation environment. Hence the number of molecules present is time dependent. Initial-product yields are usually defined experimentally by the initial linear portion of the curve of total amount of product formed vs. dose (as the dose increases from low values, the curve deviates from linearity).

The relation between initial and higher order products can be illustrated by consecutive first-order reactions from well-known chemical kinetics. Consider the idealized reaction

$$M \xrightarrow{k_A} A \xrightarrow{k_B} B \qquad (4.2)$$

where M is the substance irradiated, A is an initial product, B is a second-order product, and the k's are the rate constants for formation of products A and B. Figure 4.2 shows concentrations as a function of reaction time

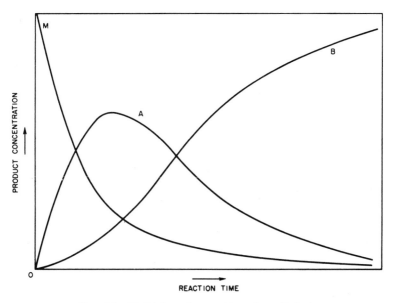

FIG. 4.2   Multiple-order reactions in radiolysis
$$(M \xrightarrow{k_A} A \xrightarrow{k_B} B, \text{ where } k_A > k_B).$$

(proportional to dose) for the case of $k_A > k_B$. If the consecutive series of reactions is extended to higher orders, the concentration–time curves become more complex.

All the primary and secondary processes shown in Fig. 4.1 occur in essentially zero time on the scale in Fig. 4.2. The yield of A is usually assumed to be linear for a short time. Thus the initial slope of the curve is taken to be the initial-product yield. This initial-rate technique has been widely used in conventional kinetic studies. In radiation chemistry a similar treatment is applied. Low doses (corresponding to less than 1% reaction) are generally required for this purpose.

In chemical kinetics the reaction may be carried out to near completion in cases where few side (parallel) reactions occur. There are few such cases in radiation chemistry because the primary species comprise a broad spectrum of excited molecules, radicals, and ions. Numerous side reactions are thus possible.

Radiolysis Yield: The slope of a given curve in Fig. 4.2 is the reaction rate (mole/liter/second) familiar from conventional kinetics. In radiation chemistry the radiolysis yield, G, is defined as

$$G = \frac{\text{No. of molecules}}{100 \text{ ev of energy absorbed}} \tag{4.3}$$

The reaction rate, R, can be obtained by multiplying the G value by the dose rate, I,

$$R\left[\frac{\text{molecules}}{\text{liter/sec}}\right] = G\left[\frac{\text{molecules}}{100 \text{ ev}}\right] I\left[\frac{100 \text{ ev}}{\text{liter/sec}}\right] \tag{4.4}$$

The total number of molecules of a product present in a reaction vessel is shown in Fig. 4.3 as a function of absorbed dose in units of 100 ev. The

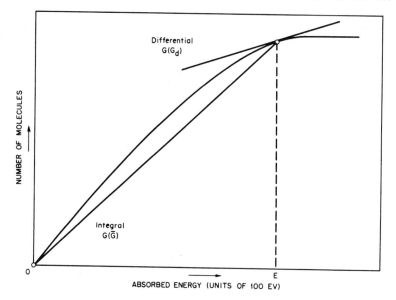

FIG. 4.3   Yields of radiolysis products

$$\left(\bar{G} = \frac{1}{E} \int_0^E G_d \, dE\right).$$

instantaneous slope of this curve is G_d, the differential G value. A G value refers to a particular molecule, e.g., G_A refers to the number of molecules of A produced per 100 ev. The symbol G_{-M} is commonly used to represent the disappearance of the starting molecules. G values have also been used to refer to the number of molecules, M, forming an unspecified polymer $(G_{M \to polymer})$.

There are many cases where too few experimental points were obtained to reveal a curvature such as shown in Fig. 4.3. In these cases, the total or integral G value, $\overline{G}$, is specified. This[99] is the average G value over the range of absorbed energy 0 to E:

$$\overline{G} \equiv \frac{1}{E} \int_0^E G_d \, dE \qquad (4.5)$$

Figure 4.3 also illustrates $\overline{G}$. Differential and integral G values are equivalent in the linear region but can be considerably different at doses high enough to allow appreciable consecutive reactions. Values range from 0 to 10,000, but for most reactions G is less than 5.

Ion-pair Yield: In early work the ionic or ion-pair yield was reported. This applied quite well to gas-phase radiolysis where the number of ions formed was easily measured. The yield was given as

$$\frac{M}{N} = \frac{\text{No. of molecules reacting}}{\text{No. of ion pairs produced}} \qquad (4.6)$$

Observed values of M/N usually range from 1 to 5. The energy necessary to produce one ion pair in gases is 25 to 34 ev for most substances. Thus the conversion factor to change ionic yields to G values is 3 to 4. If ionic yields are reported for a liquid, it is generally assumed that the conversion factor of 3 applies even though ions cannot be directly measured in the liquid phase.

4-1.2 RADIOLYSIS PRODUCTS

It is convenient to classify these products into three molecular-weight groups:

1. Low (e.g., gases formed by bond cleavage)
2. Intermediate (e.g., products formed by hydrogenation, dehydrogenation, or rearrangements)
3. High (e.g., polymer formed by condensation, polymerization, or cross linking)

There are few cases of complete quantitative analysis of radiolysis products because of the difficulty in analyzing complex mixtures of compounds produced in low yield. Gas yields are relatively easy to obtain and have almost always been reported. Lately, yields of certain intermediate- and high-molecular-weight products have been reported in the literature.

The mass spectrometer (MS) has been the most valuable single instrument for characterizing radiolysis products. High-vacuum distillation simplifies the complex radiolyzed mixture prior to MS analysis. Recently gas chromatography (GC) has been developed as a valuable analytical technique. The combination of GC and MS promises to afford good data for intermediate- and high-molecular-weight products. Such data are currently very sparse, and the high-molecular-weight materials are usually lumped together and called "high boilers," "tar," or "polymer." Polymer is defined in each instance in terms of the technique by which it is isolated.

The course of radiolysis and, hence, the major products are influenced by molecular structure. Chemical bonds are not broken randomly even though the excitation energy may exceed the bond dissociation, e.g., the C—I bond in alkyl iodides is cleaved preferentially. This general statement has certain exceptions where the statistical rule may be applied: in the absence of special chemical effects, all bonds have equal probability of rupture (Ch. 3, Sect. 3-4.1). The statistical rule assumes that fragments from bond rupture all (or at least the same fraction of each) acquire hydrogen atoms to become measurable products. The frequency of bond rupture is then related to the number of bonds in the molecule, and the products are related to the frequency of occurrence of parent groups in the radiolyzed molecule. This is the group-to-product correlation. Even in the absence of special chemical effects, the rule is an oversimplification because the fragments may have other fates, as shown in Fig. 4.1. Sometimes the statistical rule can be applied to one part of the molecule; i.e., the major structural factor is unchanged, whereas the number and/or kinds of bonds in the rest of the molecule are varied. Then a group-to-product correlation involving only the part of the molecule varied can be made; e.g., H_2 and CH_4 yields have been correlated with the C—H and C—CH_3 bonds in alkylbenzenes (see Sect. 4-2).

4-1.3 ENVIRONMENTAL FACTORS

These factors of interest in radiation chemistry include physical state (Ch. 3, Sect. 3-2), linear energy transfer (LET) (Ch. 3, Sect. 3-3), the presence of substances other than the starting material (e.g., additives), temperature, flux geometry, and dose rate. These factors influence product yields that are of first importance in the study of radiolysis mechanisms. For example, radical scavengers (additives) suppress thermal radical reactions occurring outside the spur or track (see Ch. 3, Sects. 3-1.5.2 and 3-4.5). The scavenger-radical adduct indicates what thermal radicals are produced, and the disappearance of scavenger is a measure of the yield of radicals. In practical use the interest may be in radiation protection. Therefore additives are sought which reduce the over-all decomposition. On the other hand, radiation processing or synthesis may be of interest. High conversions are then important, and sensitizers are added which direct the course of radiolysis to form desirable products.

Both LET and dose-rate effects can be considered in terms of two competing reactions:

$$R + R \xrightarrow{k_1} \text{products} \tag{4.7}$$

$$R + S \xrightarrow{k_2} \text{products} \tag{4.8}$$

where R is a reactive intermediate (e.g., radical) and S is a stable molecule present in macro amounts (e.g., a scavenger). Reaction 4.7 will be favored by high concentrations of R. If R is a primary species, it will be produced in high concentration by high dose rates. On a micro scale this is achieved at high LET; on a macro scale, at high (homogeneous) dose rates. It follows that LET and dose-rate effects can be expected for those systems in which competing first- and second-order reactions of R (4.8 and 4.7) are important in the mechanism. The unimolecular elimination shown in Fig. 4.1 is similarly a competing first-order reaction.

In chain reactions the dose-rate effect is most evident and is treated in some detail in the discussion of pure monomer polymerization (Sect. 4-3.4.1). Dose-rate effects are less obvious in other radiolysis reactions, but several instances will be cited in which this variable was posed as a possible rationalization of observed effects. Many times the effects of LET and dose rate are difficult to separate because both are changed simultaneously. Thus a radioactive source like Co^{60} gives 10^3- to 10^4-fold lower dose rates than accelerated charged-particle beams, and at the same time the LET is about 25-fold lower.

The radiation-flux geometry in the irradiation vessel can also have an important influence. Thus the G values of certain unsaturated gases from the radiolysis of n-pentane depend upon the spatial homogeneity of the radiation.[57] This may be important in comparing the effects of Co^{60} gamma rays with charged-particle beams.

The effect of temperature deserves some comment. It has been common to think of all reactions in radiolysis as "hot" (high energy) and, hence, temperature independent because of the large amount of available energy relative to bond strength.[77] However, if the fragments born with excess kinetic or vibrational energy are thermalized before reacting, the reaction rate will depend on competitive reactions and so may be temperature dependent. Even radical recombinations may show a temperature dependence if diffusion away from the spur is a controlling factor. For example, the escape of an iodine atom liberated from alkyl iodides involves diffusion out of the cage of surrounding molecules. If the atom escapes, an observable reaction occurs; if it does not escape, it will back-react to form the starting material again. Cage-escape efficiency increases with increasing temperature.

The influence of temperature on the rate of thermal reactions is usually expressed by the Arrhenius equation in which the reaction rate is a function of an activation energy E, the ideal gas constant R, and the absolute temperature T:

$$\ln (\text{rate}) = -\frac{E}{RT} + \text{constant} \qquad (4.9)$$

The expression for the rate of diffusion as influenced by temperature is similar to Eq. 4.9; i.e., an activation energy (2 to 5 kcal/mole) is associated with the diffusion of molecules past one another.[62] When possible in this chapter, the effect of temperature on radiolysis rates will be treated in terms of an activation energy.

4-1.4 FORMAT

In the sections to follow, the radiation chemistry of organic compounds will be treated separately by classes. The emphasis will be on observed products and their relation to the mechanism of radiolysis rather than on primary processes. The use of radiation to promote chemical reactions (e.g., polymerization and halogenation) is treated only incidentally, as is the effect of additives (mixtures). The illustrations on radiolysis mechanism are not meant to imply finality. Indeed the state of knowledge is far from complete and so are the mechanisms shown. These illustrations are intended merely to summarize some of the suggestions in the literature. For the sake of simplicity, reactions are discussed in terms of radicals only. Some degree of selection was made because experimental data have disproved proposed mechanisms in certain cases. The tables of product yields are likewise far from complete by design (completeness would demand a separate book) and should be taken only as typical of the available data. Comparative product yields are rare—too many times they were not obtained under equal conditions.

Irradiation environment and conditions are important, and these factors will be brought out whenever possible in the sections entitled "Effect of Experimental Variations." Structural factors and such group-to-product correlations as can be made will be pointed out; tables of G values will be presented. Thus the reader can obtain some idea of which chemical bonds are broken and how often they are broken under irradiation. He will be in a better position to make general predictions of what might happen in the particular systems of interest to him.

4-2 Saturated Hydrocarbons

Irradiation breaks both C—H and C—C bonds to form a broad spectrum of low-molecular-weight gaseous compounds. Intermediate- and high-molecular-weight materials are also produced. Hydrogen and methane have sometimes been the only gases reported, but the current trend is to

Table 4.1 — TYPICAL RADIOLYSIS YIELDS FROM HYDROCARBON (RH) IRRADIATIONS IN GAS PHASE

Compound	Methane	Ethane		Propane	
Reference	140	36	140	36	140
Radiation	γ	e^-	γ	e^-	γ
Temperature, °F	72	NR[a]	72	NR[a]	72
Dose, 10^6 rads	NR[a]	~45	NR[a]	45	NR[a]
G_{H_2}	6.4	5.6	6.8	3.8	5.9
G_{CH_4}		0.56	0.6	1.3	1.5
G_{dimer}	2.1	1.4	1.0		
G_{R_uH}[b]			0.05		0.2

[a] Not reported.
[b] R_u = unsaturated alkyl group.

make much more complete analyses. Irradiations at very low doses have shown significant yields of unsaturated gases (Refs. 5, 13, 36, and 37). These unsaturates probably are produced with measurable initial yields but then reach an undetectably low "steady-state" concentration at the higher doses. Progress has also been made in the analysis of nongaseous products. The great diversity of substances formed increases with the molecular weight of the target.[41] Isomerization has also been observed.[40]

Table 4.2 — EFFECT OF PHYSICAL STATE ON RADIOLYSIS YIELDS FROM HYDROCARBON (RH) IRRADIATIONS

Compound	n-Pentane		Neopentane		n-Hexane		Cyclohexane	
Reference	56	38	82	129	55	55	107	44,115
Radiation	e^-	e^-	e^-	γ	e^-	e^-	α	α
Temperature, °F	~72	~72	80	85	NR[a]	NR[a]	226	~72
Dose, 10^6 rads	NR[a]	24-96	100-500	0.5-2	NR[a]	NR[a]	0.2-1	20-100
Phase	Gas	Liquid	Gas	Liquid	Gas	Liquid	Gas	Liquid
G_{-M}					9.5			
G_{H_2}	>6	4.2	4.3	1.57	4.3	5	8.0	5.25
G_{CH_4}	0.7	0.22	1.8	3.72	0.5	0.13	0.13	
$G_{C_2H_2}$	0.5	<0.05			0.2	0.15	0.65	
$G_{C_2H_4}$	1.5	0.36	0.31	<0.01	1.1	0.63	2.48	
$G_{C_2H_6}$	1.1	0.27	2.3	0.33	0.9	0.63		
$G_{C_3H_8}$	2.0	0.33	0.54	0.01	1.4	0.67	0.95	
G_{dimer}			1.2			<0.69		2.0
G_{R_uH}							0.77	2.4

[a] Not reported.

The major gaseous product is hydrogen, and G_{H_2} ranges from 3 to 9 for *n*-alkanes. Tables 4.1 and 4.2 list representative G values for light-particle (electrons or gamma rays) irradiations of hydrocarbon gases and liquids. Note the high yields (second only to G_{H_2}) of dimer (carbon skeleton) in the methane and ethane exposures in Table 4.1. The lack of agreement between the two sets of data for a given compound is typical of work conducted by different people. The discrepancies may be due to different irradiation conditions (which are not always reported), such as dose (or percentage of conversion), dose rate, and temperature.

4-2.1 MECHANISMS

Figure 4.4 presents a summary of several reaction mechanisms that have been suggested for the radiolysis of saturated hydrocarbons. The

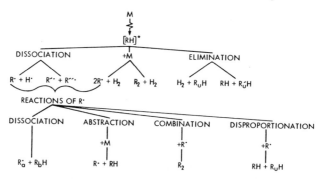

FIG. 4.4 Possible mechanism of saturated hydrocarbon radiolysis. R = alkyl group; R_u = unsaturated alkyl group.

presentation is in terms of free radicals, although the fragments may include ions. The nature of M^* is not specified but may include the excited singlet or triplet state and neutral and ionic species.

4-2.2 EFFECT OF STRUCTURE

Yields have been measured as a function of the length of the saturated hydrocarbon chain. Hydrogen evolution decreases only slightly or not at all with increasing chain length, whereas methane yields drop off sharply. The trend for hydrogen is shown in Figs. 4.5 and 4.6. The rather large discrepancies may be due to differences in experimental conditions. In Fig. 4.5, for example, some irradiations were carried to 15 to 68% conversion of the target hydrocarbon,[88] whereas others[5] were carried to only 0.1% conversion. In Fig. 4.6 the decrease in G_{H_2} noted in early work[113] was not confirmed in later work.[41]

Hydrogen and methane yields from saturated hydrocarbons exhibit a group-to-product correlation, as shown in Fig. 4.7. Curves are given for

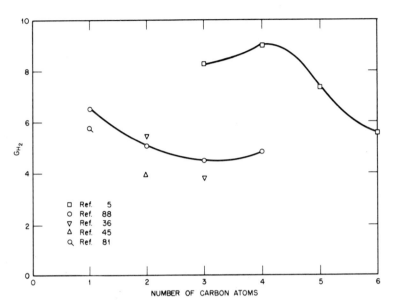

FIG. 4.5 Hydrogen yield from the irradiation of saturated hydrocarbon gases as reported by various workers.

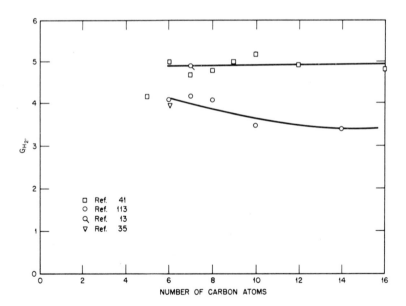

FIG. 4.6 Hydrogen yield from the irradiation of saturated hydrocarbon liquids as reported by various workers.

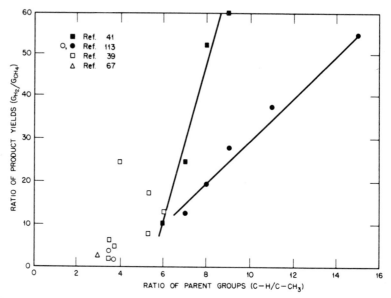

Fɪɢ. 4.7 Group-to-product correlation for saturated hydrocarbons as reported by various workers. Solid points are for *n*-alkanes; open points are for branched-chain compounds.

early[113] and for recent work.[41] In both cases the correlation is good for the normal hydrocarbons (solid points) but not for branched-chain compounds (open points), showing that branching influences the radiolysis reaction. Methane yields increase with branching, and there is a preference for C—C bond rupture adjacent to the branching site.[39]

Other product distributions reflect the sensitivity of secondary C—H bonds relative to the primary bond, consistent with bond strengths.[36,41] Mainly *trans*-vinylene double bonds

$$\left(\begin{matrix} \text{H} \\ | \\ \text{R}\overset{}{\text{C}}\!\!=\!\!\text{CR} \\ | \\ \text{H} \end{matrix}\right)$$

form from *n*-alkanes, but branched hydrocarbons form mainly vinylidene

$$\left(\text{CH}_2\!\!=\!\!\text{C}\diagup_{\text{R}}^{\text{R}}\right)$$

and vinyl

$$\left(\text{CH}_2\!\!=\!\!\text{C}\diagup_{\text{H}}^{\text{R}}\right)$$

unsaturation.[39] In spite of this bond specificity, the diversity of products formed from normal hydrocarbons has been cited as support for the over-all random nature of radiation attack.[41] Thus at least 27 compounds are formed in n-hexane radiolysis.[55] In contrast, only three major products were observed from cyclohexane radiolysis.[41,51] This illustrates that fragmentation of the ring structure is more selective even though the over-all decomposition is about the same as for n-hexane.[130]

4-2.3 EFFECT OF EXPERIMENTAL VARIABLES

The effect of temperature on the radiolysis of saturated hydrocarbons has been studied. Low temperatures ($-319°F$) were found to inhibit the formation of the dimer and intermediate-molecular-weight products in the radiolysis by electrons of n-hexane in the solid phase.[43] Double-bond production was independent of temperature. Figure 4.8 shows the variation

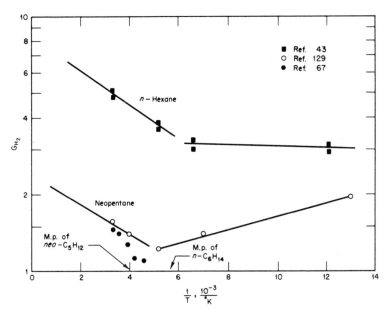

FIG. 4.8 Effect of temperature on radiolytic hydrogen yield as reported by various workers.

with physical state and temperature of hydrogen yield from n-hexane and neopentane. In the solid phase no effect was observed for G_{H_2} in n-hexane irradiations,[43] but the hydrogen yield actually increased at lower temperature in the case of neopentane.[129] This may have resulted from a reaction that competes for H atoms at intermediate temperatures with the combination reaction which forms H_2. G_{CH_4} increased with temperature in neopentane[67,129] and cyclohexane[67] irradiations. The slope of the liquid-phase portion of the curve corresponds to an activation energy of ~ 3 kcal/mole, about the same as for diffusion processes. No temperature effect was observed for liquid[40] and gaseous products[67] from cyclohexane.

An effect of physical state implies that the mechanism of product formation or rates of competitive reactions are not the same in the various phases. The temperature independence in the solid phase suggests that the mechanism does not involve a diffusion process. Products from liquid- and vapor-phase radiolysis are shown for n-pentane, neopentane, n-hexane, and cyclohexane in Table 4.2. The differences observed have not yet been explained in terms of mechanism, but they do illustrate the necessity for exercising great care in applying the general principle noted in Ch. 3, Sect. 3-2.2: gas-phase G values are larger than those from liquid-phase irradiations.

The LET of an incident particle probably does not affect the kinds of products observed but does affect their yields. Even then, however, G values are not strongly dependent on LET. The different levels of yields shown in Figs. 4.5 and 4.6 may be caused partly by differences in LET. However, the available evidence on the LET effect in saturated hydrocarbons is not clear cut. For example, early work on gaseous methane and butane using 12-Mev deuterons and Rn^{222} alphas showed no differences in product yields; lower over-all decomposition, however, was noted with deuterons.[73] More recently, alpha particles (from Cm^{242} and Po^{210}) and X rays (250 kvp) were compared in gas-phase irradiations of n-butane, isobutane, n-pentane, and n-hexane.[5] There was a qualitative similarity, but the ratio G_{H_2}/G_{CH_4} was up to two times higher for alphas. On the other hand, 14-Mev helium ions and 2-Mev electrons were found to give the same product distribution[38] from liquid pentane. The effect of geometry of the radiation flux with respect to the irradiation vessel may obscure the comparison of gamma rays and beams of electrons.[57]

Experimentally it is not always easy to change the bombarding particle without simultaneously varying the dose rate. Varying the dose clouds the interpretation of results, of course, as in the following case of n-hexane and cyclohexane. Yields were similar when effects of electrons, deuterons, and helium-ion beams were compared;[44,115] however, Co^{60} gamma rays gave lower yields of cyclohexene and bicyclohexyl from cyclohexane and lower yields of intermediate-molecular-weight products from n-hexane. These results were attributed to the lower dose rate of the Co^{60} source. This dose-rate effect was later confirmed in cyclohexane radiolysis.[48] With Co^{60} sources of different intensities, the steady-state concentration of cyclohexene increased slowly with dose rate, although the initial $G_{cyclohexene}$ is independent of dose rate. Thus it appears that cyclohexane radiolysis is not dependent upon LET. Another example of a dose-rate effect is the case of liquid cyclopentane–cyclohexane mixtures with Co^{60} gammas and 2-Mev electrons. A pronounced dependence of cyclopentylcyclopentane and cyclohexylcyclohexane yields was noted[117] as the intensity varied by about 10^5.

External conversion (energy transfer) type protection was first observed by Schoepfle[113] and is typified by the protection afforded cyclohexane by benzene. The excitation energy is transferred from at least one excited state of cyclohexane (by external conversion or perhaps by charge exchange) to the benzene molecule.[53] The latter dissipates the energy by internal conversion without decomposition, thus imparting radiation stability to the solution in excess of its mole fraction (Refs. 20, 21, 23, 53, and 89).

Negative-ion formation by an additive with high electron affinity may be the mechanism by which hydrogen evolution from cyclohexane is reduced 40% by $<10^{-3}M$ iodine, alkyl iodides, or sulfur dioxide.[114] In this case the ultimate neutralization of the cyclohexane ions can be accomplished with (negative) additive ions, rather than electrons. The resulting excited molecule may possess less energy (by the electron affinity) and, hence, may be less likely to decompose. The additive is used up in the process.

Molecules containing unshared electron pairs act as radical scavengers. Schuler *et al.*[49,51,135] suggested the use of iodine to count the number of radicals produced in radiolysis. Iodine functions to low concentrations ($<10^{-3}M$), and its consumption is related to $G_{radical}$. Oxygen is also a good radical counter, forming carbonyl and hydroxyl groups, which are readily measured.[40] Ferric chloride has been proposed as a radical scavenger.[30] Stable free radicals, such as diphenyl(picryl)hydrazyl (DPPH), have been used extensively to measure free-radical concentrations.[10]

Sometimes a product scavenges its own or other precursors. This is illustrated in cyclohexane radiolysis.[48,54] The product cyclohexene, when added to cyclohexane, inhibits its own formation and also that of H_2 (but to a lesser extent); other G values are also altered.

4-3 Unsaturated Hydrocarbons

Both C—H and C—C bonds of unsaturated hydrocarbon are broken in irradiation, but the characteristic reaction is polymerization. The reactive species formed by bond rupture may simply dimerize (cross link) or chain react to form a high-molecular-weight polymer. There is some evidence for radiation-induced cyclization.[79] Chain reactions, i.e., the polymerization of monomers, will be treated in Sect. 4-3.4.

Less gas is produced from unsaturated hydrocarbons than from saturated hydrocarbons (G_{H_2} is about one-fourth as great), but total decomposition is greater (G_{-M} ranges from 11 to 10,000). Several available G

values are listed in Table 4.3. These numbers were obtained under different experimental conditions, and it is not always clear that initial-product yields were reported. As indicated by the G_{-M} values, polymerization does not always occur via a chain mechanism. The G_{-M} for acetylene has been established as a reference in gas-phase dosimetry.[82] In ethylene radiolysis, yields of products containing an even number of C atoms predominate.

Table 4.3 — TYPICAL YIELDS FROM UNSATURATED HYDROCARBON IRRADIATIONS

Compound	Acetylene	Ethylene	1-Hexene	Cyclohexene
Reference	46	83	79	54
Radiation	β	e⁻	e⁻	γ
Temperature, °F	78	77	~72	75
Dose, 10^6 rads	0.9-38	3-32	19-64	4
Phase	Gas	Gas	Liquid	Liquid
G_{-M}	71.9	15	10.5	
G→polymer	57		6.9	8
G_{H_2}		1.2	0.8	1.2
G_{CH_4}		0.13		
$G_{C_2H_2}$		1.5		0.022
G (cyclohexane)				1.0
G (cyclohexene)	5.1			
G (bicyclohexyl)				1.36

This shows the importance of "doubling" reactions in which C—C bonds are not ruptured. Product yields from cyclohexene also bear this out, as does the production of dimer, trimer, tetramer, and pentamer in 1-hexene radiolysis.[79]

4-3.1 MECHANISMS

Speculations on the mechanism of radiolysis of unsaturated hydrocarbons are summarized in Fig. 4.9. Dissociation to give hydrogen followed by addition to a multiple bond is basic to the radiation chemistry of unsaturates. Even with acetylene, from which no H_2 is evolved, C—H bonds rupture, as evidenced by exchange between acetylene and deuteroacetylene.[46] The radicals so formed then enter into various reactions to form both higher and lower molecular weight products. If the hydrogen atom formed is in an excited state, it may abstract another hydrogen atom[54] to give H_2.

For acetylene two independent paths may be responsible for benzene and polymer (cuprene) formation.[47] Benzene may result from the trimerization of an excited acetylene by addition to neighboring acetylene

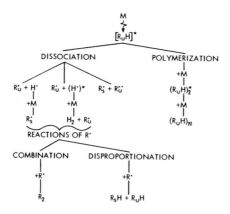

FIG. 4.9 Possible mechanism of unsaturated hydrocarbon radiolysis. R, R_u, and R_s = alkyl, unsaturated alkyl, and saturated alkyl groups, respectively.

molecules. Cuprene may come by a chain reaction via an ionic mechanism.[47,79] The existence of C_6H_n species in the mass spectrum of acetylene suggests this ionic chain reaction for cuprene formation.[7,110] If this is correct, a case of different primary processes, i.e., ionization and excitation, leading to the formation of different final products is involved.

The mechanism of ethylene radiolysis has been studied in detail because of its prospective commercial importance (Refs. 69, 71, 83, 85, and 96). Of the four most abundant gaseous products, ethane occurs via free radicals, but hydrogen, acetylene, and n-butane probably do not.[141] The major products isolated account for only about one-third the ethylene consumed. The rest forms polymer. This polymerization has been studied at high conversions under a wide variety of conditions of temperature and pressure.[69,85] G values are markedly dependent on dose and can be as high as 10,000. Polyethylene is formed through a free-radical chain mechanism.[69]

4-3.2 EFFECT OF STRUCTURE

The response of unsaturated hydrocarbons to radiolysis depends on the position of the unsaturation in the molecule. Compounds such as ethylene and acetylene, with unsaturation on a terminal carbon atom, polymerize by a chain reaction. Here, radiation takes part only in the initiation process. If the unsaturation is not at the end of the carbon chain, dimerization or cross linking takes place as with saturated hydrocarbons; and no chain reaction is involved.

Polymerization is easier for a molecule having two double bonds rather than one. *Trans* isomers cross link more readily than *cis* isomers, and irradiation converts both *trans* and *cis* forms into a mixture containing about 35% *trans* after 5×10^8 rads. The energy required to form a cross link with olefins (19 ev) is nearly independent of length of the carbon chain.[27] The average energy per cross link decreases in the order single-bond > double-bond > triple-bond molecules.

4-3.3 Effect of Experimental Variables

Decreasing the pressure below 0.03 atm in acetylene radiolysis with electrons reduced benzene formation. This was attributed to a wall effect. Thus a precursor of benzene (monomer or dimer) diffuses to the wall, where it may be deactivated.[47] No such yield diminution of low-molecular-weight products occurred in either acetylene[46] or ethylene[83] radiolysis at ~0.1 to 0.5 atm. Polyethylene yield (from ethylene) increases with pressure.[69]

Increasing the temperature (80 to 460°F) considerably increases (100-fold) the ethylene polymerization rate using gamma rays.[69,85] The corresponding over-all activation energy is 15 kcal/mole, and this has been interpreted in terms of a detailed reaction mechanism.[69]

4-3.4 Polymerization by Chain Reaction

A full treatment of radiation-induced polymerization[28] is beyond the scope of this book. In this chapter the discussion is limited to the effects of radiation on monomers. The radiolysis of polymers, elastomers, etc., is discussed in later chapters.

The lure of commercial exploitation has stimulated a great deal of work on polymerization by radiation-induced chain reactions. Interest stems from the possibility of process savings and/or unique products by this route. In nonradiation chain reactions, heat must be supplied to decompose the catalyst, and the temperature must be carefully adjusted to control the polymerization rate. Radiation, on the other hand, can initiate the reaction at both low pressures and low temperatures, which need not be precisely controlled. Moreover, no catalyst fragments are left in the polymer to impair its properties.

Other advantages also exist for radiation polymerization. Initiation is possible even in the solid phase. This is useful for obtaining block or graft polymers. Some monomers that do not polymerize under ordinary conditions do so under the influence of radiation, e.g., certain perfluoroolefins.[125] Initiation can also be induced *in situ* using radiation, and this aids in casting intricately molded products. Finally, the average chain length and, hence, the molecular weight of a polymer can be easily controlled in the radiation process because these depend upon radiation dose rate.

Important differences prevail in objectives and methods used between polymerization and other radiolysis studies. In basic radiolysis research, low dose is important to prevent contamination of the compound studied with its own degradation products. In polymerization, however, high conversion of the starting monomer to polymer is desirable. Radicals produced from the polymer result in an increase in the average molecular weight with increase in conversion.[10] Because the objective has been to produce a polymer and to study its properties, specific product yields have not received as much attention as they have in other radiation-chemistry studies.

4-3.4.1 *Kinetics and Mechanisms*

Hydrocarbons with unsaturation on a terminal carbon atom polymerize via a free-radical chain or addition reaction. The mechanism for addition polymerization (as contrasted to condensation polymerization) consists of three steps: initiation, propagation, and termination. These are written

Initiation: $M \text{ \leavevmode } \longrightarrow N$ (4.10)

Propagation: $N + M \rightarrow NM$
$$NM + M \rightarrow NM_2 \tag{4.11}$$

or simply $N + mM \rightarrow NM_m$

Termination: $wNM_m \rightarrow P$ (4.12)

The initiator N can be either a free radical or an ion. The chain reaction is propagated by the addition of a monomer, M, to active chain carriers, NM. Termination produces polymer, P, by combination with another radical, hydrogen abstraction, disproportionation, etc. The order of the termination step (with respect to chain carrier) is w.

Radiation polymerization by an ionic mechanism has been studied as a means of making unique polymers. Little is known about ionic polymerizations compared to radical polymerizations; yet ionizing radiation should produce ionic initiators in abundance. Experimentally, ionic mechanisms can be characterized in several ways: (1) the usual free-radical scavengers (O_2, I_2, DPPH, quinone) do not inhibit the reaction, (2) increasing the dielectric constant of the medium increases the rate, (3) a unique polymer is produced, and (4) the kinetics are different for ionic and free-radical polymerizations.

The dependence of conversion of monomer to polymer on radiation intensity is different in ionic vs. radical polymerizations. The rate of each step (initiation, propagation, and termination, Eqs. 4.10, 4.11, 4.12) can be written in terms of rate constants (k_i, k_p, k_t) for the three steps and concentration of the reacting species. Then the over-all reaction (conversion) rate is usually assumed to be the same as the propagation rate

$$\text{Rate} = \left[k_p \left(\frac{k_i}{k_t} \right)^{1/w} \right] (M)(I)^{1/w} \tag{4.13}$$

The monomer concentration is M; w is the order of the chain-breaking process; and I is the dose rate, or intensity, of the absorbed radiation. For free-radical mechanisms, growing chains are assumed to terminate in bimolecular collisions of two such chains, i.e., $w = 2$; and the rate equation reduces to the simple square-root dependence seen in Ch. 3, Eq. 3.36. On the other hand, $w = 1$ for ionic mechanisms. The square-root law for free-radical polymerizations has been experimentally verified only at low intensities and for cases in which the polymer is soluble in the monomer. If the monomer precipitates,[29,34] w may be between 1 and 2, as in Ch. 3, Eq. 3.37.

The temperature dependence of polymerization rate is another way of telling ionic and radical mechanisms apart. According to Eq. 4.9, the rate constants vary exponentially with temperature and activation energy. As seen from the collection of k's in Eq. 4.13, the over-all activation energy, E, can be written in terms of the activation energy for initiation, propagation, and termination: E_i, E_p, E_t

$$E = E_p + \frac{1}{w}(E_i - E_t) \tag{4.14}$$

Free-radical chains terminate when two radicals collide ($E_t = 0$) and E is positive. In ionic polymerizations, however, termination involves molecular arrangement (E_t is large) so that E is close to 0 or negative.

The chain length is an important but ill-defined concept. It is a measure of the molecular weight of the polymer, but it is here defined to be the polymerization rate divided by the initiation rate. This results in the following:

$$\text{Chain length} = \frac{k_p k_i^{(1/w)-1}}{k_t^{1/w}} (M)(I)^{(1/w)-1} \tag{4.15}$$

Note that this is somewhat similar to Eq. 4.13. If the chain length is measured as a function of dose rate, a free-radical mechanism ($w = 2$) can be distinguished from an ionic ($w = 1$) mechanism.

4-3.4.2 Irradiation of Pure Monomers

Table 4.4 lists information on some of the monomers studied. Little is known about primary species or initial products, but considerable work has been done to determine if the chain reaction is free radical or ionic in character.

Table 4.4 — TABULATION OF GAMMA-RAY-INITIATE
POLYMERIZATION REACTIONS

Reference	Monomer	Temp., °F	Pressure, psig	Polymerization conditions	Polymer, mol. wt.
70	Styrene	162	14.7	Bulk	$1.6-5 \times 10^5$
		113	14.7	Emulsion	$1.2-2 \times 10^6$
70	Methyl methacrylate	167	14.7	Bulk	380,000
70	Methyl methacrylate	86	14.7	Bulk	~70,000
70	Ethylene	374	14.7	Gas phase	
		68	1900	Gas phase	20,000
		392	1200	Gas phase	Liquids
93	Ethylene	68	720	Gas	70,000
93	Ethylene	68	810	Emulsion	200,000
70	N-Vinylpyrollidone	122	14.7	H_2O solution	~50,000
70	Acrylamide	86	14.7	Solid	236,000
70	Perfluoropropylene	86	14.7	Bulk	600
70	Perfluorobutadiene	86	14.7	Bulk	"Grease"
70	Acrylonitrile[a]	68	14.7	H_2O solution	Solid
70	Acetylene	86	14.7	Gas phase	Powder
109	Trifluorochloroethylene	59-73	Vac.	Bulk	
109	Vinylidene fluoride	59-73	Vac.	Bulk	
33	Isobutene	-108	Vac.	Bulk	
26	Vinyl acetate	57	Vac.	Bulk	
26	Vinyl chloride	57	Vac.	Bulk	
26	Methyl acrylate	57	Vac.	Bulk	

[a] X-ray initiated.

Ethylene polymerization has been studied under a wide variety of conditions using alphas, electrons, and gamma rays. The radiolysis products were discussed earlier. Gas-phase (Refs. 69, 85, 87, and 92) and solution (Refs. 71 and 93) polymerizations have been reported. Polyethylene made by irradiation is markedly different from the conventional product in appearance and properties, which depend on conditions of pressure, temperature, radiation intensity, and whether or not gamma or particulate radiation is used. In general, the strength is higher and the elongation is less than those of the conventional product—probably owing to branching of the chain and cross linking.[70]

Isobutylene deserves special mention because work with it helped to

establish that radiation can induce ionic as well as free-radical polymerization. With ordinary initiators isobutylene polymerizes via cationic intermediates. Radiation studies of the reaction rate, activation energy, and
inhibition by additives show that the mechanism is ionic.[33,37]

Radiolytic polymerization in the solid phase has been accomplished with
acrylamide,[6,95] styrene, methyl methacrylate, acrylonitrile,[95] and tetra-
ethylene glycol dimethacrylate.[112] A postirradiation polymerization occurs
with solid acrylamide. This results from the trapping and slow release of
radicals in the crystal lattice.[8] The state of aggregation affects the reaction
in the case of vinyl stearate. A discontinuity occurs at the melting point in
the temperature dependence of the molecular weight and reaction rate.[14]
Radiation polymerization does not occur if conducted at sufficiently low
temperatures. If acrylonitrile is irradiated at low temperature and then
warmed, a chain reaction sets in. The reaction can proceed with explosive
violence as the trapped free-radical initiators in the solid matrix are released upon warming. The polymers thus formed are less soluble than if
the polymerization occurred during irradiation. Such a postirradiation effect
is also observed when acrylonitrile is polymerized in a precipitating
medium.[9]

4-3.4.3 *Irradiation of Mixtures*

Solvents have an important effect on radiation polymerization of unsaturated materials. Radiation acts randomly on both solvent and monomer
to give chain initiators. More free radicals can sometimes be produced from
the solvent than from the monomer, e.g., in dilute solutions, and the reaction accelerates accordingly. Thus the $G_{-C_2H_4}$ in the presence of solvents is
fivefold to eightfold higher than in the gas phase.[93] When the initiators
are produced independently (not generally true), the initiation rate,
$G_{radical}$, depends on the sum of the free radicals produced from the monomer
and those produced from the solvent.[25] Many monomers have been polymerized in solution: methyl methacrylate in a variety of solvents,[26,121]
acrylonitrile in methanol,[26] and ethylene in several solvents and emulsions.

A copolymer can be formed from the irradiation of solutions of two
monomers. The mechanism of the reaction was studied in the special
styrene–methyl methacrylate case.[120] The copolymer would be expected to
be derived from equal amounts of each monomer if the reaction involves
free radicals, 99% styrene if it involves a cationic mechanism, and 99%
methyl methacrylate if it is anionic.[134] Radiation-produced material actually is derived from equal amounts of the two monomers and hence is
produced by a free-radical mechanism.

Free-radical production rates, $G_{radical}$, have been determined by measuring the polymerization rate of vinyl monomers, e.g., styrene, methyl
methacrylate, and vinyl acetate, which are efficient radical scavengers.[25]
As shown in Eq. 4.13, the rate constants (k_p and k_t) for the propagation

and termination steps must be known in order to calculate the radical production rate, k_i.

Irradiation of chemical catalysts produced little effect in most cases studied. However, some metal oxides (ZnO, SiO_2, MgO) accelerate isobutylene radiolytic polymerization.[139] Metal oxides do not affect free-radical reactions; so the acceleration is evidence of an ionic mechanism. Apparently the oxides capture electrons, resulting in increased lifetime for the cations and the polymerization initiators.

4-4 Aromatic Hydrocarbons

Studies of the radiolysis of aromatic compounds have been confined chiefly to benzene, alkylbenzenes, and the discrete-ring polyphenyls (compounds having two or more benzene ring units joined together in a chainlike structure). Polyphenyls are of interest as organic coolants for nuclear reactors because they are the most resistant class of organic compounds to radiation and heat. Table 4.5 shows G values that have been reported for liquid-phase irradiations of some aromatic systems. G_{-M} may be approximated as the sum of $G_{\rightarrow \text{polymer}}$ and $G_{\text{total gas}}$. G_{-M} is about 0.2 for polyphenyls, tenfold less than for other compound types. This reflects the well-known correlation between stability and aromatic content.

In polyphenyls the C—H bonds break on radiolysis in preference to

Table 4.5 — PRODUCT YIELDS FROM THE IRRADIATION (GAMMA OR ELECTRON) OF AROMATIC SYSTEMS IN LIQUID PHASE

Compound[a]	ϕH	ϕ_2	ϕ_2	ϕCH_3	$o\text{-}\phi_3$	$m\text{-}\phi_3$	$p\text{-}\phi_3$
Reference	64	15	65,66	89	15	15	15
Temperature, °F	~85	570	180	~70	570	570	570
Dose, 10^6 rads	b	~1500	30	~50	~1500	~1500	~1500
$G_{\rightarrow \text{polymer}}$	0.94	0.38	0.26	0.92	0.18	0.21	0.18
$G_{\text{total gas}}$	0.051	0.021	0.0073		0.023	0.015	0.015
G_{H_2}	0.044		0.0067	0.13			0.014
G_{CH_4}				0.0077			0.00036
G_{C_2}				0.0043			0.00072
$G_{C_2H_2}$	0.0073		0.0006				
G_{ϕ_2}	0.093						
$G_{\phi_2H_2}$	0.011[c]		>0.00028				
$G_{\phi_2H_4}$	0.004[c]		>0.000057				
$G_{\phi_2H_6}$	0.024[c]		>0.0000049				
$G_{\phi_2H_8}$	0.0024[c]						

[a] ϕ means phenyl or phenylene group.
[b] Dose not meaningful because products continuously removed.
[c] Calculated from authors' data.

rupture of a benzene ring or of the C—C bond joining two rings together. Some ring fission occurs, however, as small amounts of hydrocarbon gases are produced (see Table 4.5). When alkylbenzenes are irradiated, decomposition occurs principally in the side group, which is less stable than the benzene ring. The C—C bond once removed from the ring is preferentially ruptured. (This is also true in photochemistry and in low-energy electron bombardment in the mass spectrometer.) Polymer formation is the dominant reaction in the radiolysis of aromatics. This can be seen by comparing $G_{\rightarrow polymer}$ and $G_{total\ gas}$ yields in Table 4.5. Polymer formation has been taken as the principal index of stability in comparing candidate reactor coolants (see Ch. 8).

Evolved gases (Table 4.5) have received the most attention.[15,32] Much work has also involved characterizing the gross polymer by its properties, such as average molecular weight, carbon–hydrogen ratio, and unsaturation.[64,104] In the polymer from biphenyl, polyphenyls with even numbers of phenyl rings are more abundant than those with odd numbers of rings.[66] At high doses ($\sim 10^{10}$ rads), the average molecular weight is at least twice that of the starting molecule, and products are higher polyphenyls (principally dimer) and alkylpolyphenyls.[15]

4-4.1 MECHANISMS

Figure 4.10 shows the various reactions that have been postulated for benzene and polyphenyls. Studies with deuterobenzene show that at least two mechanisms are necessary to account for hydrogen and acetylene production: one involving free hydrogen atoms and one involving a rearrangement process.[63] As pointed out before, C—H bond rupture is the most likely of the dissociation reactions. Hydrogen atoms (primarily from an

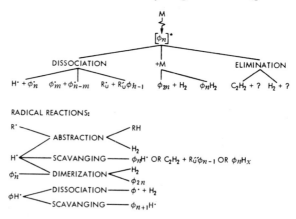

Fig. 4.10 Possible mechanism of benzene and polyphenyl radiolysis. ϕ = phenyl or phenylene group; subscripts m and n = integers; R and R_u = alkyl and unsaturated alkyl groups.

alkyl substituent, if present) dissociated from C—H bonds are scavenged rapidly by surrounding aromatic molecules.[18] The addition products are intermediates that form hydrogenated products (by continued hydrogen-atom scavenging) and polymer (by reaction with nearby aromatic molecules). The aromatic fragment remaining after loss of a hydrogen atom may also be scavenged by neighboring aromatics, giving rise to polymer. The average molecular weight of the polymer produced from benzene increases with dose, while double-bond formation decreases. Thus the polymer is probably built up via intermediates containing double bonds.[104]

4-4.2 EFFECT OF STRUCTURE

Little difference in stability among the terphenyl isomers is shown in Table 4.5. There is some evidence that stability increases in going from o-terphenyl to the *meta* and *para* isomers. It also increases as the length of the polyphenyl chain is increased.[32] When an alkyl group is added to the benzene ring, the yield of C_2 hydrocarbons drops and the CH_4 yield rises. Thus, if the C_2's come principally from ring rupture, the radiation must prefer to decompose the alkyl group. This intramolecular energy transfer corresponds to the intermolecular transfer that exists in the radiolysis mixtures of aliphatic and aromatic compounds.

A series of alkylbenzenes was irradiated, and yields of H_2, CH_4, and C_2 hydrocarbons were measured.[72,128] A group-to-product correlation for hydrogen and methane similar to that shown in Fig. 4.7 for saturated hydrocarbons is presented in Fig. 4.11. The yield ratio is plotted against the

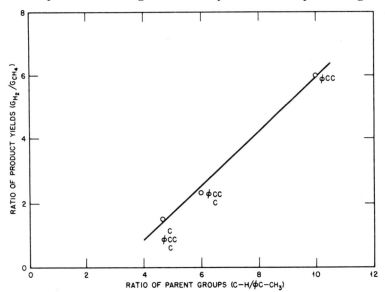

Fig. 4.11 Group-to-product correlation for alkylbenzenes. ϕ = phenyl group.

ratio of C—H bonds in the molecule to the C—C bonds once removed from the ring. The latter bonds are preferentially broken in the photochemistry and mass spectrometry of alkylbenzenes. The three alkylbenzenes in Fig. 4.11 acted as expected statistically if it is assumed that the same fraction of C—H and C—CH₃ bond ruptures result in hydrogen and methane formation for each compound tested.

4-4.3 Effect of Experimental Variables

The literature on aromatic compounds is confused by the large variations in radiation dose used by different people. Benzene and alkylbenzenes were studied at low doses ($\sim$50 megarads); the polyphenyls, however, were irradiated at much larger doses ($>$1500 megarads). The objectives were different: the high doses simulated conditions in an organic-cooled reactor; low doses minimized secondary reactions in basic studies of initial products.

With polyphenyls the total gas yield decreases with increasing dose up to 10^{10} rads and levels off at higher doses. This reflects a decrease in G_{H_2}, although G_{CH_4} and G_{C_2} actually increase with dose.[15] As the polymer builds up in the irradiated material at very high doses, the decomposition rate decreases, as shown in Fig. 4.12. The slopes of the curves give $G_{\rightarrow polymer}$

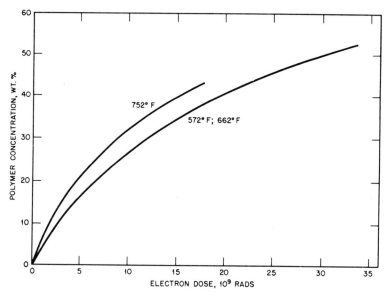

FIG. 4.12 Increase in radiolytic polymer from irradiation of p-terphenyl in liquid phase.[15]

values that become less as the polymer builds up. At high (up to 50%) concentrations, the polymer exerts a protective influence on the mixture.

Over the limited range investigated (twofold for benzene[104] and eightfold for polyphenyls[15]), there is no indication that dose rate plays a role in the radiolysis of aromatics.

The temperature of irradiation affects yields, as is shown by the Arrhenius plot in Fig. 4.13. The slopes correspond to activation energies of

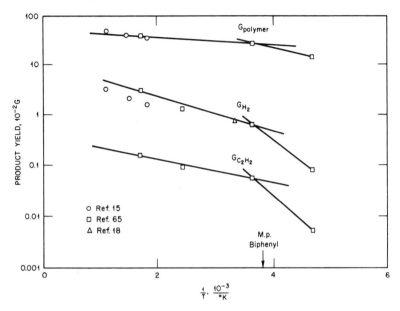

FIG. 4.13   Temperature dependence in biphenyl radiolysis.

about 3, 2, and 0.7 kcal/mole for H_2, C_2H_2, and polymer. The hydrogen yields from British work[15] fall below the line, reflecting the high doses employed. The indifference to irradiation temperature of polymer formation is also shown in Fig. 4.12. Below 660°F variations in temperature had little effect in p-terphenyl radiolysis. More polymer is formed at 750°F as the threshold of damage is approached. (The threshold is the critical temperature above which decomposition is markedly dependent on irradiation temperature. This is discussed in more detail in Ch. 8, Sect. 8-3.1.)

The effect of phase in biphenyl radiolysis is also indicated in Fig. 4.13. The solid-phase points fall below an extrapolation of the liquid-phase points. Total gas and polymer yields[32] from the terphenyls are less at 85°F than at 660°F. This may reflect the differences between solid- and liquid-phase irradiations as well as a temperature effect. Irradiations of benzene in the vapor state were found to yield a higher hydrogen-to-acetylene ratio than those in the liquid state (0.07 vs. 1.6).[89]

Although a case for equal energy–equal damage, i.e., absence of LET effect, has been made,[32] evidence continues to accumulate in support of a

LET effect in aromatics. A comparison of electron and reactor radiation was made for several alkylbenzenes.[127] The results summarized in Table 4.6 were interpreted in terms of either differences in initial excitation or a LET effect. The reactor radiation resulted in higher yields of C_2 hydrocarbons and in a higher hydrogen-to-methane ratio. Comparisons of gas yields and polymer production for reactor irradiation and 1-Mev electrons have been made.[15] Some of these results are also given in Table 4.6. The differences observed were attributed to the greater damaging effect of fast neutrons in the reactor irradiation. Recent data from the irradiation of benzene at low doses seems to confirm a LET effect for the production of H_2, C_2H_2, and hydrogenated biphenyls.[59]

<h4 align="center">4-4.4 IRRADIATION OF MIXTURES</h4>

In general, an aromatic compound will enhance the stability of a less-stable compound in a mixture. The case of intramolecular protection in alkylbenzenes was treated in Sect. 4-2. An example of intermolecular protection is the reduction of G_{H_2} when benzene is added to cyclohexane.[22] Concentrated ($\sim$50 wt. %) m-terphenyl decreased G_{H_2} in benzene radiolysis (1.5-Mev electrons, liquid) from 0.036 to 0.027, but p-terphenyl and naphthalene were without effect. Iodine added to benzene as a radical scavenger did not decrease hydrogen production in dilute solutions; but in concentrated solutions (0.2M), G_{H_2} was decreased by 20%. This effect of iodine in aromatic systems is much less than with aliphatic hydrocarbons. Such is expected from the fact that aromatics are themselves better scavengers than are the aliphatics.

4-5 Oxygen-containing Compounds

4-5.1 ALCOHOLS

The principal bond rupture occurs at the alpha carbon atom, i.e., at the carbon atom to which the OH group is attached. In aliphatic alcohols, C—O bond rupture is only one half as probable as is rupture of the other bonds at the alpha carbon on irradiation. The alpha C—H bond is more labile than a corresponding C—C bond.

An extensive survey[90,91,100] of the radiation chemistry of C_1 to C_{10} aliphatic alcohols was conducted. An attempt was made to obtain a balance of oxidation and reduction products as well as a mass balance. Some water and hydrogen could not be accounted for. Table 4.7 shows typical G values.

The major products from alcohol radiolysis are hydrogen, carbonyl-containing compounds, and glycols. Gas production ($3.5 \leqslant G_{gas} \leqslant 4.5$) is not far different from that with normal paraffins. Glycols having OH groups on adjacent carbon atoms, i.e., "vicinal" glycols, are the only ones formed. Hydrocarbons containing one less carbon atom than the parent alcohol are

Table 4.6 — EFFECT OF RADIATION TYPE ON PRODUCT YIELDS FROM AROMATIC COMPOUNDS

Compound	Toluene		Ethylbenzene		Isopropylbenzene		tert-Butyl-benzene		Biphenyl		p-Terphenyl	
Reference	127	127	127	127	127	127	127	127	15	15	15	15
Radiation	e⁻	Reactor	e⁻	Reactor	e⁻	Reactor	e⁻	Reactor	e⁻	Reactor	e⁻	Reactor
Temperature, °F	~80	~80	~80	~80	~80	~80	~80	~80	570	570	570	570
Dose, 10^6 rads	30-300		30-300		30-300		30-300		1400	850	1400	850
G_{H_2}	0.13	0.16	0.18	0.22	0.17	0.21	0.11	0.16			0.014	0.048
G_{CH_4}	0.008	0.006	0.030	0.023	0.073	0.050	0.070	0.045			0.00036	0.0079
G_{C_2}	0.001	0.016	0.004	0.022	0.009	0.011	0.009	0.018			0.00072	0.0058
G_{gas}									0.021	0.112	0.015	0.062
$G{\rightarrow}$polymer									0.38	0.82	0.18	0.47

Table 4.7 — PRODUCT YIELDS FROM NORMAL ALCOHOLS (RCH_2OH) IRRADIATED IN THE LIQUID PHASE

Compound	Methanol		Ethanol		1-Propanol	1-Butanol	1-Octanol	1-Decanol
Reference	91	90	100	91	91	91	91	91
Radiation	α	γ	α	α	α	α	α	α
Temperature, °F	≥65	72	61–77	≥65	≥65	≥65	≥65	≥65
Dose, 10^6 rads	120	0.07–0.29	5.9	120	120	120	120	120
$G \rightarrow polymer$				0.06		0.2		
G_{-M}	5.8			4.7	6.1	4.2		
$G_{total\ gas}$	4.48	4.0	4.10	4.47		4.26	3.68	3.63
G_{H_2}	3.5			3.5	2.8	3.6	3.5	3.5
G_{CO}	0.23	0.16	0.09	0.11	0.10	0.07	0.05	0.04
G_{H_2O}	0.9			0.8	0.9	0.6	0.4	0.3
G_{CH_4}	0.36	0.2	0.43	0.43	0.07	0.06	0.02	0.02
G_{RCH_3}	0.36		0.18	0.17	0.15	0.12		
G_{RH}			0.43	0.43	0.54	0.46		
$G_{aldehyde}$	1.4	1.3		2.2	2.1	1.5	0.7	1.0
$G_{total\ carbonyl}$	1.7			2.1	2.1	1.5	0.87	0.76
$G_{vic\text{-}glycol}$	1.8	3.0	1.4	1.1	0.9	0.9	0.56	0.51
$G_{R=CH_2}$				0.17	0.14	0.09		

formed when C—C bonds rupture at the alpha carbon atom. The other fragment, i.e., that containing the C—OH group, may then dimerize to glycol or oxidize further to a carbonyl compound. Decomposition yields for the radiolysis of alcohols are in the range $3 \leqslant G_{-M} \leqslant 6$ except for the self-irradiation of C^{14}-labeled methanol[131] for which $G_{-M} = 12$.

Methanol G values are still uncertain despite the attention of a number of investigators (Refs. 1, 86, 90, 91, 94, and 123). For example, in gamma radiolysis, values for G_{H_2} range[94] from 4.0 (as shown in Table 4.7) to 5.4. Attempts to resolve this disparity by very careful control of dose and impurities in the methanol resulted[86] in an intermediate value of 4.6. Discrepancies also occur in the yields of other major products and emphasize the difficulty in obtaining accurate numbers for "pure" methanol.

4-5.1.1 *Mechanisms*

The scheme for alcohol radiolysis is shown in Fig. 4.14. Struck alcohol molecules may either dissociate or rearrange to eliminate a stable molecule. Six radicals may thus be produced from primary alcohols: H•, RC•HOH, HO•, RC•H₂, HC•HOH, and R•. The relative importance of each of the

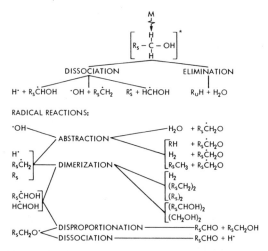

FIG. 4.14 Possible mechanism of primary aliphatic alcohol radiolysis. R_s and R_u = saturated and unsaturated alkyl groups, respectively.

reaction paths shown in Fig. 4.14 depends on the structure of the particular alcohol. The primary dissociation of a hydrogen atom is largely from the alpha carbon atom as shown.[17] (Incidentally, hydrogen is also lost from the alpha carbon with low-energy electrons in the mass spectrometer.) Several likely reactions of the initially produced radicals and RCH_2O• are also shown in Fig. 4.14. Glycol can be formed by combination of two RC•HOH's. The generally higher yield of aldehyde (see Table 4.7) is possibly due to its formation via two routes, i.e., by disproportionation of either RC•HOH or RCH$_2$O$^\bullet$. Such free-radical schemes will account for H$_2$, RH, and RCH$_3$ production. With one exception saturated and ethylenic hydrocarbons derivable from the same radical are produced in about a 2 to 1 ratio. This is taken to mean that an alkyl radical has about twice the probability of abstracting a hydrogen atom as dissociating. The exception is the case of hydrocarbons containing the same number of carbon atoms as the original alcohol. Here, the ethylenic hydrocarbons are just as abundant or more so. This is attributed to an additional molecular elimination of water (as in classical chemistry[91]

$$\underset{|}{\overset{H}{\underset{|}{\overset{|}{C}}}}\text{—CH—OH} \rightsquigarrow \quad \diagup\diagup\text{C}\!\!=\!\!\text{CH}_2 + \text{H}_2\text{O} \qquad (4.16)$$

Various deuterated ethanols have been irradiated in a study of radiolytic hydrogen formation.[17] The results were interpreted as showing molecular elimination of H$_2$ to be unimportant and hydrogen gas to be produced via abstraction of a hydrogen atom from the —OH group of ethanol leaving a CH$_3$CH$_2$O$^\bullet$ residue.

4-5.1.2 *Effect of Structure*

The nature of the R group in the molecule RCH$_2$OH is important. Reactivity of the bonds from the alpha carbon decreases in the order hydrogen, ethyl, methyl, and phenyl.[91,126] For benzyl alcohol the stability of the benzyl radical (ϕC$^\bullet$H$_2$) makes it possible to break the C—O bond in radiolysis. The ϕC$^\bullet$H$_2$ radicals formed from C—O fission dimerize to dibenzyl and also combine with ϕC$^\bullet$HOH radicals to give 1,2-diphenylethanol. Even so, aldehydes and glycols are the major products just as with aliphatic alcohols.

Table 4.7 shows that the aldehyde and glycol yields from alcohols decrease with increasing length of the carbon-atom chain. Possibly the influence of the —OH group is lessened as it is diluted by greater numbers of carbon atoms. The hydrogen yield is constant at 3.46 to 3.59 as the chain length is increased, except for *n*-propyl alcohol, the only odd carbon alcohol irradiated. Branching decreases the hydrogen yield. In fact, hydrogen is the largest gaseous product from primary and secondary alcohols; but methane exceeds hydrogen for *tert*-butyl alcohol (there is no alpha C—H bond in *tert*-butyl alcohol; and since the alpha position is the most active, an alpha C—C bond will break rather than C—H bonds elsewhere in the molecule).

In the radiolysis of alcohols, a correlation is expected between the frequency of bond breakage and the number of bonds, as shown in Fig. 4.15. The correlation implies that bond ruptures at the all-important alpha C result in H$_2$ and RH product, or at least the same fraction of these materials ends up as product for each compound studied. This is evidently not the case with the two points that do not fall on the curve.

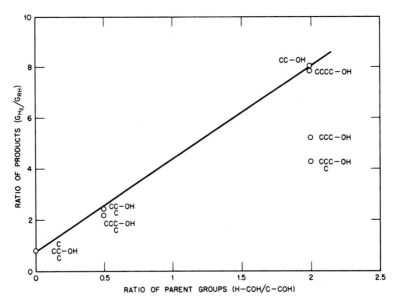

FIG. 4.15 Group-to-product correlation for alcohols of varying structure.

The $RCH_2O^{\cdot}$ intermediate shown in Fig. 4.14 gives rise to carbonyl products. The substituent on the alpha carbon determines the type of carbonyl formed. Thus secondary alcohols give both aldehydes and ketones:

$$R_2CHO^{\cdot} \begin{cases} \xrightarrow{\text{dissociation}} R_2CO + H^{\cdot} \text{ or } RCHO + R^{\cdot} & (4.17) \\ \xrightarrow{\text{disproportionation}} R_2CO + R_2CHOH & (4.18) \end{cases}$$

Primary alcohols give aldehydes and tertiary alcohols give ketones.[91] The glycol yields from primary alcohols are higher than those from secondary and tertiary alcohols. This effect may be caused either by a steric hindrance in the dimerization of $R_2C^{\cdot}OH$ or by a lowering of activation energy for disproportionation to favor formation of the carbonyl compound.

As shown in Fig. 4.14, molecular elimination of water produces olefins and involves a hydrogen on a beta carbon. The C—O bond is ruptured as in the production of saturated hydrocarbons. A C—O rupture, then, can result in either an olefin or the corresponding saturated hydrocarbon (assuming the alkyl radical abstracts a hydrogen):

$$\begin{array}{c} H \\ | \\ -C-CH_2-OH \end{array} \begin{cases} \xrightarrow{\text{elimination}} \begin{array}{c} \backslash \\ C=CH_2 + H_2O \\ / \end{array} & (4.19) \\ \xrightarrow{\text{dissociation}} \begin{array}{c} H \\ | \\ =C-\overset{\cdot}{C}H_2 + HO^{\cdot} \\ | \end{array} & (4.20) \end{cases}$$

The group-to-product correlation between alkene-to-alkane ratio and beta C—H bonds is shown in Fig. 4.16. The alkane yield from ethyl and *sec-*

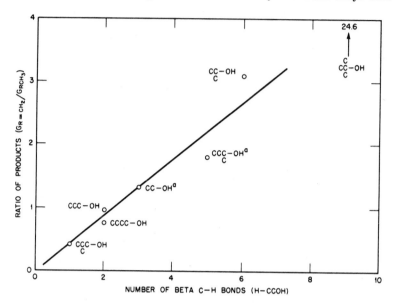

FIG. 4.16 Group-to-product correlation for alcohols.
[[a]G_{RCH_3} has been corrected for contribution by dimerization.]

butyl alcohols was corrected for the contribution from radical-radical dimerizations.[91]

4-5.1.3 *Effect of Experimental Variables*

Yields of most products from He[++] irradiations (especially hydrogen, carbonyl, and glycols) decreased as the total dose was increased over the range of 6 to 550 megarads.[100] At lower levels (0.03 to 0.4 megarad), the effect of dose is not clear cut.[1,86] These considerations make it difficult to arrive at satisfactory initial-product yields.

The effect of temperature on alcohol radiolysis has been given little attention. In one study methanol was irradiated at 32°F and at 70°F with no change in formaldehyde yield but with a decrease in glycol at the lower temperature.[90]

Ethanol vapor has also been irradiated with alphas at 108°C and 0.08 to 0.6 megarad.[108] The yields of hydrogen, RH (methane), and CH_2O were found to be 300 to 400% higher than in the higher dose liquid-phase irradiations (Table 4.7). The cause was attributed to the lack of cage recombination of the R and CH_2OH fragments. Yields of other products were also higher.

In general, beta and gamma rays give different product yields than do alpha particles. The self-irradiation of C^{14}-labeled methanol gave hydrogen and ethylene glycol as major products; no formaldehyde was produced.[123] Similarly, gamma rays gave much less formaldehyde, in comparison with glycol, than did alpha irradiations.[90] By implication glycol production is favored by low concentrations of radicals, i.e., glycol formation may take place in the bulk of the irradiated solution rather than in the tracks and spurs. This is consistent with the reduction of glycol yield observed previously at a lower exposure temperature because diffusion of glycol precursors into the bulk of the solution is inhibited as temperature is lowered. However, the implication does not reconcile with the mechanism, shown in Fig. 4.14, of the combination of $RC^{\bullet}HOH$ to give glycol, which should be favored by high radical concentrations in the tracks and spurs.

4-5.1.4 *Effect of Additives*

Radical production has been studied by the use of several additives including iodine, ferric chloride, sulfuric acid, acetone, benzoquinone, and diphenyl(picryl)hydrazyl (DPPH). $G_{radical}$ values were calculated from yield reductions when the scavengers were present. The product yields that persisted were ascribed to "molecular" processes, e.g., elimination of a stable molecule. Iodine, which functions as a scavenger for free radicals or electrons,[94] reduced yields of all products, except carbon monoxide, from methanol. Ferric chloride and benzoquinone decreased the yields of all products except formaldehyde.[1,2,19] Acetone added to isopropanol decreased G_{H_2}, but G_{CH_4} and G_{CO} were almost unaltered because of hydrogen-atom trapping by the additive.[124] Two of the radiolysis products of ethanol were used as additives to discover why product yields changed as the dose was increased. Thus both acetaldehyde and 1-hexene decreased hydrogen evolution from ethanol with little change in the yields of other products.[100]

When sulfuric acid was added to methanol containing benzoquinone or ferric chloride, hydrogen-atom production increased, but the methyl-radical yield decreased. An ionic mechanism was invoked to explain this effect. In acid solution methanol may add a hydrogen ion, which is then neutralized by an electron to form a hydrogen atom. Otherwise, the electron is captured by a neutral methanol molecule to form methyl radicals.[1]

4-5.2 ETHERS

Newton has made a systematic study of the aliphatic ethers.[97,99] This section is based almost entirely on his work. As measured by product yields, rupture of the C—O bond in ether molecules occurs twice as frequently as rupture at other sites. This is in contrast to the stronger C—O bond in alcohols which usually survives radiation attack. The major products include hydrogen, unsaturates, alcohols, carbonyl compounds, and "polymer."

G_{-M} has been estimated[130] to be about seven. Table 4.8 lists selected G values for four ethers.

Table 4.8 — PRODUCT YIELDS FROM THE He^{++} IRRADIATION OF ETHERS (RCH$_2$OCH$_2$R') IN THE LIQUID PHASE[a]

Compound (ether)	Ethyl	Ethyl n-butyl		n-Butyl	Ethyl $tert$-butyl
Temperature, °F	77–86	77–86	61–68	61–68	61–68
Dose, 10^6 rads	5.9	5.6	67	92	72
$G_{\longrightarrow polymer}$			~1.6	~2.2	~1.0
G_{H_2}	3.62	3.25	2.94	2.71	1.96
G_{CH_4}	0.24	0.095	0.104	0.061	0.77
G_{CO}	0.127	0.070	0.087	0.055	0.099
$G_{C_2H_2}$	0.091	0.037	0.042	0.026	0.034
G_{RCH_3}	0.62	0.31	0.27	0.39	0.45
$G_{R'CH_3}$	0.62	0.29	0.14	0.39	0.22
$G_{R=CH_2}$	1.07	0.52	0.42	0.38	0.32
$G_{R'=CH_2}$	1.07	0.29	0.18	0.38	0.71
$G_{total\ carbonyl}$			1.13	0.94	2.47
$G_{total\ hydroxyl}$			1.32	1.4	0.62

[a] From A. S. Newton, *Journal of Physical Chemistry*, Ref. 97.

4-5.2.1 *Mechanisms*

Figure 4.17 shows some of the primary reactions that have been proposed for ethers. Note the similarity to the scheme for alcohols (Fig. 4.14).

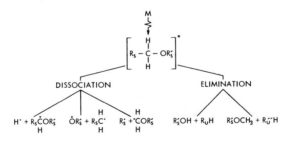

FIG. 4.17 Possible mechanism of aliphatic ether radiolysis. R_s and R_u = saturated and unsaturated alkyl groups, respectively.

Radical reactions of the various species may account for the observed products. Reactions are not shown for the ethers because it is not yet clear which are the major paths.

The molecular elimination of an alcohol, R'OH, from ethers[97] parallels the elimination of H_2O in the radiolysis of alcohols.[91] In both cases a hydrogen atom migrates from a beta carbon atom to the oxygen atom with the formation of a double bond:

$$\overset{\textcircled{H}}{-\text{C}}-\text{CH}_2-\text{OR'} \ \text{\small\leftwavy} \longrightarrow \ \overset{|}{\underset{|}{\text{C}}}=\text{CH}_2 + \text{R'OH} \qquad (4.21)$$

This reaction accounts for the high product ratio of alkenes to alkanes with the same number of carbon atoms. In like manner a CH_3 group may migrate in higher ethers forming methyl ethers and adding to the alkene production:

$$\overset{\textcircled{CH}_3}{-\text{C}}-\text{CH}_2-\text{OR'} \ \text{\small\leftwavy} \longrightarrow \ \overset{|}{\underset{|}{\text{C}}}=\text{CH}_2 + \text{R'OCH}_3 \qquad (4.22)$$

Another methyl rearrangement perhaps accounts for the high yield of propane from ethyl *tert*-butyl ether and ethane from methyl *tert*-butyl ether:

$$\text{CH}_3-\overset{\overset{\textstyle\textcircled{CH}_3}{|}}{\underset{|}{\text{C}}}-\text{OR'} \ \text{\small\leftwavy} \longrightarrow \ \text{R'CH}_3 + \text{CH}_3\text{COCH}_3 \qquad (4.23)$$
$$\qquad\quad\ \text{CH}_3$$

4-5.2.2 *Effect of Structure*

Branching in the alkyl group decreases hydrogen evolution but increases hydrocarbon yields. This behavior is similar to that observed with hydrocarbons and with alcohols. A group-to-product correlation is shown for H_2 and CH_4 yields in Fig. 4.18.

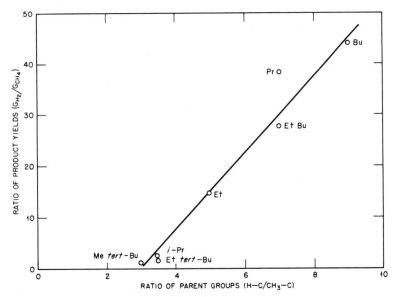

FIG. 4.18 Group-to-product correlation for ethers of varying structure.

Branching also increases the ratio of alkenes to alkanes with the same number of carbon atoms. In Sect. 4-5.2.1 double-bond formation was said to depend upon beta hydrogen atom migration. Figure 4.19 shows this beta hydrogen dependence of the alkene–alkane yields.

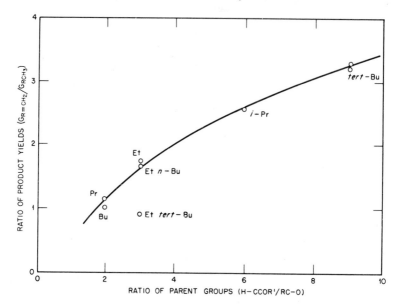

FIG. 4.19   Group-to-product correlation for ethers.

Some aromatic ethers were irradiated[132,133] to about 10^9 rads. The high doses were used because these ethers are promising as base stocks for radiation-resistant lubricants that must perform at high doses (see Ch. 9, Sect. 9-2.7). Diphenyl ether was irradiated with 1-Mev electrons and gave principally polymer, $G_{\rightarrow polymer} = 0.5$. This contained polyphenyl ethers and bis(phenoxy)biphenyl types of products. The $R=CH_2$ species does not form from aromatic ethers, but the analogous $R'CH_3$ and hydroxyl types are represented by benzene and phenol. Their G values are only 11 and 25% of the $G_{\rightarrow polymer}$, i.e., they are relatively much less abundant than the analogs from the aliphatic ethers shown in Table 4.8.

4-5.2.3 Effect of Experimental Variables

As noted before, the build-up of radiolysis products through increased dose may influence observed yields. Table 4.8 shows that ethers are no exception.[97] In other work the dose was raised 30-fold (from about 4.7 to 140 megarads), whereas $G_{acetylene}$ increased 3-fold, $G_{propene}$ decreased 2-fold, and G_{H_2} remained about the same.[99] Decreasing the dose ($\sim$0.2 megarad) resulted in a 4-fold increase in carbonyl compounds.[111]

Methyl *tert*-butyl ether was irradiated in both the vapor and liquid phases. The yield of most products was greater in the vapor phase. This presumably results from less immediate back reaction or recombination of primary radicals. In the gas phase the primary species are not contained by a cage (see Ch. 3, Sect. 3-2.2).

The effect of temperature was studied for isopropyl ether at 75 and 175°F. Product yields increased with temperature. This is caused by a more rapid diffusion of primary radicals away from their point of origin in tracks or spurs to produce more primary radical recombinations.

The use of helium ions, electrons, or gamma rays gave markedly different product yields in isopropyl ether radiolysis. (Chapter 3, Table 3.3, shows some of the data comparing helium ions with gamma rays.) The effect of helium ions and electrons was about the same, but this may have been an experimental artifact of saturation of the solution with excited species during each pulse of electrons. In this way the resulting density of excited species approached that expected along alpha-particle tracks (see Ch. 3, Sect. 3-1.1). Gamma irradiation results in a diffuse distribution of excited species; thus radical–radical reactions are minimized. The yield of propylene was found independent of LET. This is consistent with propylene formation via Eq. 4.21, monomolecular elimination.

4-5.2.4 *Effect of Additives*

Benzoquinone, added as a radical scavenger, reduced G_{H_2} and G_{CH_4} in diethyl ether radiolysis by gamma rays.[2] Both acetaldehyde and iodine were added to isopropyl ether in He[++] irradiations.[99] Iodine decreased the yield of most products. The aldehyde, a product of radiolysis, added in an amount corresponding to that formed in a 6-megarad irradiation caused marked changes in G values.

4-5.3 ALDEHYDES AND KETONES

Relatively little information is available on the radiolysis of aldehydes and ketones. Studies[3,92,103] of the volatile radiolysis products showed C—H bonds and bonds to the carbonyl carbon atom to be broken. The major products are H_2, CO, and hydrocarbons. Table 4.9 lists pertinent G values. G_{-M} has been estimated[130] to be ~7. Note that alkanes are prominent and correspond to the alkyl group in the parent. Early work[92] on formaldehyde and acetaldehyde indicated that the initial major reaction is polymerization. The polymer subsequently decomposes to give gaseous products similar to those shown in Table 4.9.

4-5.3.1 *Mechanisms*

A radiolysis mechanism for aldehydes and ketones is quite speculative at present because of the limited amount of available data. Figure 4.20

Table 4.9 — PRODUCT YIELDS FROM ALDEHYDES AND
KETONES IRRADIATED IN THE LIQUID PHASE

Compound	Acetone		Methyl ethyl ketone	Diethyl ketone	Propion-aldehyde
Reference	124	3	3	3	103
Temperature, °F	~72	81	81	81	~72
Dose, 10^6 rads	80	2.7	2.8	2.6	~4
Radiation	γ	γ	γ	γ	e^-
$G_{total\ gas}$	3.30				
G_{H_2}	0.84	0.88	1.2	1.2	1.2
G_{CH_4}	1.9	2.6	0.85	0.12	0.11
G_{CO}	0.63	0.84	0.83	1.5	1.6
$G_{C_2H_4}$			0.47	0.53	0.33
$G_{C_2H_6}$		0.48	2.8	4.0	1.1
$G_{C_3H_8}$			0.42		0.05
$G_{C_4H_{10}}$			0.22	0.34	

summarizes some of the suggestions made.[3,103] An alkyl group (or a hydrogen in the case of aldehydes) may be split from one side of the carbonyl leaving an R·CO fragment, which, in turn, decomposes into carbon monoxide and an alkyl radical. The relative effects of C—H and C—C bonds attached to the carbonyl group have not been determined directly, i.e., comparable aldehydes and ketones have not been studied simultaneously.

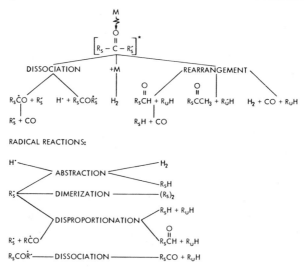

Fig. 4.20 Possible mechanism of ketone and aldehyde radiolysis. R_s and R_u = saturated and unsaturated alkyl groups, respectively.

The radical reactions shown are also tentative. Presumably, they are similar to those discussed before; i.e., the radicals may dissociate, dimerize, disproportionate, or abstract hydrogen atoms from a neighboring molecule. Most of the methane is formed via hydrogen abstraction by methyl radicals. Ethane may be produced either by hydrogen abstraction or by combination of two methyl radicals.

The mechanism of hydrogen evolution is noteworthy since the carbonyl group is itself a good hydrogen-atom scavenger.[124] Work with added scavengers and also with deuteroacetone suggests that the hydrogen gas arises via hot hydrogen atoms or other bimolecular reactions. An additional possibility[103] is unimolecular rearrangement giving $H_2 + C_2H_4 + CO$.

4-5.3.2 Effect of Structure

The series comprising formaldehyde, acetaldehyde, and acetone was irradiated in the gas phase with electrons.[92] Hydrogen, CO, and CO_2 were the principal products from formaldehyde. Replacing one or both hydrogen atoms of the formaldehyde molecule with CH_3 groups (giving acetaldehyde or acetone) resulted in lower radiolytic production of CO_2 and H_2 but gave substantial yields of alkanes and alkenes. This is qualitatively as expected on the basis of a group-to-product correlation.

The yield of hydrogen is greater for methyl ethyl ketone and diethyl ketone than for acetone. This probably results[3] from the presence of secondary C—H bonds in the first two compounds; such C—H bonds are absent in acetone. Indeed, C_{H_2} has been found to increase with the number of secondary hydrogen atoms.[105] It also appears that cyclo substituted and unsaturated ketones are more resistant to radiation than saturated ketones.[105]

4-5.3.3 Effect of Experimental Variables

Yields of gaseous products from aldehydes and ketones depend upon the total absorbed dose as with other classes of compounds. In Co^{60} irradiations of acetone shown in Table 4.9, G_{H_2} was unchanged even though doses differed by a factor of 30. However, G_{CO} and G_{CH_4} fell off as the dose was increased from 80 to 240 megarads.[124] The decrease was possibly a dose-rate effect because the higher dose work was with a 10-fold stronger source.

The yields of H_2, CO, CH_4, and C_2H_6 from low-molecular-weight ketones were only slightly different at 81 and $-112°F$ exposure temperatures. Above 81°F the yields of most products increased.[3] In liquid- and vapor-phase irradiations, the major products were the same, although their yields differed. Minor products, such as acetylene and propylene, were most apparent when the irradiation was carried out in the gas phase. Aldehydes were found in vapor but not in liquid-phase exposures.[3]

Table 4.10 — PRODUCT YIELDS FROM ACETATES IRRADIATED IN THE LIQUID PHASE

Compound	Methyl acetate		Ethyl acetate	Isopropyl acetate		n-Propyl acetate		Benzyl acetate
Reference	76	80	2	101	80,132	80,132	80,132	80,132
Radiation	γ	e^-	γ	α	e^-	e^-	e^-	e^-
Temperature, °F	~72	50–86	64	77	50–86	50–86	50–86	50–86
Dose, 10^6 rads	<10–344	350–570	>0.047	2.1	370–570	50	370–510	370–510
G_{-M}	4.1	1.82			2.99	3.35	2.7	2.77
$G{\rightarrow}$polymer				0.34		3.84	2.5	
G_{gas}	5.57[a]	3.40		5.55[a]	3.62	3.97	2.4	2.66
G_{H_2}	0.87	0.63	0.90	0.86	0.51	0.77	0.7	0.09
G_{CO}	1.57	1.20	1.13	1.17	0.76	1.14	0.55	0.15
G_{CO_2}	0.78	0.40		0.75	0.60	0.55	0.3	1.58
G_{CH_4}	2.07	0.82		0.94	0.95	0.41	0.41	0.75
$G_{C_2H_6}$	0.27	0.29	1.58	0.57	0.29	0.63	0.16	0.07
G_{R_uH}	2.07			0.77	0.19	0.13	0.05	
$G_{R'H}$	0.50	0.82		0.152	0.15	0.17	0.09	0.07
G_{RCOOH}	0.42	0.56		0.9	1.35	1.45	0.7	
G_{HCHO}	0.2							
G_{RCHO}	0.42	0.07		1.67		0.26	0.1	
$G_{ROR'}$				0.26				
$G_{HCOOR'}$	0.19	0.11						
G_{RCOR}		<0.01		0.65	0.44			
$G_{R'OH}$		0.35			0.22	1.39	0.7	
G_{ROH}		0.35				0.12	0.14	
$G_{R'CH_3}$	0.27	0.29		0.25	0.10	0.079	0.03	0.20

[a] Calculated from author's data.

A single early experiment bearing on the LET effect consisted of increasing the energy of a beam of electrons up to 160 kev in exposures of low-molecular-weight ketones.[92] Only changes in the over-all decomposition rate were observed. There was no change below 80 kev, but an increase occurred above this critical energy.

4-5.3.4 *Effect of Additives*

Iodine and diphenyl(picryl)hydrazyl (DPPH) radical scavengers have been used[3] to study radical yields from low-molecular-weight ketones. The magnitude of the effect depends upon irradiation temperature and scavenger concentration. Yields of most products were reduced. The formation of alkanes, both in the presence and absence of scavengers, may mean that they are produced via radical-combination reactions in the track or are products of hot or high-energy radicals.

Benzene exerted no protective effect when added to propionaldehyde, but actually sensitized ethane production. This is consistent with the energy-transfer picture of protection. Because the lowest excitation potential of benzene is probably higher than that of propionaldehyde,[103] energy transfer takes place from the benzene to the aldehyde molecule.

4-5.4 ESTERS

The most labile bond in the alkyl esters is the carbon–alkoxy bond, C—OR. Products derived from this cleavage are present in two or three times higher yield than those resulting from rupture of the alkyl–oxygen bond, O—R. For example, compare CO with CO_2 yields[101] among the data for esters in Table 4.10. Also note the wide distribution of products in significant yields. Unfortunately the available data were obtained under a variety of conditions; hence the G values are not necessarily initial yields.

4-5.4.1 *Mechanisms*

Figure 4.21 shows the principal reactions suggested for ester radiolysis.[4,101] There are some similarities between these reactions and those for aldehydes and ketones. For example, the $R\cdot CO$ radicals dissociate to form CO and $R\cdot$ radicals. Similarities with ethers also exist. If a methyl radical shifts from the acid part of the ester, a hydrocarbon is formed with one more carbon atom than the parent grouping. Equation 4.23 shows a similar rearrangement in the radiolysis of *tert*-butyl ethers.[97]

4-5.4.2 *Effect of Structure*

Decomposition is influenced by chain branching, double bonds, and phenyl groups in both the acid and the alcohol parts of the ester. A comparison of the CO-to-CO_2 ratio for *n*-propyl, isopropyl, and benzyl acetates

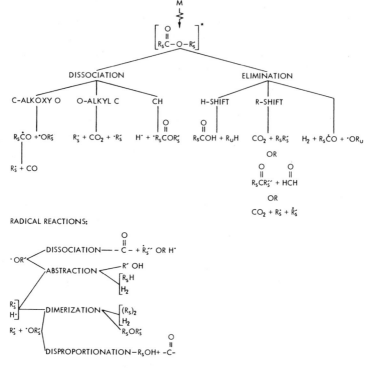

Fig. 4.21 Possible mechanism of ester radiolysis. R_s and R_u = saturated and unsaturated alkyl groups, respectively.

(see Table 4.10) and several dibasic esters[132] shows that branching or phenyl substitution in the alcohol part increases the chances of breaking the oxygen–alkyl bond. That is, the reactivity is shifted somewhat from the C—OR to the CO—R bond. A phenyl group in the alcohol part has no large effect on total gassing and decomposition (compare G_{gas} and G_{-M} in Table 4.10). A double bond in the alcohol part increases the chances of breaking the C—OR bond[101] and reduces gassing, presumably because the double bond is a good radical scavenger. However, there is increased production of low-molecular-weight polymer containing only three or four monomer groups.

A phenyl group in the acid part of the ester reduces total gas formation, but total decomposition is about the same. For example, G_{gas} decreases from 2.1 to 0.6, but G_{-M} remains at 1.3 when a phenyl group replaces the methyl group in the n-propyl esters.[132] It is worth noting that in this and the above instance the inclusion of a phenyl group did not lend stability to the molecule.

4-5.4.3 *Effect of Experimental Variables*

Over the dose range of 2 to 100 megarads, most G values from ester radiolysis do not change with total absorbed dose. Exceptions include yields of acetaldehyde and of acetone from isopropyl acetate[101] and methane from methyl acetate,[4] all of which decrease as the dose increases. For the higher dose range of 50 to 500 megarads, a few experiments showed large (up to sevenfold) differences in most product yields, varying inversely with dosage.[132]

Methyl acetate was irradiated for a range of temperatures spanning the solid, liquid, and vapor states;[4] differences in yields were attributed to phase changes. Yields were generally lowest in the solid but changed in both directions in going from the liquid to the vapor state. The effect of iodine in reducing the yield of certain products was different in the vapor and liquid states.

Increasing the temperature of radiolysis increases the yields of most products from methyl and isopropyl acetate.[4,101] A few G values vary inversely with temperature.

Comparisons have been made of electrons with gamma rays at fairly high doses (50 to 500 megarads) for three acetates and an adipate. Electrons and neutrons were also compared at 32 megarads for *n*-propyl acetate.[132] In general, the same compounds are produced but the G values are different. The electron and gamma dose rates differed by a factor of $\sim 10^5$, and it was suggested that at least part of the effect was due to the dose-rate difference.

Iodine and DPPH were added to methyl acetate as radical scavengers.[4] Iodine reduced yields when the irradiations were carried out in the vapor phase, but only G_{CH_4} was found to be reduced in the liquid phase. The effect of DPPH (liquid phase) was about the same as that of iodine. Benzoquinone reduced radiolytic yields from ethyl acetate.[2]

4-5.5 CARBOXYLIC ACIDS

Interest in the radiolysis of fatty acids was stimulated by a suggestion[88] that, if geological conditions were right, radioactivity may have acted on gaseous hydrocarbons to produce petroleum. To investigate this idea, the American Petroleum Institute (API) set up Project 43C, which included the study of the effect of alpha particles on a series of solid fatty acids.[136] The carbon chain length ranged from 2 to 30 carbon atoms. This work also included trimethyl acetic acid,[11] a naphthenic acid (cyclohexylcarboxylic),[12] an aromatic acid (benzoic), a dicarboxylic acid (sebacic),[11] and an unsaturated acid (oleic acid).[24] The alkyl–carbon bond (R—COOH) was found to break preferentially in the radiolysis of carboxylic

Table 4.11 — PRODUCT YIELDS FROM CARBOXYLIC ACIDS (RCOOH) IRRADIATED WITH ALPHA PARTICLES

Acid	Acetic		Propionic		Octanoic	Dodecanoic	Hexadecanoic	Eicosanoic	Docosanoic	Triacontanoic
Reference	98	136	98	136	136	136	136	136	136	136
Temperature, °F	77	32	77	-108	~72	~72	~72	~72	~72	~72
Dose, 10^6 rads	4.2	100	6.5	~100	~100	~100	~100	~100	~100	~100
Phase	Liquid	Solid	Liquid	Solid	Solid	Solid	Solid	Solid	Solid	Solid
G_{H_2}	0.52	0.9	0.79	0.7	1.4	1.5	1.7	1.4	1.2	2.3
G_{H_2O}	2.15		1.58		0.2	0.1	0.4	0.2	0.2	0.2
G_{CO}	0.38	0.5	0.28		0.5	0.4	0.3	0.2	0.1	0.2
G_{CO_2}	4.04	2.8	3.94	2.4	2.2	1.5	1.3	0.7	0.5	0.8
G_{CH_4}	1.38		0.53							
G_{RH}	1.38		1.07	0.9		0.8	0.5	0.4	0.2	0.3

acids. This may be contrasted to the rupture of carbon–alkoxy bonds (C—OR) in esters.

Table 4.11 lists representative G values for several acids. Absorbed doses were not reported, although other API work[73] was done at about 100 megarads. The major reaction is decarboxylation, giving CO_2 and the corresponding hydrocarbon RH. Hydrogen, CO, H_2O, and low-molecular-weight hydrocarbons are also produced. Ketones, aldehydes, and esters have been detected, but little unsaturation was found. Although the two sets of G values for acetic and propionic acids were obtained under vastly different conditions, the higher G_{H_2O} values[98] probably prevail throughout the series of solid-phase irradiations.[136] In the API series only the unsaturated acid (oleic) gave a recoverable amount of polymer.[24] Oleic acid *trans*-isomerizes.[102]

4-5.5.1 *Mechanisms*

Figure 4.22 is based on the API work[73] and that of Garrison *et al.*[58] Three modes of bond rupture result in six fragments. Some abstraction and dissociation reactions are also shown. The detection of ketones among the

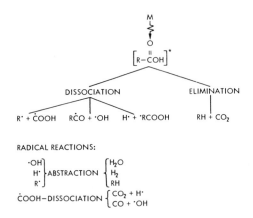

FIG. 4.22 Possible mechanism of carboxylic acid radiolysis.

radiolysis products suggests that carbony–alkoxy bonds break, forming R·CO radicals as in the case of esters.[58] These presumably could also form CO. Irradiation of labeled acetic acid has established that methane is formed mainly via ·CH_3 radicals and hydrogen via H· atoms.[16]

4-5.5.2 *Effect of Structure*

The variation in product yields as the length of the carboxylic acid hydrocarbon chain increases is complex.[136] However, a group-to-product correlation can be drawn from the data in Table 4.11. Figure 4.23 shows the dependence of yields of H_2 (primarily from C—H ruptures) relative to the yields of CO, CO_2, and H_2O (primarily from C—COOH ruptures) on the ratio of C—H bonds to C—COOH bonds (molecular weight) in the

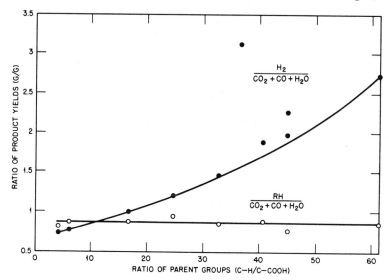

FIG. 4.23 Group-to-product correlation for acids. (From W. L. Whitehead, C. Goodman, and I. A. Breger, *Journal de chimie physique*, Ref. 136.)

molecule. As expected, the yields of RH relative to the yields of other products primarily from C—COOH rupture are not dependent upon molecular weight; the number of C—COOH bonds is the same in each molecule.

The phenyl group appears to confer stability to the carboxylic acids. Thus $G_{\rightarrow polymer} = 0.22$ and $G_{CO_2} = 0.29$ for benzoic acid (gamma rays).[130] Although comparative polymer yields have not been reported for the fatty acids, they are probably higher than for benzoic acid. This is in contrast to the ester case cited (Sect. 4-5.4.2) in which n-propyl benzoate was found to be less stable than n-propyl acetate.

4-5.5.3 *Effect of Experimental Variables*

When acetic acid was irradiated with gamma rays,[2] G values did not change over the range of 0.03 to 0.19 megarads. A dose of 1.6 megarads gave about 10% lower H_2 and CH_4 yields.[16] The discrepancy may be related to the 10-fold difference in absorbed dose.

The effect of temperature was studied for hexadecanoic ($C_{15}H_{31}COOH$) and docosanoic acids ($C_{22}H_{45}COOH$) (Rn alphas, solid phase).[136] The results for docosanoic acid are difficult to interpret because yields of H_2, CO_2, and CO go through first a maximum and then a minimum as the temperature increases. The results for hexadecanoic acid are shown in Fig. 4.24, which is an Arrhenius plot (Eq. 4.5). The points at the three higher temperatures define good straight lines with activation energies of 1, 2, and 7 kcal/mole for H_2, CO_2, and CO. There is no apparent reason for the nonconformance of the points at the right in the figure (32°F).

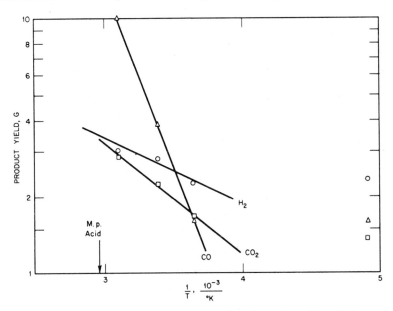

FIG. 4.24   Temperature dependence in hexadecanoic acid radiolysis.

Benzoquinone and ferric chloride were added to acetic acid as radical scavengers to measure H· and $H_3C·$ yields.[2] G_{H_2} and G_{CH_4} were reduced[16] by the scavengers; this is consistent with a radical mechanism noted in Sect. 4-5.5.1. The scavengers did not affect G_{CO_2}, G_{CO}, or $G_{C_2H_6}$.

4-6 Halogen Compounds

Organic halides are among the most studied of organic compounds. This is especially true of the iodides owing to (1) the simple spectrophotometric method for iodine determination and (2) the possibility of employing I^{131} in tracer studies. Emphasis has been on G_{I_2} measurements; total-product analysis has received little attention.

Except for the C—F bond, the carbon–halogen (C—X) bond is ruptured preferentially in organic halides. Thus the relatively small number of major products and small yields of low-molecular-weight hydrocarbons observed in butyl bromide radiolysis is explicable in terms of predominant C—Br bond ruptures.[137] This specificity is in contrast to the situation with butanes, which give a large number of products in comparable yields.[78]

Rupture of the C—I bond has been clearly demonstrated[60] by exchange experiments using I^{131}. The C—Br and C—Cl bonds also cleave readily. On the other hand, the C—F bond is more stable than the C—C or C—H bonds. Thus perfluoro organics give only relatively small amounts of gas.[52,122] The stability of the C—F bond is probably related to its higher bond energy. Table 4.12 presents G values for some alkyl iodides. Although the halides rank with the most radiation sensitive compounds on the basis of radical yields,[121] product yields are similar to those from other organic classes.[131] This may result from a cage effect that favors recombination.

Table 4.12 — PRODUCT YIELDS FROM ALKYL IODIDES (RI) IN THE LIQUID PHASE[a] AT ABOUT 72 °F

Compound	Methyl iodide		Ethyl iodide		n-Propyl iodide	Isopropyl iodide
Dose, 10^6 rads	0.1	16	0.1	16	0.2	0.2
Radiation	X	γ	X	γ	X	X
G_{I_2}	1.2	1.26	3.03	2.12	1.44	2.65
G_{HI}		0.01		0.33		
G_{H_2}	0.08	0.060	0.20	0.23	0.26	0.25
G_{CH_4}	0.57	0.77	0.007	0.01	0.015	0.015
$G_{C_2H_2}$	0.03		0.11	0.09	0.04	0.00
$G_{C_2H_4}$	0.08	0.081	2.00	2.20	0.13	0.004
$G_{C_2H_6}$	1.05	1.11	1.12	1.92	0.005	0.004
$G_{C_3H_6}$	0.001		0.00		1.27	2.25
$G_{C_3H_8}$	0.005		0.007	1.03	1.89	
G_{RH}	0.57	1.12	1.03	1.89		
G_{R_uH}			2.00		1.27	2.25
G_{isomer}					0.28	0.06
G_{R_2}	1.05	1.11		0.33		

[a] From R. H. Schuler and R. C. Petry, *Journal of the American Chemical Society*, Ref. 118.

Table 4.12 shows that the principal hydrocarbon produced (RH) is the one corresponding to the parent (RX). Also, more unsaturates (R_uH) are produced than saturates (RH). Dimer (R_2) yields are noted only for methyl and ethyl iodides; however, dimer formation was not investigated in other cases. The halogen may appear on radiolysis as halogen gas (X_2) or acid (HX) or both, depending upon its identity, and in the case of bromides, as vicinal dibromides.

Isomerization also can occur giving isoalkyl halides. The G value for isomerization is 0.2 to 4.5 for the butyl bromides[137] and is as high as about 60 for propyl chlorides.[138] The technique of scavenging propyl radicals with I_2[131] gave[118] G_{isomer} values of 0.06 to 0.3.

In both the radiolysis and the photolysis of alkyl iodides (compare with alkylbenzenes, Sect. 4-4.2), the C—I bond is preferentially broken[34] and iodine yields correlate with structure in a similar manner.[31] There is little isomerization in either radiolysis or low-energy (3261 A) photolysis, whereas significant isomerization occurs at slightly higher (2537 A) energy. It thus seems that the free radicals produced in radiolysis have taken only a small fraction of the high-energy radiation.[118] However, in photolysis methane and diiodides are formed in high yield, and iodine and hydrocarbon are formed in minor yields. The situation is reversed in radiolysis. Another difference is that no trapped radicals were detected in the photolysis of solid ethyl iodide; they were positively identified in radiolysis.[84] This may be an experimental artifact, however, because of local heating in photolysis.

4-6.1 MECHANISMS

Various reactions proposed in the literature are shown in Fig. 4.25. The scheme is far from complete, even though the halides have been studied a great deal. As already noted, very little C—X rupture occurs in fluorides.

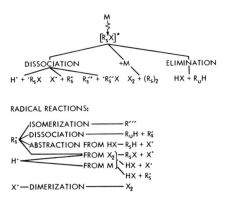

FIG. 4.25 Mechanism of organic halide radiolysis. R_s and R_u = saturated and unsaturated alkyl groups, respectively.

With iodides, both the HI and I_2 initially produced act as radical scavengers; and their competition for alkyl radicals governs the ultimate yield of I_2. At least in the case of alkyl iodide radiolysis, HX does not add to the double bond. The isomerization reaction ($G \cong 60$ for alkyl chlorides) has been interpreted by a radical chain mechanism;[138] a primary radical initially produced rearranges to a secondary radical, or, if one starts with a secondary halide, the initial secondary radical rearranges to the more stable tertiary alkyl radical. These more stable radicals can abstract halide from the initial compound to form more primary radicals. This is the propagating step in a chain reaction.

Much has been said concerning ion–molecule reactions in the case of alkyl halides, and the experimental evidence has been summarized.[77] For instance, 16 ion–molecule reactions were proposed to account for several ions whose molecular weight is greater than that of the parent.[106] In the decomposition of gaseous n-propyl chloride by neutron capture in the chlorine atom, 15 different organic chlorides containing Cl^{38} produced were attributed to ion–molecule reactions.[77]

Ion–molecule reactions in the liquid phase remain obscure because it is still impossible experimentally to distinguish ion–molecule from hot radical or track reactions; all give "unscavengeable" products. On the other hand, organic radicals may actually be observed. Thus the electron-spin resonance spectra of irradiated ethyl iodide show ethyl radicals ($G_{C_2H_5} \cong 1$). Hydrogen atoms were also found in about 50-fold lower yield.[84]

4-6.2 EFFECT OF STRUCTURE

In radiolysis, as in photolysis,[31] iodine yields from alkyl iodides increase with the number of hydrogen atoms attached to beta carbon atoms. The explanation is not as straightforward as a group-to-product relationship. Indeed, a plot of G_{I_2} vs. fraction of hydrogen atoms in the beta position gives a poorer curve than if plotted against total number of such hydrogen atoms. The increased I_2 production results from increased HI yield via the following[68] (see Fig. 4.25):

$$R^\cdot + HI \rightarrow RH + I^\cdot \tag{4.24}$$
$$I^\cdot + I^\cdot \rightarrow I_2 \tag{4.25}$$

The bromine yield from carbon tetrabromide is greater than the chlorine yield from carbon tetrachloride. This is in line with relative bond energies.[142]

The effect of structure was studied for the four isomeric butyl bromides.[137] The two straight-chain compounds gave high yields of normal butane, whereas the two branched-chain compounds showed large yields of isobutene, presumably formed by HBr elimination. The high stability of the tertiary radical was again demonstrated because isobutyl bromide gave higher isomerization yields ($G = 4.5$) than the other bromides ($G = 0$ to 0.2).

4-6.3 EFFECT OF EXPERIMENTAL VARIABLES

The effect of absorbed dose on the radiolysis of alkyl halides has been studied. For certain alkyl iodides, G_{I_2} values were found to be constant to about 0.1 megarad and then to decrease with increasing dose.[75] Similarly,[119]

G_{Cl_2} from carbon tetrachloride was dose independent up to about 0.2 megarad but decreased[142] at higher doses, 30 to 180 megarads.

The effect of dose rate has also been investigated for carbon tetrachloride. The exchange of chlorine between CCl_4 and Cl_2 was unaffected[119] by gamma dose rate in the range of 0.0012 to 0.067 megarad/hr. However, G_{Cl_2} dropped off as the dose rate increased from 240 to 2500 megarads/hr, but, here,[142] the total dose also varied, obscuring the intensity effect.

In the liquid-phase radiolysis of ethyl, isopropyl, isobutyl, and sec-butyl iodides with gamma rays, G_{I_2} was temperature independent from $-108°F$ to room temperature and above.[75] On the other hand, crystalline-phase irradiations exhibited a temperature dependence for G_{I_2}. This indicates iodine formation is not diffusion controlled in the liquid phase but that there is an activation energy in the crystalline state probably associated with a steric effect. In another study,[50] G_{Br_2} from CCl_3Br was temperature sensitive with an activation energy of about 3 kcal/mole. This suggests that cage escape of $\cdot Br$ and $\cdot CCl_3$ fragments is important in the mechanism of Br_2 production.

Differences between liquid- and gas-phase irradiations can also be traced to caging of fragments in the liquid phase. Thus, when methane solutions of iodine are exposed to neutrons, only methyl iodide is observed in the gas phase; both methyl and ethyl iodides are found in liquid-phase exposures because of caging.[74] Another factor that may explain phase effects is the lifetimes of radical fragments with respect to hydrogen abstraction. For example, the longer lifetimes of bromine and iodine atoms allow them to escape the liquid cage and react with other thermal atoms.[77] In going from liquid- to solid-phase exposures, there is no set pattern; sometimes the gross organic halogen yield is increased (e.g., with C_3H_7Br, CCl_4, $BrCCl_3$, Br_2CCl_2, and RCl), and sometimes there is no change (e.g., with C_2H_5I, iso-C_4H_9I, sec-C_4H_9I). In studies[142] of CCl_4 the temperature effect is interwoven with a phase change, but there appears to be less dose and dose-rate dependency in the solid than in the liquid phase.

Some very interesting observations have been made on ethyl iodide in the glass and crystalline states.[75,77,84] About 30 to 40 times more ethyl radicals are produced in the glass phase, and G_{HI} and G_{I^2} are greater in the glass phase at the same temperatures (Co^{60} gamma rays, liquid-nitrogen temperature). Thus, hot ethyl radicals can attack only certain adjacent parts of the ethyl iodide lattice; and so a particular orientation favors a hot reaction, which competes with cage escape, or, possibly, cage escape is simply more difficult. In the organized crystalline lattice, the situation is even more complicated: G_{I_2} from solid alkyl iodide depends upon the previous history of the sample. If a sample is first irradiated as a liquid, is frozen, and then is reirradiated, the yield is different than if the first irradiation is of the solid.[77]

The effect of LET was studied in CCl_4 radiolysis.[142] For comparable dose, G_{Cl_2} was twice as high for Co^{60} gamma rays as for radon alpha particles. On the other hand, experiments at $-305°F$ showed no difference in G_{Cl_2} between radon alphas and electrons. This work is complicated by the fact that the alpha particles were 100 to 1000 times lower in intensity than the electrons used.

4-6.4 EFFECT OF ADDITIVES

Triphenylmethane, added as a radical scavenger in liquid ethyl bromide radiolysis with electrons and X rays, resulted[116] in a 10-fold increase in the formation of HBr. The aromatic compound probably scavenged the bromine atoms in a displacement reaction.

In several experiments radiolysis products were added to see if they entered into reactions with initial products.[68] Iodine yields from ethyl iodide were unaltered by small amounts of ethylene dibromide and ethyl bromide, but small concentrations of iodine decreased the initial rate of iodine production by 54%. As the irradiation proceeded, G_{I_2} increased toward the normal rate. In like manner added HI increased the initial rate; but, as the irradiation proceeded, the G_{I_2} fell off toward the normal rate. This study led to the abstraction scheme shown in Fig. 4.25, which involves a competition between I_2 and HI for thermal radicals. Similar experiments were conducted with labeled iodine additives. Using I_2^{131}, the exchange reaction was established and found to proceed at a slower rate when HI^{131} was originally present (no added I_2). This is consistent with the exchange proceeding via reaction of radicals with I_2 rather than with HI. Hydrogen iodide and iodine added to other alkyl iodides gave qualitatively similar results.

The exchange of Cl between Cl_2 and CCl_4 was also studied[119] using tagged Cl_2 (Co^{60} gammas). The rate of exchange was taken as a measure of the radical yield because of the independence of exchange rate with initial Cl_2 concentration. This shows that all radicals (assumed to be $^{\bullet}CCl_3$) escaping the cage undergo exchange, i.e., they are scavenged by the tagged Cl_2 molecules:

$$^{\bullet}CCl_3 + Cl_2^{36} \rightarrow CCl_3Cl^{36} + {}^{\bullet}Cl^{36} \qquad (4.26)$$

In other carbon tetrachloride work, CBr_4 was added, and the free-halogen yield was observed.[142] The data were analyzed in terms of a displacement reaction:

$$Cl^{\bullet} + CBr_4 \rightarrow CBr_3Cl + Br^{\bullet} \qquad (4.27)$$

It was assumed that no transfer of energy occurred. This was demonstrated by the irradiation of mixtures of C_2Cl_3 and CCl_4 where the total free-chlorine yield was equal to the amounts that would have been formed if each component had been separately irradiated.

4-7 Principles

It is not possible to cite principles for the radiation chemistry of pure compounds in the same sense that "principles of application" are cited in later chapters. This results in part from a basic difference between radiation chemistry and radiation effects (engineering). Radiation chemistry is devoted to the study of mechanisms of radiolysis. Here low radiation doses are employed, and careful product analyses are performed. On the other hand, engineering studies are concerned primarily with changes in physical properties. High radiation doses are necessary to effect measurable changes in properties. At such high doses much more complex products are present as a result of the radiolysis of initial products. In spite of these differences, it is hoped that the survey of the radiation chemistry of pure compounds in Ch. 4 will provide additional background for the understanding of radiation effects.

To be able to formulate extensive principles generally applicable to the radiation chemistry of organic compounds would be helpful, but available knowledge will not yet permit such laws to be written. Nevertheless, some useful generalizations on the sites of principal radiolytic attack are noted in Table 4.13. Thus, when a functional group is present in the organic

Table 4.13 — MAIN BONDS BROKEN IN RADIOLYSIS
OF PURE ORGANICS

Compound type	Main attack site	Approx. G_{-M}
Hydrocarbons: Saturated	$C-H$, $C-C$ bonds	6-9
Unsaturated	$C-H$, $C-C$ bonds; polymerization or cross linking	11-10,000
Aromatic	$C-H$ bonds; side chain $C-C$ bonds	0.2-1
Alcohols	$H-COH$, $C-COH$ bonds	3-6
Ethers	$C-H$, $C-OR$ bonds	~7[a]
Aldehydes and ketones	$C-H$, $C\overset{\text{O}}{\underset{\|}{-}}C$ bonds	~7[a]
Esters	$C-H$, $\overset{\text{O}}{\underset{\|}{C}}-OR$ bonds	~4[a]
Carboxylic acids	$C-H$, $C-\overset{\text{O}}{\underset{\|}{C}}OH$ bonds	~5[a]
Halogen compounds: Fluorides	$C-H$, $C-C$ bonds	~3
Others	$C-H$, $C-X$ bonds	~3

[a] Reference 130.

molecule, e.g., $-\overset{|}{\underset{|}{C}}-OH$, $-OR$, $>C=O$, or $-CO_2H$ group, the principal attack, aside from C—H ruptures, is at its point of attachment to the rest of the molecule. The main exceptions to this are the attack on the ArC—C rather than the Ar—C group in alkyl aromatic compounds and on the —COH rather than the C—OH bond in alcohols.

All classes of compounds exhibit the effects of molecular structure in the yields of specific products. Only in special cases can one see products derived strictly from a random or statistical attack. It is evident that the bond ruptured is not necessarily the weakest in the molecule. Thus high-energy radiation may have a specific effect on the molecule which is different from that produced from other methods of excitation, e.g., light. On the other hand, there are cases of similarity between normal chemical, photochemical, and radiation chemical reactions. This applies principally to secondary reactions of primary molecular fragments.

Environmental factors certainly are important in radiation chemistry, perhaps more so than in engineering studies. This is a consequence of the low radiation doses used in radiation chemistry and the interest in changes of small magnitude. The absence of adequate control of environmental conditions is a valid criticism of many experiments reported in the literature. Consequently, if a specific question need be answered within about 10% accuracy, a new experiment should be conducted.

References

Several of the following were cited in the text as authority for statements made. Others were not quoted but are included because they contain pertinent information. All were consulted in the preparation of this chapter.

1. Adams, G. E., and Baxendale, J. H., Radical and Molecular Yields in the γ Irradiation of Liquid Methanol, *J. Am. Chem. Soc.*, *80*(16): 4215 (August 1958).
2. Adams, G. E., Baxendale, J. H., and Sedgwick, R. D., Some Radical and Molecular Yields in the γ Irradiation of Some Organic Liquids, *J. Phys. Chem.*, *63*(6): 854 (June 1959).
3. Ausloos, P., and Paulson, J. F., Radiolysis of Simple Ketones, *J. Am. Chem. Soc.*, *80*(19): 5117 (October 1958).
4. Ausloos, P., and Trumbore, C. N., Radiolysis of CH_3COOCH_3 and CH_3COOCD_3 by Cobalt-60 γ Rays, *J. Am. Chem. Soc.*, *81*(15): 3866 (August 1959).
5. Back, R. A., and Miller, N., The Radiolysis of *n*-Pentane and Other Hydrocarbons in the Gas Phase, *Trans. Faraday Soc.*, *55*(6): 911 (June 1959).
6. Ballantine, D. S., Glines, A., and Metz, D. J., The Conversion of High Energy Radiation to Stored Chemical Energy and Its Utilization in the Formation of Graft Copolymers, *Proceedings of the Second International Conference on the Peaceful Uses of Atomic Energy, Geneva, 1958*, Vol. 29, p. 322, United Nations, New York, 1959.
7. Barker, A., Hamill, W. H., and Williams, R. R., Jr., Ion-Molecule Reactions of 1,3-Butadiene, of Acetylene, and of Acetylene-Methane Mixtures, *J. Phys. Chem.*, *63*(6): 825 (June 1959).
8. Baysal, B., Adler, G., Ballantine, D., and Colombo, P., Solid State Polymerization

of Acrylamide Initiated by γ-Radiation, *J. Polymer Sci.*, *44*(143): 117 (May 1960).

9. Benasasson, R., and Bernas, A., Polymerization Radiochimique de L'acrylonitocle Quelques Observations Sur Le Post-Effect, *J. Polymer Sci.*, *30*(121): 163 (July 1958).

10. Bouby, L., Chapiro, A., Magat, M., Migirdicyan, E., Prevot-Bernas, A., Reinisch, L., and Sebban, J., The Chemical Reactions Induced by Ionizing Radiation in Various Organic Substances, *Proceedings of the First International Conference on the Peaceful Uses of Atomic Energy, Geneva, 1955*, Vol. 7, p. 526, United Nations, New York, 1956.

11. Breger, I. A., Transformation of Organic Substances by Alpha Particles and Deuterons, *J. Phys. Chem.*, *52*(3): 551 (March 1948).

12. Breger, I. A., and Burton, V. L., The Effects of Radioactivity on a Naphthenic Acid, *J. Am. Chem. Soc.*, *68*(8): 1639 (August 1946).

13. Brodsky, A. M., Kolbanovsky, U. A., Freatona, E. D., and Tchernysheva, A. S., Radiolysis of Normal Heptane and Its Inhibition by Dibenzyl Sulfide and Dibenzyl Additions, *Intern. J. Appl. Radiation and Isotopes*, *5*(1): 57 (February 1959).

14. Burlant, W. J., and Adicoff, A., Polymerization of Vinyl Stearate by High Energy Electrons, *J. Polymer Sci.*, *27*(115): 269 (January 1958).

15. Burns, W. G., Williams, T. F., and Wild, W., The Effects of Fast-Electron and Pile Irradiation on Polyphenyls at High Temperatures, *Proceedings of the Second International Conference on the Peaceful Uses of Atomic Energy, Geneva, 1958*, Vol. 29, p. 266, United Nations, New York, 1959.

16. Burr, J. G., The Radiolysis of Deuterated and Tritiated Acetic Acids, *J. Phys. Chem.*, *61*(11): 1481 (November 1957).

17. Burr, J. G., The Radiolysis and Mass Spectrometry of Several Deuterated Ethanols, *J. Phys. Chem.*, *61*(11): 1477 (November 1957).

18. Burr, J. G., and Scarborough, J. M., The Radiolysis of Deuterated Biphenyls: Mechanism of Hydrogen Formation, *J. Phys. Chem.*, *64*(10): 1367 (October 1960).

19. Burr, J. G., and Strong, J. D., The Radiolysis of Organic Solutions: II, The Benzophenone-Propanol-2 System, *J. Phys. Chem.*, *63*(6): 873 (June 1959).

20. Burton, M., Chang, J., Lipsky, S., and Reddy, M. P., Radiation Protection in Cyclohexane, *Radiation Research*, *8*(3): 203 (March 1958).

21. Burton, M., Chang, J., Lipsky, S., and Reddy, M. P., Radiolysis of Mixtures: Cyclohexane-Benzene-Iodine, *J. Chem. Phys.*, *26*(5): 1337 (May 1957).

22. Burton, M., and Patrick, W. N., Radiation Chemistry of Luminescent Solutions, *J. Chem. Phys.*, *22*(6): 1150 (June 1954).

23. Burton, M., and Patrick, W. N., Radiation Chemistry of Mixtures: Cyclohexane and Benzene-d₆, *J. Phys. Chem.*, *58*(5): 421 (May 1954).

24. Burton, V. L., The Effects of Radioactivity on Oleic Acid, *J. Am. Chem. Soc.*, *71* (12): 4117 (December 1949).

25. Chapiro, A., Determination of Free Radical Yields in the Radiolysis of Mixtures by the Polymerization Method, *J. Phys. Chem.*, *63*(6): 801 (June 1959).

26. Chapiro, A., Sur la Polymerisation des Composes Vinyliques Amorcee par les Rayons (II), *J. chim. phys.*, *47*: 764 (1950).

27. Charlesby, A., The Effect of Ionizing Radiation on Long-Chain Olefins and Acetylenes, *Radiation Research* *2*(1): 96 (February 1955).

28. Charlesby, A., *Atomic Radiation and Polymers*, Pergamon Press, Inc., New York, 1960.

29. Charlesby, A., Effect of Radiation on Behavior and Properties of Polymers, in

The Effects of Radiation on Materials, Harwood, J. J., Hausner, H. H., Morse, J. G., and Rauch, W. G., (Eds.), p. 268, Reinhold Publishing Corp., New York, 1958.

30. Cherniak, E. A., Collinson, E., Dainton, F. S., and Meaburn, G. M., Ferric Chloride as a Radical Scavenger in the Radiolysis of Organic Compounds, *Proc. Chem. Soc., 1958:* 54 (February 1958).

31. Cochran, E. L., Hamill, W. H., and Williams, R. R., Jr., Photolysis and Radiolysis of Liquid Alkyl Iodides, *J. Am. Chem. Soc., 76*(8): 2145 (April 1954).

32. Colichman, E. L., and Gercke, R. H. J., Radiation Stability of Polyphenyls, *Nucleonics, 14*(7): 50 (July 1956).

33. Collinson, E., Dainton, F. S., and Gillis, H. A., The Radiation-Induced Polymerization of Isobutene: A Liquid Phase Ionic Reaction, *J. Phys. Chem., 63*(6): 909 (June 1959).

34. Collinson, E., and Swallow, A. J., The Radiation Chemistry of Organic Systems, *Chem. Revs., 56*(3): 471 (June 1956).

35. Davison, W. H. T., The Radiolysis of Liquid Paraffins, *Chem. & Ind. (London), 1957* (21): 662 (May 1957).

36. Davison, W. H. T., The Formation and Reactions of Free Radicals in the High Energy Irradiation of Hydrocarbons in the Gas Phase, *Chem. Soc. (London) Spec. Publ. No. 9,* p. 151, 1958.

37. Davison, W. H. T., Pinner, S. H., and Worrall, R., Polymerization of Isobutene with High Energy Radiation, *Chem. & Ind. (London), 1957* (38): 1274 (September 1957).

38. de Vries, A. E., and Allen, A. O., Radiolysis of Liquid n-Pentane, *J. Phys. Chem., 63*(6): 879 (June 1959).

39. Dewhurst, H. A., Radiation Chemistry of Organic Compounds: III, Branched Chain Alkanes, *J. Am. Chem. Soc., 80*(21): 5607 (November 1958).

40. Dewhurst, H. A., Radiation Chemistry of Organic Compounds: IV, Cyclohexane, *J. Phys. Chem., 63*(6): 813 (June 1959).

41. Dewhurst, H. A., Radiation Chemistry of Organic Compounds: I, n-Alkane Liquids, *J. Phys. Chem., 61*(11): 1466 (November 1957).

42. Dewhurst, H. A., Radiation Chemistry of n-Hexane and Cyclohexane Liquids, *J. Chem. Phys., 24*(6): 1254 (June 1956).

43. Dewhurst, H. A., Radiation Chemistry of Organic Compounds. II: n-Hexane, *J. Phys. Chem., 62*(1): 15 (January 1958).

44. Dewhurst, H. A., and Schuler, R. H., A Comparison of the Decomposition of Hexane and Cyclohexane by Different Types of Radiation, *J. Am. Chem. Soc., 81*(13): 3210 (July 1959).

45. Dorfman, L. M., Radiolysis of Ethane: Isotopic and Scavenger Studies, *J. Phys. Chem., 62*(1): 29 (January 1958).

46. Dorfman, L. M., and Shipko, F. J., The β-Particle Radiolysis of Acetylene, *J. Am. Chem. Soc., 77*(18): 4723 (September 1955).

47. Dorfman, L. M., and Wahl, A. C., The Radiation Chemistry of Acetylene: I, Rare Gas Sensitization and II, Wall Effect in Benzene Formation, *Radiation Research, 10*(6): 680 (June 1959).

48. Dyne, P. J., and Fletcher, J. W., Radiation Chemistry of Cyclohexane: II, Dose Rate Effects on the Formation and Destruction of Cyclohexene, *Can. J. Chem., 38*(6): 851 (June 1960).

49. Fessenden, R. W., and Schuler, R. H., On the Use of Iodine as a Radical Detector in Hydrocarbon Radiolysis, *J. Am. Chem. Soc., 79*(2): 273 (January 1957).

50. Firestone, R. F., and Willard, J. E., The Radiolysis of CCl₃Br with Gamma Rays,

Abstracts 127th Meeting American Chemical Society, April 1954, Paper No. 53, Div. of Physical and Inorganic Chemistry.

51. Forsyth, P. F., Weber, E. N., and Schuler, R. H., Radiation-Induced Reaction Between Iodine and Heptane, *J. Chem. Phys.*, *22*(1): 66 (January 1954).

52. Florin, R. E., Wall, L. A., and Brown, D. W., Gamma Irradiation of Hexafluorobenzene, *J. Research Nat. Bur. Standards*, *64A*(4): 269 (July–August 1960).

53. Freeman, G. R., Radiolysis of Cyclohexane: I, Pure Liquid Cyclohexane and Cyclohexane-Benzene Solutions, *J. Chem. Phys.*, *33*(1): 71 (July 1960).

54. Freeman, G. R., The Radiolysis of Cyclohexane: II, Cyclohexane–Cyclohexene Solutions and Pure Cyclohexene, *Can. J. Chem.*, *38*(7): 1043 (July 1960).

55. Futrell, J. H., High Energy Electron Irradiation of *n*-Hexane, *J. Am. Chem. Soc.*, *81*(22): 5921 (November 1959).

56. Futrell, J. H., Gas Phase Radiolysis of *n*-Pentane, *J. Phys. Chem.*, *64*(11): 1634 (November 1960).

57. Futrell, J. H., Secondary Processes in Gas Phase Radiolysis of Hydrocarbons, *J. Phys. Chem.*, *65*(3): 565 (March 1961).

58. Garrison, W. M., Bennett, W., Cole, S., Haymond, H. R., and Weeks, B. M., Indirect and Direct Action of Heavy Particle Radiation on Acetic Acid in Aqueous Solution, *J. Am. Chem. Soc.*, *77*(10): 2720 (May 1955).

59. Gäumann, T., Schuler, R. H., The Radiolysis of Benzene by Densely Ionizing Radiations, *J. Phys. Chem.*, *65*(4): 703 (April 1961).

60. Gevantman, L. H., and Williams, R. R., Jr., Detection and Identification of Free Radicals in the Radiolysis of Alkanes and Alkyl Iodides, *J. Phys. Chem.*, *56*(5): 569 (May 1952).

61. Gillis, H. A., Williams, R. R., Jr., and Hamill, W. H., Ionic and Free Radical Processes in the Radiolysis of Liquid Methyl and Ethyl Iodides, *J. Am. Chem. Soc.*, *83*(1): 17 (January 1961).

62. Glasstone, S., Laidler, K. J., and Eyring, H., *The Theory of Rate Processes*, 1st ed., p. 522, McGraw-Hill Book Company, Inc., New York, 1941.

63. Gordon, S., and Burton, M., Radiation Chemistry of Pure Organic Compounds: Benzene and Benzene-d₆, *Discussions Faraday Soc.*, *1952*(12): 88 (1952).

64. Gordon, S., Van Dyken, A. R., and Doumani, T. F., Identification of Products in the Radiolysis of Liquid Benzene, *J. Phys. Chem.*, *62*(1): 20 (January 1958).

65. Hall, K. L., California Research Corporation, unpublished data, 1959–1960.

66. Hall, K. L., and Elder, F. A., Some Observations on Biphenyl Radiolysis, *J. Chem. Phys.*, *31*(5): 1420 (November 1959).

67. Hamashima, M., Reddy, M. P., and Burton, M., Radiolysis of Neopentane and Cyclohexane by Co⁶⁰ Radiation: Effect of Temperature, *J. Phys. Chem.*, *62*(2): 246 (February 1958).

-68. Hanrahan, R. J., and Willard, J. E., Quantitative Treatment of the Elementary Process in the Radiolysis of Alkyl Iodides by γ Rays, *J. Am. Chem. Soc.*, *79*(10): 2434 (May 1957).

69. Hayward, J. C., Jr., *Polymerization of Ethylene Initiated by Gamma Radiation*, USAEC Report NYO-3313, Yale University, June 1955.

70. Henley, E. J., and Barr, N. F., Ionizing Radiation Applied to Chemical Processes and to Food and Drug Processing, in *Advances in Chemical Engineering*, Drew, T. B., and Hoopes, J. W., Jr., (Eds.), Vol. I, p. 369, Academic Press, Inc., New York, 1956.

71. Henley, E. J., and Ng, C. C., Gamma Radiation Induced Solution Polymerization of Ethylene, *J. Polymer Sci.*, *36*(130): 511 (April 1959).

72. Hentz, R. R., and Burton, M., Studies in Photochemistry and Radiation Chem-

istry of Toluene, Mesitylene, and Ethylbenzene, *J. Am. Chem. Soc.,* 73(2): 532 (February 1951).

73. Honig, R. E., and Sheppard, C. W., An Experimental Comparison of the Chemical Effects of Deuterons and of Alpha Particles on Methane and *n*-Butane, *J. Phys. Chem.,* 50(3): 119 (March 1946).

74. Hornig, J. F., Levey, G., and Willard, J. E., Reactions of Methane with Iodine Activated by Radiative Neutron Capture, *J. Chem. Phys.,* 20(10): 1556 (October 1952).

75. Hornig, E. O., and Willard, J. E., Effects of Structure, Product Concentration, Oxygen, Temperature, and Phase on the Radiolysis of Alkyl Iodides, *J. Am. Chem. Soc.,* 79(10): 2429 (May 1957).

76. Hummel, R. W., The Radiolysis of Liquid Methyl Acetate with Co^{60} Gamma Radiation, *Trans. Faraday Soc.,* 56 (Part 2, 446): 234 (February 1960).

77. Jones, T. O., Luebbe, R. H., Wilson, J. R., and Willard, J. E., The Effect of Phase on Reactions Induced by Radiation in Organic Systems, *J. Phys. Chem.,* 62(1): 9 (January 1958).

78. Keenan, V. J., Lincoln, R. M., Rogers, R. L., and Burwasser, H., Irradiation of Petroleum Hydrocarbons: I, Electron Bombardment of Liquid Butanes, *J. Am. Chem. Soc.,* 79(19): 5125 (October 1957).

79. Kharasch, M. S., Chang, P. C., and Wagner, C. D., Radiolysis of 1-Hexene, *J. Org. Chem.,* 23(5): 779 (May 1958).

80. Kinderman, E. M., *Effects of High-Energy, High-Intensity Electromagnetic Radiation on Organic Liquids,* Report WADC-TR-57-465, Stanford Research Institute, September 1957.

81. Lampe, F. W., High Energy Electron Irradiation of Methane. Remarks on the Reaction Mechanism, *J. Am. Chem. Soc.,* 79(5): 1055 (March 1957).

82. Lampe, F. W., High-Energy Electron Irradiations of Neopentane, *J. Phys. Chem.,* 71(7): 1015 (July 1957).

83. Lampe, F. W., The Direct Radiolysis and the Radiation-Sensitized Hydrogenation of Ethylene, *Radiation Research,* 10(6): 691 (June 1959).

84. Luebbe, R. H., Wilson, J. R., and Willard, J. E., Temperature and Phase Effects on the Photolysis of Ethyl Iodide, *J. Am. Chem. Soc.,* 81(4): 761 (March 1959).

85. Lewis, J. G., Martin, J. J., and Anderson, L. C., Gamma-Activation of Syntheses-Polymerization of Ethylene, *Chem. Eng. Progr.,* 50(5): 249 (May 1954).

86. Lichtin, N. N., Radiolysis of Methanol and Methanolic Solutions by Co^{60} γ-Rays and 1.95×10^6 Volt Van de Graaff Electrons, *J. Phys. Chem.,* 63(9): 1449 (September 1959).

87. Lind, S. C., *The Chemical Effects of Alpha Particles and Electrons,* The Chemical Catalogue Co., New York, 1928.

88. Lind, S. C., and Bardwell, D. C., The Chemical Action of Gaseous Ions Produced by Alpha Particles: IX, Saturated Hydrocarbons, *J. Am. Chem. Soc.,* 48 (9): 2335 (September 1926).

89. Manion, J. P., and Burton, M., Radiolysis of Hydrocarbon Mixtures, *J. Phys. Chem.,* 56(5): 560 (May 1952).

90. McDonell, W. R., and Gordon, S., Decomposition of Methyl Alcohol by Co^{60} Gamma Radiation, *J. Chem. Phys.,* 23(1): 208 (January 1955).

91. McDonell, W. R., and Newton, A. S., The Radiation Chemistry of the Aliphatic Alcohols, *J. Am. Chem. Soc.,* 76(18): 4651 (September 1954).

92. McLennan, J. C., and Patrick, W. L., The Action of High-Speed Cathode Rays on the Simpler Alcohols, Aldehydes, and Ketones, and on Ethylene, *Can. J. Research,* 5(4): 470 (October 1931).

93. Medvedev, S. S., Radiation Polymerisation, in *Radioisotopes in Scientific Research*, R. C. Extermann (Ed.), Vol. 1, p. 161, Pergamon Press, New York, 1958.

94. Meshitsuka, G., and Burton, M., Radiolysis of Liquid Methanol by Co^{60} Gamma-Radiation, *Radiation Research*, 8(4): 285 (April 1958).

95. Mesrobian, R. B., Ander, P., Ballantine, D. S., and Dienes, G. J., Gamma-Ray Polymerization of Acrylamide in the Solid State, *J. Chem. Phys.*, 22(3): 565 (March 1954).

96. Mikhailov, B. M., Tarasova, L. V., Kiselev, V. G., and Bogdanov, V. S., The Reactions of Gaseous Saturated Hydrocarbons and Ethylene Under the Effect of Fast Electrons, *Proceedings of the First All-Union Conference Radiation Chemistry, Moscow 1957*, English translation, p. 199, Consultants Bureau, New York, 1959.

97. Newton, A. S., A Survey of the Radiation Chemistry of Some Aliphatic Ethers, *J. Phys. Chem.*, 61(11): 1485 (November 1957).

98. Newton, A. S., Note on the Helium-Ion Radiolysis Products of Liquid Acetic and Propionic Acids, *J. Chem. Phys.*, 26(6): 1764 (June 1957).

99. Newton, A. S., Some Aspects of the Radiolysis of Isopropyl Ether, *J. Phys. Chem.*, 61(11): 1490 (November 1957).

100. Newton, A. S., and McDonell, W. R., The Radiolysis Products from Ethyl Alcohol; Effect of Total Energy Input on the Radiolysis Products, *J. Am. Chem. Soc.*, 78(18): 4554 (September 1956).

101. Newton, A. S., and Strom, P. O., The Radiation Chemistry of Isopropyl Acetate and Isopropenyl Acetate, *J. Phys. Chem.*, 62(1): 24 (January 1958).

102. Pan, H. P., Goldblith, S. A., and Proctor, B. E., Trans-Isomerization of Oleic Acid and Potassium Oleate by Ionizing Radiation, *J. Am. Oil Chemists' Soc.*, 35(1): 1 (January 1958).

103. Patrick, W. N., and Burton, M., Radiation Chemistry of Mixtures: Propionaldehyde and Benzene-d_6, *J. Phys. Chem.*, 58(5): 424 (May 1954).

104. Patrick, W. N., and Burton, M., Polymer Products in Radiolysis of Benzene, *J. Am. Chem. Soc.*, 76(10): 2626 (May 1954).

105. Pitts, J. N., Jr., and Osborne, A. D., Structure and Reactivity in the Radiolysis of Ketones, *J. Am. Chem. Soc.*, 83(14): 3011 (July 1961).

106. Pottie, R. F., Barker, R., and Hamill, W. H., Ion-Molecule Reactions of Methyl and Ethyl Iodides, *Radiation Research*, 10(6): 664 (June 1959).

107. Ramaradhya, J. M., and Freeman, G. R., Radiolysis of Cyclohexane. III: Vapor Phase, *J. Chem. Phys.*, 34(5): 1726 (May 1961).

108. Ramaradhya, J. M., and Freeman, G. R., The Radiolysis of Ethanol. I: Vapor Phase, *Can. J. Chem.*, 39(9): 1836 (September 1961).

109. Roberts, R., Dalton, F. L., Hayden, R., and Hills, P. R., Some Recent Advances in the Chemical Utilization of Fission Products, in *Proceedings of the Second International Conference on Peaceful Uses of Atomic Energy, Geneva, 1958*, Vol. 29, p. 408, United Nations, New York, 1959.

110. Rudolph, R. S., and Melton, C. E., Mass Spectrometer Studies of Ionic Intermediates in the α-particle Radiolysis of C_2 Hydrocarbons: I, Acetylene, *J. Phys. Chem.*, 63(6): 916 (June 1959).

111. Saraeva, V. V., Ladygin, B. Ya., and Sun, N. C., Radiolysis and Radiation-Induced Oxidation of Diisopropyl Ether, *J. Phys. Chem. (USSR)*, 34(4): 359 April 1960).

112. Schmitz, J. V., and Lawton, E. J., Initiation of Vinyl Polymerization by Means of High Energy Electrons, *Science*, 113(2947): 718 (June 1951).

113. Schoepfle, C. S., and Fellows, C. H., Gaseous Products from Action of Cathode Rays on Hydrocarbons, *Ind. Eng. Chem.*, *23*(12): 1396 (December 1931).

114. Schuler, R. H., The Effect of Solutes on the Radiolysis of Cyclohexane, *J. Phys. Chem.*, *61*(11): 1472 (November 1957).

115. Schuler, R. H., and Allen, A. O., Radiation-Chemical Studies with Cyclotron Beams, *J. Am. Chem. Soc.*, *77*(2): 507 (January 1955).

116. Schuler, R. H., and Hamill, W. H., The Fast Electron and X-Ray Decomposition of the Alkyl Halides, *J. Am. Chem. Soc.*, *74*(24): 6171 (December 1952).

117. Schuler, R. H., and Muccini, G. A., On the Effect of Dose Rate on the Radiolysis of Liquid Hydrocarbons, *J. Am. Chem. Soc.*, *81*(15): 4115 (August 1959).

118. Schuler, R. H., and Petry, R. C., Decomposition of the Liquid Alkyl Iodides by 120 kvp X-Radiation, *J. Am. Chem. Soc.*, *78*(16): 3954 (August 1956).

119. Schulte, J. W., Radiation-Induced Exchange of Chlorine with Carbon Tetrachloride, *J. Am. Chem. Soc.*, *79*(17): 4643 (September 1957).

120. Seitzer, W. H., Goeckermann, R. H., and Tobolsky, A. V., β-Ray Initiation of Polymerization of Styrene and Methyl Methacrylate, *J. Am. Chem. Soc.*, *75*(3): 755 (February 1953).

121. Seitzer, W. H., and Tobolsky, A. V., The Interaction of β-Particles with Organic Liquids in the Presence of Vinyl Monomers, *J. Am. Chem. Soc.*, *77*(10): 2687 (May 1955).

122. Simmons, J. H., and Taylor, E. H., The Action of Reactor Radiation on Saturated Fluorocarbons, *J. Phys. Chem.*, *63*(4): 636 (April 1959).

123. Skraba, W. J., Burr, J. G., and Hess, D. N., The Decomposition of Methanol-C^{14} Under the Influence of Its Own Radiation, *J. Chem. Phys.*, *21*(7): 1296 (July 1953).

124. Strong, J. D., and Burr, J. G., The Radiolysis of Organic Solutions: I, Acetone as a Trap for Hydrogen Atoms, *J. Am. Chem. Soc.*, *81*(4): 775 (February 1959).

125. Swallow, A. J., *Radiation Chemistry of Organic Compounds*, pp. 61–147, Pergamon Press, New York, 1960.

126. Swan, G. A., and Wright, D., The Chemical Effects of γ-Radiation on Organic Systems: Part II, The Action of Radiation on Benzyl Alcohol Alone or Mixed with Acetone or Bromo-Benzene, *J. Chem. Soc.*, *1958*: 4673 (December 1958).

127. Sworski, T. J., and Burton, M., A Study of Impingment-Particle Velocity in Radiolysis of Some Aromatic Hydrocarbons, *J. Am. Chem. Soc.*, *73*(8): 3790 (August 1951).

128. Sworski, T. J., Hentz, R. R., and Burton, M., Studies in Photo-Chemistry and Radiation Chemistry of *i*-Propylbenzene and *t*-Butylbenzene, *J. Am. Chem. Soc.*, *73*(5): 1998 (May 1951).

129. Taylor, W. H., Mori, S., and Burton, M., Radiolysis of Liquid Neopentane, *J. Am. Chem. Soc.*, *82*(22): 5817 (November 1960).

130. Tolbert, B. M., and Krinks, M. H., Chemical Effects of Ionizing Radiation on Pure Organic Compounds, *Radiation Research, Supp. 2*, 586 (1960).

131. Tolbert, B. M., and Lemmon, R. M., Radiation Decomposition of Pure Organic Compounds, *Radiation Research*, *3*(1): 52 (September 1955).

132. Wagner, R. M., and Towle, L. H., *Effects of High Energy, High Intensity Electromagnetic Radiation on Organic Liquids*, Report WADC-TR-58-683, Stanford Research Institute, March 1959.

133. Wagner, R. M., and Towle, L. H., *Effects of High Energy, High Intensity Electromagnetic Radiation on Organic Liquids*, Report WADC-TR-58-206, Stanford Research Institute, June 1958.

134. Walling, C., Briggs, E. R., Cummings, W., and Mayo, F. R., Copolymerization

(XIV) by Nonradical Mechanisms, *J. Am. Chem. Soc., 72*(1): 48 (January 1950).

135. Weber, E. N., Forsyth, P. F., and Schuler, R. H., Radical Production in the Radiolysis of the Hydrocarbons, *Radiation Research, 3*(1): 68 (February 1955).

136. Whitehead, W. L., Goodman, C., and Breger, I. A., The Decomposition of Fatty Acids by Alpha Particles, *J. chim. phys., 48:* 184 (1951).

137. Wilcox, W. S., The Radiolysis of Butyl Bromides, *Radiation Research, 10*(2), 112 (February 1959).

138. Wiley, R. H., Miller, W., Jarboe, C. H., Jr., Harrell, J. R., and Parish, D. J., Gamma Radiation-Induced Isomerization of *n*-Propyl Chlorides, *Radiation Research, 13*(3): 479 (September 1960).

139. Worrall, R., and Pinner, S. H., Heterophase Radiation Polymerization of Isobutene and Methyl Methacrylate, *J. Polymer Sci., 34*(127): 229 (January 1959).

140. Yang, K., and Manno, P. J., The Role of Free Radical Processes in the Gamma-Radiolysis of Methane, Ethane, and Propane, *J. Am. Chem. Soc., 81*(14): 3507 (July 1959).

141. Yang, K., and Manno, P. J., γ-Radiolysis of Ethylene, *J. Phys. Chem., 63*(5): 752 (May 1959).

142. Zimin, A. V., Action of Radioactive Radiations on CCl_4 and All Mixtures CCl_4 + C_2Cl_6, CCl_4 + CBr_4, *Symposium on Radiation Chemistry,* Academy of Sciences of the USSR, Division of Chemical Science, Moscow, 1955, English translation, Consultants Bureau, New York.

CHAPTER 5

Polymers

By Oscar Sisman, William W. Parkinson, and C. Daniel Bopp

5-1 Introduction

Polymeric substances make up possibly the most important class of organic materials, technically and economically. The familiar plastics, fibers, elastomers, and biological materials that surround us attest to this importance. Such substances, which are composed of a great many identical groups or repeating units, are known as "high polymers." Polymers composed of more than one kind of repeating unit are termed "copolymers."

Polymeric materials are profoundly affected by ionizing radiation. The radiation-induced changes result from disturbance of the distinctive molecular or chemical structure of these materials. These unique structural features and the characteristic properties that they confer on polymeric materials are described in this chapter. This is background for the general discussion given here of chemical and physical changes produced by radiation. Detailed discussions of radiation effects on individual polymers and of the applications of these materials have been reserved for later chapters on elastomers, textiles, paints, etc. Because of the importance of polymers in subsequent presentations, some background is also given on the behavior of polymers in nonradiation environments.

The earliest studies, around 1930, of the effects of high-energy radiation on polymers[62,82] were motivated by the possibility of vulcanizing rubber by this means. Davidson and Geib[45] investigated in 1948 the changes in natural and synthetic rubbers subjected to the mixed radiation of a nuclear reactor. Thereafter the ever increasing variety of nuclear reactors created a need for data from which the service lifetimes of materials in radiation fields could be predicted. This led to comprehensive studies of the changes in the engineering properties of plastics and elastomers resulting from radiolysis.[16,22,92]

The large changes produced in plastics and elastomers by radiation stimulated basic investigations of the reactions involved in radiation effects. Cross linking in polymers that become hard and brittle and cleavage in polymers that weaken or soften under irradiation were elucidated by Alexander, Charlesby, and coworkers,[5,34,38] Lawton et al.,[72] and by Little.[74] Dole and coworkers[52] investigated the chemical reactions occurring in poly-

127

ethylene as a result of irradiation. There have been many later workers in this field, and the extensive information now available forms the subject of two recent books.[20,33]

Although polymeric materials are substances made up of a large number of repeating monomer units, the chainlike macromolecules are not of unlimited length. In practice, chain lengths of the order of a hundred thousand monomer units are not uncommon. Branched or network structures are present in polymers containing polyfunctional monomer units. The density of branches or cross links depends upon the concentration of the polyfunctional units. Most supposedly linear commercial polymers have a small amount of branching because of polyfunctional impurities in the starting material or side reactions during the polymerization process.

This macromolecular nature of polymeric materials accounts for a number of their unusual properties. Tensile elongations of linear polymers at temperatures above the glassy region run several hundred per cent. This susceptibility to drawing allows the formation of fibers of high tensile strength as a result of orientation of the molecular chains. Partly crystalline polymers possess rigidity, stiffness, and strength because the submicroscopic crystals serving as a hard filler are interlaced with the long molecular chains, each of which may traverse many crystals. Polymers of sufficient irregularity do not crystallize but remain soft and liquidlike. Here the phenomenon of high elasticity is exhibited by light cross linking. Fourfold to sixfold reversible extensions are common in the familiar natural and synthetic rubbers.

The unusual properties of polymeric materials immediately suggest many applications. The uses of plastics and elastomers are generally familiar. The moderate melting points of the linear polymers lead to uses in a wide variety of molded and extruded objects. The solubility of these materials in suitable solvents enables them to be used as paints, coatings, and films.

Fiber and fabric possibilities have already been pointed out, and both synthetic and natural products are well known as the basis for large industries. The elasticity, flexibility, toughness, and abrasion resistance of the elastomers make them uniquely suitable for tires, hoses, gaskets, and similar items.

The covalent atomic bonds of polymeric materials confer electrical and thermal resistance; thus these substances find application as electrical and thermal insulators. The rigidity and hardness of cross-linked polymers have long been utilized in molded objects, which can be produced economically by thermally initiated cross-linking reactions within the mold. Recently developed additives cross link liquid polymers under low heat and pressure conditions in extremely simple molding operations.

5-2 Chemical Structures[58]

Polymers can be separated into two major chemical types. The simplest type (or class) comprises the addition polymers. Such polymers have no functional groups in the main chain. They are formed by the simple addition of monomer molecules in such a way that the repeating units of the polymer are identical in elemental composition with the monomer molecules. The other class of polymers, condensation polymers, contains functional-group linkages within the main chain. They are formed by reactions between monomers having two or more functional groups. These combine by eliminating simple molecular products. Polymers from cyclic compounds, e.g., anhydrides, ethers, and intramolecular esters and amides, which do not yield small molecules on polymerization, are also included.

5-2.1 ADDITION POLYMERS

The monomer units here may be hydrocarbons or their derivatives containing only one double bond, e.g., ethylene ($H_2C{=}CH_2$) or isobutylene $[H_2C{=}CH(CH_3)CH_3]$, or they may be more complex structures reacting through conjugated double bonds, e.g., butadiene ($H_2C{=}CH{-}CH{=}CH_2$) or isoprene $[H_2C{=}C{-}CH(CH_3){=}CH_2]$. After polymerization of the latter class of monomers, each monomer unit retains one double bond. This residual unsaturation constitutes additional reaction sites, which can lead to intermolecular bridges or cross links. Typical addition polymers are listed in Table 5.1.

Table 5.1—CHEMICAL STRUCTURE
OF TYPICAL ADDITION POLYMERS

Name	Structure
Polyethylene	$-CH_2CH_2-$
Polypropylene	$-[CH_2CH(CH_3)]-$
Polystyrene	$-\left[CH_2CH(\langle \bigcirc \rangle)\right]-$
Poly(methyl methacrylate)	$-[CH_2C(CH_3)(C(O)OCH_3)]-$
Polybutadiene	$-CH_2CH{=}CHCH_2-$
Natural rubber	$-CH_2CH{=}C(CH_3)CH_2-$
Poly(vinyl chloride)	$-[CH_2CH(Cl)]-$
Polyacrylonitrile	$-[CH_2CH(CN)]-$

The reaction mechanism in addition polymerization is usually a free-radical process in which a molecular fragment having an unpaired electron adds to the double bond of a monomer unit. This addition to the double bond produces another unpaired electron or free-radical site to propagate the chain reaction and increases the growing molecule by one monomer unit as well. This process is illustrated by the following reactions:

$$M^* + RCH{=}CH_2 \rightarrow M\overset{R}{C}HCH_2{}^* \tag{5.1}$$

$$\overset{R}{M}CHCH_2{}^* + RCH{=}CH_2 \rightarrow M\overset{R}{C}HCH_2\overset{R}{C}HCH_2{}^* \tag{5.2}$$

where M^* can be a free radical from a chemical initiator or an actively growing polymer chain.

Such reactions are usually very rapid and can produce molecular weights of several million under favorable conditions. The rapid growth of relatively few activated molecules leads to a heterogeneous distribution of molecular weights in which a large fraction of the available monomer is incorporated into a small number of large molecules. This deviates from a "most-probable" distribution. Thus, with this type reaction product, the summation of the weight fraction of each molecular species multiplied by its mass is frequently larger than the summation of the mole fraction of each species times its mass. The former quantity is defined as the "weight-average" molecular weight and the latter as the "number-average" molecular weight.

5-2.2 CONDENSATION POLYMERS

The main chain of these polymers differs from that of addition polymers in that it contains regularly recurring functional-group linkages. These polymers are frequently the products of esterification or amidation reactions or condensations involving a carbonyl group. Examples of condensation polymers are given in Table 5.2.

The reactions yielding condensation polymers are usually slower than addition reactions; therefore molecular weights of synthetic condensation polymers are generally lower than those of addition polymers. (In contrast, natural condensation polymers may have very high molecular weights.) The polar nature of the functional groups causes strong intermolecular forces, which promote the tendency to crystallize. Toughness, stiffness, and tensile strength, therefore, can be achieved through crystallinity in the condensation polymers only at moderate molecular weights.

In reactions that form condensation polymers, each molecule has equal probability for growth. Thus a most probable molecular-weight distribution is produced. This is also the distribution prevailing in random cleavage of an infinitely long molecule. Molecular-weight measurements are, therefore, not likely to be affected by changes in distribution when applied to degradation of condensation polymers; but chain branching may affect measurements that are sensitive to molecular shape (e.g., solution viscosity).

Table 5.2—CHEMICAL STRUCTURE
OF TYPICAL CONDENSATION POLYMERS

Name	Polymer structure
Poly(ethylene terephthalate)	$-[OCH_2CH_2OC(O) \langle\text{benzene}\rangle C(O)]-$
Poly(hexamethyleneadipamide)(nylon 66)	$-[NH(CH_2)_6\,NHC(O)(CH_2)_4C(O)]-$
Protein	$-[NHCH(R)C(O)]-$
Polysulfide	$-SSSSCH_2CH_2-$
Polydimethylsiloxane (silicone)	$-[OSi(CH_3)_2]-$
Cellulose	$-OCH \underset{\diagdown CH(OH)CH(OH)}{\overset{\diagup CH(CH_2OH)O\diagdown}{}} HCH-$
Phenol formaldehyde	(network polymer)

5-2.3 NETWORK POLYMERS

With both addition and condensation polymers, branching or cross linking into essentially infinite three-dimensional networks can take place if the starting monomers contain more than one functional group. These network polymers have unique characteristics. They are insoluble and infusible, although decomposition may give them the appearance of melting. Furthermore, they have a strong tendency to retain their shape through rubberlike elasticity in materials with a low density of cross links or through high rigidity and hardness in heavily cross-linked materials.

Polymers capable of network formation are available commercially in partially reacted form both as liquids and solids. After the material has been shaped into final form, either with or without a filler, reaction is completed to produce objects having final properties that depend considerably on the polymer and filler used. If heat is used to perform the final cross-linking reaction, the polymer or resin is termed "thermosetting." Solid polymers that are not susceptible to cross linking soften when heated and are known industrially by the term "thermoplastic."

5-2.4 MOLECULAR WEIGHT

High molecular weight is the unique property of polymeric substances. Thus it is desirable to characterize polymers by molecular weight. A common method used is to measure osmotic pressures of polymer solutions. This essentially counts molecules and gives number-average molecular weights. A more sensitive method is to measure the light scattering of solutions. This depends nonlinearly on particle size, as well as on number, and yields weight-average molecular weights.[†] A much more convenient, but usually not absolute, method is to measure the viscosity of dilute solutions. Although the viscosity method is usually calibrated against one of the other methods, it can be used on an absolute basis by a method described by Edelmann.[54]

5-3 Physical State

5-3.1 INFLUENCE OF CHEMICAL STRUCTURE

The mechanical properties of polymers are intimately connected with the physical state of these materials, i.e., their crystalline, glassy, liquid, or rubbery nature. This physical state is governed primarily by the chemical structure of the constituent molecules and, to a lesser degree, by previous heat and mechanical treatment. Two factors associated with chemical structure are most important: (1) forces between molecules and (2) molecular shape or symmetry.

Intermolecular forces arise from three sources:

1. The most powerful force is the attraction between permanent dipoles formed by the unbalanced charge distribution in valence bonds between atoms of different electronegativity. Because of its source this attractive force is dependent on orientation and is markedly affected by thermal agitation. It is this type of interaction between plasticizer molecules and polymer which enables plasticizers to reduce the rigidity and hardness of plastics containing polar groups. One example of dipole interaction, hydrogen bonding, exerts such a strong influence when its existence is possible that it deserves special mention. When hydrogen is attached to an electronegative atom, such as oxygen or nitrogen, the electron cloud shows greater density around the electronegative atom; and a dipole is set up. If a second polar group is accessible, particularly a carbonyl group, a strong attraction occurs. This is adequate to produce a partial sharing of the proton with

---

[†] These averages can be represented as the number average,

$$\overline{M}n = \sum \frac{n_i}{N} M_i = \frac{\Sigma n_i M_i}{\Sigma n_i}$$

and the weight average,

$$\overline{M}w = \sum \frac{w_i}{W} M_i = \frac{\Sigma n_i M_i^2}{\Sigma n_i M_i}$$

where n_i is the number of moles of each molecular species, M_i is its molecular weight, n_i/N is its mole fraction, and w_i/W is the weight fraction of each species.

the second polar group. Large intermolecular forces are produced this way in amides, carboxylic acids, cellulose, etc.

2. Another intermolecular force results from the asymmetry of charge distribution around any atom at a given instant owing to orbital motion of the electrons. This attractive force increases more rapidly than the permanent dipole force as molecules approach each other and may exceed the latter for solid or liquid polymers containing few or only weakly polar groups. This force is dependent only on distance and is independent of temperature.

3. The third intermolecular force is the result of the polarizability of molecules. Induced dipoles are produced by interaction with the field of neighboring polar groups. This induced dipole force is only slightly temperature dependent but varies strongly with distance of separation.

The sum of these interactions is the driving force that produces crystallization or the glassy state. The intermolecular forces per unit chain length for some typical polymers are listed in Table 5.3. Materials with cohesive

Table 5.3—COHESIVE FORCES
OF TYPICAL HIGH POLYMERS[10,78]

Substance	Groups responsible for lateral attraction	Molar cohesion per 5-A chain length, kcal/mole
Polyethylene	(CH_2)	1.0
Polyisobutylene	$(CH_2),(CH_3)$	1.2
Polybutadiene	$(CH_2),(CH{=}CH)$	1.1
Rubber	$(CH_2),[CH{=}C(CH_3)]$	1.3
Polychloroprene	$(CH_2),(CH{=}CCl)$	1.6
Polyvinyl chloride	$(CH_2),(CHCl)$	2.6
Polyvinyl acetate	$(CH_2),[C(O)OCH_3]$	3.2
Polyvinyl alcohol	$(CH_2),[CH(OH)]$	4.2
Polystyrene	$(CH_2),(C_6H_5)$	4.0
Cellulose	$(OH),(CHOCH_2)$	6.2
Cellulose acetate	$[CH_3C(O)O],(CHOCH_2)$	4.8
Polyamides	$(CH_2),[C(O)NH]H$	5.8
Silk fibroin	$[CH(R)],[C(O)NH]H$	9.8

energies of less than about 2 kcal are soft and rubbery. Polymers having cohesive energies above 5 kcal have high elastic moduli, tend to be crystalline, and tend to form fibers on elongation.

The other major aspect of chemical structure which determines the physical state is molecular shape. Bulky side groups or groups producing irregularities in the main chain strongly hinder crystallization. The hydrocarbon polymers furnish several examples. Although polystyrene has strong intermolecular forces, the bulky benzene ring prevents close packing of the chains. This results in formation of an amorphous glass. Polyethylene, which can be obtained with less than one side chain per thousand carbon atoms, is more than 90% crystalline for this linear form. The regularity of the polymer chains permits crystallization, although the intermolecular forces are comparatively low. The more highly branched forms of this polymer (up to 35 branches per 1000 carbon atoms) range down to 55% crystalline.

The effect of main-chain shape can be illustrated by the difference between *cis*-polyisoprene (natural rubber) and *trans*-polyisoprene (balata and gutta percha). These natural polymers have very regular structures of the repeating unit $-CH_2CH=C(CH_3)CH_2-$. The crystallinity of the regular form of polypropylene, $-CH_2CH(CH_3)-$, is an indication that the small methyl side group is inadequate to preclude crystallization. However, rubber, which is all, or nearly all, the *cis* isomer, crystallizes only with difficulty unless oriented by elongation. Balata and gutta percha, the *trans* form, are ordinarily partially crystalline.

Polymers containing polar groups along the main chain, e.g., the polyesters and polyamides, show a strong tendency toward crystallinity. These materials, with more or less definite melting points, tend to be hard and tough. In general, the melting or softening points of polymers in the molecular-weight range of commercial products are independent of molecular weight. However, the viscosity of the melt and the melting point of low-molecular-weight materials increase with molecular weight.

5-3.2 INFLUENCE OF CRYSTALLINITY

The dimensions of the crystals in polymeric materials are small compared to the average length of the polymer molecules. The crystallites are regular arrays of segments of polymer chains. Individual polymer molecules thread their way through many crystallite and amorphous regions. Thus crystallinity has an important effect on mechanical properties.

Several methods have been devised for measuring the amount of crystallinity. Light scattering can be used, although not commonly, for quantitative work. Density or specific-volume measurements have been correlated with crystallinity for many polymers. X-ray diffraction determinations give crystallinity directly. Refractive index and infrared absorption measurements are also used. Certain of the infrared absorption peaks are altered in the crystalline regions because the regular close packing of the crystal lattice alters the force field surrounding the atoms and sometimes modifies their oscillations. Infrared crystallinity determinations require calibration against some other method.

5-3.3 MOBILITY OF THE POLYMER MOLECULE

The physical state, as well as governing mechanical properties, influences the rate of chemical reactions. From free-radical polymerization processes, it is known that when the viscosity of the reaction medium rises to large values, further addition to the free-radical chain ends is inhibited. The mobility of polymer chain segments, then, is important in both ordinary and radiation-induced reactions.

Bulky side groups at frequent intervals along the polymer chain not only stiffen the chain but also hinder reaction at certain points in the molecule. Crystal regions permit only low-amplitude vibrational motions and, in some cases, preclude reaction where penetration by a second reactant is involved. Translational and rotational motion of molecular segments is also low in the glassy state owing to the strong intermolecular forces already described. In general, in the amorphous regions of polymers, the mobility of chain segments is determined by the size of side groups and by forces between molecules.

5-3.4 STABILITY OF COMMON POLYMERS

The chemical structure of polymers controls their stability both to chemical attack and to atmospheric aging. Although the great variety of materials and conditions makes a detailed discussion impractical here, it is important to point out general behavior. It should be understood that radiation resistance does not correlate with resistance to chemical degradation. Furthermore, additives to improve physical or aging properties may play a part in changes produced by radiation.

The inert hydrocarbon structures of polyethylene and polystyrene are resistant to water and aqueous reagents, except strongly oxidizing acids. Moderate intermolecular forces allow solubility in organic solvents, at room temperature for polystyrene and at 140 to 176°F for polyethylene. The softening temperatures of both materials are low. In common with the unsaturated rubber hydrocarbons, polystyrene and polyethylene undergo atmospheric oxidation in sunlight. Additives can be used in polyethylene and in the rubbers; but, since the applications of polystyrene frequently are dependent on transparency, opaque agents cannot be used in it. Opaque additives are usually carbon black or metallic oxides, which simply limit light penetration. In addition, antioxidants are employed to reduce the attack by oxygen or ozone on the polymer molecule. In rubber the susceptibility to oxidation of stressed sulfur cross links leads to cracking and stress relaxation. The antioxidants are usually complex aromatic amines or phenols and may react with radiation-produced molecular fragments to modify radiation effects.

For transparent objects exposed to sunlight, poly(methyl methacrylate)† is employed because of its resistance to discoloration. The polar ester group renders it less resistant to absorption of moisture than polystyrene and hence inferior for certain electrical applications. As in the case

† Plexiglas, Lucite, etc.

of polyethylene and polystyrene, the moderate intermolecular forces allow low softening temperatures and solubility in many organic solvents.

In general, for resistance to oxidation, unsaturation must be kept to a minimum. This means that unreacted monomer, as well as unsaturated groups in polymer molecules, should be reduced as far as practical. Reactive species from polymerization initiators, catalysts, etc., may serve to initiate degrading reactions under extremes of temperature or long exposure periods.

Higher softening temperatures are produced by cross-linked structures or by those having strong intermolecular forces and high crystallinity. The densely cross-linked phenol-formaldehyde resins[†] have high softening tem-

Table 5.4—STABILITY OF COMMON PLASTICS[a]

Material	Heat stability (max. temp. for continuous exposure), °F	Action by chemical agents [b] Acids[c]	Alkalies[c]	Organic solvents
Phenol-formaldehyde:				
Unfilled or fabric filled	220-250	A	A	N
Glass filled	350-450	A[d]	A	N
Urea-formaldehyde (cellulose filled)	170	A[e]	A	N
Melamine-formaldehyde	210	A	A	N
Alkyds	250[f]	A[d]	A	Some
Polyamides	270-300	A	N	N
Poly(vinyl chloride)	120-160	N	N	Some
Poly(vinyl acetate)	[g]	A[e]	A	A
Poly(vinylidene chloride)	160-200[f]	N	N	N
Polystyrene	150-205	A[d]	N	Some
Poly(methyl methacrylate)	140-190	A[d]	N	A
Ethyl cellulose	115-185	A	A	A
Cellulose acetate	150-220[f]	A	A	Some
Polyethylene (high and low density)	212-250[f]	A[d]	N	A
Poly(tetrafluoroethylene)	500[f]	N	N	N
Poly(chlorotrifluoroethylene)	390	N	N	Some

[a] From The Plastics Properties Chart, G. Kline (Ed.), Modern Plastics, Ref. 81.
[b] A, attacked or soluble; N, not attacked or insoluble.
[c] Strong reagents; weak reagents have little effect.
[d] Strong oxidizing acids.
[e] Attacked by hot water.
[f] Heat distortion point below continuous-exposure temperature.
[g] Heat distortion temperature = 100 °F.

peratures, are highly resistant to solvents, and have moderate water absorption in spite of the presence of the polar hydroxyl group. This group is susceptible to attack by strong alkalies. Hydrophilic fillers, although they may raise the maximum operating temperatures, also increase moisture absorption.

† Bakelite, Redmanol, Indur, etc.

The highly crystalline and inert structures of polytetrafluoroethylene[†] and polychlorotrifluoroethylene[‡] are among the most resistant to attack by solvents, acids, and alkalies and show very low moisture absorption. The useful temperature limits are also high, although the hardness is less than for the cross-linked thermosetting resins. The polyamides,[§] which are also highly crystalline and have strong intermolecular forces, similarly have high softening points and are resistant to most solvents. These materials are resistant to alkalies, but the polar nature of the molecule makes water absorption high and permits decomposition by strong acids. Thermal characteristics of polymers are listed in Table 5.4 along with their resistance to acids, alkalies, and organic solvents.

5-4 Mechanical Properties of High Polymers

The structure of a polymer, long chain or network, contributes certain unusual characteristics to its mechanical properties. Likewise, crystallinity and orientation play a part. The mechanical behavior of polymers is more strongly dependent on temperature than is the behavior of most other materials.

5-4.1 STRESS RESPONSE OF AMORPHOUS HIGH POLYMERS

Amorphous linear high polymers above the brittle temperature (Fig. 5.1) are fundamentally much the same as liquids; i.e., they have short-range order and long-range disorder.[10] They possess the viscous-flow properties of liquids under stress but also possess some of the elastic properties of crytalline solids. Viscoelastic response is a characteristic of polymeric materials.

The process of diffusion with a liquid of low molecular weight involves molecules' jumping into holes.[10] Since the amorphous polymer molecule is too large to move in this manner, it is a segment of the molecule that jumps.[66] After many segments have jumped, the molecule itself will have moved, and, in addition, it will have changed its shape. The motion of the chain segments, which is quite rapid, is termed "micro-Brownian" movement. The motion of the center of gravity of the molecule, which is relatively slow, is termed "macro-Brownian" movement.[69] In the presence of a stress, both the micro- and the macro-Brownian movements are affected. Stress-biased micro-Brownian movement is recoverable but not instantly. This retarded elastic response is sometimes called "configurational elasticity." The response to stress is then threefold: (1) instantaneous elasticity, (2) retarded elasticity, and (3) viscous flow.

The instantaneous elastic response is given by the slope of the first

[†] Teflon.
[‡] Kel-F.
[§] Nylon.

part of the stress–strain curve (Fig. 5.2), Young's modulus. Theoretically, not only is the response to ordinary elasticity instantaneous, but also the elasticity is completely reversible instantaneously. The mechanism of elasticity in a molecular lattice is generally thought to be by displacement of the molecules relative to each other against van der Waals' forces and by the deformation of primary valence bonds and bond angles.

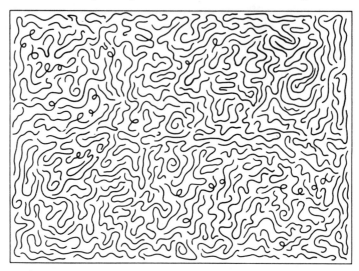

FIG. 5.1 Schematic diagram of linear amorphous high polymer. Many configurations are possible because of flexibility. Most molecules are neither tightly curled nor fully extended.

The elasticity in retarded elastic response is also completely reversible, but the time lag may be very long.[10,55] This time delay, or retardation time, is required for the uncoiling and reorientation of the polymer molecules. The retarded response dominates the portion of the stress–strain curve in Fig. 5.2 just before the yield stress is reached. It is usually not possible to describe the action of a material by one retardation time. Thus a spectrum of retardation times is used. The retardation time, τ, is defined by the following equation:

$$y = y_0(1 - e^{-t/\tau}) \tag{5.3}$$

where y is the deformation at time t after application of stress and y_0 is the equilibrium value of deformation.[10,61]

Qualitatively, viscous flow may be viewed simply as a stress-biased diffusion.[10] In the force field generated by a shear or tensile stress, the jumping of the molecular segments is no longer random but is biased in one direction. If a movement of the center of gravity of the molecule results, the strain is not recoverable; and such macro-Brownian movement

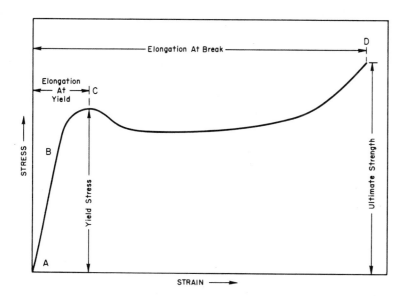

Fig. 5.2 Polymer stress–strain curve. AB = elastic response; BC = viscoelastic response; and CD = viscous or plastic flow.

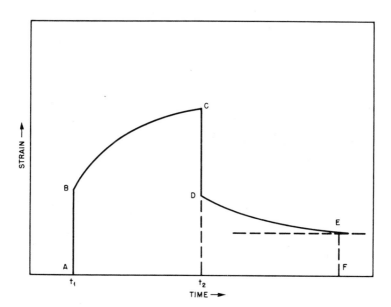

Fig. 5.3 Strain–time curve at constant stress. Stress applied at t_1 and released at t_2. AB = CD = instantaneous elastic response; DE = retarded elastic response; and EF = plastic flow.

is termed "true flow." Viscous flow occurs beyond the yield stress point in Fig. 5.2.

The combined elastic, viscoelastic, and flow properties are illustrated by the strain–time curve (Fig. 5.3). If a stress is applied at time t_1, there is first an instantaneous strain AB and then a time-dependent combined recoverable and flow response. When the stress is removed at time t_2, there is an instantaneous recovery of CD = AB and a time-dependent viscoelastic recovery DE. The nonrecoverable strain due to flow is represented by EF.

The linear amorphous high polymers, which are fusible and soluble, include the noncrystalline thermoplastics and unvulcanized rubber. The thermosetting materials and vulcanized rubber are three-dimensional networks. A brief comparison will be made of the loose network structure to the amorphous linear structure. The very tight network structures may be treated as crystalline low-molecular-weight solids, the ultimate in tightness being graphite. The theory of structures of intermediate tightness is more complex.

5-4.2 STRESS RESPONSE OF NETWORK POLYMERS[10,59]

A three-dimensional network is pictured in Fig. 5.4. The cross links consist of molecular bonds between polymer molecules. One molecule can be bonded in this way to several others or more than once to one other

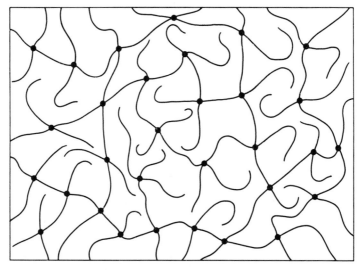

FIG. 5.4 Schematic diagram of polymer network structure.

molecule or even back onto itself. The bond can be directly between carbon atoms of the backbone chain or through an intermediate atom or molecular segment. In the early stages of cross linking, the molecular weight increases. In a true network structure, there are enough cross links to effectively make the polymer into one large molecule interspersed with material of low molecular weight or with linear polymer molecules.

The instantaneous elastic response of cross-linked polymers is less affected by cross linking than the retarded elastic response. The wide distribution of retardation times necessary to describe the viscoelastic behavior of linear polymers is reduced to a much narrower spectrum for cross-linked polymers. This is true because in the linear polymer the orientation and configuration of segments and molecules of all lengths are involved; in the cross-linked material, however, only the sections between cross links and parts of these sections are involved. As the temperature is increased, the retarded elastic response of linear polymers gradually becomes dominated by flow, whereas the retarded elastic response of the cross-linked polymers merely becomes less retarded. The cross-linked polymers cannot flow unless primary valence bonds are broken.

5-4.3 EFFECT OF CRYSTALLINITY[10,78]

It is often convenient to consider high polymers as completely amorphous materials. This is, however, seldom the case in the temperature range of interest because many polymers do attain a very high degree of crystallinity. The following is a brief description of crystallinity in polymers and its contribution to their mechanical properties. This information is background for the role that crystallinity plays in the effects of radiation on polymers.

A crystallite in a high polymer is a region in which the structural units are ordered, as in other crystalline solids. The structural units, however, are neither atoms nor molecules, but are segments of molecules. A given molecule may be part of several crystallites. In between crystallites the molecule lies in amorphous regions because a high polymer is never completely crystalline. Furthermore, the molecule does not necessarily pass from a completely crystalline region to a completely amorphous region. A crystalline polymer is, therefore, a mixture of regions of various degrees of the orders shown in Fig. 5.5 where crystalline regions are indicated by heavy parallel lines.

If a crystalline polymer is stretched or if, by some other means, the crystallites are made to line up in the same direction, an oriented crystalline polymer is produced. In the oriented state the molecular segments between crystallites are straightened so that the tendency toward crystallinity is higher. In the unoriented state the crystallites have a more or less random direction, and the part of the molecule between crystallites is coiled up as is typical of the amorphous material. Here the influence of one crystallite on the next through the connecting portion of the molecule is very slight since a stress on one will only cause a change in configuration of the coiled molecular segment. In the oriented case the connecting portion of the molecule is not so coiled; therefore it can exert a much greater influence on the attached crystallite.

The crystallite can be considered a more or less rigid inclusion in the amorphous polymer. The rigid crystallite has no viscoelastic response and no flow if it is to remain crystalline. For small strain the response is entirely from the amorphous regions. Large strains must, however, cause phase changes; i.e., the crystallites will grow or they will melt away.

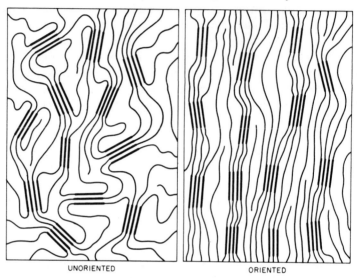

UNORIENTED   ORIENTED

Fig. 5.5 Schematic diagram of crystalline polymer.

Crystalline high polymers have a broad melting range because the melting temperature is dependent on the crystallite size. The melting range can be changed somewhat by applying a compressive stress, but it can be changed much more by applying a tensile stress (which increases the crystallinity). If the phase change by deformation is neglected, it is easy to see why crystallinity inhibits flow. The crystallites effectively act as cross links and bind the polymer together in a networklike structure.

Crystallinity plays an important role in radiation-induced reactions. This role is most often explained by the foregoing discussion of the crystalline structure of polymers, which, in turn, is based on the fringed micelle model. Recent studies have introduced a slightly altered picture of the structure of crystallinity in polymers.[53] It has been observed that the long-chain molecule folds back upon itself many times before leaving a crystallite. The length of the molecular segment in the fold determines the thickness of the crystal. A typical single crystal is shown in Fig. 5.6. Sometimes a fibrous structure is observed for which the fibril diameter is of the same order as the thickness of the crystallites.

FIG. 5.6 Crystallinity in polyethylene. (From A. Keller, in *Growth and Perfection of Crystals*, John Wiley & Sons, Inc., Ref. 53.)

FIG. 5.7 The spherulitic-structure birefringence pattern. (From A. Keller, in *Growth and Perfection of Crystals*, John Wiley & Sons, Inc., Ref. 53.)

The most recent studies have shown a spherulitic structure. This is thought to result from the arrangement of fibrils into a bundle that fans out at the ends. The molecules in the spheroids effectively run in a circular pattern around the center of the spheroid. There results the birefringence pattern shown in Fig. 5.7.

5-4.4 Effect of Temperature

Both the low- and the high-molecular-weight amorphous polymers have temperature ranges in which they pass from hard and brittle to softer materials having rubberlike elasticity. At the brittle-point temperature, the micro-Brownian movement is frozen in. The range where this occurs usually depends on the speed of testing.[10] Below this temperature range the polymer is often termed "glassy"; this transition occurs at the "glass transition temperature."

Polymers have good tensile strength and poor impact strength at low temperatures because they are hard and brittle. Above the brittle temperature the tensile strength is reduced, but the impact strength is much improved. This is sometimes called the "leathery region" in contrast to the glassy region. Further increase in temperature of an amorphous polymer will cause melting; but, if the polymer is lightly cross linked, it becomes elastomeric.

5-4.5 Elastomeric Materials

The concepts presented here are oversimplified because they apply only to an ideal material; they are especially inadequate at large rates of strain and at large deformations. At very high strain rates, all polymers behave like glasses. Theories of rubber elasticity have been developed for a better understanding of the mechanism of large elastic deformation in elastomers.[67,98,99]

An elastomeric material is distinguished by its ability to recover rapidly from large deformation. An elastomer is a polymer with a loose network structure that is cross linked at infrequent points. Between these pinning points there are long sections of loose, random molecules, which have a high freedom of motion. When stressed, the polymer behaves much like an amorphous material with no cross links. However, the molecules that make up the network structure cannot find a new random configuration because they are still held at pinning points. When the stress is removed, the original configuration is completely recovered. This is a reversible macro-Brownian movement.

The restoring force for high elasticity is from the thermal motion of the chain segments; the restoring force for ordinary elasticity is from van der Waals' bonding and valence bonding. Elastomers are sometimes described as liquidlike materials which are held together only by the few cross links that give a network structure. When stretched, however, the elastomer exhibits crystallinity because the stretching increases orientation.

In the random structure of the amorphous linear high polymer, there is much intermingling and entwining of the molecules.[59] The entanglements do not impede the macro-Brownian motion in polymers not cross linked because the molecules can fairly readily slip by each other. In the lightly cross-linked elastomeric materials, the entanglements greatly affect the properties of the polymer. When the polymer is strained, the entanglements, being locked in by cross links, contribute to the restoring force.

5-4.6 Tensile and Impact Properties[10,26]

The tensile properties of polymers are very important in engineering applications. However, analytical treatment of these properties is difficult. The generalized stress–strain curve was given in Fig. 5.2. In the initial straight portion of the curve, the polymer is nearly perfectly elastic and obeys Hooke's law. The slope here (Young's modulus) is a measure of the rigidity or stiffness of the material. The point where the curve departs from linearity is called the "proportional limit," and elongation beyond this point is not immediately recoverable (see Fig. 5.3). The "yield point" is the load at which the slope of the stress–strain curve first becomes zero. At this point plastic flow and permanent deformation become appreciable. The stress at rupture gives the ultimate strength of the material if it is greater than the yield stress. The strain at rupture is called "elongation."

Thus materials represented by Fig. 5.2 would typically have characteristics as follow:

1. If the yield stress is high, the polymer will be hard and ductile.
2. If the yield stress is low but the strain at break is high, the material will be soft and ductile.
3. The curve for a hard, brittle material will terminate at A.
4. Soft, weak materials have low slopes and break before much extension.

The stress–strain curve depends both on the temperature of the test and on the speed of testing. Slow testing favors plastic failure (failure after the yield point), whereas high rates of strain will cause early fracture.

The impact strength test is often used to determine the fracture characteristics of a material. This test is empirical.[65] The specimens are often notched to concentrate the stress and to assure fracture. The stress concentration is favored in an impact test since the load is applied so quickly that there is no time for stress relaxation by plastic flow. In general, a very hard material is likely to have low impact strength. This is not always true, however, because the behavior of the material also depends on the rate of application of stress. If the time for viscoelastic response is a little below the ordinary test time but above the impact test time, the polymer will look brittle in the impact test yet flexible in a slow test.

The dependence of the tensile strength of high polymers on the average molecular weight is better understood than their dependence on molecular-weight distribution. As the molecular weight increases, the strength increases roughly in proportion to the chain length, up to a nonlinear region. Within this region the strength increases asymptotically to a maximum value; beyond this region further increase in molecular weight results in no change in strength.

Molecular weight also influences the method of fracture. It is thought that a low-molecular-weight material breaks largely by the pulling apart of intertwined groups of chain ends but that a high-molecular-weight polymer breaks by the rupture of molecular chains.[10,78] With short molecules the primary valence forces within a chain are very much stronger than the intermolecular forces between neighboring molecules; thus, the chains will tend to slip past each other. With long molecules, however, the accumulated effect of the intermolecular forces over the length of the chain may result in the fracture of the chains before slip.

5-4.7 EFFECTS OF PLASTICIZERS[3,78]

The addition of certain low-molecular-weight materials (plasticizers) to high polymers changes the mechanical properties. In a nonpolar material the plasticizer is quite randomly distributed through the polymer. The effect of increasing plasticizer content is to change a hard, rigid polymer first to a viscoelastic material and then to a rubbery, flexible product. Further addition of plasticizer changes the material to a liquid. The general effect is to increase the retarded elastic or viscoelastic response by decreasing the irrecoverable viscous flow.

In polar materials plasticizers are not distributed randomly but tend to cluster around the polar groups of the polymer. This has the effect of neutralizing the polar group and reducing the strong intermolecular attraction. The plasticizer molecule, however, is not as free to diffuse around as in the nonpolar case. The net result is a softening action, the same as in the nonpolar case but brought about in a different manner. A significant difference is that the plasticized polar material exhibits elasticity without much increase in flow.

Many organic polymers are hygroscopic to varying degrees. Water will act as a powerful plasticizer for many polymers, resulting in a loss in strength and in elastic modulus but in an increase in ductility and in toughness. The extent of this effect is roughly proportional to the amount of water absorbed.

5-5 Electrical, Optical, and Thermal Properties

Rigid organic polymers have dielectric constants† of between 2 and 4. For polar materials this constant can be increased by raising the temperature or by adding plasticizer. It can be decreased by lowering the frequency. Nonpolar materials are not much changed by temperature or frequency. The dielectric loss factor varies from 0.0001 for polystyrene (nonpolar) to above 0.1 for plasticized vinyl chloride (polar). As with the dielectric constant, the loss factor for polar materials will change with frequency and temperature. It will also show peaks at transition points.[68,81]

The dielectric strength of a material is its ability to withstand an applied voltage without breakdown by puncture. This strength (expressed in volts per unit thickness) decreases with increasing thickness. For $\frac{1}{8}$-in.-thick specimens of organic polymers, the dielectric strength is a few hundred volts per mil.

The electrical conductivity (Ch. 13, Sect. 13-2) of polymers is low except when ionic impurities are present. For a polystyrene the volume resistivity is very high, 10^{18} to 10^{21} ohm-cm, depending on the ionic impurity content and the length of time of measurement. Most polymers have resistivity values[81] above 10^{10} ohm-cm. The resistivity decreases markedly with increase in temperature and with increased humidity of the atmosphere.

Most high polymers transmit visible, infrared, and ultraviolet light well. Amorphous high polymers are transparent, often clear, water white, but sometimes have a yellowish or bluish tinge. As the crystallinity is increased, the clarity is lowered because of the internal reflection of the crystallites. Thus crystalline polymers are translucent but not transparent. The degree of transparency is often measured as "haze," the percentage of incident light that is scattered.

The index of refraction of a high polymer is the same order as that of ordinary glass. Polymers, however, have the characteristic of having different refractive indexes in the directions parallel and perpendicular to the polymer chains. The resulting double refraction, or birefringence, can be used to study the orientation of the stress concentration in the polymer. The spherulitic structure of high polymers was illustrated by birefringence[53,68] in Fig. 5.7.

The specific heat of organic polymers can be estimated reasonably by adding the specific heats of the atoms in the monomer unit and dividing by the average atomic weight. The specific heat of polymers is higher than that of metals on a per gram basis but lower on a volume basis. The ther-

† See Ch. 13, Sect. 13-2, for a discussion of dielectric properties.

mal conductivity of most organic polymers is lower than that for asbestos or wood. It can be increased considerably by the addition of conducting filler. The coefficient of thermal expansion for organic polymers is three to ten times that for most metals.

5-6 Radiation Effects

Predominantly, the effect of high-energy radiation on organic polymers is to produce ionization and excitation. Subsequent rupture of chemical bonds yields fragments of the large polymer molecules which may retain unpaired electrons from the broken bonds. The free radicals thus produced may react to change the chemical structure of the polymer and alter the physical properties of the material. The polymer may undergo cleavage or scission, i.e., the polymer molecules may be broken into smaller fragments. It also may undergo cross linking, i.e., the molecules may be linked together into larger molecules.[27,30,49] Low-molecular-weight fragments (gases) and unsaturation are important side results of these reactions.

The general form of the cross-linking reaction is illustrated by Eq. 5.4:

$$2RCH_2CH_2R^* \rightarrow H_2 + RCH_2\overset{R}{C}H\overset{R}{C}HCH_2R \qquad (5.4)$$

where the asterisk designates an excited or ionized molecule and R is an alkyl group. The mechanism of cross linking has been postulated in detail only for polyethylene. A simple view has the hydrogen radical abstract another hydrogen from a nearby molecule to form the hydrogen molecule. The two polymer radicals then join to form the cross-linked molecule, as in Eq. 5.4.

At present there is strong evidence that the cross-linking reaction is favored at the site of a double bond. Dole and coworkers[50,52] have shown that vinylene (in-chain, $-CH=CH-$) double bonds build up to an equilibrium value. They may be formed by radiation-produced hydrogen atoms abstracting other hydrogen atoms at the closest site in the same molecule or by the removal of two nearby hydrogens in the same radiation event at the same time. The vinyl (end, $-CH=CH_2$) double bonds and the vinylidene (side group, $CH_2=C<$) double bonds quickly become exhausted. During the early stages of irradiation, when the vinyl and vinylidene unsaturation is being destroyed, the cross linking also progresses faster. A detailed discussion of cross linking in polyethylene is given in Ch. 6.

Mechanisms for cleavage have been postulated for poly(methyl methacrylate) in some detail, but none has proved to be very satisfying. The general form of the scission reaction is as follows:

$$R-C_3H_6-R^* \rightarrow RCH_3 + CH_2=CHR \qquad (5.5)$$

The polymer molecule is broken in the main chain. The structure of a polymer molecule that undergoes scission must be somehow different from one that prefers to cross link. This is discussed in Sect. 5-8.

5-6.1 CROSS LINKING AND SCISSION

5-6.1.1 *Methods of Measurement*

Molecular-weight determinations can be used to establish the extent of cross linking and scission in irradiated polymers. The osmotic-pressure, light-scattering, and viscosity (of dilute solutions) methods were described briefly in Sect. 5-2.4. Because of its relative convenience, the viscosity method is most frequently used. This method, however, is not entirely applicable when cross linking has proceeded to the point of rendering some of the polymer insoluble. There are also other difficulties in interpreting the solution viscosity data to give molecular weights quantitatively;[86,91] but, for a most-probable molecular-weight distribution, the viscosity average is about equal to 1.9 times the number-average molecular weight.

The gel point, the point at which the cross-linking process first produces insoluble material, can also be used to determine the degree of cross linking.[58] The cross-linking index (γ) is a common parameter for this purpose. It is defined as the number of cross-linked units per number-average molecule. With a most-probable distribution, the weight-average molecular weight is twice the number average; and at the gel point $\gamma = \frac{1}{2}$. Thus there is one cross link for every four original number-average molecules. The point at which insoluble material first appears in a cross-linking polymer is obviously a function of molecular weight. Furthermore, the number of cross links required per number-average molecule (but not per weight-average molecule) is also a function of the molecular-weight distribution.

For degrees of cross linking higher than the gel point, the ratio of soluble to insoluble material can be measured. Charlesby[37,39] has developed expressions for the gel–sol ratio as a function of cross linking for a most-probable molecular-weight distribution. This treatment includes equations allowing for scission of the main chain concurrent with cross linking. Figure 5.8 shows the solubility relation[37] for an initially most-probable distribution for various ratios of scission to cross linking. At high radiation doses, if scission and cross linking both occur, the soluble fraction decreases to an asymptotic value characteristic of the ratio of cross linking to scission. It was concluded that it is just possible to form insoluble material if the rate of cross linking exceeds one-fourth the rate of scission.

When cross linking has progressed to the point of complete insolubility, the extent of cross linking can be determined by the equilibrium swelling

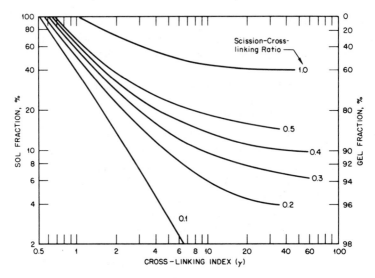

FIG. 5.8   Theoretical curves of gel fraction vs. γ (number of cross-linked units per number-average molecule) for various ratios of scission to cross linking, assuming a most-probable molecular-weight distribution initially. [From A. Charlesby, *Proceedings of the Royal Society (London)*, Ref. 37.]

of the polymer in a solvent. A theoretical formula[40] for V, the swelling ratio (weight of polymer plus solvent/polymer dry weight), is

$$V^{2/3} = (0.5 - \mu) \frac{M_c}{\rho v} \qquad (5.6)$$

where μ is a constant that depends on the interaction between solvent and polymer, M_c is the average molecular weight of the polymer between cross links, ρ is the density of the dry polymer, and v is the molar volume of the solvent. This approximate formula is not valid for high densities of cross links when the swelling ratio is small or for lightly cross-linked networks in which a significant amount of the original material has not been bound into the network structure. More complicated equations have been derived which are more adaptable to smaller swelling ratios (but not very small) and for lower degrees of cross linking.

For highly elastic networks equilibrium-stress measurements can be used to determine M_c, the average molecular weight between cross links.[58,67] The relation between the applied stress, f, and the extension at equilibrium, α, is given by

$$f = \frac{\rho RT}{M_c} \left[\alpha - \left(\frac{1}{\alpha^2} \right) \right] \left[1 - \left(\frac{2M_c}{M_n} \right) \right] \qquad (5.7)$$

where R is the gas constant, T is the absolute temperature, ρ is the density, α is the ratio of the extended length to the original length, and M_n is the initial number-average molecular weight of the polymer. The expression $[1 - (2M_c/M_n)]$ is a correction for end effects.

Stress-relaxation measurements have been traditionally used for studies with elastomeric materials because they afford a way of assessing the amount of cleavage in the presence of concurrent cross linking (see Ch. 7, Sect. 7-2.5). Here the stress is allowed to change in order to maintain the extension constant. Measurements can be made in a radiation field this way, the advantage of this method being that the orientation of the molecular chains and the forces on the molecules are not changed except by the radiation effect.

One of the new tools for studying the mechanical properties of solids is the measurement of the vibration characteristics. The properties studied are the dynamic elastic modulus and internal friction. A vibrating solid has a characteristic resonance frequency, which depends on the elastic modulus of the material. The frequency of the resonance vibration determines the elastic modulus. The broadness of the resonance peak is a measure of the internal friction. The equations of motion of the vibrating body depend on the mode of vibration, which, in turn, depends on the shape of the specimen, method of clamping, and method of driving. The concentration of cross links in a polymer can be estimated from Young's modulus measured at a temperature where the polymer exhibits rubberlike elasticity. The relation is expressed in Eq. 5.7, which reduces at small strain to

$$f = \frac{\rho R T}{M_c} \tag{5.8}$$

Proton magnetic-resonance measurements have recently been applied to cross linking and other radiation effects. In this method the specimen is placed in a strong magnetic field, which interacts with the magnetic moment of the nuclei. The specimen is subjected also to an alternating electromagnetic field oscillating at frequencies in the microwave region. The strong magnetic field is varied until the resonant condition is realized for the spin inversion of the hydrogen nucleus in a quantum-mechanical transition. The data are recorded as radio-frequency energy absorbed as a function of the magnetic-field intensity. Because of interaction between atoms, a broad peak occurs when the atoms are stationary, as in a crystal; but a narrow peak denotes atoms that are in thermal motion, as in a liquid.[64,104] The motion of atoms in amorphous areas of partially crystalline polymers is liquidlike, but motion is more restricted in crystalline regions. Thus two peaks are observed in crystalline polymers. The narrower is associated with motion in the amorphous portions; the broader, with the crystalline regions.

Obviously, cross linking will have a strong influence on the motion in polymeric materials. A low degree of cross linking increases the intensity and reduces the width of the amorphous peak by increasing the concentration of defects, and consequently, the motion, in the crystalline regions. Extensive cross linking broadens and decreases the intensity of the amorphous peak because the effects in the crystalline portion are overcompensated by the reduction in motion in the amorphous region.

5-6.1.2 *Kinetics of Reaction*

It has been pointed out (Ch. 3, Sect. 3-4.4; Ch. 4, Sect. 4-3) that the kinetics of radiation-induced reactions in polymers are much more complicated than just a consideration of the rates of cross linking and cleavage.[51] For example, cross linking is predominant in polyethylene. Here the number of cross links should equal the number of molecules of gas less the

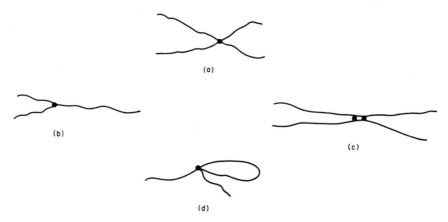

Fig. 5.9   Comparison of true cross link with various pseudo cross links. (a) Normal cross link. (b) End link. (c) Square link (two cross links on adjoining carbon atoms or cross links so close together that they act as one). (d) Ring link (link in a chain that doubles back on itself).

number of double bonds formed. The gas yield, however, is considerably larger than predicted from this. Such may be attributed to certain kinds of cross links (not properly termed cross links at all) which do not result in a change in property in the material even though gas is evolved. These other kinds of cross links have been termed "end links," "square links," and "ring links" (Fig. 5.9).

Possibly the most convincing argument for free-radical reactions comes from evidence of stored free radicals. At low temperatures free radicals may be stored in large numbers for long periods of time.[1,2] The concentration of radicals has been measured by electron-spin resonance, and the decay of the free radicals can be followed by this method and by the ensuing chemical reactions.[71] Postirradiation aging characteristics have been observed in many materials. This effect is frequently a continuation of the reaction that took place under irradiation; however, for irradiation under vacuum and subsequent exposure to oxygen, reaction with oxygen may result. For thick specimens the rate of reaction will depend on the rate that oxygen can diffuse into the specimen. Postirradiation reaction is illustrated in Fig. 5.10.

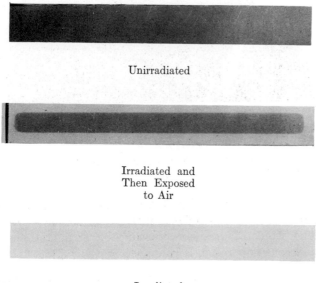

Unirradiated

Irradiated and
Then Exposed
to Air

Irradiated
in Vacuum

Fig. 5.10 Postirradiation reaction in polystyrene. Irradiated in Oak Ridge Graphite Ridge Graphite Reactor at about 77°F in an inert atmosphere.

The rate of radiation-induced reactions also depends on the physical state of the polymer, i.e., whether the polymer is crystalline or amorphous, glassy or rubbery. This is discussed in the next section.

5-6.1.3 *Effects of Cross Linking*

Cross linking increases the molecular weight of the polymer, decreases the solubility, and increases the softening temperature. When enough cross links have formed to bind the material into one large molecule, it is completely insoluble but will swell when placed in a solvent.[40]

Further irradiation, beyond that which cross links the polymer into one large molecule, will bind the material into a three-dimensional network.[31] As cross linking progresses, the network becomes more rigid. The properties of the polymer are now very little governed by chemical structure but become a function of the density of cross links in the network structure.[18,30]

As the density of cross links is increased, a liquidlike, soft, amorphous polymer will change to a rubbery material and then to a hard, glassy substance. The latter transition is illustrated in Fig. 5.11.

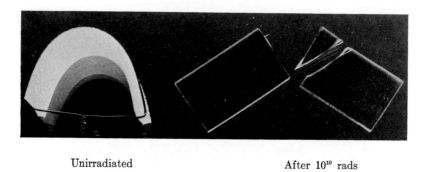

Unirradiated   After 10^{10} rads

FIG. 5.11   Effect of cross linking in polyethylene. Irradiation without stress with gammas at about 77°F in an inert atmosphere.

The stress–strain curves in Fig. 5.12 also show the effect of cross linking.[92] The curve for the unirradiated material is characteristic of a soft, ductile product. Moderate irradiation produces a harder, stronger material. Most of the viscous flow region is gone (see Fig. 5.1). Both the yield point

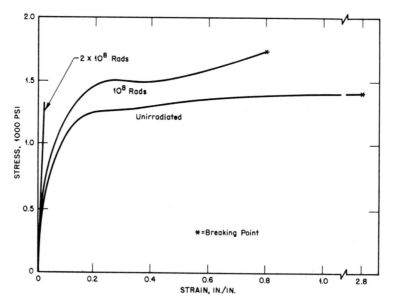

FIG. 5.12   Stress–strain curves for polyethylene. Irradiated without stress in Oak Ridge Graphite Reactor at about 77°F in an inert atmosphere.

and the ultimate strength are increased. The values of the retardation times for viscoelastic behavior are increased; and Young's modulus (the slope of the initial portion of the curve) is increased.[16,17,36] The highest irradiation dose has produced a material that will break before the yield point.

If a thermoplastic polymer that has been given a moderate degree of radiation cross linking (see Fig. 5.12) is heated, it shows rubber elasticity. The change in a cured natural rubber caused by radiation-induced cross linking is shown by the tensile-strength curve[16] of Fig. 5.13. As the cross linking progresses, the material passes from an elastomeric to a leathery and finally to a glassy state.

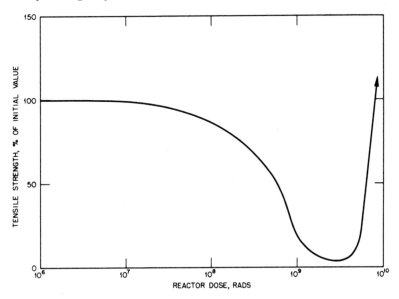

FIG. 5.13 Tensile strength of an irradiated natural-rubber compound.[16] Irradiated without stress in Oak Ridge Graphite Reactor at about 77°F in an inert atmosphere.

In addition to the stress–strain test, there are three methods commonly used to study the viscoelastic behavior of a material.[55] These are (1) the step-function, constant-stress (creep) experiment; (2) the constant-strain (stress-relaxation) experiment; and (3) sinusoidal application of stress (dynamic mechanical properties). Creep and stress-relaxation measurements are most used in radiation-effects studies for elastomers (see Ch. 7, Sect. 7-2.5). Dynamic mechanical measurements are used for all types of polymeric materials and have proven to be an excellent tool in this work.

The dynamic mechanical properties of a polymer depend on the molecular weight, degree of branching, amount of crystallinity, extent of

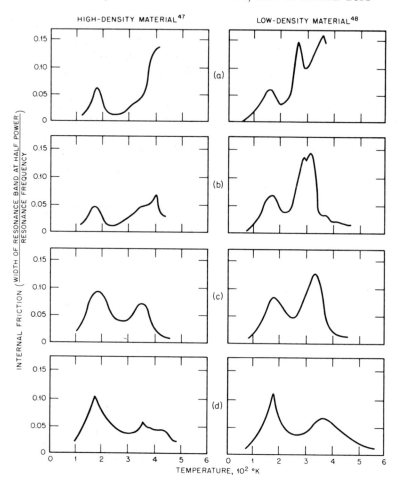

Fig. 5.14 Effect of irradiation on internal friction of polyethylene. Irradiated in Brookhaven Graphite Research Reactor at 104 to 122°F in vacuum. (a) Unirradiated. (b) About 1×10^9 rads. (c) About 3×10^9 rads. (d) About 6×10^9 rads. (From C. W. Deeley *et al., Journal of Applied Physics,* Ref. 47, and *Journal of Polymer Science,* Ref. 48.)

cross linking, and orientation of the molecules. Information on some of these can be obtained from resonance-frequency measurements. When the resonance frequency for low-density polyethylene is plotted against temperature, the following three transitions are clearly indicated by changes in the slope of the curve:[24]

1. The transition at low temperature occurs at the glass transition point and is attributed to the development of segmental motion in amorphous areas involving alternative configurations.

2. The peak at intermediate temperatures is attributed to diffusional

motion of the chain segments containing branch points and indicates softening of the amorphous regions.

3. The transition at high temperature is associated with the melting of the crystallites or an elastic motion in the amorphous regions.

These transitions are most clearly shown as peaks in the internal friction or damping vs. temperature plot. The temperature at which the damping peaks occur varies somewhat, the variation being dependent on the material and the method of measurement.

The damping curves of low-density and high-density polyethylene from work by Deeley and coworkers[47,48] are shown in Fig. 5.14. The low-density material was about 50% crystalline, and the high-density material was about 90% crystalline. With increased radiation dose the low-temperature peak shifts to higher temperatures and becomes more prominent for both types of material. The other two peaks in the low-density material first merge and finally become less prominent. In the highly crystalline material (which has less branching), the peak attributed to branch points is absent. An indication of a peak at about 400°K can be seen for the lowest irradiation period when some of the crystallinity has been destroyed. In both materials the crystallinity is progressively destroyed and disappears completely at high-radiation doses. At low doses this destruction of crystallinity is the major factor in altering the mechanical properties of high-density polyethylene. After much of the crystallinity has been destroyed, the increased restraints produced by the cross linking are more significant than further loss in crystallinity. A fourth small peak, which is more noticeable at doses below those shown here, has also been postulated as resulting from crystalline melting.

The effect of cross linking is to draw the molecules closer together and, therefore, to decrease the specific volume.[35] The hardness also increases, and the resultant material has glassy properties. The hard cross-linked polymer will, of course, have very poor impact strength, in contrast to lightly cross-linked polymers.[17]

5-6.1.4 *Effects of Scission*

In most respects the influence of scission on the properties of polymers is just the opposite to that of cross linking. When the scission reaction breaks the molecule into smaller fragments, this decreases the molecular weight, increases solubility, and lowers the melting point. The mechanical properties of a polymer are also changed by scission. The shortened chains and greater number of chain ends lead to weakening and often to embrittlement even though the material may have become somewhat softer. The stress–strain curves in Fig. 5.15 for poly(methyl methacrylate) are illustrative of the effects of scission. The strength is progressively decreased by irradiation as is typical for hard, brittle materials.[92]

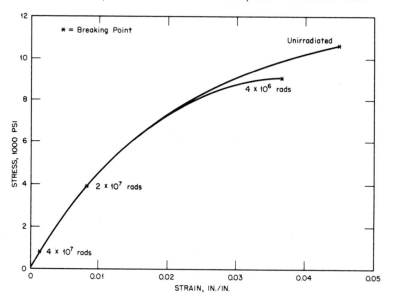

FIG. 5.15 Stress–strain curves for poly(methyl methacrylate).[92] Irradiated in Oak Ridge Graphite Reactor at about 77°F in an inert atmosphere.

The stress–strain curves for poly(vinyl chloride acetate) in Fig. 5.16 illustrate extreme softening, which occurs in some polymers.[92] Scission here has the effect of reducing the yield stress and increasing viscous flow. The strength is progressively decreased, and with longer irradiations the viscous flow is also decreased. Young's modulus is decreased and the flow proper-

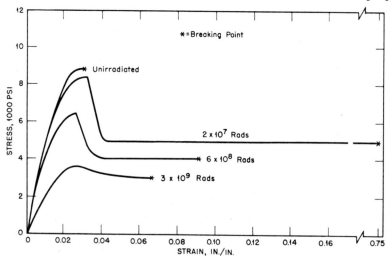

FIG. 5.16 Stress–strain curves for poly(vinyl chloride acetate).[92] Irradiated in Oak Ridge Graphite Reactor at about 77°F in an inert atmosphere.

ties are changed as a result, perhaps, of a decrease in molecular weight for poly(vinyl chloride acetate).

Crystallinity can be increased in polymers that undergo scission because there is less restraint on the shortened molecules. Thus they are more easily oriented into the crystal structure. An increase in crystallinity will cause an increase in density. Cross linking also increases the density but for a different reason, as already described. There is no evidence of any radiation-produced decrease in density for any polymer except through foaming by gas formation. The impact strength of poly(tetrafluoroethylene), which scissions, is markedly increased after short radiation doses,[92] presumably because of an increase in crystallinity. Further irradiation, however, reduces the impact strength. Most polymers that are scissioned by radiation are reduced in impact strength concurrently with a reduction in tensile strength.

5-6.2 OPTICAL AND ELECTRICAL PROPERTIES

Almost all polymers are colored to some extent by radiation. In some cases the material will become opaque after prolonged exposure. Some, like poly(methyl methacrylate), require oxygen to produce coloration, whereas others, like polystyrene, fade if exposed to oxygen after irradiation. Polyethylene and nylon, which have a high haze value owing to their crystallinity, are increased in transparency by irradiation because the crystallinity is destroyed[17,28] (Fig. 5.17).

Postirradiation measurements of the volume resistivity and dielectric

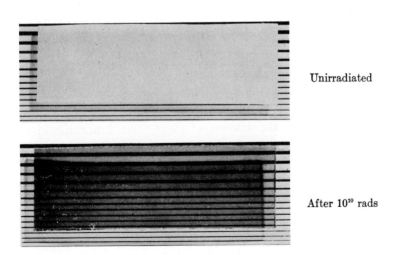

Unirradiated

After 10^{10} rads

FIG. 5.17 Destruction of crystallinity in nylon. Irradiated in Oak Ridge Graphite Reactor at about 77°F in an inert atmosphere.

strength have shown very large changes in some polymers.[92] For example, poly(vinyl chloride acetate) changes from 10^{17} ohm-cm to 10^6 ohm-cm in resistivity for modest radiation exposure. Changed electrical properties result from the production of cracks or other flaws. Chemical breakdown can also yield conducting products.

The electrical resistance of polymers under irradiation drops to a value that is a function of the intensity of the radiation field.[60,77,84] In high-flux fields the decrease can amount to a factor of 100 or 1000 for good insulators. This drop, which is recovered when the radiation is removed, is caused by ionization. This provides mobile charges, which are available for conduction. These charges give properties similar to semiconductors to the polymer and result in nonohmic resistance, as well as photovoltages.[84]

Little is known at present of changes in thermal properties of polymers caused by radiation, but only a small effect is expected.

5-6.3 OTHER REACTIONS

The evolution of gases is commonly observed in the decomposition of polymers, whether by irradiation or by other means. The thermal decomposition of addition polymers produces substantial quantities of monomer. In the case of poly(methyl methacrylate), yields of monomer close to 100% have been obtained. In contrast to this thermal effect, irradiation produces low-molecular-weight products having no similarity to the monomer. Polymeric products of cross linking or scission are also produced, as already described.

The gaseous radiolysis products have been identified for a number of materials, but little effort has been made to identify nonvolatile products. The most thoroughly studied substance, logically, has been the simplest, polyethylene. From 85 to 99% of the gas from polyethylene is hydrogen; low-molecular-weight hydrocarbons are the other constituents.[52] This spread in the hydrogen yield results from the effect of different kinds of radiation, different irradiation conditions, and/or different starting materials. The composition and total quantity of the hydrocarbon fraction were shown[73] to depend on the amount of short-chain branching in the polyethylene. Linear polyethylene evolves about 99% hydrogen regardless of the type of radiation involved. About four molecules of gas are produced for every 100 ev of energy absorbed. Gas evolution has also been studied for poly(methyl methacrylate). The composition and yield suggest that one ester side group is destroyed for each main chain scission.[5,100]

As would be expected from the copious evolution of hydrogen from polyethylene and other saturated hydrocarbon polymers, unsaturation develops during the irradiation. The growth and decline of various isomeric configurations of the $>C=C<$ groups in polyethylene during irradiation are discussed in Ch. 6, Sect. 6-1.

The production of approximately two $>C=C<$ groups for every chain scission in polyisobutylene was demonstrated[6] by chemical methods, but the connection of this process with postulated mechanisms for the scission reaction is still uncertain. The appearance of doubly bonded carbon groups conjugated with the carbonyl group in irradiated poly(methyl methacrylate) has been suggested by ultraviolet absorption spectra. Although the production of unsaturation accompanies chain scission in proposed reaction mechanisms[90] for poly(methyl methacrylate), quantitative measurements of unsaturation have not been made.

The growth of aliphatic unsaturation and the decline of aromatic groups in polystyrene during reactor irradiation have been reported, as has the conversion of *cis*- to *trans*-unsaturation in natural rubber.[87] A decrease in terminal $>C=C<$ groups in styrene-butadiene rubber and polybutadiene and a destruction of *cis*-groups[88] in the latter have also been observed as a result of exposure in a reactor. Thus the development of, or changes in, unsaturation appears to be as basic a part of radiation effects as cross linking and cleavage.

5-7 Influence of Chemical Structure on Radiation-induced Reactions

The controlling factor in the behavior of polymeric materials under irradiation, as under most other environmental influences, is the chemical structure. Whether molecular weight increases or decreases on radiolysis depends upon the presence or absence of frequently recurring quaternary or halogenated carbon atoms in the main chain. Another correlation requires the presence of at least one hydrogen atom on the carbon atom adjacent to a methylene group (e.g., —CHCH$_2$—) for cross linking to be favored.[41]

The mechanism of scission of polymers of methacrylates, isobutylene, α-methylstyrene, etc., is still unsettled. Wall and Brown[100] have pointed out that the polymers that contain quaternary carbons and that also undergo scission show reduced heats of polymerization from the steric strain of the substituents. If momentary disruption of the main chain occurs during irradiation, it is suggested that steric hindrance at the quaternary carbon prevents the recombination usually induced by the Frank–Rabinowitch cage effect (see Ch. 3, Sect. 3-2.2). The possibility of resonance with the substituent groups to stabilize the free radical formed on chain scission has also been advanced to account for the scission of this class of polymers.[79] A one to four diradical process involving ejection of one of the substituent groups has also been proposed:[90]

$$R_1-\overset{\overset{\displaystyle H}{|}}{\underset{\underset{\displaystyle H}{|}}{C}}-\overset{\overset{\displaystyle CH_3}{|}}{\underset{\underset{\displaystyle CH_3}{|}}{C}}-\overset{\overset{\displaystyle H}{|}}{\underset{\underset{\displaystyle H}{|}}{C}}-\overset{\overset{\displaystyle CH_3}{|}}{\underset{\underset{\displaystyle CH_3}{|}}{C}}-R_2 \longrightarrow CH_4^* + R_1-\overset{\overset{\displaystyle H}{|}}{\underset{\underset{\displaystyle H}{|}}{C}}-\overset{\overset{\displaystyle CH_3}{|}}{\underset{\underset{\displaystyle \cdot C}{|}}{C}}-\overset{\overset{\displaystyle H}{|}}{\underset{\underset{\displaystyle H \cdot C}{|}}{C}}-\overset{\overset{\displaystyle CH_3}{|}}{\underset{\underset{\displaystyle H_2}{|}}{C}}-R_2 \longrightarrow R_1-\overset{\overset{\displaystyle H}{|}}{\underset{\underset{\displaystyle H}{|}}{C}}-\overset{\overset{\displaystyle CH_3}{|}}{\underset{\underset{\displaystyle H}{|}}{C}}=\overset{\overset{\displaystyle H}{|}}{C}+\overset{\overset{\displaystyle CH_3}{|}}{\underset{\underset{\displaystyle H_2}{||}}{C}}-R_2 \tag{5.9}$$

The influence of various substituent groups on the behavior of polymers is detailed for various classes of compounds in the remainder of this section. Initial emphasis is on substituents attached to the main polymer chain. This is followed by compounds having substituents in place of the main-chain carbon atoms to form links in the chain itself.

5-7.1 HALOGENATED POLYMERS

Halogenated polymers, which are common among polymers, have high radical yields. Poly(vinyl chloride) has been found to show changes indicative of both cross linking and scission, depending on the composition of the starting material. Complete halogenation, e.g., as with polytetrafluoroethylene, leads to scission at a high rate. No conclusive generalizations are yet possible for polymers of intermediate degrees of halogenation. Poly(vinylidene chloride) has shown net scission, whereas copolymers of vinylidene fluoride and monomers of higher halogen contents, e.g.,

$$\overset{\text{CF}_3}{\underset{|}{}}$$
$$-CH_2CF_2CFClCF_2-, \quad -CH_2CF_2CF_2CF-$$

vulcanize or cross link on irradiation. The cross linking of

$$\underset{-CH_2CH-}{\overset{O=COCH_2(CF_2)_2CF_3}{\underset{|}{}}}$$

indicates that halogen atoms in the side chain do not promote net scission. Obviously, more definitive experiments need to be performed to resolve the influence of halogenation.

Experimental work, however, agrees that low-molecular-weight halogen compounds are evolved in the radiolysis of the halogenated polymers. This is important in electrical applications of these polymers. These new products are capable of forming halide ions with moisture present. Thus the electrical resistance of the polymers decreases rapidly upon irradiation. The gaseous products, whether they be hydrogen halide acids or elemental halogens, are also corrosive to metals.

5-7.2 POLYSTYRENES AND PROTECTIVE EFFECTS OF AROMATIC RINGS

The outstanding material in regard to its resistance to ionizing radiation is polystyrene. This material graphically demonstrates the stabilizing effect of a regularly recurring phenyl group on the main chain. The energy dissipated per cross link in polystyrene is 1400 to 1800 ev, about thirty times the 45 to 60 ev per cross link in polyethylene. There are indications that poly(α-methylstyrene) undergoes scission in a radiation field at a much slower rate than poly(methyl methacrylate) or polyisobutylene.[14] The behavior of these materials suggests energy transfer to the benzene ring, a point that was mentioned in Ch. 3, Sect. 3-4.5.

Burton and coworkers[23,76] have shown that benzene is able to accept energy absorbed initially by other molecules that have higher ionization or first excitation levels. This behavior was demonstrated by the irradiation of mixtures of benzene with aliphatic compounds. A part of the stability of polystyrene must be assigned to the low mobility of the molecular segments in the solid. In this connection both the polymer yield of benzene and the yield for the exchange of hydrogen atoms between the benzene ring and the ethyl group are several-fold greater than the cross-linking yield for polystyrene.[94]

A similar protective effect was demonstrated by Alexander and Charlesby[4] in the cross linking of hydrocarbons. The radiation energy required to produce gel formation was measured for dodecanes substituted with a saturated bicyclic group or with a naphthyl group at various positions. Almost twice as much radiation was required for gelation in the aromatic substituted compound as in the aliphatic when the substituent was centrally located. The protective effect decreased considerably when the naphthyl group was at the chain end. This latter observation is cited as evidence that absorbed energy cannot be transferred efficiently over chain lengths of more than about six carbon atoms. The same authors[7] investigated the protection against scission by irradiating copolymers of isobutylene and styrene. Styrene was found to protect isobutylene over distances of one to two isobutylene units.

Bauman and Glantz[12] synthesized copolymers of butadiene and styrene and measured gelation and solvent swelling after various exposures to gamma radiation. They concluded that radiation-induced cross linking was retarded by the benzene ring in these copolymers also.

The probable role of in-chain unsaturated groups in the cross-linking reaction was discussed in Sect. 5-6. The —C≡N group retarded cross linking through certain ranges of composition and radiation dose.[12] The protective effect of this group, however, is not as clear cut as is that of the aromatic ring.

5-7.3 POLYACRYLATES

A systematic study by Shultz and Bovey[89] deals with the effect in the radiolysis of polyacrylate polymers of varying the side-chain structure. The energy per scission was approximately constant for polymers from methyl, the four butyls, and neopentyl acrylate. When the hydrogens on the carbinol carbon atom were replaced with an alkyl substituent, the energy per cross link increased markedly. This indicates the removal of these hydrogens to play a part in the cross-linking reaction.

The side-chain structure has also been observed to affect the energy dissipation in scission of polymethacrylates.[90] The *tert*-butyl side chain lowers the apparent scission energy over that for a methyl side chain, but the normal butyl group raises it. Polymethacrylates of long-chain alcohols predominantly cross link[90] under irradiation. Evidently the cross linking in the long-chain portion offsets the scission of the main chain.

5-7.4 OTHER POLYVINYL COMPOUNDS

Polyvinyl alcohol, together with its esters, ethers, and acetals, comprises a class having an electronegative atom substituted on alternate main-chain carbon atoms $[—CH_2CH(OR)—]$. All this class, except the parent poly(vinyl alcohol), predominantly cross link. Probably the attachment of an ester, ether, or acetal group to alternate carbon atoms of the main chain gives less increase in the scission to cross linking ratio than does the attachment of a halogen atom or hydroxyl group; but a comparison in the absence of more definitive measurements is not justified. Polyvinyl pyrolidone

$$H_2C——CH_2$$
$$H_2C\diagdown_N\diagup C\diagup\!\!=\!\!O$$
$$\underset{|}{N}$$
$$—CH_2CH—$$

with an amine group attached to alternate main-chain carbons cross links.

5-7.5 POLYETHERS AND OTHER POLYESTERS

The substitution of atoms other than carbon in the main chain might be expected to have a greater effect on the results of irradiation than the substitution of atoms attached to the chain. This, however, has not always been observed. Ether type oxygen linkages occur in the main chain in poly(ethylene oxide), $—OCH_2CH_2—$. Pearson[83] found this material to gel upon irradiation. A considerably higher dose is required for the gel point here than for polyethylene of equivalent molecular weight. The ether structure apparently shows fewer cross-linking sites and requires more energy for the formation of cross links than does polyethylene.

A different order of substitution is represented by ester linkages in the main chain, e.g., poly(ethylene terephthalate),

$$(-\overset{O}{\overset{\|}{C}}\!\!\!\diagup\!\!\!\overline{}\!\!\!\diagdown\!\!\!\overset{O}{\overset{\|}{C}}OCH_2CH_2O-).$$

Experience with the polyacrylates suggests that radiation should disrupt the ester group. This prediction is borne out for poly(ethylene terephthalate) by infrared measurements; however, solubility tests suggest that cross linking predominates,[42] probably through linkage at the benzene ring. Crystallization studies[74,75] show that the net rate of cross-link production cannot be high. Apparently both cross linking and scission take place slowly, but further experiments are necessary to prove which process ultimately predominates. Maleic acid–glycol polyesters cross linked with styrene show a loss of hardness at high doses. This suggests scission, but cross-link density was undoubtedly high before this evidence of degradation appeared.[92] More quantitative measurements of cross-link density are needed.

5-7.6 CELLULOSE DERIVATIVES

These materials embody a high degree of oxygen substitution both within and on the main chain. Cellulose is made up of glucose residues joined through acetal linkages (ether links formed between hydroxyl and carbonyl groups; see Ch. 11 for discussion on textiles). Bovey[20] found that cellulose and the common cellulose esters and ethers undergo scission at a relatively high rate under irradiation. One glucose unit is destroyed per scission. This probably results from a break in the acetal link rather than simple rupture of the glucose ring. Rupture of bonds at two points in the ring would be required to produce scission. Since poly(ethylene oxide) with its ether linkage shows predominant cross linking rather than scission, the higher degree of oxidation of the carbohydrates apparently makes the polymer much more susceptible to scission.

5-7.7 NITROGEN COMPOUNDS

The substitution of a nitrogen atom for carbon in the main chain is found in the commercial aniline–formaldehyde polymer, $-CH_2N(C_6H_5)-$. The strength was found to change only very slowly under reactor irradiation,[92] but slight increases in elastic modulus and shear strength indicate that this material undergoes cross linking. This polymer changes somewhat more rapidly in a radiation field than does polystyrene.

The amide linkage, $-R_1C(O)NHR_2-$, a structural part of nylon type polymers and of the proteins, represents a more highly substituted main chain than the amine type. A number of workers have shown that cross linking is dominant during irradiation of nylon (see Ch. 11 for nylon in textiles). Little[75] observed a low-molecular-weight fraction after irradiation. This indicates that scission also takes place. Upon recrystallization the irradiated samples showed a diffraction pattern and a changed density which showed that chain branching had occurred concurrently with scission. The mechanical properties, e.g., elastic modulus, of nylon 66 were found to change at a rate not much different from those of polyethylene.[92]

On the other hand, dynamic vibrational studies above the crystalline melting point have indicated the initial rate of cross linking of nylon to be about half the rate for polyethylene.[46,48] However, this relative rate for nylon decreases at high radiation doses. Gel-point measurements of poly-caprolactam (nylon 6)[80] and end-group determinations give 290 ev as the energy required per cross link. This is five or six times the energy dissipated per cross link in polyethylene. The net cross-linking rate in amides appears to be reduced by concurrent scission at the amide linkage.

The proteins have received attention for a number of years because of their biological importance. Most investigations have been in aqueous media; but studies of dry wool, silk, and casein show that scission is dominant. The mechanical properties of casein[92] decline at about the same rate as those of poly(methyl methacrylate). Apparently the more closely spaced amide groups in the protein structure, as compared with nylon, promote a larger degree of scission. Data are lacking on polypeptides having long alkyl side chains irradiated in dry condition. Such side chains would probably cross link under irradiation in the same manner as the methacrylate esters of the higher alcohols.

5-7.8 Sulfur and Silicon Compounds

The polysulfide elastomers have still another type of main-chain linkage, a series of sulfur atoms ($-CH_2CH_2SSSS-$). The physical properties of these materials indicate that the polar forces of the polysulfide groups are lower than those of the amides or esters. Most of the experimental work has been on commercial formulations, and the changes observed show that such rubbers scission under moderate radiation exposure.[16] In contrast, an ethylene–propylene polysulfide[43] was cross linked at low exposure by reactor radiation, as indicated by a reduction in solubility. Ethylene polysulfide and the mixed ethylene–diethyl formal polysulfide irradiated in the vulcanized state showed no change in solubility or swelling after moderate radiation exposures. In other irradiations of commercial materials,[85] property changes have suggested cross linking or only slow scission. Evidently the dominance of cross linking or scission in commercial vulcanized stocks depends on the nature of the cross-linking agent. The conditions of the irradiation, such as temperature and accessibility of oxygen, also exert an influence.

A highly substituted structure, in fact one that does not contain a carbon–carbon main chain at all, is represented by the polysiloxanes or, commonly, the silicones, $-OSi(R)_2OSi(R)_2-$. Bueche and coworkers[21,96] measured the cross-linking yield for low-molecular-weight methyl siloxane liquids. They found 40 ev required per cross link. This is in fair agreement with the values of earlier workers. The cross-linking rate for the rubbery solid polymers should be similar to that for these liquids. Thus the cross-link yield for the methyl silicone polymers is of the same order as that for polyethylene, although the main chain does not contain carbon

Table 5.5—RADIATION RESISTANCE OF COMMON
POLYMERS THAT PREDOMINANTLY CROSS LINK

(Listed in Order of Decreasing Resistance to Net Molecular-weight Change)

Polymer	Structure	Energy absorbed per cross link (E_{XL}), ev	Energy absorbed per scission (E_d), ev
Poly(vinyl carbazole)	—[CH$_2$CH(N(C$_6$H$_4$)$_2$CH$_2$)]—	?	?
Polystyrene	—[CH$_2$CH(C$_6$H$_5$)]—	1400-1800	5000-7000
Aniline-formaldehyde	—[CH$_2$N(C$_6$H$_5$)]—	?	?
Nylon	—NH(CH$_2$)$_6$NHC(O)(CH$_2$)$_4$C(O)]—	250-300 (net)	?
Poly(methyl acrylate)	—[CH$_2$CH[C(O)OCH$_3$]]—	160-200	560-600
Polyacrylonitrile [a]	—[CH$_2$CH(CN)]—	?	?
Poly(dihydroperfluorobutyl acrylate) [a]	—[CH$_2$CH[C(O)OCH$_2$(CF$_2$)$_2$CF$_3$]]—	80-160	400-800
SBR rubber (styrene-butadiene) [a]	—[[CH$_2$CH(C$_6$H$_5$)]$_x$[CH$_2$CH=CHCH$_2$]$_y$]—	60-100	500-700
Polybutadiene [a]	—CH$_2$CH=CHCH$_2$—	50-70	600-750
Natural rubber (cis-polyisoprene)	—CH$_2$CH=C(CH$_3$)CH$_2$—	30-40 (net)	?
NBR rubber (nitrile-butadiene)	—[CH$_2$CH(CN)]$_x$(CH$_2$CH=CHCH$_2$)$_y$]—	?	?
Poly(ethylene oxide)	—CH$_2$CH$_2$O—	?	?
Poly(vinyl acetate)	—[CH$_2$CH[OC(O)CH$_3$]]—	?	?
Poly(vinyl methyl ether)	—[CH$_2$CH(OCH$_3$)]—	?	?
Polyethylene	—CH$_2$CH$_2$—	45-60	90-120
Silicone[poly(dimethyl siloxane)]	—Si(CH$_3$)$_2$O—	40	High

[a] Formulations containing commercial compounding. Rankings and energy values are only approximate.

Table 5.6—RADIATION RESISTANCE OF COMMON POLYMERS
THAT ARE BORDERLINE BETWEEN PREDOMINANT CROSS
LINKING AND SCISSION

(Listed in Order of Decreasing Resistance to Net Molecular-weight Change)

Polymer	Structure	Energy absorbed per cross link (E_{XL}), ev	Energy absorbed per scission (E_d), ev
Polysulfide rubber	$-CH_2CH_2SSSS-$	$0.5\,E_d < E_{XL} < 4E_d\,^a$	
Poly(ethylene terephthalate)	$-C(O)\!\!\bigcirc\!\!C(O)CH_2CH_2O-$	?	?
Poly(vinylidene fluoride-perfluoropropylene)	$-[CH_2CF_2CF_2CF(CF_3)]-$	$0.5\,E_d < E_{XL} < 4E_d\,^a$	
Poly(vinyl chloride)	$-[CH_2CH(Cl)]-$	$0.5\,E_d < E_{XL} < 4E_d\,^a$	
Poly(vinylidene chloride)	$-[CH_2C(Cl)_2]-$	$\,?$	?
Polypropylene	$-[CH_2CH(CH_3)]-$	100-150	100-120

^{a} If $E_{XL} > 4\,E_d$, it is not possible to form insoluble material by irradiation (see Sect. 5-6.1.1).

and, indeed, infrared evidence suggests that the cross links are not even between pairs of carbon atoms.

With the exception of the siloxane polymers, substitution of atoms other than carbon in the main chain gives a net reduction in cross linking. This is probably through acceleration of scission. If several electronegative atoms form the linking group, as in amides or polysulfides, the polymer is decidedly more susceptible to scission.

5-7.9 ROLE OF UNSATURATION

Unsaturation plays an important part in the mechanism of cross linking, as already noted. Internal double bonds participate in the cross-linking process but do not profoundly increase cross-link yields under irradiation.[44] However, there is a significant yield increase for double bonds at the end of chains.[25] The rubbers, both synthetic and natural, present the best examples of hydrocarbon polymers with regularly recurring, but not con-

Table 5.7—RADIATION RESISTANCE OF COMMON
POLYMERS THAT SCISSION PREDOMINANTLY

(Listed in Order of Decreasing Resistance to Net Molecular-Weight Change)

Polymer	Structure	Energy absorbed per cross link (E_{XL}), ev	Energy absorbed per scission (E_d), ev
Phenol-formaldehyde[a]		?	?
Poly(α-methyl styrene)	$-[CH_2C(CH_3)(C_6H_5)]-$		500-100
Poly(methyl methacrylate)	$-[CH_2C(CH_3)[C(O)OCH_3]]-$	>600	60-80
Poly(vinyl alcohol)	$-[CH_2CH(OH)]-$	?	?
Polytetrafluoro-ethylene (Teflon)	$-CF_2CF_2-$		?
Polyisobutylene (butyl rubber)	$-[CH_2C(CH_3)_2]-$	>200	15-20
Cellulose		>100	~10

[a] Specimens already densely cross linked before irradiation.

jugated, double bonds. The available experimental evidence shows that cross linking proceeds at about the same rate in the base polymers of rubbers as in polyethylene. No increase in cross-linking yield was observed in polyethylene containing 5% polybutadiene.[103] Not only is this behavior unexpected because the double bond appears to be a precursor of cross links, but it contrasts with the findings for unsaturated monomers. In the latter materials, free-radical type chain-propagated polymerization is initiated by radiation. The high yields observed in such processes are discussed in Ch. 4, Sect. 4-3.

5-7.10 CONCLUSIONS

It is apparent that many structural features of the polymer determine the nature or the rate of the changes produced by irradiation. Of obvious importance are the elements making up the main chain and the side chains or substituent groups. In Tables 5.5, 5.6, and 5.7 are listed the chemical structures of common polymers in the order of their resistance to the predominant radiation-induced process, either cross linking or scission.

5-8 Influence of Other Variables on Radiation-induced Reactions

5-8.1 TEMPERATURE AND MOBILITY EFFECTS

Reactions involving free radicals are affected by anything that changes the mobility of the species, e.g., temperature. However, the rate of production of free radicals in a given material is independent of mobility and is determined only by the intensity of the radiation. Radical recombination competes with other reactions, e.g., cross linking. Thus, with a given radical production rate, if the cross-linking rate is decreased by lowering the temperature, a greater fraction of the free radicals must recombine. The result is a greater net energy required per cross link.

Both the rate of cross linking in polyethylene and the rate of scission in polymethacrylate and polyisobutylene are strongly temperature dependent.[15,32,102] It is not clear, however, that scission and cross linking should increase at the same rate with increase in temperature. In fact, scission should be less affected by increased mobility than cross linking because it involves a single-molecule reaction, whereas cross linking involves at least two molecules. If cross linking is favored at high temperatures and scission at low temperatures, the radiation effect would be completely altered in character by temperature alone. No such effect has been noted; but effects of substituent groups or stress, which also change the rigidity of the polymer, may be due at least in part to a change in the mobility of the molecules. The increased rigidity due to cross linking might be expected to retard further cross linking, but this effect is not observed.[56]

Some investigators believe that in polyethylene most of the cross links are formed in the amorphous regions[70] and that very little cross linking occurs in the crystalline regions. Evidence now favors equal amounts of cross linking in the crystalline and the amorphous regions.[27,29,56]

5-8.2 OXYGEN AND THICKNESS EFFECTS

The reactive species in radiation-induced processes should be highly sensitive to the presence of oxygen (or air). The effect should vary with materials and with conditions. Polyisobutylene was found to undergo scission at the same rate in vacuum as in air.[6] On the other hand, poly(methyl methacrylate) requires about twice as much radiation per scission in the presence of air as in vacuum.[101] However, in the experiment cited the effect of oxygen may have been somewhat dependent on the presence of benzene impurity in the specimens.[8] In another experiment irradiation of pure powdered poly(methyl methacrylate) in air yielded 25% less scission than that in a vacuum.

The accessibility of oxygen is important because, for example, the dissolved oxygen in bulk poly(methyl methacrylate) (1 cm thick) is insufficient to affect the scission rate.[8] For thin films and powdered material, the diffusion of oxygen into the sample is adequate to retard the scission rate in air irradiations. The diffusion rate of oxygen at high dose rates limits the oxygen effect. Quantitative experimental measurements of rate relations are lacking at present.

Wall and Brown[101] found that additional scission occurred in poly-(methyl methacrylate) films that dissolved in dilute solutions of *tert*-butylcatechol following irradiation in air. Apparently during irradiation oxygen combines with active sites on the polymer chains to form peroxide links or bridges to reduce the net scission rate. The peroxide links are then subject to reduction by the *tert*-butylcatechol, but the scission produced by such postirradiation decomposition is not equal to the difference between the scission yields in air and in vacuum.

Polyethylene and polystyrene, which normally cross link under irradiation, show an oxygen effect that is dependent on thickness and dose rate in the manner just described for poly(methyl methacrylate). Investigation[9,97] has shown that cross linking is retarded considerably by irradiation of polystyrene films in air, compared to irradiation in vacuum. However, thicker polymer specimens (1-cm-diameter rods) were considerably less affected by oxygen. Some of the earliest work on polyethylene demonstrated that surface oxidation of films occurred during irradiation in air. More recently the gel–sol relations of polyethylene film irradiated in air have been measured.[9] These results point to an increase in the scission rate by oxygen with no effect on the rate of cross linking.

Several mechanisms have been suggested for the action of oxygen both on polymers that cross link and on those that undergo scission.[20] One assumes that cross linking is unaffected by oxygen and that the initial act of scission is a rapid process that is also unaffected. In this mechanism the broken chain ends recombine by a relatively slow process; but, in the presence of oxygen, instead of recombining they react with oxygen to produce scission. By this scheme the apparent reduction in scission of poly(methyl methacrylate) by oxygen is accomplished by the formation of oxygen and peroxy cross links at reactive sites between neighboring chains. The cross linking gives a net reduction in the scission yield, although the actual chain-rupture process is not affected by oxygen.

The effect of oxygen on the radiation-induced changes in polytetrafluoroethylene (Teflon) is unusually large. The increase in density and the loss of tensile strength may be ten times as rapid in air as in vacuum in a given radiation field.[95] Both these changes probably result from scission of the original molecules to give a reduction in molecular weight. The increased density very probably is due to an increase in the fraction of the material in the crystalline phase. The reduced restraints among the smaller molecules would produce this increase in crystallinity.

Infrared studies show that radiation-induced oxidation produces a variety of products, hydroxy and carbonyl compounds and probably hydroperoxides and peroxides. Chemical evidence supports the indication of the peroxy compounds, as well as the other oxidation products. It is known that radiation produces ozone in air and that ozone preferentially attacks double bonds under certain conditions. The stress relaxation in stretched natural rubber is much greater in air than in the absence of oxygen.[13,16]

There is much evidence for the existence of free radicals and perhaps other reactive species after organic solids have been irradiated. When exposed to air, such samples oxidize readily, in some cases over protracted periods. Infrared data show that the postirradiation products differ in abundance from the products of irradiation in air but are similar in kind, i.e., they are aldehydes, ketones, and alcohols.[87]

5-8.3 EFFECT OF ADDITIVES

The production of reactive or excited intermediates by high-energy radiation permits additives to influence radiation-induced changes to an appreciable degree.[13] On the general basis of participation in radiation-induced processes, additives and nonpolymer components can be divided into two categories, active and inert materials.

Active additives can be further subdivided into two classes, the energy-sink materials and the chemical reactants. Obviously the aromatic ring, in the instances already cited (see Sect. 5-7.2), acts as an energy sink incorporated intramolecularly in the polymer. Alexander and Toms[9] made a thorough study of the reduction of scission of poly(methyl methacrylate) by aromatic compounds, namely, hydroxyquinoline and naphthalene, dissolved in the polymer. They found that the protection of the polymer was dependent on the concentration of the additive and that reduction of scission was not accomplished by linking of the additive into the polymer. The evidence indicated that the aromatic protector absorbed some of the excitation or ionization energy from the base polymer thereby reducing decomposition. Energy transfer has been verified in the case of scintillation solutes.

Protection against the effects of radiation by reactive additives has been observed by Bauman and Born[19] in rubber stocks (see Ch. 7, Sect. 7-3.2.3 and 7-4.7). These stocks contained carbon black and phenyl-2-naphthylamine (~0.6%), as well as about 3% of the protective agent. The protective agents were compounds of the antioxidant type used in the rubber industry. Probably the reduction of the cross-linking yield is due to combination of the protector with radiation-produced free radicals to prevent their further reaction. On the other hand, no reduction was shown in cross linking of polyethylene by allylthiourea or certain aromatic compounds.[8,9] The only observation with these materials was a reduction in the effect of air on the cross-link yield.

The importance of such additives is obvious where commercial materials are to be exposed to radiation; antioxidants and aromatic stabilizers and plasticizers are very frequently used to enhance durability or mechanical properties. Plasticizers may make up 30 to 40% of the weight of poly(vinyl chloride) items and may be a determining factor in the behavior under irradiation. Polyethylene and hydrocarbon rubbers normally require a small quantity of an antioxidant for stability during hot processing, and ultraviolet stabilizers are occasionally incorporated in polystyrene and poly(methyl methacrylate).

The inert additives or fillers need little discussion. These materials play a part in radiation effects simply by making up a portion of the mass in which the radiation energy is deposited. Since such materials serve both as reinforcing agents and as economical extenders, they are frequently encountered in commercial items. Common reinforcing agents and fillers are carbon black, silica, glass fiber, cellulose fiber, talc, asbestos, and wood flour. If the filler makes up an appreciable weight fraction of the fabricated article, the filler will absorb a portion of the radiation energy and, in the case of the inorganic fillers, will reduce the radiation effects in the exposed item. In the case of the cellulosic fillers, these may deteriorate faster than the resin binder and so accelerate radiation damage.[92]

5-9 Variables of the Radiation Field

The interaction of radiation with matter was discussed in Ch. 2, where the importance of the ionization effect with organic materials generally was emphasized. Irradiation variables and effects that are important with regard to solid materials are presented here.

There is no difference in basic reaction mechanism between the interaction of gamma radiations and the interaction of electrons with organic solids. Both radiations lose most of their energy through ionization and excitation and cause very few displacements by recoils. The electron, however, is completely stopped in the surface of a relatively thick specimen, whereas the photon will penetrate large thicknesses of organic matter. The electron effect, being concentrated at the surface, will also be much enhanced if oxygen is available. The electrons, and all charged particles, build up a charge in the specimen which, if not bled off, can produce more extensive changes than the initial absorption.

Heavy particles can also be penetrating (neutrons) or short ranged (protons or alpha particles). In addition, the heavy particles produce a considerable number of displacements. The effect of the displacements in organic polymers has never been carefully assessed. It will be more important in reactor exposures than in other common radiation sources.

The neutrons in a reactor are born with energies in the million electron volt range and are degraded to thermal energies. The thermal neutrons only have an effect when they are captured by an atom being bombarded. This is generally a small part of the over-all effect in the reactor for hydrocarbon polymers (of small sample size). The epithermal neutrons, particularly the fast end of the spectrum, are so important for most inorganic materials that their effect overshadows all others. The important reactions with inorganic materials are the creation of interstitial atoms, vacancies, impurity atoms, and thermal spikes; ionization is less important. With a hydrocarbon polymer the radiation effect in the reactor may also be largely due to fast neutrons, but it is by ionization instead of displacements.[14,93] The proportion of the radiation effect caused by fast neutrons and gamma radiation in a reactor depends, of course, on the ratio of gamma flux to neutron flux. It also depends on the hydrogen content of the material exposed because the neutrons are scattered primarily by the hydrogen (for equal numbers of hydrogen and of carbon atoms, ten times as much energy is lost to the hydrogen). In a graphite-moderated reactor, most hydrocarbon materials will receive from neutrons about half the total energy absorbed. The remaining half will come from gamma radiation.[92]

There are reasons why the effect of reactor radiation might be different from that of gamma radiation alone. If the polymer is extremely hard and rigid so that ionization contributes only a minor effect, the displacement of atoms by fast neutrons would become more important. It is not clear that any polymer falls into this category. Another difference between the neutron and gamma reaction is that the proton (the secondary particle from neutron exposures) leaves a much denser ionization track than does the electron (the secondary particle from photon exposures). This means that for equal energy deposited the number of ionization tracks by the neutrons will be much fewer, but the number of events within the track will be much greater.

It has been observed that for equal energy absorbed, gassing of polymers is greater in the reactor than in a gamma-radiation source.[14] In some instances a higher ratio of hydrogen to methane was evolved in the reactor.[52,73] Also, the destruction of crystallinity was accomplished faster in a reactor than in a gamma-radiation source.[28]

If the higher intensity of radiation in the ionization track from the proton causes a different radiation effect, should there not be a difference also in exposures at high dose rates with any kind of radiation? There is little data to substantiate such a contention. In fact irradiations of polyethylene at relatively low dose rates with gamma radiation and very high dose rates with electrons have given essentially the same value for energy per cross link.[11] The scission of poly(methyl methacrylate) also is accomplished with the same energy per scission at very high and low dose rates. Certain reactions, notably the cleavage of polytetrafluoroethylene, have been enhanced at low dose rates by the presence of oxygen. The data here are very skimpy; but, perhaps, at low dose rates for a fixed dose, the oxygen has more time to enter into the reaction.

A rule of thumb for estimating the change in organic polymers (or any organic material) for a given exposure condition from data obtained under different conditions has been this: "for equal energy absorbed, there will be equal radiation effect." This, of course, is not true, especially if there are big differences in temperature or if one irradiation was made in the presence of oxygen and the other not. The rule is strictly applicable to like irradiation conditions with a single radiation type. Nevertheless, for many engineering purposes it yields good approximations even when not strictly applied. This is possibly because much of the existing data on the radiation-induced changes in polymers is not very quantitative. It must be recognized, however, that reactor radiation may have a somewhat different effect than electrons and that extreme differences in dose rate should be avoided when the rule is applied.

5-10 Principles

A large part of this chapter is background for chapters to follow on plastics, elastomers, adhesives, textiles, paints, and wood products. Polymers are major building blocks for such articles of commerce. Specific items concerning these applications will be found in the pertinent succeeding chapter. There are, however, certain principles applying to almost all polymers undergoing radiolysis. These principles, given below, will aid the reader in evaluating new data as they appear.

1. The reaction of radiation with polymers and the resultant changes in the chemical structure and physical properties are very strongly dependent on the chemical structure of the starting material, the physical state of the material during irradiation, and the conditions of the irradiation (i.e., temperature, atmosphere, kind of radiation, and intensity of the radiation field).

2. Polymers predominantly either cross link or scission on irradiation (a few show little net effect at reasonable doses). Materials with recurring quaternary or halogenated carbon atoms in the main polymer chain tend to scission. Those containing at least one hydrogen atom on a carbon adjacent to a methylene ($-CH_2-$) group tend to cross link.

3. Scission or cleavage:[93]

    Decreases Young's modulus
    Reduces yield stress for viscous flow
  It usually causes
    Decreased tensile strength
    Increased elongation
    Decreased hardness
    Increased solubility
    Decreased elasticity
  It sometimes causes
    Embrittlement
    Gas formation

4. Cross linking:[93]

    Increases Young's modulus
    Impedes viscous flow
  It usually causes
    Increased tensile strength
    Decreased elongation
    Increased hardness
    Increased softening temperature
    Decreased solubility
    Gas formation
    Embrittlement
    Decreased elasticity

5. Polymers containing a high percentage of aromatic rings are the most resistant to radiolysis; those with a highly aliphatic structure are the least resistant.

6. Additive materials, generally of the antioxidant and/or aromatic type, can be used to improve the resistance of polymers to radiolysis.

References

Several of the following were cited in the text as authority for statements made. Others were not quoted but are included because they contain pertinent information. All were consulted in the preparation of this chapter.

1. Abraham, R. J., and Whiffen, D. H., Electron Spin Resonance Spectra of Some γ-Irradiated Polymers, *Trans. Faraday. Soc., 54*(9): 1291 (September 1958).

2. Abraham, R. J., Melville, H. W., Ovenall, D. W., and Whiffen, D. H., Electron Spin Resonance Spectra of Free Radicals in Irradiated Polymethyl Methacrylate and Related Compounds, *Trans. Faraday. Soc., 54*(8): 1133 (August 1958).

3. Aiken, W., Alfrey, T., Janssen, A., and Mark, H., Creep Behavior of Plasticized Vinylite VYNW, *J. Polymer Sci., 2*(2): 178 (March–April 1947).

4. Alexander, P., and Charlesby, A., Energy Transfer in Macromolecules Exposed to Ionizing Radiations, *Nature, 173*(4404): 578 (March 1954).

5. Alexander, P., Charlesby, A., and Ross, M., The Degradation of Solid Polymethyl Methacrylate by Ionizing Radiation, *Proc. Roy. Soc. (London), A223* (1154): 392 (May 1954).

6. Alexander, P., Black. R. M., and Charlesby, A., Radiation-Induced Changes in the Structure of Polyisobutylene, *Proc. Roy. Soc. (London), A232*(1188): 31 (October 1955).

7. Alexander, P., and Charlesby, A., Radiation Protection in Copolymers of Isobutylene and Styrene, *Proc. Roy. Soc. (London), A230*(1180): 136 (June 1955).

8. Alexander, P., and Toms, D. J., Protection Provided by Added Substances Against the Direct Action of Ionizing Radiations, *Radiation Research, 9*(5): 509 (November 1958).

9. Alexander, P., and Toms, D. J., The Effect of Oxygen on the Changes Produced by Ionizing Radiations in Polymers, *J. Polymer Sci., 22*(101): 343 (November 1956).

10. Alfrey, Turner, Jr., *Mechanical Behavior of High Polymers*, p. 358, Interscience Publishers, Inc., New York, 1948.

11. Atchison, G. J., Dose Rate Effect on Cross Linking of Polyethylene with High Energy Electrons in Vacuo, *J. Polymer Sci., 35*(129): 557 (March 1959).

12. Bauman, R. G., and Glantz, J. A., The Effect of Copolymer Composition on Radiation Cross Linking, *J. Polymer Sci., 26*(114): 397 (December 1957).

13. Bauman, R. G., and Born, J. W., The Mechanism of Radiation Damage to Elastomers. Part I: Chain Scission and Antirad Action, *J. Appl. Polymer Sci., 1*(3): 351 (May–June 1959).

14. Binder, D., Oak Ridge National Laboratory, unpublished data, 1960.

15. Black, R. M., Effect of Temperature Upon the Cross-Linking of Polyethylene by High Energy Radiation, *Nature, 178*(4528): 305 (August 1956).

16. Bopp, C. D., and Sisman, O., *Radiation Stability of Plastics and Elastomers*, Supplement to ORNL-928, USAEC Report ORNL-1373, Oak Ridge National Laboratory, July 1953.

17. Bopp, C. D., and Sisman, O., Radiation Stability of Plastics and Elastomers, *Nucleonics, 13*(7): 28 (July 1955).

18. Bopp, C. D., and Sisman, O., How Radiation Changes Polymer Mechanical Properties, *Nucleonics, 13*(10): 50 (October 1955).

19. Born, J. W., *USAF-WADC Quarterly Progress Report No. 1*, The B. F. Goodrich Company, July 1958.

20. Bovey, F. A., *The Effects of Ionizing Radiation on Natural and Synthetic High Polymers*, Interscience Publishers, Inc., New York, 1958.

21. Bueche, A. M., An Investigation of the Theory of Rubber Elasticity Using Irradiated Polydimethylsiloxanes, *J. Polymer Sci.*, *19*(92): 297 (February 1956).

22. Burr, J. G., and Garrison, W. M., *The Effect of Radiation on the Physical Properties of Plastics*, USAEC Report AECD-2078, Argonne National Laboratory, 1943.

23. Burton, M., and Patrick, W. N., Radiation Chemistry of Mixtures: Cyclohexane and Benzene-d_6. *J. Phys. Chem.*, *58*(5): 421 (May 1954).

24. Butta, E., and Charlesby, A., Dynamic Mechanical Properties of Irradiated Polyethylene. *J. Polymer Sci.*, *33*(126): 119 (December 1958).

25. Chang, P. C., Yang, N. C., and Wagner, C. D., Direct Dimerization of Terminal Olefins by Ionizing Radiation, *J. Am. Chem. Soc.*, *81*(9): 2060 (May 1959).

26. Carswell, T. S., and Nason, H. K., Effect of Environmental Conditions on the Mechanical Properties of Organic Plastics, in *Symposium on Plastics, Feb. 22-23, 1944*, pp. 22–46, American Society for Testing Materials, 1944.

27. Charlesby, A., and Swallow, A. J., Radiation Chemistry, in *Ann. Rev. Phys. Chem., 10*: 289–330 (1959).

28. Charlesby, A., and Callaghan, L., Crystallinity Changes in Irradiated Polyethylenes, *J. Phys. and Chem. Solids, 4*(4): 306 (1958).

29. Charlesby, A., von Arnim, E., and Callaghan, L., Effect of Crystallinity on Radiation Effects in Polyethylene, *Intern. J. Appl. Radiation and Isotopes, 3*(3): 226 (1958).

30. Charlesby, A., Effect of Radiation on Behavior and Properties of Polymers, in *Effects of Radiation on Materials*, p. 261, Reinhold Publishing Corp., New York, 1958.

31. Charlesby, A., A Theory of Network Formation in Irradiated Polyesters, *Proc. Roy. Soc. (London), A241*(1227): 495 (September 1957).

32. Charlesby, A., and Davison, W. H. T., Temperature Effects in the Irradiation of Polymers, *Chem. & Ind. (London), 1957*(8): 232 (1957).

33. Charlesby, A., *Atomic Radiation and Polymers*, Vol. 1, Pergamon Press, New York, 1960.

34. Charlesby, A., Cross Linking of Polyethylene by Pile Radiation, *Proc. Roy. Soc. (London), A215*(1121): 187 (November 1952).

35. Charlesby, A., and Ross, M., The Effect of Cross-Linking on the Density and Melting of Polyethylene, *Proc. Roy. Soc. (London), A217*(1128): 122 (March 1953).

36. Charlesby, A., and Hancock, N. H., The Effect of Cross-Linking on the Elastic Modulus of Polythene, *Proc. Roy. Soc. (London), A218*(1133): 245 (June 1953).

37. Charlesby, A., Gel Formation and Molecular Weight Distribution in Long-Chain Polymers, *Proc. Roy. Soc. (London), A222*(1151): 542 (March 1954) and The Cross-Linking and Degradation of Paraffin Chains by High Energy Radiation, *Proc. Roy. Soc. (London), A222*(1148): 60 (Feb. 1954).

38. Charlesby, A., Molecular Weight Changes in the Degradation of Long-Chain Polymers, *Proc. Roy. Soc. (London), A224*(1156): 120 (June 1954).

39. Charlesby, A., Solubility and Molecular Size Distribution of Crosslinked Polystyrene, *J. Polymer. Sci., 11*(6): 513 (December 1953).

40. Charlesby, A., Swelling Properties of Polystyrene Crosslinked by High Energy Radiation, *J. Polymer. Sci., 11*(6): 521 (December 1953).

41. Charlesby, A., *Actions Chimiques et Biologiques des Radiations*, Troisieme Serie, Chapitre III, Masson et Cie, Paris, 1958.

42. Charlesby, A., Effect of High Energy Radiation on Long-Chain Polymers, *Nature, 171*(4343): 167 (January 1953).

43. Charlesby, A., and Groves, D., *Rubber Technology Conference Proceedings, Third*, pp. 317–333, W. Heffer & Sons, Ltd., Cambridge, 1956.

44. Charlesby, A., Effect of Ionizing Radiation on Long-Chain Olefins and Acetylenes, *Radiation Research, 2*(1): 96 (February 1955).
45. Davidson, W. L., and Geib, I. G., The Effects of Pile Bombardment on Uncured Elastomers, *J. Appl. Phys., 19*(5): 427 (May 1948).
46. Deeley, C. W., Woodward, A. E., and Sauer, J. A., Effect of Irradiation on Dynamic Mechanical Properties of 6-6 Nylon, *J. Appl. Phys., 28*(10): 1124 (October 1957).
47. Deeley, C. W., Sauer, J. A., and Woodward, A. E., Dynamic Mechanical Behavior of Irradiated Polyethylene, *J. Appl. Phys., 29*(10): 1415 (October 1958).
48. Deeley, C. W., Kline, D. W., Sauer, J. A., and Woodward, A. E., Effect of Pile Irradiation on the Dynamic Mechanical Properties of Polyethylene, *J. Polymer Sci., 28*(116): 109 (February 1958).
49. Dole, M., Williams, T. F., and Arvia, A. J., The Radiation Chemistry of a Typical Macromolecule, Polyethylene, *Proceedings of the Second International Conference on the Peaceful Uses of Atomic Energy, Geneva, 1958,* Vol. 29, p. 171, United Nations, New York, 1959.
50. Dole, M., Milner, D. C., and Williams, T. F., Irradiation of Polyethylene. Part II: Kinetics of Unsaturation Effects, *J. Am. Chem. Soc., 80*(7): 1580 (April 1958).
51. Dole, M., Milner, D. C., and Williams, T. F., Cyclization in Gamma Ray Irradiated High Density Polyethylene, *J. Am. Chem. Soc., 79*(17): 4809 (September 1957).
52. Dole, M., Keeling, C. D., and Rose, D. G., The Pile Irradiation of Polyethylene, *J. Am. Chem. Soc., 76*(17): 4304 (September 1954) and Dole, M., and Keeling, C. D., Long-Range Migration of Chemical Activity in the Solid State, *J. Am. Chem. Soc. 75*(23): 6082 (December 1953).
53. Doremus, R. H., Roberts, B. W., and Turnbull, D., *Growth and Perfection of Crystals,* John Wiley & Sons, Inc., New York, 1958.
54. Edelmann, K., The Absolute, Entirely Viscometric Determination of the Molecular Weight of High Polymers, *Rubber Chem. and Technol., 30*(2): 470 (April–June 1957).
55. Eirich, F. R., *Rheology Theory and Application,* Academic Press, Inc., New York, 1958.
56. Epstein, L. M., Electron Crosslinking of Polyethylenes of Two Different Densities, *J. Polymer Sci., 26*(114): 299 (December 1957).
57. Feng, P. Y., and Kennedy, J. W., Electrical and Chemical Effects of β-Radiation in Polystyrene, *J. Am. Chem. Soc., 77*(4): 847 (February 1955).
58. Flory, P. J., *Principles of Polymer Chemistry,* Cornell University Press, Ithaca, New York, 1953.
59. Flory, P. J., Network Structures and the Elastic Properties of Vulcanized Rubber, *Chem. Rev., 35*(1): 51 (February 1944).
60. Fowler, J. F., X-ray Induced Conductivity in Insulating Materials, *Proc. Roy. Soc. (London), A236*(1207): 464 (September 1956).
61. Frith, E. M., and Tuckett, R. F., *Linear Polymers,* Longmans, Green & Co., Inc., New York, 1951.
62. Fromandi, G., The Effect of Silent Electric Discharge on Rubber and Decalin, *Kolloidchem. Beih., 27:* 189 (1928).
63. Fuschillo, N., and Sauer, J. A., Nuclear Magnetic Resonance, Radiation Damage, and Rigidity in Branched Polyethylene as a Function of Temperature, *J. Appl. Phys., 28*(10): 1073 (October 1957).
64. Fuschillo, N., Rhian, E., and Sauer, J. A., Nuclear Magnetic Resonance and Crystallinity in Polyethylene, *J. Polymer Sci., 25*(110): 381 (August 1957).

65. Gilkey, H. J., Murphy, G., and Bergman, E. O., *Materials Testing*, McGraw-Hill Book Company, Inc., New York, 1941.
66. Glasstone, S., Laidler, K. J., and Eyring, H., *The Theory of Rate Processes*, McGraw-Hill Book Company, Inc., New York, 1941.
67. James, H. M., and Guth, E., Theory of the Elastic Properties of Rubber, *J. Chem. Phys.*, *11*(10): 455 (October 1943) and An Experimental Varification of the Network Theory of Rubber Elasticity, *J. Polymer Sci.*, *24*(107): 479 (May 1957).
68. Kinney, G. F., *Engineering Properties and Applications of Plastics*, John Wiley & Sons, Inc., New York, 1957.
69. Kuhn, W., Uber die Gestalt fadenförmiger Molekule in Löesengen, *Kolloid-Z.*, *68*(1): 2 (July 1934).
70. Lawton, E. J., Balwit, J. S., and Powell, R. S., Effect of Physical State During the Electron Irradiation of Hydrocarbon Polymers. Part I: The Influence of Physical State on Reactions Occurring in Polyethylene During and Following the Irradiation, *J. Polymer Sci.*, *32*(125): 257 (November 1958).
71. Lawton, E. J., Powell, R. S., and Balwit, J. S., Effect of Physical State During the Electron Irradiation of Hydrocarbon Polymers. Part II: Additional Experiments and Discussion Pertaining to Trapped Radicals in Hydrocarbon Polymers, *J. Polymer Sci.*, *32*(125): 277 (November 1958).
72. Lawton, E. J., Bueche, A. M., and Balwit, J. S., Irradiation of Polymers by High Energy Electrons, *Nature*, *172*(4367): 76 (July 1953).
73. Lawton, E. J., Zemany, P. D., and Balwit, J. S., *J. Am. Chem. Soc.*, *76*(13): 3437 (July 1954).
74. Little, K., Irradiation of Linear High Polymers, *Nature*, *170*(4338): 1075 (December 1952).
75. Little, K., Some Effects of Irradiation on Nylon and Polyethylene Terephthalate, *Nature*, *173*(4406): 680 (April 1954).
76. Manion, J. P., and Burton, M., Radiolysis of Hydrocarbon Mixtures, *J. Phys. Chem.*, *56*(5): 560 (May 1952).
77. Mayburg, S., and Lawrence, W. L., The Conductivity Change in Polyethylene During Irradiation, *J. Appl. Phys.*, *23*(9): 1006 (September 1952).
78. Mark, H., and Tobolsky, A. V., *Physical Chemistry of High Polymeric Systems*, 2nd ed., p. 150, Interscience Publishers, Inc., New York, 1950.
79. Miller, A. A., Lawton, E. J., and Balwit, J. S., Effect of Chemical Structure of Vinyl Polymers on Crosslinking and Degradation by Ionizing Radiation, *J. Polymer Sci.*, *14*(77): 503 (November 1954).
80. Majury, T. G., and Pinner, S. H., The Irradiation of Polycaprolactam with γ-Rays and Electrons, *J. Appl. Chem. London*, *8* (Part 3): 168 (March 1958).
81. *Modern Plastics*, *36*(1A), Encyclopedia Issue (September 1958).
82. Newton, E. B., assigned to the B. F. Goodrich Company, *Vulcanizing Rubber*, U. S. Patent 1,906,402, May 1933.
83. Pearson, R. W., The Effect of Gamma-Irradiation Upon Poly(ethylene Oxides), *First UNESCO Conference on Radioisotopes in Scientific Research*, Paris, 1957, Vol. 1, p. 151, Pergamon Press, Inc., 1958.
84. Pigg, J. C., Bopp, C. D., Sisman, O., and Robinson, C. C., The Effect of Reactor Irradiation on Electrical Insulation, *Trans. Am. Inst. Elec. Engrs., Part I*, *74*(1): 717 (1955).
85. Ryan, J. W., Effect of Gamma Radiation on Certain Rubbers and Plastics, *Nucleonics*, *11*(8): 13 (August 1953).
86. Saito, Osamu, On the Effect of High Energy Radiation to Polymers, *J. Phys. Soc. Japan*, *13*: 1465 (1958).

87. Sears, W. C., and Parkinson, W. W., Post-Irradiation Oxidation in Rubber and Plastics, *J. Polymer Sci.,* 21(98): 325 (August 1956).

88. Sears, W. C., Oak Ridge National Laboratory, unpublished data, 1960.

89. Shultz, A. R., and Bovey, F. A., Electron Irradiation of Polyacrylates, *J. Poly. Sci.,* 22(102): 485 (December 1956).

90. Shultz, A. R., High-Energy Radiation Effects on Polyacrylates and Polymethacrylates, *J. Polymer Sci.,* 35(129): 369 (March 1959).

91. Shultz, A. R., Roth, P. I., and Rathmann, G. B., Light Scattering and Viscosity Study of Electron-Irradiated Polystyrene and Polymethacrylates, *J. Polymer Sci.,* 22(102): 495 (December 1956).

92. Sisman, O., and Bopp, C. D., *Physical Properties of Irradiated Plastics,* USAEC Report ORNL-928, Oak Ridge National Laboratory, June 1951.

93. Sisman, O., and Wilson, J. C., Engineering Use of Damage Data, *Nucleonics,* 14(9): 58 (September 1956).

94. Kang, Y. S., Pravednikov, A. N., and Medvedev, S. S., Mekanism zaschitnogo deistvida benzol'nik kolets pri radiolise polistirola, *Doklady Akad. Nauk S.S.S.R.,* 127(3): 595 (July 1959).

95. Tsvetkov, U. D., Issledovanie spektrov E.P.R. nekotorik polimerov, obluchennik pri 77°K, *Doklady Akad. Nauk S.S.S.R.,* 122(6): 1053 (October 1958).

96. St. Pierre, L. E., Dewhurst, H. A., and Bueche, A. M., Swelling and Elasticity of Irradiated Polydimethylsiloxanes, *J. Polymer Sci.,* 36(130): 105 (April 1959).

97. St. Pierre, L. E., and Dewhurst, H. A., Oxygen Effects in the Radiation Chemistry of Polyethylene, *J. Chem. Phys.,* 29(1): 241 (July 1958).

98. Wall, F. T., Statistical Thermodynamics of Rubber, *J. Chem. Phys.,* 10(2): 132 (February 1942).

99. Wall, F. T., Statistical Thermodynamics of Rubber, III, *J. Chem. Phys.,* 11(11): 527 (November 1943).

100. Wall, L. A., and Brown, D. W., Chemical Activity of Gamma-Irradiated Polymethyl Methacrylate, *J. Research Nat. Bur. Standards,* 57(3): 131 (September 1956).

101. Wall, L. A., and Brown, D. W., γ-Irradiation of Polymethyl Methacrylate and Polystyrene, *J. Phys. Chem.,* 61(2): 129 (February 1957).

102. Williams, T. F., and Dole, M., Irradiation of Polyethylene. Part III: Influence of Temperature and Phase, *J. Am. Chem. Soc.,* 81(12): 2919 (June 1959).

103. Williams, T. F., and Dole, M., Inhibition of Crystallization in Polyethylene Subsequent to Gamma Irradiation, *J. Am. Chem. Soc.,* 80(11): 2595 (June 1958).

104. Wilson, C. W., III, and Pake, G. E., Nuclear Magnetic Relaxation in Polytetrafluorethylene and Polyethylene, *J. Chem. Phys.,* 27(1): 115 (July 1957).

CHAPTER 6

Plastics

BY C. DANIEL BOPP, WILLIAM W. PARKINSON, AND OSCAR SISMAN

6-1 Introduction

The changes that occur in commercial plastics as a result of exposure to high-energy radiation are discussed in this chapter. Quantitative values are given insofar as possible for changes in properties useful in engineering design. A large amount of literature was studied in an effort to correlate the available data and arrive at the best numbers. Many conflicting and often confusing data were encountered. The rule was to make a choice in all cases and not to present conflicting values. The choice was sometimes easy (one experiment may have been performed before the importance of oxygen or temperature was recognized, or one set of data may have been different from two or three others that checked each other); but often it was quite difficult and was based on the authors' best judgment of what they thought to be the best experiment. On the other hand, often only one set of data existed; and it was used unless some flaw was recognized in the experiment.

The largest uncertainty in most experiments is in the measurement of radiation dose. This, coupled with uncertainties in environmental conditions, prompted the use of the "degree of change" when the materials were rated. Absolute values have been reserved for the text where the reader finds them more closely associated with pertinent experimental conditions. Only a few critical mechanical properties are listed in the tables of data; other properties, where known, are presented in the text.

The materials are grouped according to similarities of chemical composition or molecular structure rather than according to the dominance of cross linking or scission. Polyethylene is discussed thoroughly as an example of a material that cross links; poly(methyl methacrylate) is discussed as representative of materials that undergo scission. Much is known about these two plastics, and it is felt that much can be inferred by analogy for other materials where data are lacking.

6-2 Effects of Radiation on Mechanical Properties

It was pointed out in the preceding chapter that the mechanical properties of polymers depend on the forces between atoms of neighboring molecules and on the mobility of segments of molecules. The intermolecular forces are largely determined by the nature of the atoms and are only slightly changed by the cross linking and scission induced by radiation. The mobility of molecular segments, however is certainly reduced by cross linking. This reduction decreases the viscoelastic response in tensile tests (see Ch. 5, Sect. 5-4.1). The resulting reduction in creep or elongation is accompanied by an increase in ultimate tensile strength if the polymer initially is of such molecular weight that tensile breaking occurs through slippage of molecules by each other rather than through rupture of main polymer chains. Commercial, hard, glassy plastics have molecular weights in the range where normal breaking is primarily by chain rupture.

The relation between mobility and retardation time and the time scale of testing was explained in Ch. 5, Sect. 5-4.1. Cross linking increases retardation time as well as hardness and elastic modulus. Impact tests have a time scale that is comparable to the retardation times in soft, rubberlike plastics, but short compared to hard, glossy plastics. Impact strength is likely to be changed by cross linking only in the former class of polymers. On the other hand, impact strength may be affected by low-molecular-weight decomposition products that have a plasticizing action.

Scission increases molecular mobility and affects mechanical properties under certain conditions, e.g., under test times long enough to allow molecular motion to be a controlling factor. In general, the tensile strength and elongation are reduced by scission to a greater degree than the elastic modulus and hardness. It appears that the large increase in the impact strength of Teflon at low radiation dose is caused by an increase in crystallinity as a result of scission.[14] Cross linking destroys crystallinity very effectively.

The mobility of molecular segments also influences the rates of radiation processes. The only available data relating mobility and radiation-induced processes are measurements of mechanical properties of polyethylene at various temperatures (Ch. 5, Fig. 5.14). These may be coupled with the influence of temperature on cross-linking rates (Fig. 6.1). The cross linking yield shows[44] rate changes at the temperatures of two of the three changes of slope in the mechanical properties of Fig. 5.14.

Plasticizer and filler contents of commercial plastics influence the rates of cross linking and scission. Plasticizers are commonly low-molecular-weight compounds, and they may be much more susceptible to radiation decomposition than the base polymer, particularly if they are heavily halogenated. Not only does such depletion of the plasticizer alter the mechanical properties of the plastic, but halogen or hydroxy radicals, where these may be radiolysis products from the plasticizer, accelerate decomposition of the base polymer. The influence of plasticizers was discussed more thoroughly in Ch. 5, Sect. 5-4.7. The part played by fillers,

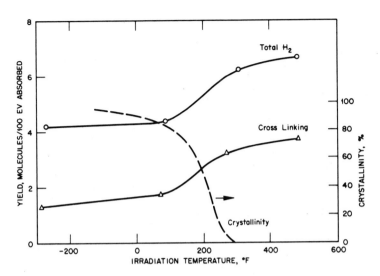

Fig. 6.1 Radiation processes in polyethylene (Marlex-50). Electron dose, 6.7 megarads. (From E. J. Lawton, *Journal of Polymer Science,* Ref. 44.)

both inert and active, in the radiation-induced changes in plastics was also explained (see Sect. 5-8.3). It was pointed out that inorganic or mineral fillers serve largely as energy absorbers and as supporting or reinforcing structures. The energy absorption retards the radiation effects, and the reinforcement is most influential in reducing the softening of plastics in which the polymer undergoes scission.

6-3 Radiation Effects on Electrical and Optical Properties

Permanent changes in the electrical resistance of plastics can be produced by the cracks, bubbles, and similar flaws that result from radiation damage. In addition, the irradiation of halogenated polymers in moist air appears to give rise to ionic products which reduce the electrical resistance many orders of magnitude. During irradiation, electrons are excited to an essentially free state (the conduction band) to produce photoconduction. These electrons may become loosely bound at trapping sites within the plastic. Whether they are trapped or free, their effect on the resistivity at room temperature is limited to periods of a day or two after irradiation.[34]

These loosely bound trapped electrons would be expected to produce optical coloration much like the color centers in ionic crystals. The free radicals resulting from radiation-induced rupture of polymer molecules have electrons with unpaired spins. Such species may also give optical coloration. In addition, the unsaturation produced by evolution of hydrogen or by other decomposition will eventually yield conjugated groups. Such groups have electron excitation levels in the visible spectral range and will also produce discoloration and reduction in light transmission. On the other hand, the microcrystals of crystalline materials scatter light and reduce transparency. Since cross linking reduces crystallinity, this radiation-induced process increases light transmission.[14]

6-4 Use of Plastics in Radiation Fields

Mild radiation doses may enhance certain properties in some plastics. Large doses of radiation will invariably be deleterious. Whether the radiation effect is considered damaging or not depends on the use to which the material is being put, as well as on the radiation dose. In essence, an evaluation must be made for each application as it arises since very few generalizations can be made at this time. From the standpoint of use in a radiation field, it is preferable that the properties of the material not change with time. This is not always possible, even in the absence of radiation. It can be considered that the radiation simply shortens the use time; i.e., it has an accelerated aging effect.

High radiation intensities are encountered in nuclear reactors, particle accelerators, and radioactive-material handling facilities. Plastics are used here in exactly the same ways that they are used away from radiation: containers, hoses, gaskets, electrical and thermal insulation, etc. In reactor applications plastics have an additional use as moderator and neutron-shield materials. The reaction that slows down neutrons, however, yields energetic charged particles that react to damage polymers. Thus these applications are limited to radiation fields of moderate intensity.

Before the problem of evaluating the desirability of using a plastic for a specific application is considered, the radiation dose that the material will receive must first be determined. Once the dose is known, the change in the property or properties most sensitive in the specific use can be estimated if this estimation always takes into account the particular conditions of temperature, pressure, atmosphere, and dose rate. An example will serve to illustrate these points: it is assumed that polyethylene will be used for a diaphragm in a pressure-sensing device that will receive a radiation dose of 10^7 rads in an inert atmosphere. Under these conditions the mechanical properties of the polyethylene will not change enough to preclude its use, but enough gas will evolve to interfere with the pressure-sensing function.

If radiation damage is excessive for a given material, ways of reducing the radiation effect may be sought or the equipment may be redesigned to use another material. The radiation effect may sometimes be reduced by excluding oxygen or by changing the temperature or stress, but usually it is necessary to reduce the intensity of the radiation field either by moving the equipment or shielding it.

Normally, plastics are not used inside reactors. The radiation intensity is usually much too high, and the temperature is usually also too high for these materials. Applications of interest then are near the reactor core but not in it. Problems with plastics are most acute for mobile reactors where space requirements are critical and shielding is kept to a minimum. To avoid the use of plastics in such instances complicates design problems; and, therefore, it is important to know when they can be used and when their use must be avoided.

6-5 Improvement of Properties by Irradiation

If the result of the radiation-induced reaction is scission, the changes in the properties of the material exposed are generally not desirable ones. The strength is decreased because of the shortening of the molecular chains. It was observed that for a specific radiation dose in air polytetrafluoroethylene (Teflon) was increased in impact strength (probably owing to an increase in crystallinity[52]). This improvement, however, is the exception rather than the rule.

Cross linking causes desirable changes in many materials if they are irradiated to the proper degree. The Young's modulus and the tensile strength are increased. The yield strength usually is increased also. Cross linking causes an improvement in the resistance to heat distortion[43] and increased resistance to solvent action. Associated with these improvements in properties may be some undesirable effects. The hardness is increased by cross linking, and the impact strength is decreased. Elongation before break may be drastically reduced, even to the extent that the material will have no yield point.

There is the possibility of using nonpenetrating radiation to change the surface of a material for the better. The surface of one polymer can be hardened or toughened while the base material is left soft and pliable. Another polymer can be grafted to the surface of the original by irradiation; or a polymer can be used to hold together a bulk filler, such as wood pulp, by polymerizing with penetrating radiation. Surface treatment with radiation may also make a material more capable of holding a dye.

In spite of the fact that some deleterious effects may be associated with any improvements that result from irradiating plastics, there is a distinct possibility of developing improved properties by irradiation. When a new material is produced by radiation, it must be compared with similar products made by more conventional means. If the irradiated material cannot be produced more cheaply or if it does not have unique properties, it will not compete successfully in the commercial market.

6-6 Radiation Protection

Selected additives to base polymers can minimize radiation damage to finished plastics, as discussed in Ch. 5, Sect. 5-8.3. Thus mineral fillers, which are frequently mixed with the base polymer in the finished product, can give radiation protection to the polymer through dilution. Also, stabilization can be built into the base polymer by copolymerizing an aromatic monomer with the major aliphatic monomeric constituent. Thus, the ability of the aromatics to dissipate energy without decomposition is combined with desirable physical properties of the aliphatic polymers. It is also feasible to copolymerize monomers that undergo cross linking with those that undergo scission so that the net result of the competing processes is a minimum change in gross physical properties.

The most thoroughly studied method of radiation protection is the addition of chemical reagents to polymers (see Ch. 7, Sect. 7-3.2.3). From the results with poly(methyl methacrylate), rates of scission may be reduced by one-half or more by certain protective additives.[6] Estimates of the effect on mechanical properties cannot be made precisely since these are not a linear function of molecular weight. A difficulty with protectors is that they become depleted after extended exposure to radiation. The best procedure in fabricating radiation-resistant articles is to utilize a resistant base polymer, if this is possible.

Another factor that influences radiation-induced changes is the atmosphere during irradiation. The thickness of the specimen determines to a large extent the importance of atmosphere. Scission is the dominant process when thin films of some materials are irradiated in air, even though thick specimens of the same materials show cross linking under these conditions.

6-7 Hydrocarbon Polymers

6-7.1 POLYETHYLENE

6-7.1.1 *General*

The crystallinity of polyethylene is inversely related to the degree of chain branching.[2] Conventional low-density polyethylene prepared by the older high-pressure process has two types of branching: long branches of average size comparable with the main chain, about one per molecule, and short branches only a few carbon atoms in length, of which there may be as many as 30 for every 1000 chain atoms. The newer low-pressure polymerization process yields an unbranched polyethylene of high crystallinity and density. In this type product, the number of terminal groups per molecule ranges from 2.0 (the theoretical number for polymethylene) to 2.5. The crystallinity and low-temperature embrittlement of high-density (linear) polyethylene decrease somewhat at very high molecular weight, but the crystallinity of low-density (branched) polyethylene is less sensitive to molecular weight. Linear polyethylene softens at about 265°F; branched polyethylene, at about 230°F. The crystallinity of branched polyethylene decreases gradually with increasing temperature, but a large

degree of crystallinity is retained by linear polyethylene to near the softening point. Both types are insoluble at room temperature but become soluble
in hydrocarbon solvents above 120°F. Solubility increases with temperature
and with the degree of branching.

In branched polyethylene, a small vinylene (in-chain, —CH_2CH_2CH=
$CHCH_2CH_2$—) concentration and a smaller vinylidene (side chain,

$$—CH_2CH_2\overset{\overset{\textstyle CH_2}{\textstyle \|}}{C}CH_2CH_2—)$$

concentration are present. The unsaturation in
linear polyethylene is sensitive to the process of manufacture. For Marlex-
50, which has been the subject of extensive radiation studies, the unsaturation is largely vinyl (chain end, —CH_2CH_2CH=CH_2—) with a much
smaller concentration of vinylene. The oxidative degradation of both linear
and branched polyethylenes is severe after several days' exposure at 300°F.

Compared to other plastics, polyethylene is soft, flexible, and tough.
The linear material is much harder and more rigid than the branched
polymer, however, and still retains the high impact strength characteristic
of the branched product. Polyethylene has very good molding characteristics, but its low softening point limits its usefulness to temperatures below
212°F. The chemical inertness of polyethylene has already been mentioned; but, in outdoor applications, antioxidants, ultraviolet stabilizers,
and opaque fillers, such as carbon black, are required. The chemical structure confers very desirable properties as an electrical insulator.

The properties of polyethylene and its moderate price make it suitable
for a broad range of commercial applications. It is used in an immense
variety of small molded items where rigidity is of secondary importance.
Large quantities go into insulation for electrical wire. Packaging applications also consume large amounts of sheeting and molded items.

6-7.1.2 Radiation Chemistry

Hydrogen is the principal gas evolved in the radiolysis of polyethylene.
Hydrocarbons account for a larger fraction of the gas evolved from
branched (5 to 15%) than from linear polyethylene (0.5 to 1%).[50,65] The
temperature dependence of yield[87] is an important consideration when gas
evolution is used as a monitor of radiation exposure. Other factors also
effect the gaseous hydrocarbon yield, e.g., the solubility of the gases and
their rate of diffusion out of the specimen. In thin specimens the apparent
yield increases with dose,[65] apparently from the effect of solubility. The
rate of diffusion decreases as cross linking progresses. Therefore the measured gas yield decreases with increasing dose for thicker specimens.[74]

Vinylene unsaturation is the only type of unsaturation that is produced
in polyethylene by high-energy radiation (though both vinylene and vinyl
are produced with ultraviolet radiation).[10] Other types of unsaturation,

which may be present initially, decay. The vinylene concentration builds up to a limiting value at moderate exposure, as shown in Fig. 6.2. It has been postulated that a steady-state concentration results when the rates of formation (zero order) and decay (first order) are equal. The steady-state vinylene concentration has inverse temperature dependence since the temperature dependence is greater for its decay than for its formation.[28]

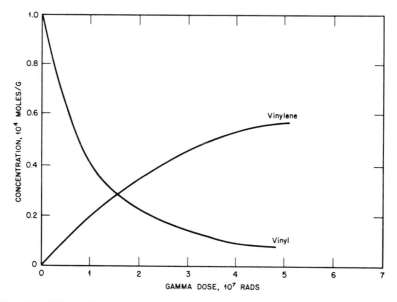

FIG. 6.2   Effects of dose on unsaturation in linear polyethylene (Marlex-50). (From M. Dole, *Journal of the American Chemical Society*, Ref. 28.)

The decay rates of vinyl (chain end) and vinylidene (side chain) unsaturation are about equal and are three times the decay rate of vinylene (in-chain) unsaturation. The higher decay rate for vinyl and vinylidene probably results from the higher mobility or accessibility of these groups. The yield for vinyl decay is too high for an ionization mechanism unless a chain reaction is postulated.[28] Evidence of the presence of charge and energy carriers that might participate in a chain reaction is given by the radiation-induced increase in conductivity (Ch. 5, Sect. 5-5). The conductivity decays after removal of the vinyl from the radiation field.[34]

   1. *Cross Linking.* Possible mechanisms of the cross-linking process were discussed in Ch. 3, where both ion–molecule and free-radical mechanisms were outlined. Experimentally, there is evidence for two concurrent mechanisms. The first is a strongly temperature-dependent excitation or ionization mode (U) in which unsaturation is destroyed as follows:†

_____

† Wavy arrow denotes ionizing radiation.

$$— CH_2CH_2CH_2CH_2— \qquad — CH_2CH=CHCH_2— \qquad — CH_2CH_2CHCH_2—$$

$$\text{—} \wedge\wedge\wedge \blacktriangleright \qquad + H_2 \text{—} \wedge\wedge \blacktriangleright \qquad \Big| \qquad + H_2$$

$$— CH_2CH_2CH_2CH_2— \qquad — CH_2CH_2CH_2CH_2— \qquad — CH_2CH_2CHCH_2—$$

The vinylene production reaction is included in the scheme because of its usefulness in the material balance to be discussed. There are many possible intermediate processes by which the reactions may take place; thus the steps presented should not be viewed rigidly. The second mechanism is a free-radical process (R) in which unsaturation is not involved:

$$— CH_2CH_2CH_2CH_2— \qquad — CH_2CH_2CHCH_2— \qquad —CH_2CH_2CHCH_2—$$

$$\text{—} \wedge\wedge\wedge \blacktriangleright \qquad \binom{H}{H} \qquad \longrightarrow \qquad \Big| \qquad + H_2$$

$$— CH_2CH_2CH_2CH_2— \qquad — CH_2CH_2CHCH_2— \qquad —CH_2CH_2CHCH_2—$$

Destruction of unsaturation does not involve decay of radicals. This is shown by a lack of change in vinylene concentration when radicals trapped by low-temperature irradiation decay on warming.[28] Furthermore, unsaturation is not destroyed ordinarily by the addition of molecular hydrogen to double bonds since there is no increase in the hydrogen yield corresponding to the disappearance of the initial unsaturation. Therefore the decay of unsaturation appears to be principally by the intermolecular (cross linking) reaction (XL) or intramolecular (ring linking) reaction (U). A material balance, then, between vinylene decay and hydrogen evolution permits a comparison of linking by (U) to that by the radical reaction (R).

A material balance is reached as follows: a molecule of hydrogen is assumed to evolve for each linking reaction when the steady-state concentration of unsaturation is reached. (The hydrogen yield reaches a constant value at very low doses.[27]) Under these conditions the hydrogen yield, G_{H_2}, can be taken as the total linking yield. At the steady-state condition of unsaturation, the vinylene decay is equal to the rate of formation, G_V. This latter rate can be taken from the measurements of Dole and coworkers[28] (Fig. 6.2) during the initial stages of irradiation of a linear polyethylene (Marlex-50). (It is assumed, as mentioned above, that the rate of vinylidene formation is independent of dose.) If this value is substituted along with the hydrogen yield in the equation

$$\frac{G_{XL_R}}{G_{XL}} = \frac{G_{H_2} - G_V}{G_{H_2}}$$

a value of 0.42 is obtained for

$$\frac{G_{XL_R}}{G_{XL}}$$

the fraction of total linking by mechanism (R). This method takes into account intramolecular linking (ring linking) in addition to cross linking, but it neglects any linking by the decay of the initial vinyl and vinylidene unsaturation. The neglect of the decay of the initial unsaturation is valid only for long exposures.

The same quantity, (G_{XL_R}/G_{XL}), can be estimated by a second method, which is based on the apparent temperature dependence of the cross-linking yield. The ionized or excited states involved in mechanism (U) are assumed to have such short lifetimes that cross linking by this mechanism does not occur at very low temperature. However, the radicals involved in mechanism (R) are trapped during irradiation at low temperature and react upon subsequent warming (a necessary reaction for the measurement of the cross-linking yield). For these reasons irradiation at liquid-nitrogen temperature will give cross linking only by mechanism (R) allowing the determination of G_{XL_R}. From the data of Lawton and coworkers,[44] G_{XL_R}/G_{XL} is 0.41, in agreement with the value from the method cited previously.

For branched polyethylene the ratio of cross-linking yield at low temperature to that at room temperature was 0.32 in the exposure range of 25 to 40 megarads.[19] This lower fraction for the radical mechanism may result from the contribution to cross linking by the decay of the vinylidene unsaturation, which is present in considerably larger concentration in the branched polymer. In support of this a decrease in the growth of the elastic modulus has been observed corresponding to the decrease in the initial vinylidene concentration.[24]

There is evidence for the participation of the allylic free radical in the cross-linking process from the amount of unsaturation in the gel fraction of solid paraffins.[72] Additional evidence comes from an electron-spin resonance study of the radical trapped in the low-temperature irradiation of polyethylene.[78] This radical was tentatively identified as $-CH_2\dot{C}HCH_2-CH_2-$. Its transformation to an allylic radical, $-CH_2\dot{C}HCH=CH-$, offers a plausible explanation of the change in fine structure which occurs when the polyethylene is warmed to room temperature.

In this discussion the ratios of cross-linking yields at different temperatures rather than absolute yields have been presented. The accuracy of the absolute cross-link yields is limited by the accuracy of the mean molecular weights. The sol-fraction method of estimating the cross-linking yield, which involves the number-average molecular weight, gives a lower result than the gel-point method (see Ch. 5, Sects. 5-2.4 and 5-6.1.1) which involves the weight average.[20] At least part of this discrepancy results from the difference in radiation doses involved in the two methods. The decay of the initial vinylidene unsaturation contributes significantly to cross linking only at the lower doses employed in the gel-point method. It is significant that the two methods are in best agreement for linear polyethylene in which the initial vinylidene concentration is small.

Almost equal cross-linking yields for linear and branched polyethylene,

$G_{XL} = 1.6$, were obtained by a determination based on the growth in the modulus of rubberlike elasticity in the exposure range from 20 to 100 megarads.[33] A sol-fraction determination[20] gave $G_{XL} = 1.6$ for branched and $G_{XL} = 2.1$ for linear material. This similarity for the two types of polyethylene indicates that the high crystallinity of the linear material does not retard cross linking.

The hydrogen yield for polyethylene is about 1.5 to 2.0 times the cross-linking yield at room temperature $(G_{H_2} = 3.1)$.[27] This suggests that the yields of ring links and cross links are of the same order, since hydrogen production was equated to the sum of cross linking and ring linking.

An explanation of the broad range of cross-linking yields reported by various authors $(G_{XL} = 0.5$ to $4.0)$ lies in the difference in the measuring techniques employed. Where the gel–sol ratio is used as an index of cross linking, degradation during the extraction procedure sometimes affects the apparent cross-linking yield. In one extraction method a higher gel yield was obtained for linear polyethylene when the extraction was performed immediately after irradiation than when the sample was exposed to air for a week before extraction.[44] Apparently the yield was affected by oxidative degradation that occurred during the extraction procedure. The method of Charlesby and Pinner[20] gave the same yields with and without a 30-day exposure of the irradiated samples to air. This second method, a bottle extraction, featured a short preheat of specimens to destroy peroxide links and then an extraction in the dark with xylene containing di-β-naphthyl-phenylenediamine as an antioxidant.

The study of cross linking in polymers by means of nuclear-spin resonance was introduced in Ch. 5, Sect. 5-6.1.1. Cross linking alters the thermal motion of atoms; this affects the interaction of a proton with its neighbors. In amorphous polyethylene the motion is liquidlike. This reduces interaction between atoms and yields a narrow spin resonance line shape. In crystalline polyethylene atomic motion is more restricted and interaction broadens the line shape considerably (see Fig. 6.3).[36] At low doses the only effect appears to be an increase in motion in the crystalline regions owing to the introduction of defects. This change is seen as a further sharpening of the narrow line. At higher doses the restriction of motion by cross linking dominates, and the narrow line disappears. The latter effect can be correlated with changes in the mechanical properties, specifically with the internal friction peaks of the vibrational measurements (Ch. 5, Fig. 5.14). As the dose increases, there is a reduction in the internal-friction peaks at the higher temperatures in the low density (branched) polyethylene. These peaks correspond to the motion of branch points in the amorphous regions (Ch. 5, Sect. 5-6.1.3).

2. *Oxidation.* The irradiation of polyethylene films at temperatures well below the softening point produces trapped radicals that initiate

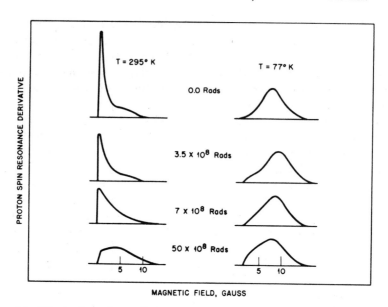

FIG. 6.3 Effect of reactor radiation on resonance of branched polyethylene (only positive half of line shape shown). (From J. A. Sauer, *Journal of Applied Physics,* Ref. 36.)

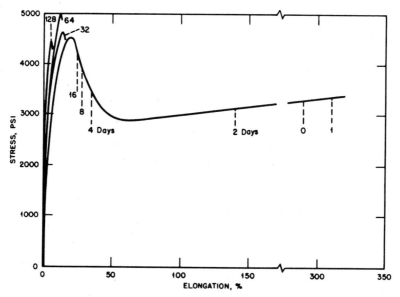

FIG. 6.4 Aging of irradiated polyethylene (Marlex-50) in air. Irradiated and tested at 77°F; cross head, 0.5 in./min. (From E. J. Lawton, *Journal of Polymer Science,* Ref. 44.)

oxidative degradation upon exposure to air. Deterioration of the mechanical (see Fig. 6.4) and electrical properties[63] continues for several months. Postirradiative degradation can be avoided by irradiation in a vacuum or in an inert atmosphere and by annealing before exposure to air (an annealing temperature of about 285°F is employed for linear polyethylene).[44]

The rate of oxidative scission in thin films of polyethylene irradiated in air (Ch. 5, Sect. 5-8.2) is dependent on film thickness,[6] dose rate, and oxygen pressure.[62] The low rate of diffusion of oxygen into the polymer results in the near absence of an oxygen effect for thick sheets irradiated in air at high dose rates.[20,28] The ratio of vinylene to carbonyl formation is severalfold more for deuteron than for gamma radiation. This probably results from a lower carbonyl yield in the dense deuteron track since the vinylene yield is nearly independent of track density.[26] An analogous effect occurs in the radiation oxidation of ferrous sulfate solutions.[16] For the processes of hydrogen evolution, vinyl-group decay, and vinylene growth, there is not much difference between irradiation under a small pressure of oxygen and irradiation in a vacuum.[47]

6-7.2 POLYPROPYLENE

This polymer may be regarded as being derived from polyethylene by the substitution of methyl groups on alternate carbon atoms:

$$\begin{array}{cc} CH_3 & CH_3 \\ | & | \\ \end{array}$$
$$-CH_2CHCH_2CH-$$

The material is termed "isotactic" if the methyl groups are on the same side of the chain and "atactic" if the arrangement is random. Isotactic polypropylene has higher crystallinity, a higher melting point, and a higher glass transition temperature. The isotactic polymer is the only type that has appeared on the commercial market. Its properties closely resemble those of linear polyethylene. It can be expected to have similar uses once these have had an opportunity to develop. The tensile strength and rigidity of oriented polypropylene fibers and films seem likely to open up textile and packaging applications not favorable for polyethylene.

For isotactic polypropylene the initial apparent scission yield ($G = 4.95$) is nearly the same as for polyisobutylene. It decreases with increasing dose. The cross-linking yield was estimated to be $G = 0.9$ to 1.3 after a dose of 10^8 rads.[79]

The apparent scission yield of isotactic polypropylene is equal to the vinylidene yield. This observation has been explained on the basis of the following:

$$-CH_2CHCH_2CH-$$

If cross linking is solely by vinylidene decay, a steady-state vinylidene concentration would be reached when the rate of cross linking (involving vinylidene destruction) equals the rate of scission (involving vinylidene

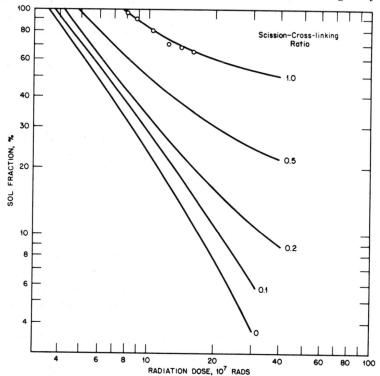

Fig. 6.5 Solubility of irradiated polypropylene compared with theoretical curves for various ratios of chain fracture to cross linking. [From R. M. Black and B. J. Lyons, *Proceedings of the Royal Society (London)*, Ref. 13.]

production). Gel-fraction measurements indicate[13] that the rate of cross linking approaches the rate of scission, as shown in Fig. 6.5.

6-7.3 POLYSTYRENE

This polymer can be regarded as a substituted polyethylene with phenyl groups on alternate carbon atoms:

$$
\begin{array}{cc}
CH_3 & CH_3 \\
| & | \\
-CHCH_2CHCH_2-
\end{array}
\xrightarrow{\hspace{1cm}}
\left(
\begin{array}{cc}
CH_3 & \overset{*}{}CH_3 \\
| & | \\
-CHCH_2- & CHCH_2-
\end{array}
\right.
$$

$$
\begin{array}{cc}
CH_3 & CH_3 \\
| & | \\
-C=CH_2 + & CH_2CH_2-
\end{array}
$$

Polystyrene is highly rigid at room temperature, but the rigidity may be decreased and the elongation and impact strength increased by plasticizers. Since no radiation-effects work has been reported for isotactic polystyrene, this discussion is confined to the atactic material.

The rigidity, moldability, transparency, and low cost of polystyrene make it one of the most abundantly used of all thermoplastic resins, although its low softening temperature limits its uses as in the case of polyethylene and poly(methyl methacrylate). Its low impact strength can be improved significantly by incorporating plasticizers or by copolymerizing with olefin monomers. It can be used in moldings for radios, clocks, and a wide variety of other household and industrial items. Stabilizers are required to improve the weathering characteristics of formulations for panels and other shapes for outdoor use.

The electrical-insulating properties and the chemical inertness of polystyrene lead to its use in many small electrical components. Its chemical and moisture resistance, along with its low cost, have been responsible for widespread use in container and other packaging items.

The preponderant radiation effect in polystyrene is cross linking, although a small amount of scission has been found by sol-fraction measurements.[73] For irradiation in air the amount of scission probably depends on the specimen thickness and the dose rate. Various exposure variables affect the cross-linking yield. It can be increased by the use of selected additives in the presence of air or by heating the specimen in air after it has been exposed to large doses in vacuum.[55,60] Much higher cross-linking yields are obtained for certain polystyrene solutions, but the scission-to-cross linking ratio is often greater in solution than in the solid state. The presence of dissolved oxygen in solutions greatly increases the amount of scission.[31]

Wall and Brown[82] irradiated polymers prepared from styrene deuterated in various positions. It was found that when the main polymer chain was completely deuterated the rate of cross linking and evolution of hydrogen were reduced to about 60% of the values for undeuterated polymers. A similar reduction in the cross-linking rate was observed for polystyrene with deuterium in the *para* position of the aromatic ring. Deuteration in this position produced only a slight reduction in the hydrogen–deuterium yield, however. The results suggest that the *para* position of the aromatic ring plays a part in cross linking, perhaps without concomitant production of hydrogen. The main polymer chain seems to be involved in both hydrogen production and cross linking. The rate of cross-link formation was found to be about twice the rate of hydrogen production, in contrast to the relation for polyethylene. The results (coupled with infrared measurements showing a reduction in aromatic rings[55,66]) point to cross linking through the benzene ring with destruction of aromatic unsaturation.

The mechanical properties of polystyrene are changed very little by irradiation. The tensile strength and elongation at break of unmodified polystyrene are reduced by only 5 to 10% by exposures of 5×10^9 rads. High-impact polystyrene, which contains modifiers, shows greater susceptibility to radiation damage. Although the tensile strength is not reduced by high doses, the elongation and impact strength show marked losses at 10^7 rads.

6-7.4 POLY(α-METHYLSTYRENE)

This polymer

resembles polystyrene in mechanical properties; but, although it has a higher softening point, it is less stable to depolymerization on high-temperature aging. Its uses are similar to those of polystyrene.

The predominant radiation effect on poly(α-methylstyrene) is scission. This is expected for polymers containing quaternary carbon atoms, as discussed in Ch. 5, Sect. 5-7. However, the scission rate for poly(α-methylstyrene) is severalfold less than for many other polymers having alternate quaternary carbon atoms. For vacuum irradiation the initial monomer yield (G of unsaturation soluble after precipitation with methanol = 25) is much larger than the yield of primary chain scissions ($G = 0.25$ by viscometry and osmometry after monomer separation).[42] The monomer yield is very much less and the yield of primary scissions is about 50% less for irradiation in air than for irradiation in vacuum.

Effects of radiation on the mechanical properties of poly(α-methylstyrene) have not been studied as extensively as for many other polymers.

The shear strength decreases much more rapidly than that of both unmodified and high-impact polystyrene.

6-8 Nitrogen-containing Polymers, Polyamides (Nylon)

The high flexural modulus (stiffness) and the high impact strength of the typical polyamide, nylon,

$$
\begin{array}{ccccc}
H & & H & O & & O \\
| & & | & \| & & \| \\
-N-(CH_2)_n-N-C-(CH_2)_m-C-
\end{array}
$$

account for its use in most applications other than in textiles. Knobs, gears, and other mechanical parts are made from nylon because its low friction coefficient and high softening point are advantageous when coupled with its strength properties. Its high cost, however, restricts its use as a plastic; the large usage is as a fiber or textile raw material (see Ch. 11 for discussion of textiles).

Because of the strong interchain bonding at amide groups, the melting point is higher for polyamides than for polyethylene. For the same reason, nuclear magnetic resonance studies show that molecular motion is not liquidlike in the amorphous regions at room temperature, in contrast to polyethylene.[25,36] Since the polar amide groups provide sites for the attachment of hydrogen bonding molecules, both the solubility in polar solvents and the equilibrium water content are greater for polyamides than for polyethylene, Conditioning over water before drying increases the crystallinity because of the plasticizing action of absorbed moisture.[25]

The ratio of cross linking to scission on radiolysis is somewhat less for polyamides than for polyethylene. Qualitatively, however, the initial changes in mechanical properties are strikingly similar for both polymers. In contrast to the behavior of polyethylene, in polyamides the growth of high-temperature rubberlike elasticity drops off extensively at high doses.[25] The increase in the concentration of terminal amino groups suggests that scission occurs at the N–C bond.[45] The production of free radicals in nylon was studied photometrically and by paramagnetic resonance.[88]

The high polarity of the amide group allows the study of chain properties of polyamides by dielectric measurements.[15] The dielectric-loss peak in the high-frequency region is associated with a mechanical-loss peak observed in measurements of dynamic mechanical properties. The latter involve motion in amorphous regions.[25] The dielectric-loss peak is destroyed by 10 times the gel-point radiation dose. This corresponds to a cross link for every 15 amide groups if the cross linking is linear with exposure. Figure 6.6 shows this effect.[15]

As for polyethylene at least three types of radiation change would be expected to affect the molecular motion of polyamides: (1) increase in the amorphous content by the destruction of crystallinity, (2) introduction of defects within crystallites, and (3) formation of a tight network. Of these, network formation is most important for the electrical-loss measurements

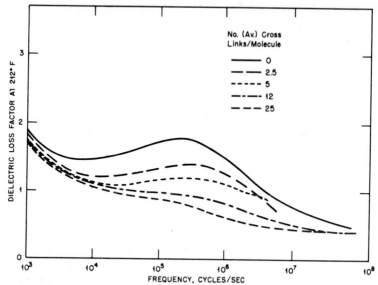

FIG. 6.6   Effect of cross linking of electron-irradiated dry 66 nylon on dielectric loss. (From R. H. Boyd, *Journal of Chemical Physics*, Ref. 15.)

at high frequency. For nylon, as for polyethylene, the most pronounced change is hardening from cross linking. However, the higher ratio of scission to cross linking for nylon makes its radiation stability poorer with respect to retention of strength and elongation.

Other nitrogen-containing thermoplastics that have been studied for radiation effects are proteins and aniline-formaldehyde. Very little information on radiation effects is available for other nitrogen-containing thermoplastics. Because of their biological importance, the work on proteins (polyamides) with the exception of casein is almost all from the viewpoint of the biologist. The data on casein[14] and aniline-formaldehyde plastics is too limited to warrant discussion beyond that in Ch. 5, Sect. 5-7.7, and a listing in the summary tables in this chapter.

6-9 Oxygen-containing Polymers

6-9.1 GENERAL

This section treats the thermoplastic polymers containing only oxygen in addition to carbon and hydrogen. The addition polymers discussed include the acrylates, methacrylates, and poly(vinyl alcohol) and its derivatives. The condensation polymers covered include poly(ethylene oxide), polyesters, and cellulosics. The thermosetting plastics are discussed in a separate section.

The properties of the oxygen-containing materials vary over a considerable range. The acrylates are amorphous and have sufficient flexibility in the main chain to be soft and rubberlike. The methacrylates, with less chain flexibility, are hard and glassy. The derivatives of poly(vinyl alcohol) are amorphous, flexible materials and are more common in commercial use than poly(vinyl alcohol) itself because of its solubility in water. Poly(ethylene oxide) is the only polyether in general industrial usage. It is waxy, fibrous, and water soluble because of the ether linkage. The only thermoplastic polyester important commercially is poly(ethylene terephthalate). It is hard, crystalline, and fiber forming because of the regularity of the chain and the high intermolecular forces.

Cellulose and its derivatives are used in tremendous quantities as natural and synthetic fibers and, in less volume, as film, sheeting, paints, and molded items. Fibrous materials, paints, and wood are discussed in Chs. 11, 12, and 15. Explosive derivatives of cellulose are also included in Ch. 15. Thus only molded and extruded cellulose derivatives are dealt with in this chapter.

The diverse nature of the molecular structure of the materials covered here leads to varied behavior under irradiation. The most extraordinary radiation-induced process observed in these materials is the rapid reduction in molecular weight of the methacrylates and cellulosics. This scission process is accompanied by a marked loss in important mechanical properties. The case of the oxygen main-chain linkage of the polyethers and polyesters is not so clear cut. Certainly this linkage represents a point along the chain which is not available for cross linking; but the tendency for the linkage to serve as a cleavage point probably depends on the nature of adjacent groups. Therefore conclusions about the radiation behavior of this class of materials are best left to a detailed discussion of the individual materials.

6-9.2 POLYACRYLATES

The simpler structure of these polymers suggests that they be discussed before the polymethacrylates, although the latter are used in greater quantity and have been investigated under irradiation much more thoroughly.

The polyacrylates are derivatives of acrylic acid, $H_2C{=}C{-}\overset{\overset{\displaystyle H}{|}}{}\overset{\overset{\displaystyle O}{||}}{C}OH$; and the simplest of these, poly(methyl acrylate), is

$$\begin{array}{c} O \\ \| \\ COCH_3 \\ | \\ -CH_2CHCH_2CH- \\ | \\ C-OCH_3 \\ \| \\ O \end{array}$$

They are transparent, amorphous polymers, softer than the polymethacrylates because of the greater flexibility of the polymer chain. Because of their extensibility and toughness, the polyacrylates are used (frequently in methyl methacrylate copolymers) as coatings or paints. These properties have also led to the use of poly(ethyl acrylate) as a component of synthetic rubbers in which resistance to oils and high temperatures is important. Molding powders and extruded items are also made from the acrylate ester polymers.

A large part of the work on the radiolysis of polyacrylates has been fundamental, instigated by the extreme sensitivity to radiation of the related compound, poly(methyl methacrylate). This effort has dealt with the effect of variations in the ester side chain on the rate of radiation-induced cross linking and scission. Shultz and Bovey[69] irradiated a series of polyacrylates comprising polymers of the methyl ester, the four isomeric butyl esters, and the neopentyl ester. The molecular weights of the materials were determined, and the energy absorbed per cross link was calculated from the radiation dose at the gel point. The gel–sol ratio as a function of dose beyond the gel point gave the ratio of scission to cross linking.

The energy per scission did not show a significant trend among the different polyacrylates. The values varied from 430 to 615 ev, which was about the range for the experimental accuracy of the determination. On the other hand, the energy per cross link was about 190 ± 30 ev for all the polymers except the *tert*-butyl ester. Here, about 600 ev per cross link was absorbed to indicate that some unique feature of the structure of poly(*tert*-butyl acrylate) is important in the cross-linking process. This polymer

$$\begin{array}{c} O \\ \| \\ COC(CH_3)_3 \\ | \\ -CH_2CHCH_2CH- \\ | \\ COC(CH_3)_3 \\ \| \\ O \end{array}$$

differs from the other poly(acrylate esters) in having no hydrogen atoms on the carbinol carbon of the ester side chain. Earlier work on the irradiation of alcohols showed the hydrogens on the carbinol carbon to be much more readily removed than hydrogen atoms in other parts of the molecule. Apparently rupture of this carbinol carbon–hydrogen bond plays an important part in the cross linking of the polyacrylates in which this bond occurs. The bulkiness of the side group is not a factor in the cross-linking rate since the neopentyl ester polymer

$$\begin{array}{cc} \overset{\displaystyle O}{\overset{\displaystyle \|}{C}}OCH_2C(CH_3)_3 & \overset{\displaystyle O}{\overset{\displaystyle \|}{C}}OCH_2C(CH_3)_3 \\ | & | \\ -CH_2CH\!-\!\!\!-\!\!\!-\!\!\!-\!\!\!-CH_2CH- \end{array}$$

did not require the high energy per cross link of the *tert*-butyl polymer but showed about the same cross-linking rate as other polyacrylates.

Similar conclusions were reported[37] based on studies of aromatic acrylate polymers. The gel-point doses were measured for benzyl, β-phenylethyl, and phenyl acrylate polymers, whose side-chain structures are

respectively. The poly(phenyl acrylate) required a fivefold to tenfold higher radiation dose for the gel point than the other polymers. Although the energies absorbed per cross link were not specifically measured, the facilitation of cross linking by hydrogens on the carbinol carbon was demonstrated again.

Measurements of the effect of radiation on the engineering and mechanical properties of polyacrylates have been made on elastomeric polymers compounded into commercial rubbers. The changes produced are discussed in Ch. 7. Polyacrylate rubber shows the changes characteristic of cross linking at a higher rate than natural rubber. A polyacrylate ester of fluorinated butyl alcohol has proved useful as a rubber where solvent resistance and high-temperature properties are important.

Aqueous solutions of acrylic and methacrylic acid polymers have been studied because of the similarity of the behavior of the latter to that of biological materials. These systems, which depend on the action of reactive species arising from the radiolysis of the water, are beyond the scope of this chapter. Solid poly(acrylic acid) cross links and reaches a gel condition upon irradiation.[49]

6-9.3 POLYMETHACRYLATES

The methacrylate ester polymers are exceptionally clear, hard, glassy plastics. They soften at temperatures over 212°F. This permits fabrication by molding and extrusion techniques but limits uses to those involving only moderate temperature. Poly(methyl methacrylate) is widely used, sometimes with plasticizer and/or small amounts of other methacrylate esters as copolymers. The resins are so widespread under the trade names of Plexiglas and Lucite in the United States and Perspex in Europe that these words have become synonymous for transparent plastic panels, windows, and windshields. The resistance of these resins to shattering and to the weather has led to their large-scale application in aircraft. Sheets, rods, tubes, and molded items find many uses where excellent transparency is needed.

6-9.3.1 *Scission and Cross Linking*

Polymethacrylates undergo scission with irradiation in contrast to most common polymeric materials, which cross link. This fact motivated extensive basic work on the simplest ester polymer, poly(methyl methacrylate). The abundant use of this material also led to several early studies of the effects of radiation on its engineering properties. Its use in X-ray equipment prompted measurements of its electrical conductivity under irradiation. The change in molecular weight of pure poly(methyl methacrylate) has been suggested for dosimetry; the change in coloration of dyed methacrylate films has also been proposed for this purpose.

A comprehensive study was conducted on the reduction in molecular weight of poly(methyl methacrylate) by both Co^{60} gamma radiation and the mixed radiation of a nuclear reactor. The molecular weights were determined before and after irradiation by measurements of the viscosity of dilute solutions in chloroform. The polymer contribution to the viscosity at high dilution, η, is related to the "viscosity-average" molecular weight by an equation of the form

$$\eta = K(M_v)^a \tag{6.1}$$

where M_v is the viscosity-average molecular weight and K and a are empirical constants, respectively, 4.8×10^{-5} and 0.8 for chloroform at 77°F. If it is assumed that the molecular-weight distribution of the polymer is random and that there is no chain branching, then the viscosity-average molecular weight is 1.9 times the number average. The number of molecules per unit mass is proportional to the reciprocal of the number-average molecular weight, and each scission produces one new molecule. Therefore, if the reciprocal of the molecular weight is plotted against the radiation dose, the slope is proportional to the radiation energy absorbed per scission. One main-chain scission was found for every 60 to 65 ev of Co^{60} radiation absorbed by the specimen at 64°F.

The validity of the determination of the rate of scission by viscosity measurements depends on the assumption that there is no cross linking or chain branching. The scission yield just cited could be accounted for[70] if scission occurred at the rate of one scission for every 36 ev absorbed and simultaneous cross linking occurred at the rate of 180 ev per cross link.

Molecular weights of electron-irradiated poly(methyl methacrylate) were measured both by viscosity and by light-scattering methods. Cross linking was shown to be negligible when the apparent molecular weights were found to be the same by both methods. The observed scission rate was 59 ev per scission, which agrees very well with the previous results.

6-9.3.2 *General Scission Mechanism*

The earlier observations that most polymers undergo cross linking but those with recurring quaternary carbon atoms undergo scission led to many attempts to prove a general scission mechanism. In Ch. 5, Sect. 5-7, possible mechanisms were cited, including steric hindrance to recombination, resonance stabilization of free-radical fragments, and 1-4 diradical or six-membered ring processes. Experimental vertification of any exclusive mechanism is lacking. Indeed it is likely that under irradiation, where various amounts of energy may be imparted to the molecular system, several processes producing scission occur to an appreciable degree.

An absorption band was observed in the ultraviolet spectrum of poly-(methyl methacrylate) as a result of irradiation.[5] The wave length indicated conjugated unsaturation. Also, the quantity and composition of the gases evolved during irradiation corresponded to the decomposition of one ester side chain for each main-chain rupture.[5,81] A 1-4 diradical mechanism (see Ch. 5, Sect. 5-7) or the equivalent six-membered ring[68] concerted decomposition is in accord with these observations:

$$(6.2)$$

The excited methyl formate undergoes decomposition to H_2, CH_4, CO, and CO_2, which are observed as gaseous radiolysis products. Reported values for the composition of the evolved gas do not agree on the H_2-to-CH_4 ratio; but they do agree[5,81] that these two components make up about half the gaseous products and CO and CO_2 make up the other half in the ratio of about 3 to 2. Differences in observed gas composition result from differences in experimental conditions employed, e.g., differences in temperature, in specimen surface-to-volume ratio, in types of radiation, and perhaps in impurity content of the samples.

Hydrocarbon polymers, which are distinctive in undergoing scission, also have low heats of polymerization and yield relatively large amounts of monomer upon thermal depolymerization.[80] Such polymers have quaternary carbon atoms alternately along the main chain. Steric hindrance reduces the bond energy at the quaternary carbon and facilitates rupture of the polymer at this point during thermal depolymerization. A possible scission mechanism based on this strain concept could include, as a first step, the excitation of one or more electrons in a localized region of a polymer molecule. This excitation energy could spread quickly over a distance of several atoms to include a quaternary carbon atom. The main-chain bond at the excited quaternary carbon could then break; recombination would be prevented by steric hindrance.

This mechanism explains the presence of the type of free radicals found in polymethacrylates after irradiation. The following radical was observed by electron-spin resonance measurements on poly(methyl methacrylate) irradiated in an inert atmosphere:

$$
\begin{array}{cc}
\mathrm{O} & \mathrm{O} \\
\parallel & \parallel \\
\mathrm{COCH_3} & \mathrm{COCH_3} \\
| & | \\
-\mathrm{CH_2C-CH_2C\cdot} \\
| & | \\
\mathrm{CH_3} & \mathrm{CH_3}
\end{array}
$$

Although many other molecular fragments could be unstable intermediates in the radiolysis, this radical indicates that some scission takes place at the quaternary carbon. The absence of the radical composed of the matching fragment

$$
\begin{array}{cc}
\mathrm{O} & \mathrm{O} \\
\parallel & \parallel \\
\mathrm{COCH_3} & \mathrm{COCH_3} \\
| & | \\
\cdot\mathrm{CH_2C-CH_2C-} \\
| & | \\
\mathrm{CH_3} & \mathrm{CH_3}
\end{array}
$$

may be explained by its probable high reactivity or by the formation of an ionized species and a trapped electron during radiolysis. It is possible that the spectrum of a trapped electron might have been broad enough to have escaped detection. Free radicals have also been detected in irradiated poly(methyl methacrylate) by chemical means.[81]

6-9.3.3 Structural Effects

Scission has been found to be influenced by several chemical structural factors. The aromatic ring in phenyl and benzyl methacrylate polymers increases the energy absorbed per scission severalfold.[37] Poly(benzyl methac-

$$- CH_2C \underset{\overset{|}{CH_3}}{\overset{\overset{O}{\parallel}}{\overset{CO}{|}}} \underset{}{\bigcirc} - CH_2C - \underset{\overset{|}{CH_3}}{\overset{\overset{O}{\parallel}}{\overset{CO}{|}}} \bigcirc \quad \text{and} \quad - CH_2C \underset{\overset{|}{CH_3}}{\overset{\overset{O}{\parallel}}{\overset{COCH_2}{|}}} \bigcirc CH_2C - \underset{\overset{|}{CH_3}}{\overset{\overset{O}{\parallel}}{\overset{COCH_2}{|}}} \bigcirc$$

rylate) was observed to require 710 ± 50 ev for each scission. Poly(phenyl methacrylate) was estimated to require around 200 ev for each scission. Thus the aromatic ring exerts a greater protective effect from scission (but not from cross linking) when it is attached to the α-carbon atom of the ester side chain than when it is attached directly to the oxygen of the ester. This effect of location was observed in the polyacrylates (see Sect. 6-9.2) where the phenyl ester absorbs more energy per cross link than does the benzyl or β-phenylethyl ester.

A somewhat smaller influence of ester side-chain structure has been found in polymethacrylates of aliphatic alcohols. Ethyl, n-butyl, and tert-butyl methacrylate polymers were studied.[68,70] If concurrent cross linking is assumed negligible, then the energy absorbed per scission is 75 ev for the ethyl, 146 ev for the n-butyl, and 43 ev for the tert-butyl polymer. The tert-butyl polymer apparently shows greater steric hindrance than poly-(methyl methacrylate) and, consequently, undergoes scission at a higher rate. The increased energies absorbed per apparent scission by the ethyl and n-butyl polymers could be the result of cross linking occurring concurrently with scission. Cross linking through the alcohol side chain was shown to result in gel formation in the case of polymethacrylates of alcohols having 12 and 18 carbon atoms.[68]

It may be concluded that the radiolysis of polymethacrylates can be influenced by the structure of the side chain in three distinct ways. The side chain may serve as an energy sink if an aromatic ring is present. Bulky side chains increase steric strain and may accelerate scission. Finally, long side chains may provide cross-linking sites.

6-9.3.4 Effects of Additives

The effect of additives in poly(methyl methacrylate) on the rate of scission under irradiation was noted by several observers.[5,6,82] Whether the impurities were added for protection or were present accidentally, scission was retarded with but one exception, methylene chloride. This material, used as a solvent in the preparation of some of the specimens, is without effect in concentrations around $\frac{1}{2}\%$.

Alexander and coworkers[5,6] cast poly(methyl methacrylate) films containing up to 10 wt. % of various substances. After irradiation the reduction in molecular weight of the films containing the protective substances was compared with that of pure polymer. The concentration dependence of protection was also studied for typical additives. An equation was developed for a protection coefficient, P, relating the energy per scission for pure polymer, E,

$$P = (100\%) \left(\frac{E_P - E}{E_P} \right) \tag{6.3}$$

Results[5,6] are presented in Table 6.1. A variety of structures can furnish substantial protection against scission for poly(methyl methacrylate). All the better protective agents are aromatic in nature. Many, but not all, are strong reducing agents, although the irradiations were conducted in vacuum.

Table 6.1 — PROTECTIVE EFFECT OF ADDITIVES IN RADIOLYSIS[a] OF POLY (METHYL METHACRYLATE)[b]

Additive	Concentration, wt. %	Protection,[c] %
Benzoic acid	1.0	76
Naphthalene	2	32
Anthracene	2.1	37
Phenanthrene	2.2	51
Biphenyl	2.5	56
Phenol	2.7	52
α-Naphthylamine	2.5	78
8-Hydroxyquinoline	2	52
Diphenylthiourea	3.6	69
α-Naphthol	5.5	82
β-Naphthol	5.3	24
Ethylurea	10.0	12
Paraffin	~10	3

[a]Exposures in vacuum in the British Experimental Pile (BEPO) (see Ch. 1, Fig. 1.2) or in Co^{60} source at 77 to 158 °F.
[b]From P. Alexander and D. J. Toms, *Radiation Research*, Ref. 6.
[c]From Eq. 6.3.

The mechanism of additive protection was studied[6] using naphthalene containing radioactive carbon (C^{14}). After incorporating this labeled naphthalene in the polymer and irradiating, only enough naphthalene was found chemically bound to the polymer to bridge one fifth of the main-chain breaks prevented by the naphthalene. Apparently the protection involves energy absorption rather than bridging between broken-chain ends. The possibility is not precluded, however, that the naphthalene combines with a reactive species that otherwise would initiate a kinetic chain reaction.

If protection involves energy absorption where the excitation is long-lived and transported large distances, the effect of protector concentration would be less than if protection involved bridging chain ruptures or scavenging reactive species. In either case a variation of protection with concentration would be expected at very low concentrations. The results of studies on samples containing various concentrations of naphthalene and 8-hydroxyquinoline[6] are shown in Fig. 6.7. A strong dependence of protection on concentration was noted only below 4% of the 8-hydroxyquinoline. The variation with concentration may extend above 5% for naphthalene, which is not as good a protector.

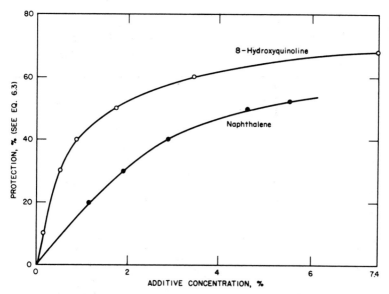

FIG. 6.7 Protection with additives in radiolysis of poly(methyl methacrylate). Exposures in British Experimental Pile to low doses in vacuum at 158°F. (From P. Alexander and D. J. Toms, *Radiation Research*, Ref. 6.)

The fact that protection is concentration dependent raises the question of whether the protector is destroyed by radiation and is therefore dose dependent, also. No dose dependence was found for naphthalene up to doses corresponding to 3×10^7 rads in a reactor facility (BEPO) for concentrations[6] as low as 0.8%. However, 8-hydroxyquinoline at concentrations of 3% and lower declined in protective effect as the dose increased; but, in concentrations of 5% and over, it, too, showed no loss of protection up to doses of about 3×10^7 rads. The decrease in protection by 8-hydroxyquinoline as the dose increased probably resulted from a depletion of the additive; naphthalene is more radiation resistant.

The effect of oxygen or air on poly(methyl methacrylate) under irradiation is still somewhat uncertain. Comparisons of specimens irradiated in vacuum and in air showed the scission rate of thin specimens (film or powder) to be reduced in air to 60 to 80% of the rate in vacuum.[6,82] This effect is somewhat dependent on the specimen thickness, but it has also been found to be influenced by impurities. With 2 to 5% of benzene impurity present, the scission rate in air was only one-half or less the rate in vacuum for identical samples. It was also demonstrated that benzene is very difficult to remove completely from even thin samples of poly(methyl methacrylate) which have been prepared from benzene solutions.[6] Protection with benzene was observed both in vacuum and in air.

6-9.3.5 *Temperature Effects*

Scission yields have been reported for poly(methyl methacrylate) irradiated at various temperatures.[6,12,82] As shown in Fig. 6.8, there is con-

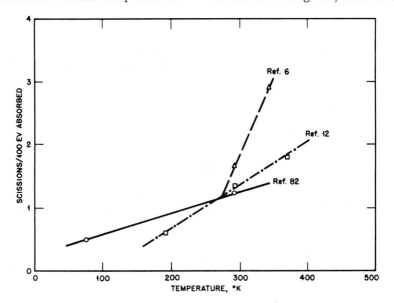

FIG. 6.8 Temperature dependence of scission for poly(methyl methacrylate).

siderable disagreement among the results at room temperature and above, and there are insufficient results at low temperatures. The discrepancies at room temperature can be attributed to differences in purity of the sample material or perhaps in the atmosphere during irradiation. About 5% benzene was contained in the specimen of Wall and Brown.[82] They found that specimens of higher purity gave much greater scission yields (2.0 to 2.5 per 100 ev absorbed). The data do indicate, however, a definite increase in the scission yield as the temperature of irradiation is increased. If the high-temperature measurements are extrapolated to lower temperatures, it is seen that the zero-yield intercept is a finite temperature. It is not likely that the scission yield actually becomes zero at 100 to 200°K. Thus the slope of the scission yield vs. temperature curve must be greater at high temperatures than at very low temperatures. This behavior agrees with the findings for the cross linking of polyethylene and the scission of polyisobutylene.

6-9.3.6 *Postirradiation Effects*

The presence of free radicals or trapped electrons in irradiated polymer raises the possibility of postirradiation effects. Electron-spin resonance measurements showed free radicals to persist for some time following irradiation and to undergo changes upon exposure to air.[1] Irradiated poly(methyl methacrylate) was also found to be capable of initiating polymerization of methacrylate or styrene monomer, even after storage for several days.[81] This chemical activity also changed after exposure to air for a week. The molecular weight of irradiated samples of commercial poly (methyl methacrylate) decreased over periods of two weeks or longer following irradiation.[54] The extent of the postirradiation scission after storage for 500 hr was 20% of the total scission yield for doses of around 10^6 rads.

In contrast to the subtle chemical changes cited, the mechanical properties of poly(methyl methacrylate) in commercial use undergo little postirradiation change. The tensile properties of specimens irradiated to moderate doses showed essentially no postirradiation change; specimens involving large doses (10^9 to 10^{10} rads) showed postirradiation changes that were negligible compared to the total damage by radiation.[14]

6-9.3.7 *Physical-property Effects*

Optical and electrical properties may undergo postirradiation changes to a degree that is important in certain uses. Optical properties are determined by the low-energy quantum levels of conjugated, unsaturated groups and by the loosely bound electrons of free radicals and solid-state traps. Electrical conductivity is determined by the number of free electrons or charge carriers, which depends partly on the concentration and energy levels of the trapped species. Thus both optical properties and conductivity would be expected to change profoundly during irradiation and to show further changes as the metastable species, free radicals, and trapped charge carriers decay following irradiation.

Poly(methyl methacrylate) was found to drop in optical transmittance from about a 90% value to 55% upon receiving 5×10^6 rads of gamma radiation in air. After irradiation, recovery to a transmittance value of about 80% occurred over an exposure-in-air period of four to five months.[64]

The electrical properties of poly(methyl methacrylate) were studied both during and after irradiation.[34,35] Observations were interpreted on the basis of a physical model consisting of a conduction band with the current carried by electrons either excited from valence levels or liberated from traps. The photoconductivity was found to vary as $R^{0.55}$, where R is the intensity of radiation. The conductivity decreased after irradiation, showing an exponential decay for periods greater than 5 hr after exposure. Conductivity was 10^{-17} (ohm-cm)$^{-1}$ at 400 rads/hr and was ohmic (currents strictly proportional to voltage) if time was allowed for attainment of equilibrium. Up to doses of 5×10^6 rads, the conductivity returned to about the preirradiation value, given sufficient time. Other postirradiation measurements showed that the conductivity, after 10^8 rads, was less than 10^{-14} (ohm–cm)$^{-1}$, the lowest conductivity measurable by the equipment used.[14]

The mechanical properties of poly(methyl methacrylate) generally deteriorate rapidly under irradiation, as shown in Fig. 6.9. This degradation

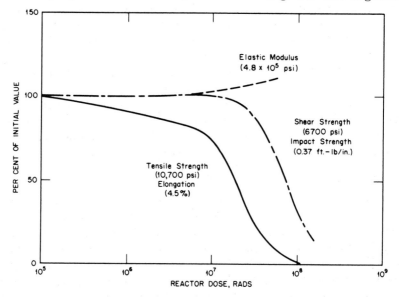

FIG. 6.9 Mechanical-property changes in radiolysis of poly(methyl methacrylate).[14] Exposures in Oak Ridge Graphite Reactor in air at about 77°F.

results from the relatively large number of breaks in the polymer chains for a given amount of energy deposited in the sample. The elastic modulus changes very little[14] as a result of irradiation, since this property depends on van der Waals' forces between atoms in this glassy material rather than on the length of the polymer chains. This effect is illustrated in Fig. 5.15 (Ch. 5), together with the loss in ultimate tensile strength as the dose increases. The hardness and density of poly(methyl methacrylate), like the elastic modulus, are not sensitive to radiation. The flexural strength, which decreases to about one-fourth the unirradiated value at 5×10^7 rads, appears to be about as sensitive as the tensile strength and elongation.[64] The heat-distortion temperature is influenced by the "plasticizing" effect of low-molecular-weight decomposition products and by the increased mobility of the ruptured polymer chains. This distortion point is fairly insensitive to radiation; 5×10^7 rads is required[64] to reduce it by 25%.

6-9.4 Poly(Vinyl Alcohol) and Its Derivatives

Poly(vinyl alcohol) is not prepared directly from the monomer, which is unstable and isomeric with acetaldehyde, the stable form. Instead, it is made by hydrolysis of poly(vinyl acetate). The outstanding property of poly(vinyl alcohol) is its solubility in water and its resistance to most organic solvents. The polymer can be cross linked by esterification or oxidation. It is tough and flexible—properties which lead to its use in solvent-resistant hoses, diaphragms, and gaskets. It is also used in coatings, in textile sizes, and as an adhesive.

The behavior of poly(vinyl alcohol) under irradiation has been investigated most frequently in aqueous solution or in air. It cross links to form a gel in aqueous solutions[11] unless the concentration is less than 0.3%. In the dry state, however, both in air and in vacuum, radiation produces scission.[22,53,67] The cross linking in solution is an indirect effect—the action of radicals from the radiolysis of water. It is not clear why the polymer degrades in the dry state, but the apparent energy absorbed per scission, assuming no cross linking, is 30 to 35 ev in both air and vacuum. The carbonyl content of the polymer has been observed to increase during irradiation in vacuum as well as in air but more rapidly in air, of course.[67] Mobile hydroxyl radicals, liberated from their side-chain locations, may oxidize the main chain to produce scission in a secondary reaction.

The effect of radiation on the mechanical properties of poly(vinyl alcohol) has not been reported. These properties would be expected to deteriorate somewhat faster than those of poly(methyl methacrylate) since the scission rate is higher for the poly(vinyl alcohol).

Powdered poly(vinyl alcohol), which has been irradiated in air, forms an insoluble gel when heated above 248°F for 10 min. Infrared spectra indicate that the carbonyl group diminishes during the heat treatment. It was suggested that intermolecular coupling takes place between the $\diagdown$C=O group and —OH groups of the adjacent chain to form ketal cross linkages.[23] Such cross linking would be expected to influence the tensile properties, especially at high temperature, as well as the solubility.

Poly(vinyl acetate) is synthesized industrially from acetylene and acetic acid. It is the parent compound, commercially, for poly(vinyl alcohol) and the acetal derivatives. The acetate has a low softening point and is soluble in aromatic, oxygenated, and chlorinated solvents but not in water or aliphatic hydrocarbons. It is used in adhesives, coatings, textile sizes, and as a bonding agent for heavily filled materials.

Radiation studies have been limited to copolymers with vinyl chloride and to heavily filled sheet stock. In both cases poly(vinyl acetate) was a minor constituent; and the experimental work does not permit an estimate of cross linking or scission.

The poly(vinyl ethers) can be made directly from the monomer. The methyl ether polymer

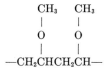

$$\begin{array}{cc} CH_3 & CH_3 \\ | & | \\ O & O \\ | & | \\ -CH_2CHCH_2CH- \end{array}$$

is soluble in water; the higher ethers decrease in solubility in water but increase in solubility in organic solvents. Commercial uses of these materials resemble those of the acetate; there is limited use for the pure solid polymer. Little work with radiation has been reported, but the materials are listed among those which gel under electron bombardment.[49] Liquid poly(vinyl methyl ether) of molecular weight 3000 to 5000 has been converted by irradiation to a rubbery solid.[30] Tensile strength was only about 100 psi and elongation about 150% at 4×10^7 rads; but fillers, such as carbon, MgO, Fe_2O_3, and SiO_2, improved the properties considerably.

The poly(vinyl acetals) are the most abundantly used plastics of this group. They are prepared from poly(vinyl acetate) by direct reaction with the aldehyde or with the aldehyde after hydrolysis. The removal of the acetate groups is not complete but usually varies from 80 to 95%. The resulting acetals

$$\begin{array}{c} R \\ | \\ CH \\ \diagup \quad \diagdown \\ O \qquad O \\ | \qquad\quad | \\ -CH_2CH-CH_2CH- \end{array}$$

have a cyclic side-chain structure, where R is hydrogen or the hydrocarbon residue of the aldehyde. The acetals are insoluble in hydrocarbon solvents. The solubility in other solvents varies with the structure of the R group.

Poly(vinyl formal) (R = —H) is used in coating electrical wire, where its superior flexibility and resistance to abrasion are advantageous. Poly(vinyl acetal) (R = —CH$_3$) is also tough and is easy to mold. It is used for bottle caps, combs, and as a binder in heavily filled molded items. Poly(vinyl butyral) ($R = -CH_2CH_2CH_3$) is a very important item of commerce as the interlayer in safety glass. The outstanding toughness and resistance to shock, to water, and to aging of this polymer, make it especially well adapted for this use. Furthermore, by a hydrolysis reaction in the manufacture, about 18% of the hydroxyl groups of the parent poly (vinyl alcohol) is left unreacted to provide excellent adhesion to glass layers without additional adhesives or bonding agents of any kind. About 2% of the original acetate groups also remain in the final product.

The behavior of thin sheet stock of poly(vinyl formal) and (-butyral) has been studied after irradiation in a reactor with somewhat restricted access to air. The work on poly(vinyl formal) is limited to sample material containing about 10% of plasticizer; thus it is not clear what the precise response of pure material would be. Irradiation reduced the elastic modulus and tensile strength by 50% at about 5×10^8 rads.[14] In this dose range the elongation at break increased by over 50% and showed a maximum when plotted as a function of dose. The weight and density also showed appreciable decreases in this dose range. These changes are indicative of chain scission but may result from decomposition of the plasticizer.

The changes observed after irradiation of poly(vinyl butyral) (purer material used) point clearly to predominant cross linking.[14] The density increased, although a weight loss was observed. An increase in the elastic modulus was accompanied by a decrease in elongation at break (50% at 3×10^8 rads). The tensile strength (50% at 10^8 rads) decreased faster on irradiation than did that of the formal.

6-9.5 POLY(ETHYLENE OXIDE)

Commercial poly(ethylene oxide), $-CH_2CH_2O-$, is waxy and fibrous. Because of its water solubility, it is used as a plasticizer and as an additive in nonpolymeric materials rather than as a base polymer. It is particularly useful in polymer irradiation studies, being readily soluble in a variety of solvents and easily characterized by end-group determinations and viscometry.[57] It is the only polyether on which radiation-effects information is available.

The presence of oxygen in the chain does not greatly increase the susceptibility of poly(ethylene oxide) to radiolysis as compared with polyethylene. This was shown by increases in solution viscosity after irradiation in a vacuum. In the measurement of viscosity, the samples must be transferred rapidly to the solvent to avoid oxidative degradation. At moderate doses irradiation in air results in a larger increase in solution viscosity than vacuum irradiation owing to the formation of peroxide cross links. Longer exposures in air result in oxidative degradation.

Samples of known molecular weight, but of unknown molecular-weight distribution, were used in this work.[53] A distribution must be assumed to calculate a cross-linking rate from the observed gel-point dose and number-average molecular weight. If the specimens did not differ greatly from a "most probable" distribution and if chain scission is ignored, the gel-point dose of 5×10^7 rads for specimens of 9000 number-average molecular weight gives $G_{XL} = 0.53$. This value for irradiation in a vacuum is about one-fourth the cross-linking rate of polyethylene. There have been no measurements of the effects of radiation on the mechanical properties of poly(ethylene oxide).

6-9.6 Poly(Ethylene Terephthalate)

This material

$$-CH_2CH_2O\overset{O}{\overset{\|}{C}}\langle\underset{}{\bigcirc}\rangle\overset{O}{\overset{\|}{C}}O-$$

is the only commercial linear polyester. It is a fibrous, partly crystalline polymer, which forms hard, tough sheets and films. It can also be drawn into strong fibers that have very desirable properties as a textile raw material. The product is marketed in Europe as Terylene and in this country as Mylar in the sheet form and as Dacron fibers and textiles. The sheets and films have high tensile strength and are used in packaging and protective applications.

The question of dominance of cross linking or scission with poly(ethylene terephthalate) under irradiation was discussed in Ch. 5, Sect. 5-7.5. Infrared spectra show that the ester linkage is destroyed in what must constitute one mode of scission.[55] The spectra also show a reduction in the crystallinity of the specimen, a thin film, after a reactor dose of about 4×10^9 rads in vacuum. After one-tenth of this exposure, Dacron textile fibers irradiated in air were not changed in crystallinity. The modulus of elasticity of these fibers increased except for those having a high degree of orientation[76] (see Ch. 11, Sect. 11-4.2). Thus orientation was established as one of the experimental conditions influencing the quantitative results of irradiation, together with atmosphere, specimen thickness, dose, and dose rate. Although the increase in modulus observed in some of the fibers is an indication of the prevalence of cross linking, the influence of crystallinity and oxygen makes the observations somewhat inconclusive.

The tensile strength and elongation of Mylar sheet stock of 0.002- to 0.010-in. thickness is reduced by irradiation in a limited supply of air. The elongation at break decreases at about the same rate as that for polyethylene, dropping to half the initial value at about 3×10^8 rads. The tensile strength, which initially is an order of magnitude higher than that of polyethylene, decreases to 50% at 5×10^8 rads and to 10% at about

2×10^9 rads. This ranks poly(ethylene terephthalate) between poly(methyl methacrylate) and polyethylene with respect to retention of original tensile strength.

6-9.7 MOLDED AND EXTRUDED CELLULOSE DERIVATIVES

Since cellulose materials are treated in later chapters (Chs. 11 and 15), only the ethyl ether, the nitrate, and three esters of cellulose will be discussed in this chapter. The ethyl ether of cellulose (ethyl cellulose) is produced by digesting cellulose fiber with sodium hydroxide, followed by reaction with ethyl chloride or other alkylating agents. The product is insoluble in water but is soluble in chlorinated and aromatic solvents and in polar materials, such as alcohols and esters, as long as the ethoxy content is less than 50%. Complete conversion of the cellulose yields a 54.9% ethoxy content, but commercial products have 46 to 50% to preserve solubility properties.

Ethyl cellulose is compatible with many other resins and with most plasticizers. It is easily molded by injection or extrusion methods into a wide variety of items for applications in which its flexibility and toughness are advantageous. These properties, along with its compatibility with cellulose nitrate, are responsible for its use in paints and as a coating for fabrics.

Ethyl cellulose sheet stock of such thickness (0.82 in.) that air had little effect showed a slight increase in elastic modulus after 4×10^7 rads.[14] At about this dose the tensile and impact strengths had dropped to one-fourth the original values, and the elongation had decreased to less than 5% of the value for unirradiated material. The hardness showed a small but measurable decrease at this dose. For a 50% reduction in tensile strength, about 2×10^7 rads is required. It is not possible to draw conclusions about cross linking or scission from these experimental measurements. These data and those for the succeeding cellulosics were on thick specimens irradiated in the Oak Ridge Graphite Reactor at about 77°F in a limited supply of air (closed air-filled container).

Three esters of cellulose are discussed, the acetate, propionate, and the mixed acetate-butyrate. Cellulose acetate is produced by esterifying the hydroxyl groups of cellulose with acetic acid and acetic anhydride. As in the case of ethyl cellulose, a small quantity of free hydroxyl groups is desirable for optimum properties in the commercial product. Complete esterification yields a material that contains 62.5% acetate groups (expressed as acetic acid), but commercial molding powders have from 56 to 59% acetate groups. The water and weather resistance of cellulose acetate is not as good as is that of most plastics, and it is not generally used above 160°F. Variations in manufacturing methods permit a considerable range in properties. In addition to the wide use of cellulose acetate as a textile (rayon), it is used as sheets, film, rods, tubes, and as molding powder for a multitude of items not subjected to severe environmental or mechanical conditions. It is also used in paints and coatings.

Cellulose acetate behaves similarly to ethyl cellulose under irradiation except that slightly higher doses are required for the same reduction in tensile strength. About 4×10^7 rads reduced[14] this property by 50%. Hardness measurements were not made on samples receiving more than 2.5×10^7 rads, and it is not known whether the decrease in hardness observed in ethyl cellulose above this dose occurs in the acetate.

Cellulose propionate is manufactured in processes like those for the acetate and has properties that are superior in some respects. Less plasticizer is required for equal flexural strengths, but the tensile strength of pure sheet stock is less in the case of the propionate. Uses are similar to those for the acetate. The irradiation behavior is comparable to that of ethyl cellulose,[14] but again the hardness measurements were not extended to the doses that produced a decrease in this property for ethyl cellulose.

Mixed esters of cellulose, such as cellulose acetate-butyrate, are superior to the acetate in regard to water resistance and the retention of some plasticizers. The solubility in certain organic solvents is greater; but the tensile strength is somewhat lower, although there is an accompanying increase in elongation at break. Applications of the mixed esters are similar to those for the acetate. As expected, the behavior of the acetate-butyrate plastic under irradiation is similar to that of the acetate.[14]

Incompletely nitrated cellulose nitrate is well known in molded objects in the form of rods, sheets, tubes, etc., and as a constituent of lacquers and photographic film. Because of its flammability and tendency to decompose at high temperatures, cellulose nitrate is not used as a compression or injection molding material.

The mechanical properties of cellulose nitrate are changed by irradiation in about the same manner and extent as are the properties of the acetate. There is a gradual increase in hardness, however, which continues beyond 1×10^8 rads.[14] This hardening differs from the behavior of ethyl cellulose. Evolution of gas on irradiation is different with the nitrate than with other cellulosics. Gas evolution is dependent on conditions of exposure; but for $\frac{1}{8}$-in. sheet at room temperature and about 10^6 rads/hr, the weight loss is 0.6% at 4×10^7 rads. Warming such a specimen to its softening temperature results in a spectacular release of gas, which may inflate the specimen, as shown in Fig. 6.10, to several times its original volume in the form of a multicellular foam or an aggregation of a few large bubbles.

The cellulose ethers, esters, and the nitrate were shown in the foregoing discussion to be relatively sensitive to irradiation like the parent compound, cellulose. The tensile properties degrade on irradiation at least 10 times as fast as those of polyethylene but not quite as fast as those of

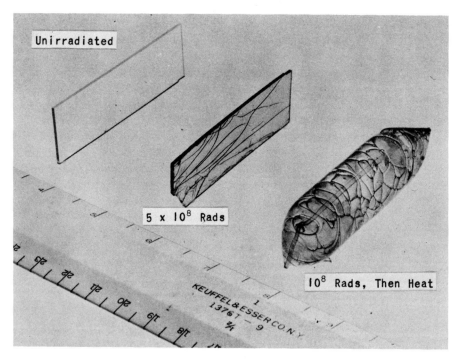

FIG. 6.10 Gas production in irradiated cellulose nitrate.

poly(methyl methacrylate). Cellulose itself undergoes scission much more rapidly than poly(methyl methacrylate). This suggests that the cellulose ethers, esters, and acetals are more resistant to radiation than cellulose itself if poly(methyl methacrylate) can be used as a reference. In support of this contention, fibers of cellulose (cotton) have been reported[76] to undergo scission and loss of tensile strength more rapidly than cellulose acetate.

6-10 Halogen-containing Polymers

6-10.1 POLY(VINYL CHLORIDE)

This polymer, —$CH_2CHClCH_2CHCl$—, contains 58% chlorine. It is somewhat crystalline in the drawn state, but crystallinity is very small in the unoriented material. Unplasticized polymer is used in applications requiring high rigidity; plasticized material is used where flexibility and toughness are desirable. Copolymerization of vinyl chloride with 5 to 20% of vinyl acetate yields a product with internal plasticization which cannot diffuse out of the finished item. The variation in properties through plasticization, the low price, and the early discovery of this polymer have made it one of the most abundantly used of all synthetic polymers. Insulation for electric wire consumes a large tonnage. It is used as a fabric coating for waterproof wearing apparel and for upholstery and similar household articles. Extruded fiber and sheeting are used without other backing for upholstery, furniture coverings, etc. Hoses and tubular items are made from very flexible resins, and molded objects consume quantities of the more rigid formulations. Thin sheeting and film are used in very large quantities for both industrial and household packaging.

Exposure to light and heat results in a loss of HCl with the production of unsaturation, but this effect is reduced by the addition of stabilizers. Irradiation also results in HCl loss; but the influence of stabilizers is much less marked than for exposure to heat, since the concentration of the initiating radicals is larger. The radiation-induced HCl loss is accompanied by both cross linking and scission. The amount of scission is less for irradiation in vacuum than for irradiation in air.[59,85] By analogy with the behavior of polystyrene, the cross-linking yield of poly(vinyl chloride) is greater when the polymer is irradiated in certain solvents than in the solid state. Radiation effects for plasticized formulations are analogous to the effects for solutions.[84] The cross-linking yield is enhanced by loading with unsaturated polyester monomer.[59]

The radiation behavior of both plasticized and unplasticized resins has been studied. Hard high-strength resins show only small losses in tensile strength at 10^8 rads; the strength is reduced by one-third at 2×10^8 rads. The impact strength is even more resistant to change.[14,17] A vinyl chloride–acetate copolymer showed a spectacular maximum (about 200%) in the elongation at break at about 5 megarads.[14] This material softened appreciably at 2×10^8 rads, at which dose the elastic modulus had also decreased to 70% of its initial value.

Some plasticized formulations harden and increase in elastic modulus[14] while the tensile strength shows about the same relative change as already cited for high-strength resins. Other compositions are more sensitive by at least an order of magnitude. The electrical properties of plasticized poly (vinyl chloride) resins deteriorate rapidly under irradiation. The resistance of a vinyl chloride–acetate copolymer was below 10^6 ohm–cm after 10^8 rads.[14]

Copolymers of vinylidene chloride and vinyl chloride are similar to vinyl chloride–acetate copolymers in being softer and more flexible than unplasticized poly(vinyl chloride). This copolymer is familiar in the chemical laboratory as Saran tubing. It differs from the acetate copolymer in having less than 50% vinyl chloride in many copolymer compositions. Mechanical tests of 0.13-in.-thick Saran samples irradiated in the Oak Ridge Graphite Reactor with limited access to air gave evidence of predominant chain scission. At about 5×10^7 rads, the elastic modulus decreased by 25% and the tensile strength even more.[14] A measurable softening was also observed at this dose. The elongation and impact strength were even more sensitive, dropping to half their initial values at about 2×10^7 rads and to 10% at 10^8 rads. Electrical resistance declined rapidly with irradiation.

6-10.2 POLY(TETRAFLUOROETHYLENE) (TEFLON) AND POLY(CHLOROTRIFLUOROETHYLENE) (KEL-F)

These two polymers are characterized by their chemical inertness. Teflon, $—CF_2CF_2CF_2CF_2—$, shows an unusually high softening temperature for an organic material. It is used for high-temperature and corrosion-resistant wire coating, pipe fittings, washers, spacers, etc. It is also used as a container for very corrosive chemical agents. Kel-F

$$
\begin{array}{cc}
Cl & Cl \\
| & | \\
\end{array}
$$
$$—CFCF_2CFCF_2—$$

is used where corrosion resistance and flexibility are required, e.g., for gaskets, diaphragms, and hoses. The cost of both materials is prohibitive at present for all applications except those in which their unique properties are required.

Electron-spin resonance studies for Teflon[61,78] indicate that the primary radical formed by irradiation in vacuum reacts in the presence of air to give peroxy type radicals. The rate of scission is an order of magnitude less in vacuum than in air. This indicates peroxy radicals to be involved in the scission of Teflon. This effect of irradiation atmosphere is more pronounced with Teflon and Kel-F than with any of the other polymers studied, although the surfaces of these two may become oxidized on exposure to air.[32] This surface oxidation is useful in the case of Teflon since it improves its ability to be dyed or grafted. In air the scission yield for Teflon is severalfold greater[78,83] than that for poly(vinyl chloride). Kel-F behaves similarly.

Infrared measurements show that, for Teflon films of 70 μ thickness irradiated in air, the ratio of vinylene formation to carbonyl formation increases with increasing intensity of irradiation.[71] This probably indicates the diffusion of oxygen to be rate limiting at high intensity. The density is increased and the melt viscosity is increased by irradiation in the presence of air.[52]

In spite of their excellent resistance to thermal and chemical degradation, Teflon and Kel-F are among the most sensitive to radiation in the presence of oxygen. Even with thick specimens, irradiation in air causes rapid deterioration of mechanical properties. The tensile strength of 0.14-in. specimens of Teflon was reduced to half the initial value at about 4×10^6 rads in the Oak Ridge Graphite Reactor;[14] and the elongation was even more susceptible, this loss showing at 2 or 3×10^6 rads. The tensile strength did not decline as rapidly after this early 50% decrease and retained 25% of its initial value up to doses of 6 or 7×10^7 rads. The elastic modulus showed little change with dose, but the impact strength was unusual in going through a sharp maximum (500% of initial value) at 3×10^6 rads. This property then decreased sharply to one-fourth its initial value at about 6×10^7 rads, the same dose at which the tensile strength suffered this loss.

Kel-F is more resistant to radiation damage than Teflon. The tensile strength was not reduced by half until 3×10^7 rads, although deterioration was quite rapid following the initial loss. The elongation and impact strength decreased to half the initial at 10^7 rads.

The importance of oxygen in the radiation sensitivity of Teflon indicates that the effect of both dose rate and thickness are likely to be very important in the case of irradiation in the presence of air. For this reason the above description of the radiation stability is confined to specimens of about 0.2-in. thickness irradiated at an intensity of 10^6 rads/hr in the presence of air.

6-11 Thermosetting Resins (Phenolics, Epoxies, and Polyesters)

The "thermosets" are insoluble and infusible because of their three-dimensional structure, as explained in Ch. 5, Sect. 5-2.3. These resins were the earliest synthetic polymers used commercially and still are among the leaders in industrial production. They are used chiefly as molding powders and as binders for laminates.

The most important thermosetting resin, historically and industrially, is phenol-formaldehyde. This product is prepared in condensation reactions in which phenol or one of its derivatives is used:

Urea and melamine condense with formaldehyde to form similar cross-linked products. The final cross-linking reaction or curing takes place under heat and pressure to give the resin its final form. Because of these favorable molding characteristics and relatively good high-temperature properties, along with low cost, these materials have wide applicability. A variety of fibrous materials, including wood flour, fabric, and asbestos, is used to improve (and sometimes to reduce the cost of) finished items.

The hardness, strength, and electrical resistance of the phenolics and other aldehyde derivatives permit their use in all types of molded household items. Laminated sheets and tubes are widely used in electrical components. The heat resistance and low flammability of filled articles make these resins very useful for molded components of industrial equipment.

Epoxies and unsaturated polyesters represent a second type of cross-linking resin that can be cured by chemical agents with little or no application of heat or pressure. They are frequently used in paints and finishes. The polyesters for such purposes are largely esters of phthalic acid but include esters of long-chain olefinic acids to permit hardening by atmospheric oxidation. The epoxies incorporate a variety of chemical curing agents in commercial formulations, including aliphatic and aromatic amines, polyhydroxyphenols, acid anhydrides, or other reactive compounds.

Recently the epoxies and polyesters of short-chain unsaturated acids have come into widespread use for molding large complex shapes reinforced with fibrous fillers and for embedding or "potting" electronic components. The polyesters are dissolved in styrene or other vinyl monomers for cross linking by addition polymerization. Typical preparative and curing reactions for the polyesters and epoxies are shown on pages 224 and 225, respectively.

The phenolics and epoxies are roughly comparable in their resistance to radiation, but the latter show marked variations depending on the curing agents employed. Thin films or coatings of the epoxies are also more susceptible to radiation degradation in oxygen than are films of phenolic resins.[41]

$$HOC-C=C-COH + HOCH_2CH_2OH \longrightarrow$$
(with O, H, H, O labels above)

$$--OC-C=C-C-O-CH_2CH_2-- + H_2O$$
(with O, H, H, O labels above; pendant $C=C$ with phenyl group)

$$--OC-C-C-C-O-CH_2CH_2-$$
(with O, H, H, O labels; HCH/CH–phenyl and HCH/HC–phenyl substituents)

Comparisons of epoxy resins cured with different reagents showed that aromatic curatives give products that are much more resistant to radiation than those with aliphatic curing agents. Gas production was about three-fold greater for the aliphatic agents than for the aromatics.[51] The most resistant resins tested were those cured with aromatic amines. Such resins retained over 60% of their initial flexural strength after about 10^9 rads in a reactor (BEPO) at 155°F in air.[3] There was evidence that scission occurred near the nitrogen atom and that the remainder of the epoxy molecule underwent cross linking slowly. Resins cured with low-molecular-weight aliphatic amines retained only 25 to 30% of their original flexural strength after 4×10^8 rads.[3,51]

Curatives having long alkyl side chains for the purpose of imparting flexibility to the cured resins degraded faster than the more rigid resins cured with more compact molecules. Resins cured with dodecenyl succinic anhydride lost about one-half their initial flexural strength when exposed[3] to 5×10^8 rads in a reactor (BEPO) in air at 155°F. Similar samples cured with other aliphatic acid anhydrides, with the maleic anhydride adduct of methylcyclopentadiene and with hexahydrophthalic anhydride, retained 80 to 85% of their initial strength at this dose.

Some commercial resins are cured with BF_3, which has a high cross section for reaction with thermal neutrons. Such a resin decreased in flexural strength to less than 25% of the initial value in a reactor irradiation that would have been less than 4×10^8 rads for ordinary materials. Actually, owing to the boron (n,α) reaction, the dose was much higher.[3]

Substantial differences that have been observed between the effects of

$$HO-\underset{}{\bigcirc}-\underset{CH_3}{\overset{CH_3}{\underset{|}{C}}}-\bigcirc-OH \;+\; CH_2CHCH_2Cl$$

$$HO-\bigcirc-\underset{CH_3}{\overset{CH_3}{\underset{|}{C}}}-\bigcirc-OCH_2\overset{OH}{\underset{|}{C}HCH_2Cl}$$

$[OH^-]$

$$HO-\bigcirc-\underset{CH_3}{\overset{CH_3}{\underset{|}{C}}}-\bigcirc-OCH_2CHCH_2 \;+\; HCl$$

$[OH^-]$ $\quad CH_2CHCH_2Cl \;+\; HO-\bigcirc-\underset{CH_3}{\overset{CH_3}{\underset{|}{C}}}-\bigcirc-OH$

$$CH_2CHCH_2\left[-O-\bigcirc-\underset{CH_3}{\overset{CH_3}{\underset{|}{C}}}-\bigcirc-OCH_2\overset{OH}{\underset{|}{C}}HCH_2-\right]_n O-\bigcirc-\underset{CH_3}{\overset{CH_3}{\underset{|}{C}}}-\bigcirc-OCH_2CHCH_2$$

$$\underset{H}{\overset{H}{N}}-R-\underset{H}{\overset{H}{N}}$$

$$-CH_2\overset{OH}{\underset{|}{C}}HCH_2\underset{\underset{HN}{\overset{|}{R}}}{\overset{\overset{CH_2\overset{OH}{CHCH_2}}{|}}{N}}\left[-O-\bigcirc-\underset{CH_3}{\overset{CH_3}{\underset{|}{C}}}-\bigcirc-OCH_2\overset{OH}{\underset{|}{C}}HCH_2-\right]_n O-\bigcirc-\underset{CH_3}{\overset{CH_3}{\underset{|}{C}}}-\bigcirc-OCH_2\overset{OH}{\underset{|}{C}}HCH_2\underset{\overset{|}{-OCH_2\overset{OH}{C}HCH_2N}}{\overset{|}{NH}}$$

accelerated electrons and gamma and reactor radiation have been explained on the basis of the difference in dose rates in the presence of air (at 85 to 160°F). Uniform specimens ($\frac{1}{8}$ in. thick) were exposed in air in an accelerator at 2×10^8 rads/hr and in a gamma source and in a reactor at 2 and 3×10^6 rads/hr, respectively. The specimens (cured with maleic anhydride adduct of methylcyclopentadiene) showed no change as a result of electron bombardment to 10^9 rads, but those receiving this dose from the gamma source and from the reactor decreased to 65% of the initial flexural strength.[4] Presumably, at the high dose rate of the accelerator, oxygen dissolved in the interior of the specimen was depleted and could not be replenished by diffusion from the surface rapidly enough to participate in radiation-induced degradative reactions. It has also been observed that thin films of epoxy resins are less resistant to radiation in air than are thick specimens.[41]

As in the case of the other thermosetting resins, fiberglass-epoxy laminates have been found more resistant to radiation than the bulk resin alone. Specimens of 30 to 35% resin content showed no loss of flexural strength after 10^9 rads of gamma radiation in air at room temperature, except for one laminate cured with dicyandiamide, an aliphatic polyamine.[77] The dielectric constant at microwave frequencies and the loss tangent of these materials were found to be unchanged in measurements carried out in the radiation field.

Lap joints of aluminum bonded with epoxy resin have been tested because of the common use of epoxies as adhesives. These[3,8] are discussed in Ch. 10, Adhesives.

6-12 Summary and Conclusions

A summary of changes in strength produced by irradiation of commercial plastics is presented in Table 6.2. Included are materials for which little is known about the nature of the radiation-induced changes. The reader is cautioned that it is more hazardous to extrapolate to other conditions of dose rate, temperature, thickness, etc., for these materials than for those for which these variables have been studied.

In the absence of appreciable effects from oxygen and water vapor, there is evidence that the amount of cross linking is insensitive to dose rate and may be correlated with high accuracy to the total dose alone (the energy absorbed from the radiation field).[9] For short exposures (less than a few weeks), oxidation effects in thick specimens of polyethylene are confined to the surface; however, unless the trapped free radicals are removed by annealing, the mechanical properties are seriously degraded after several months of postirradiation aging (Fig. 6.3). It appears that the diffusion of oxygen is rate limiting in this case and that the amount of oxidative scission depends on the concentration of oxygen in the polymer. Thus, where oxidation is involved, the amount of damage becomes a function of the dose rate and thickness as well as the total dose (all listed in Table 6.2). This greatly complicates the problem of setting tolerances for the exposure of plastics in radiation fields under these conditions.

Water vapor is analogous to oxygen inasmuch as the effect depends on the thickness and the dose rate. Humidity is an additional variable here. For certain of the irradiation studies referred to in Table 6.2, the humidity was controlled[14] at $50 \pm 5\%$.

The yield of oxidative scission is strongly dependent on the chemical structure of the polymer. For example, irradiation in the presence of air gives a much larger scission-to-cross linking ratio for polyethers than for polyethylene,[57] although cross linking predominates in the vacuum irradiation of both polymers. Also, for poly(vinyl chloride) and Teflon, the yield of main-chain scissions is increased for irradiation in the presence of air

Table 6.2 — EFFECTS OF RADIATION ON THE MECHANICAL PROPERTIES OF PLASTICS
(Irradiated in air at 77°F unless otherwise noted)

	Initial value	Dose rate, megarads/hr	Thickness, in.	Effect at rad dose[a]					Ref.
				5×10^6	10^7	10^8	10^9	10^{10}	
A. Hydrocarbon Thermoplastics									
1. High-density (linear) polyethylene									
a. Super Dylan:									
Tensile strength	3000 psi	2	0.12			C	A		55
Elongation	170 %						D		
b. Marlex-50:									
Tensile strength	4280 psi	1	0.002	A	D				38
Elongation	600 %			D					
Irradiated in vacuum:									
Tensile strength						A			
Elongation						D			
2. Low-density (branched) polyethylene									
a. Alathon:									
Tensile strength	1400 psi	2	0.19		A	B	A	B	14
Elongation	250 %				A	B	D		
Notch impact strength	11.2 ft-lb/in.						D		
b. Alathon 10:									
Tensile strength	1820 psi	2	0.13			C	A		55
Elongation	450 %						D		
c. Alathon 3:									
Tensile strength	1915 psi	1	0.003		A	B			39
Elongation	380 %				A	D			

Key: A = 80% of the initial value retained; B = 50 to 80%; C = 10 to 50%; D = <10%.

Table 6.2 (Continued)

	Initial value	Dose rate, megarads/hr	Thickness, in.	Effect at rad dose[a]					Ref.
				5×10^6	10^7	10^8	10^9	10^{10}	
Irradiated in vacuum:									
Tensile strength									
Elongation									
d. Irrathene 101:									
Tensile strength	2390 psi	1	0.010			B			39
Elongation	525%					B			
Irradiated in vacuum:		1							
Tensile strength					A	B			
Elongation					A	D			
Irradiated in air at low intensity:		0.1							
Tensile strength					A	C			
Elongation					A	D			38
3. Polystyrene									
a. Clear polystyrene:									
Tensile strength	1800 psi	2	0.12					A	14
Elongation	0.32 %							A	
b. Polyflex:									
Tensile strength	11,300 psi	1	0.002		A	B			39
Irradiated in vacuum:									
Tensile strength						B			
c. High-impact polystyrene:									
Tensile strength	3100 psi	2	0.10	A	B	B		A	14
Elongation	20 %			A	B	B	D		
Notch impact strength	0.67 ft-lb/in.						C	C	

Key: A = 80% of the initial value retained; B = 50 to 80%; C = 10 to 50%; D = <10%.

Table 6.2 (Continued)

	Initial value	Dose rate, megarads/hr	Thickness, in.	Effect at rad dose[a]					Ref.
				5×10^6	10^7	10^8	10^9	10^{10}	
4. Poly (α-methylstyrene):									
Shear strength	6000 psi	2	0.17		A	B	D		14
5. Butadiene-styrene copolymer, rubber blend (Pliotuf):									
Tensile strength	4300 psi	2	0.08					A	14
Elongation	3.8 %						A	B	
Notch impact strength	0.8 ft-lb/in.						A	B	
B. Nitrogen-containing Thermoplastics									
1. Nylon:									
Tensile strength	7600 psi	2	0.10	A	B	C	C	A	14
Elongation	62 %			A	B	C	D	D	
Notch impact strength	2.8 ft-lb/in.								
2. Aniline-formaldehyde polymer:									
Tensile strength	9200 psi	2	0.20				A	A	14
Elongation	1.8 %					A	A	A	
Notch impact strength	0.20 ft-lb/in.							A	
3. Styrene-acrylonitrile copolymer (Royalite):									
Tensile strength	4000 psi	2	0.06			A	A		14
Elongation	8.5 %						C		

Key: A = 80% of the initial value retained; B = 50 to 80%; C = 10 to 50%; D = <10%.

Table 6.2 (Continued)

	Initial value	Dose rate, megarads/hr	Thickness, in.	Effect at rad dose[a]					Ref.
				5×10^6	10^7	10^8	10^9	10^{10}	
4. Poly (vinyl carbazole):									
Tensile strength	1800 psi	2	0.15					A	14
Elongation	0.32 %							A	
Notch impact strength	0.27 ft-lb/in.							A	
5. Casein resin:									
Tensile strength	8500 psi	2	0.24		A	B	D		14
Elongation	20 %				A	B	D		
Notch impact strength	0.50 ft-lb/in.				A	C	D		
C. Oxygen-containing Thermoplastics									
1. Polycarbonate (Macrofol):									
Tensile strength	6800 psi	1	0.003		A	A			39
Elongation	75 %					B			
Irradiated in vacuum:									
Tensile strength					A				
Elongation					B				
2. Mylar A:									
Tensile strength	25,000 psi	2	0.002		A	A	C	D	14
Elongation	50 %				A	A	D		
Tensile strength	20,300 psi	1	0.003		A	B			39
Elongation	150 %				A	B			
Irradiated in vacuum:									
Tensile strength					A	B			39
Elongation					A	B			

Key: A = 80% of the initial value retained;   B = 50 to 80%;   C = 10 to 50%;   D = <10%.

Table 6.2 (Continued)

	Initial value	Dose rate, megarads/hr	Thickness, in.	Effect at rad dose[a]					Ref.
				5×10^6	10^7	10^8	10^9	10^{10}	
3. Poly(methyl methacrylate):									
a. Lucite									
Tensile strength	10,700 psi	2	0.13	A	B	D			14
Elongation	4.5 %			A	B	D			
Notch impact strength	0.37 ft-lb/in.				A	B	D		
b. Plexiglas II									
Notch impact strength	1.0 ft-lb/in.	0.5	0.25		A	C	D		64
4. Poly(vinyl formal):									
Tensile strength	7400 psi	2	0.005			A	B	C	14
Elongation	2 %						A	D	
5. Poly(vinyl butyral):									
Tensile strength	2200 psi	2	0.016		A	B	C	D	14
Elongation	220 %				A	C	C	D	
6. Cellulosics (ethyl cellulose, cellulose acetate, cellulose propionate, cellulose nitrate, cellulose acetate-butyrate):									
Tensile strength	4000-6000 psi	2	0.1-0.2		A-B	C	D		14
Elongation	1-40 %				A-B	C-D	D		
Notch impact strength	1-3 ft-lb/in.				A-B	C-D	D		

Key: A = 80% of the initial value retained; B = 50 to 80%; C = 10 to 50%; D = <10%.

Table 6.2 (Continued)

	Initial value	Dose rate, megarads/hr	Thickness, in.	Effect at rad dose[a]					Ref.
				5 x 10⁶	10⁷	10⁸	10⁹	10¹⁰	
D. Halogen-containing Thermoplastics									
1. Rigid poly(vinyl chloride):									
Tensile strength	8100 psi	0.2	0.17			A	B		17
Notch impact strength	0.5 ft-lb/in.						A		
2. Plasticized poly(vinyl chloride)									
a. (Geon 8630):									
Tensile strength	2555 psi	1	0.004	A	B	B			
Elongation	245 %			B	B	B			
b. (Geon 8630):									
Tensile strength	2735 psi	1	0.02	A	A	A			
Elongation	300 %					B			
c. (Geon 8640):									
Tensile strength	3150 psi	1	0.004	A	B	B			
Elongation	225 %				A	B			
Irradiated in vacuum:									
Tensile strength		1				B			
Elongation						B			
3. Poly(vinyl chloride) with special plasti-cizers (70 parts plasticizer per 100 parts polymer):									
a. Tritolyl phosphate:									
Tensile strength	2100 psi	0.2	0.06		A	B			84
Elongation	318 %				A	B			

Key: A = 80% of the initial value retained; B = 50 to 80%; C = 10 to 50%; D = <10%.

Table 6.2 (Continued)

	Initial value	Dose rate, megarads/hr	Thickness, in.	Effect at rad dose[a]						Ref.
				5 x 10^6	10^7	10^8	10^9	10^10		
b. Di-2-ethylhexyl phthalate:										
Tensile strength	1900 psi	0.2	0.06		B	C				
Elongation	364 %				B	C				
c. Di-2-ethylhexyl sebacate:										
Tensile strength	1300 psi	0.2	0.06		B	D				
Elongation	318 %				B	D				
d. Polypropylenyl sebacate (Reoplex 100):										
Tensile strength	2000 psi	0.2	0.06		A	B				
Elongation	342 %				B	D				
e. Polypropylenyl sebacate modified (Reoplex 110):										
Tensile strength	2000 psi	0.2	0.06		A	A				
Elongation	234 %				A	C				
4. Vinyl chloride-vinylidene chloride copolymer:										
Tensile strength	3700 psi	2	0.13	B	A	C	D			14
Elongation	200 %			B	B	C	D			
Notch impact strength	1.6 ft-lb/in.				B	C	D			
5. Poly(vinyl chloride-acetate):										
Tensile strength	9000 psi	2	0.13		A	B	C	D		14
Elongation	3.1 %				A	B	C	D		
Notch impact strength	0.5 ft-lb/in.						A	D		

Key: A = 80% of the initial value retained; B = 50 to 80%; C = 10 to 50%; D = <10%.

Table 6.2 (Continued)

	Initial value	Dose rate, megarads/hr	Thickness, in.	Effect at rad dose[a]						Ref.
				10^6	5×10^6	10^7	10^8	10^9	10^{10}	
6. Poly(tetrafluoroethylene) (Teflon):										
a. Tensile strength	3400 psi	1	0.14	B	C	C	D			14
Elongation	250 %			C	D					
b. Tensile strength	2695 psi	1	0.01	C	C					39
Elongation	165 %			C	D					
Irradiated in vacuum:										
Tensile strength					B					
Elongation					C					
7. Poly(chlorotrifluoroethylene) (Kel-F):										
Tensile strength	4900 psi	1	0.12	A	B	A	D			14
Elongation	50 %			A	B	B	D			
Notch impact strength	1.9 ft-lb/in.					B	D			
E. Thermosets										
1. Asbestos fabric-filled phenolic:										
Tensile strength	11,000 psi	1	0.12						A	14
Elongation	1.3 %								A	
Notch impact strength	3.9 ft-lb in.								A	

Key: A = 80% of the initial value retained: B = 50 to 80%: C = 10 to 50%: D = 10%.

Table 6.2 (Continued)

	Initial value	Dose rate, megarads/hr	Thickness, in.	Effect at rad dose[a]					Ref.
				5×10^6	10^7	10^8	10^9	10^{10}	
2. Linen fabric-filled phenolic:									
Tensile strength	11,000 psi	2	0.25	A	A	B	C	D	14
Elongation	4.0 %				B	C	D	D	
Notch impact strength	2.75 ft-lb/in.			A	B	C	D	D	
3. Cast phenolic:									
Tensile strength	11,000 psi	2	0.18			A	B	D	14
Elongation	2 %					A	B	D	
Notch impact strength	0.53 ft-lb/in.					A	B	D	
4. Epoxy:									
a. Aromatic amine-cured									
Flexural strength	17,000 psi	3	0.12			A	B		3,51
b. Aliphatic amine-cured									
Flexural strength	18,500 psi	3	0.12			B	D		3,51
c. Acid anhydride-cured									
Flexural strength	18,500 psi	3	0.12			A	B		3,51
d. Acid anhydride-cured (long side chain)									
Flexural strength	11,500 psi	3	0.12			B	D		3,51
e. Araldite Type B casting									
shear strength	8000 psi	2	0.16				A	B	14

Key: A = 80% of the initial value retained;   B = 50 to 80%;   C = 10 to 50%;   D = <10%.

Table 6.2 (Continued)

	Initial value	Dose rate, megarads/hr	Thickness, in.	Effect at rad dose[a]					Ref.
				5×10^6	10^7	10^8	10^9	10^{10}	
5. Mineral-filled polyester: (Plaskon Alkyd)		1	0.13						14
Tensile strength	4700 psi							A	
Elongation	0.2 %							A	
Notch impact strength	0.39 ft-lb/in.							A	
6. Cast polyester (Selectron 5038):		2	0.26						14
Tensile strength	2000 psi				A	C	A	C	
Elongation	20 %						C	D	
Notch impact strength	0.73 ft-lb/in.				A	B	C	D	
7. Allyl diglycol carbonate resin:		2	0.12						14
Tensile strength	6700 psi					A	B	D	
Elongation	2.4 %						A	C	
Impact strength	0.35 ft-lb/in.						A	C	
8. Triallyl cyanurate resin:		2	0.25						14
Shear strength	2000 psi							A	
9. Cellulose pulp-filled melamine-formaldehyde:		2	0.248						14
Tensile strength	9100 psi					A	C	D	
Elongation	0.65 %					A	C	D	
Notch impact strength	0.29 ft-lb/in.						A	D	

Key: A = 80% of the initial value retained; B = 50 to 80%; C = 10 to 50%; D = · 10%.

Table 6.2 (Continued)

	Initial value	Dose rate, megarads/hr	Thickness, in.	Effect at rad dose[a]					Ref.
				5×10^6	10^7	10^8	10^9	10^{10}	
10. Cellulose pulp-filled urea-formaldehyde		2	0.125						14
Tensile strength	7800 psi					A	C	D	
Elongation	0.5 %					A	C	D	
Notch impact strength	0.30 ft-lb/in.						A	D	
11. Furane resin, graphite-filled:		1	0.37						14
Tensile strength	2200 psi							A	
Elongation	0.39 %							A	
Impact strength	0.31 ft-lb/in.							A	
12. Silicone-glass cloth laminate;		1	0.07						14
Shear strength	13,5000 psi					A	B	C	

Key: A = 80% of the initial value retained; B = 50 to 80%; C = 10 to 50%; D = < 10%.

over that for vacuum irradiation. It appears that for polyethers and for halogen-containing polymers, the diffusion of oxygen is not as important a rate-limiting factor as it is for polyethylene.

Exposure temperature is another important irradiation variable. In the presence of oxygen, increasing exposure temperature increases the rate of oxidative degradation initiated by radiation-produced radicals. Information is inadequate on the effect of high temperatures in the absence of oxygen, but both Teflon and poly(methyl methacrylate) form sharply increased amounts of volatile materials on irradiation at temperatures near the softening point.[58] Thus for these polymers temperature becomes a factor at much lower values in the presence of radiation than in its absence.

Values for the total gas evolved from irradiated polymers are given in Table 6.3. The composition of the gas, where known, has already been given in the text. Here again the effects of oxygen and temperature are very important. The yields presented in the table are for approximately room temperature and in a limited supply of oxygen or in vacuum. The gas yields of the materials containing fillers are subject to considerably more error than the others. This results from a lack of information on the amount of filler present.

Owing to the method of measurement, all the low gas-yield values except those for polystyrene are in some doubt; and they are so marked. In addition to the error in measurement, the number of measurements was smaller than in the case of the high yields because the radiation exposure had to be very long to produce sufficient quantities of gas. The value for poly(vinyl formal) is marked as approximate, although high, because the amount of gas evolved was not proportional to the dose but appeared to be proportional to the square root of the dose between 10^8 and 10^9 rads.

The gas yield for polyethylene is perhaps the most accurate ($\pm 10\%$). The value given is for long exposure, as are those for the other materials. Short exposures give somewhat higher gas yields for polyethylene.[65] All the other values in Table 6.3 were derived by normalizing to the polyethylene value.

Gas evolution has not been studied extensively for halogenated compounds such as poly(vinyl chloride) and poly(tetrafluoroethylene). However, the gases evolved are very reactive; reaction with either the container or the polymer is immediate. The gas yield is therefore hard to measure and not very meaningful. It is well to remember that the corrosive gases evolved may cause trouble in any application.

Significant developments have been made in recent years in the clarification of the mechanism of radiation-induced reactions in polyethylene. The uncertainties involved in the cross-linking yield have been eliminated by Charlesby through cross-link determinations by two independent tech-

Table 6.3 — GAS YIELDS FROM IRRADIATED PLASTICS
AND ELASTOMERS

| Material | Gas evolved[14,58] | |
	Molecules/100 ev[a]	Ml/g (S. T. P.) at 10^9 rads[a]
Polyethylene	3.1	70
Polystyrene	0.08	1.5
Poly (α-methylstyrene)	0.08	1.5
Natural rubber[b]	0.3	7
Styrene-butadiene rubber[b]	0.15	4
Styrene-butadiene plastic	~0.08	~2
Polyisobutylene rubber[b]	0.8	17
Polyamide - nylon	1.1	25
Aniline-formaldehyde polymer	~0.08	~2
Melamine-formaldehyde polymer (cellulosic filler)	0.45	10
Urea-formaldehyde polymer (cellulosic filler)	0.8	17
Nitrile-butadiene rubber[b]	0.15	5.0
Casein plastic	0.15	4
Poly (methyl methacrylate)	1.5	35
Poly (ethylene terephthalate)	0.15	3
Allyl diglycol carbonate	1.9	40
Polyesters (general)	0.08 to 1.9	2 to 40
Cellulose acetate polymer	0.8	17
Cellulose acetate-butyrate polymer	1.2	28
Cellulose propionate polymer	1.5	35
Cellulose nitrate polymer	4.6	105
Ethyl cellulose polymer	1.5	35
Phenolic plastic (no filler)	0.1	3
Phenolic plastic (cellulose filler)	0.8	17
Phenolic plastic (mineral filler)	<0.08	<2.0
Silicone elastomer	0.9	20
Ethyl acrylate rubber[b]	1.2	28
Chloroprene rubber[b]	0.15	4
Poly (vinyl formal)	~4.3 (at 10^9 rads)	~100
Triallyl cyanurate polymer	~0.08	~2.0
Polysulfide rubber[b]	0.23	6

[a]Energy absorbed by the polymer, excluding any filler.
[b]Rubbers are compounded and vulcanized. The values are much more approximate than those for the plastics.

niques on both linear and branched material. The measurements of hydrogen production and the increase and decrease of unsaturated species by Dole have indicated how these processes are involved in the crosslinking reactions. The work of Lawton and coworkers has shown reactions that trapped free radicals can undergo.

Poly(methyl methacrylate) has been studied as a prototype of polymer in which scission predominates. Alexander has demonstrated the effect of impurities; Wall and Brown have studied the effect of atmospheric oxygen and have shown the presence of long-lived reactive species in irradiated solid polymer. Whiffen, Ovenall, and coworkers have identified these as a chain remnant by examinations of poly(methyl methacrylate) and related compounds. The effect of size of the side groups on the rates of scission and cross linking of acrylates and methacrylates has been elucidated by Shultz.

The general stabilizing effect of a frequently recurring aromatic ring as a side group has been observed by several investigators. The effect of incorporation of elements other than carbon and hydrogen in the molecular structure of a plastic on its behavior under irradiation is still uncertain.

References

Several of the following were cited in the text as authority for statements made. Others were not quoted but are included because they contain pertinent information. All were consulted in the preparation of this chapter.

1. Abraham, R. J., Melville, H. W., Ovenall, D. W., and Whiffen, D. H., Electron Spin Resonance Spectra of Free Radicals in Irradiated Polymethyl Methacrylate and Related Compounds, *Trans. Faraday Soc., 54*(8): 1133 (August 1958).

2. Aggarwall, S. L., and Sweeting, O. J., Polyethylene: Preparation, Structure, and Properties, *Chem. Revs., 57*(4): 665 (August 1957).

3. Aitken, I. D., and Ralph, K., *Some Effects of Radiation on Cast Epoxy Resin Systems,* British Report AERE-R-3085, February 1960.

4. Aitken, I. D., Ralph, K., and Sheldon, R., *Irradiation Studies on Anhydride Cured Epoxy Resin,* British Report AERE-R-3339, May 1960.

5. Alexander, P., Charlesby, A., and Ross, M., The Degradation of Solid Polymethyl Methacrylate by Ionizing Radiation, *Proc. Roy. Soc. (London), A223*(1154): 392 (May 1954).

6. Alexander, P., and Toms, D. J., Protection Provided by Added Substances Against the Direct Action of Ionizing Radiation, *Radiation Research, 9*(5): 509 (November 1958).

7. Amemiya, A., and Danno, A., Effects of Ionizing Radiations on Polyethylene, *J. Phys. Soc. Japan, 13*(6): 604 (June 1958).

8. Arlook, R. S., and Harvey, D. G., *Effects of Nuclear Radiation on Structural Adhesive Bonds,* Report WADC-TR-56-467, Wright Air Development Center, August 1956.

9. Atchison, G. J., Dose Rate Effect on Crosslinking of Polyethylene with High Energy Electrons in Vacuo, *J. Polymer Sci., 35*(129): 557 (March 1959).

10. Bakh, N. A. (Ed.), Symposium on Radiation Chemistry, *Acad. Sci. U.S.S.R.,* 1955, English translation, Consultants Bureau, New York, 1955.

11. Berkowitch, J., Charlesby, A., and Desreux, V., Radiation Effects on Aqueous Solutions of Polyvinyl Alcohol, *J. Polymer Sci., 25*(111): 490 (September 1957).

12. Black, R. M., Effect of Temperature Upon the Crosslinking of Polyethylene by High Energy Radiation, *Nature, 178*(4528): 305 (August 1956).

13. Black, R. M., and Lyons, B. J., Radiation-Induced Changes in the Structure of Polypropylene, *Proc. Roy. Soc. (London) A253*(1274): 322 (December 1959).

14. Bopp, C. D., and Sisman, O., *Physical Properties of Irradiated Plastics*, USAEC Report ORNL-928, Oak Ridge National Laboratory, June 1951; *Radiation Stability of Plastics and Elastomers*, USAEC Report ORNL-1373, Oak Ridge National Laboratory, July 1953; and *Nucleonics*, *13*(7): 28 (July 1955), *13*(10): 50 (Oct. 1955), and *14*(3): 52 (March 1956).

15. Boyd, R. H., Dielectric Loss in 66 Nylon, *J. Chem. Phys.*, *30*(5): 1276 (May 1959).

16. Burch, P. R. J., A Theoretical Interpretation of the Effect of Radiation Quantity on Yield in the Ferrous and Ceric Sulphate Dosimeters, *Radiation Research, 11* (4): 481 (October 1959).

17. Byrnes, J., *et al.*, Evolution of Halides from Halogenated Plastics Exposed to Gamma Radiation, *Ind. Eng. Chem.*, *45*(11): 2549 (November 1953).

18. Charlesby, A., Beneficial Effects of Radiation on Polymers, *Nucleonics*, *14*(9): 82 (September 1956).

19. Charlesby, A., and Davison, W. H. T., Temperature Effects in the Irradiation of Polymers, *Chem. & Ind. (London)*, *1957*(8): 232 (February 1957).

20. Charlesby, A., and Pinner, S. H., Analysis of the Solubility Behavior of Irradiated Polyethylene and Other Polymers, *Proc. Roy. Soc. (London)*, *A249*(1258): 367 (January 1959).

21. Charlesby, A., and Swallow, A. J., Radiation Chemistry, in *Ann. Rev. Phys. Chem.*, *1959*(10): 289–330.

22. Danno, A., Effects of Ionizing Radiations on Polyvinyl Alcohol. Part I: Breakdown of Main-Chain and Formation of Carbonyl Groups, *J. Phys. Soc. Japan, 13* (6): 609–613 (June 1958).

23. Danno, A., Effects of Ionizing Radiation on Polyvinyl Alcohol. Part II: Changes of Physical Properties of the Irradiated Specimen Caused by Heat Treatment, *J. Phys. Soc. Japan*, *13*(6): 614–617 (June 1958).

24. Deeley, C. W., Kline, D. W., Sauer, J. A., and Woodward, A. E., Effect of Pile Irradiation on the Dynamic Mechanical Properties of Polyethylene, *J. Polymer Sci.*, *28*(116): 109 (February 1958); Deeley, C. W., Sauer, J. A., and Woodward, A. E., Dynamic Mechanical Behavior of Irradiated Polyethylene, *J. Appl. Phys.*, *29*(10): 1415 (October 1958).

25. Deeley, C. W., Woodward, A. E., and Sauer, J. A., Effect of Irradiation on Dynamic Mechanical Properties of 6-6 Nylon, *J. Appl. Phys.*, *28*(10): 1124 (October 1957).

26. Dewhurst, H. A., and Schuler, R. H., A Comparison of the Decomposition of Hexane and Cyclohexane by Different Types of Radiations, *J. Am. Chem. Soc.*, *81*(13): 3210 (July 1959).

27. Dole, M., Williams, T. F., and Arvia, A. J., The Radiation Chemistry of a Typical Macromolecule, Polyethylene, *Proceedings of the Second International Conference on the Peaceful Uses of Atomic Energy, Geneva, 1958*, Vol. 29, p. 171, United Nations, New York, 1959.

28. Dole, M., Milner, D. C., and Williams, T. F., Irradiation of Polyethylene, II: Kinetics of Unsaturation Effects, *J. Am. Chem. Soc.*, *80*(7): 1580 (April 1958).

29. Dole, M., and Williams, T. F., Energy Transfer in Polyethylene and Polyethylene-Polybutadiene Mixtures During Gamma Irradiation, *Discussions Faraday Soc.*, No. 27: 74 (1959).

30. Duffey, D., Polyvinyl Methyl Ether Elastomers by High Energy Radiation, *Ind. Eng. Chem.*, *50*(9): 1267 (September 1958).

31. Durup, M., *et al.*, Peroxidation of Organic Compounds Induced by Ionizing Radiations, *Proceedings of the Second International Conference on the Peaceful Uses of Atomic Energy, Geneva, 1958*, Vol. 29, p. 143, United Nations, New York, 1959.

32. Ehrenberg, E., and Zimmer, K. G., Action of Ionizing Radiation on Insulating Plastics, *Acta Chem. Scand.,* 10(5): 874 (1956).
33. Epstein, L. M., Electron Crosslinking of Polyethylenes of Two Different Densities, *J. Polymer Sci.,* 26(114): 399 (December 1957).
34. Fowler, J. F., X-Ray Induced Conductivity in Insulating Materials, *Proc. Roy. Soc. (London) A236*(1207): 464 (September 1956).
35. Fowler, J. F., and Farmer, F. T., Conductivity Induced in Unplasticized Perspex by X Rays, *Nature,* 175(4455): 516 (March 1955).
36. Fuschillo, N., Rhian, E., and Sauer, J. A., Nuclear Magnetic Resonance and Crystallinity in Polyethylene, *J. Polymer Sci.,* 25(110): 381 (August 1957); Fuschillo, N., and Sauer, J. A., Nuclear Magnetic Resonance, Radiation Damage, and Rigidity in Branched Polyethylene as a Function of Temperature, *J. Appl. Phys.,* 28(10): 1073 (October 1957).
37. Graham, R. K., Gamma Irradiation of Polymers of Aryl and Alkaryl Methacrylates and Acrylates, *J. Polymer Sci.,* 37(132): 441 (June 1959).
38. Harrington, R., Damaging Effects of Radiation on Plastics and Elastomers, *Nucleonics,* 14(9): 70 (September 1956).
39. Harrington, R., and Giberson, R. C., Chemical and Physical Changes in Gamma-Irradiated Plastics, *Modern Plastics,* 36(3): 199 (November 1958).
40. Henglein, A., Crosslinking of Polymers in Solution Under the Influence of Gamma Radiation, *J. Phys. Chem.,* 63(11): 1852 (November 1959).
41. Horrocks, L. A., How Radiation Affects Six Organic Coating Materials, *Design Eng.,* 47(1): 120 (January 1958).
42. Kotliar, A. M., The Effect of Radiation on Poly-α-Methylstyrene, *J. Appl. Polymer Sci.,* 2(5): 134–142 (September–October 1959).
43. Lanza, V. L., Effect of Radiation on Polyethylene, *Modern Plastics,* 34(10): 129 (July 1957).
44. Lawton, E. J., Powell, R. S., and Balwit, J. S., Effect of Physical State During the Electron Irradiation of Hydrocarbon Polymers. Part I: The Influence of Physical State on Reactions Occurring in Polyethylene During and Following the Irradiation, *J. Polymer Sci.,* 32(125): 257–275 (November 1958); Part II: Additional Experiments and Discussion Pertaining to Trapped Radicals in Hydrocarbon Polymers, *J. Polymer Sci.,* 32(125): 277–290 (November 1958).
45. Majury, T. G., and Pinner, S. H., The Irradiation of Polycaprolactam with X Rays and Electrons, *J. Appl. Chem., (London),* 8 (Part 3): 168 (March 1958).
46. Marans, N. S., Radiation Crosslinking of Polystyrene-Additive Systems, American Chemical Society, Abstracts of Papers, 132nd Meeting, Sept. 8–13, 1957, p. 21T.
47. Matsuo, H., and Dole, M., Irradiation of Polyethylene IV, Oxidation Effects, *J. Phys. Chem.,* 63(6): 837 (June 1959).
48. Meyer, R. A., Bouquet, F. L., and Alger, R. L., Radiation Induced Conductivity in Polyethylene and Teflon, *J. Appl. Phys.,* 27(9): 1012 (September 1956).
49. Miller, A. A., Lawton, E. J., and Balwit, J. S.. Effect of Chemical Structure of Vinyl Polymers on Crosslinking and Degradation by Ionizing Radiation, *J. Polymer Sci.,* 14(77): 503 (November 1954).
50. Miller, A. A., Lawton, E. J., and Balwit, J. L., The Radiation Chemistry of Hydrocarbon Polymers: Polyethylene, Polymethylene, and Octacosane, *J. Phys. Chem.,* 60(5): 599 (May 1956).
51. Mixer, R. Y., and Parkinson, D. B., *Nuclear Radiation Effects on Structural Plastics and Adhesives,* Report WADC-TR-56-534, Part III, Stanford Research Inst., August 1957.
52. Nishioka, A., *et al.,* Effects of Gamma Radiation on Some Physical Properties of Polytetrafluoroethylene, *J. Appl. Poly. Sci.,* 2(4): 114 (July–August 1959).

53. Okamura, S., *et al.*, Effects of Gamma Radiation on Polymer Reactions, *Proceedings of the Second International Conference on the Peaceful Uses of Atomic Energy, Geneva, 1958*, Vol. 29, p. 176, United Nations, New York, 1959.
54. Parkinson, W. W., and Binder, D., Post-Irradiation Oxidation and Molecular Weight Changes in Polystyrene and Poly(Methyl Methacrylate), pp. 224–232, in Materials in Nuclear Applications, *ASTM Spec. Tech. Publ.* 276, June 1960.
55. Parkinson, W. W., *Solid State Division Annual Progress Report*, USAEC Report ORNL-2413, Oak Ridge National Laboratory, 1957, and other unpublished work.
56. Pearson, R. W., Mechanism of the Radiation Crosslinking of Polyethylene, *J. Polymer Sci.*, *25*(109): 180 (July 1957).
57. Pearson, R. W., The Effect of Gamma-radiation Upon Poly(Ethylene Oxides), *Proceedings of the International Conference on Radioisotopes in Scientific Research*, Vol. 1, Paper 1, p. 151, Pergamon Press, New York, 1958.
58. Petrov, I. Ya., and Karpov, V. L., Investigation of Gas Evolution from the Action of Nuclear Radiation on Polymers, *Proceedings of the First All-Union Conference on Radiation Chemistry*, 1957 English translation, Consultants Bureau, New York, 1959.
59. Pinner, S. H., Enhancement of Radiation-Induced Crosslinking of Polyvinyl Chloride, *Nature*, *183*(4668): 1108 (April 1959).
60. Pravednikov, A. N., Kang, Y. S., and Medvedev, S. S., The Mechanism of the Crosslinking of Polymer Chains by Gamma Irradiation, *Proceedings of the Second International Conference on the Peaceful Uses of Atomic Energy, Geneva, 1958*, Vol. 29, p. 192, United Nations, New York, 1959.
61. Rexroad, H. N., and Gordy, W. J., Electron Spin Resonance Studies of Irradiated Teflon, Effects of Various Gases, *J. Chem. Phys.*, *30*(2): 399 (February 1959).
62. St. Pierre, L. E., and Dewhurst, H. A., Oxygen Effects in the Radiation Chemistry of Polyethylene, *J. Chem. Phys.*, *29*(1): 241 (July 1958).
63. Sashin, B. E., et al., Some Properties of Gamma-Irradiated Polyethylene, *Zhur. Tekh. Fiz.*, *28*, 1991 (1958).
64. Schmidt, D. L., *Effects of Gamma Radiation on Aircraft Transparent Materials*, Report WADC-TR-56-557, Part II, Wright Air Development Center, March 1958.
65. Schumacher, K., About the Change in High and Low Density Polyethylenes from X Rays, *Kolloid-Z.* *157*(1): 16 (March 1959).
66. Sears, W. C., and Parkinson, W. W., Post-Irradiation Oxidation in Rubber and Plastics, *J. Polymer Sci.*, *21*(98): 325 (August 1956).
67. Shinohara, K., et al., Radiation Effects on Polymers, *Proceedings of the Second International Conference on the Peaceful Uses of Atomic Energy, Geneva, 1958*, Vol. 29, p. 186. United Nations, New York, 1959.
68. Shultz, A. R., High Energy Radiation Effects on Polyacrylates and Polymethacrylates, *J. Polymer Sci.*, *35*(129): 369 (March 1959).
69. Shultz, A. R., and Bovey, F. A., Electron Irradiation of Polyacrylates, *J. Polymer Sci.*, *22*(102): 485 (December 1956).
70. Shultz, A. R., Roth, P. I., and Rathmann, G. B., Light Scattering and Viscosity Study of Electron-Irradiated Polystyrene and Polymethacrylates, *J. Polymer Sci.*, *22*(102): 495 (December 1956).
71. Slovokhotova, N. A., Investigation Using Infrared Spectroscopy of Chemical Changes Occurring in Teflon Under the Effect of Ionizing Radiation, in *Action of Ionizing Radiation on Organic and Inorganic Systems*, Pshezhetskii, S. Ya., (Ed.), p. 295, Akad. Nauk S.S.S.R., Moscow, 1958.
72. Snow, A. I., and Moyer, H. C., Radiation Chemistry of Solid Paraffins, *J. Chem. Phys.*, *27*(5): 1222 (November 1957).
73. Soboleva, I. G., Makletsova, N. V., and Medvedev, S. S. (Karpov Scientific-

Research Institute of Physics and Chemistry), Light Scattering, Osmometric, and Viscosity Studies of the Structure of Polystyrene Subjected to γ-Radiation, *Kolloid. Zhur. 21,* 625–629 (September–October 1959) (in Russian).

74. Sobolev, I., Meyer, J. A., Stannett, V., and Szwarc, M., Permeability to Gases of Irradiated Polyethylene, *J. Polymer Sci., 17*(85): 417 (July 1955).

75. Taubman, A. B., and Ianova, L. P., Some Characteristics of the Radiation Destruction of Polymers, *Doklady Akad. Nauk S.S.S.R., 118*(5): 991 (February 1958).

76. Teszler, O., and Rutherford, H. A., The Effect of Nuclear Radiation on Fibrous Materials, *Proceedings of the Second International Conference on the Peaceful Uses of Atomic Energy, Geneva, 1958,* Vol. 29, p. 228, United Nations, New York, 1959.

77. Tomashot, R. C., and Harvey, D. G., *Nuclear Radiation of Reinforced Plastic Radome Materials,* Report WADC-TR-56-296, Wright Air Development Center, July 1956.

78. Tsvetkov, U. D., *et al.,* The Electron Resonance Spectrum of Polymer Irradiated at 77°K, *Doklady Akad. Nauk S.S.S.R., 122*(6): 1053 (October 1958).

79. Waddington, F. B., The Electron Crosslinking of Polypropylene and High Density Polyethylene, *J. Polymer Sci., 31*(122): 221 (August 1958).

80. Wall, L. A., Factors Influencing the Behavior of Polymers Exposed to High Energy Radiation, *J. Polymer Sci., 17*(83): 141 (May 1955).

81. Wall, L. A., and Brown, D. W., Chemical Activity of Gamma-Irradiated Polymethyl Methacrylate, *J. Research Nat. Bur. Standards, 57*(3): 131 (September 1956).

82. Wall, L. A., and Brown, D. W., Gamma-Irradiation of Polymethyl Methacrylate and Polystyrene, *J. Phys. Chem., 61*(2): 129 (February 1957).

83. Wall, L. A., and Florin, R. E., Polytetrafluoroethylene—A Radiation-Resistant Polymer, *J. Appl. Polymer Sci., 2*(5): 251 (September–October 1959).

84. Wells, H., and Williamson, I., Polyvinyl Chloride Compositions for Resistance to Intense γ-Radiation, *Brit. Plastics, 31*(7): 311 (July 1958).

85. Wippler, C., Crosslinking of Polyvinyl Chloride by Ionizing Radiation, *J. Polymer Sci., 29*(120): 585 (June 1958).

86. Williams, T. F., Matsuo, H., and Dole, M., Inhibition of Crystallization in Polyethylene Subsequent to Gamma Irradiation, *J. Am. Chem. Soc., 80*(11): 2895 (June 1958).

87. Williams, T. F., and Dole, M., Part III, Influence of Temperature and Phase, *J. Am. Chem. Soc., 81*(12): 2919 (June 1959).

88. Zimmerman, J., Spectra of Irradiated Polyamides, *J. Appl. Polymer Sci., 2*(5): 181 (September–October 1959).

CHAPTER 7

Elastomeric Materials

BY JOHN W. BORN

7-1 Introduction

For many years the development and the adaptation of rubber products to meet new needs have made important contributions to technological advancement. The latest challenge encountered is in the area of nuclear radiation effects. The unique serviceability of rubber products in conventional technology makes them important where nuclear fission has replaced the more common forms of energy. Nuclear uses, however, impose severe new demands on rubber materials: they must withstand the combined attack of heat and radiation, and, as man's power requirements increase, temperatures and radiation doses will become more severe.

Elastomeric materials may serve the nuclear scientist either as neutron shields or as components in thermal, electrical, or mechanical systems. They may appear in experimental nuclear reactor installations; in nuclear-fueled electric power plants; in the nuclear-propelled Army and Navy; and, before many years, in nuclear-powered aircraft and spacecraft. At present they are used mainly in gamma irradiation facilities, in the vicinity of particle accelerators, and in radioisotope hot cells.

Elastomeric materials are among the most sensitive to radiolysis of all construction materials (see Ch. 1, Fig. 1.1). Radiation progressively deteriorates the initially optimized properties of elastomers and rubber compounds. The general effect is to increase the modulus of elasticity and the hardness while decreasing ultimate elongation and tensile strength. The problems, if not the solutions, are clear: to understand and prevent radiation-induced damage on the one hand and to learn how to employ radiation beneficially on the other.

The first published work[55] on the effect of high-energy radiation on rubber concerned the vulcanization of natural rubber by Newton in 1929. He used accelerated electrons from a cathode-ray tube. Few papers appeared until 1948, when Davidson and Geib[25] discussed the effects of reactor radiations on uncured elastomers. From 1949 to the present, the amount of literature on this general subject has accompanied the growth of nuclear technology and engineering.

This growth has reflected several important influences: (1) the increasing availability of ionizing-radiation sources, (2) the need for elasto-meric materials in areas adjacent to reactors in nuclear-propelled aircraft and submarines, and (3) the discovery that radiation can induce improve-ments in the physical properties of some organic high polymers. High-energy radiation is becoming an increasingly valuable tool to the basic scientist in the controlled induction of physical and chemical changes, particularly in the molecular materials.

After developing a broad basis for the understanding of subsequent discussions by describing rubber technology, this chapter will present gen-eral radiation effects on elastomeric materials and discuss specific ex-amples. It will treat the beneficial applications of radiation and will con-cern itself with radiation-induced deterioration in service performance and thresholds of radiation damage to rubber products.

7-2 Rubber Technology

7-2.1 ELASTOMERIC MOLECULES

An elastomer is a chemical substance of high molecular weight, a high polymer, having the property of elasticity. It consists of repeating struc-tural units, called "monomer units," joined by chemical bonds into long chains. Elasticity, the reciprocal of rigidity, is the ability to resist and recover from deformation produced by an applied force.[68] The American Society for Testing Materials (ASTM) defines an elastomer as a material that can be stretched repeatedly to at least twice its original length at room temperature and will immediately return to its approximate original length forcefully when the stress is removed. Examples are polyisoprene (NR), polyisobutylene (IR), polychloroprene (CR), poly(styrene-co-buta-diene) (SBR), and poly(acrylonitrile-co-butadiene) (NBR). In further discussions these accepted abbreviations[3] will be used in place of the full names of the polymers.

The repeating structural units of these five elastomers are as follows:

NR   IR   CR

SBR   NBR

The latter two examples are copolymer units resulting from the combination of two different monomers. The distribution of the different comonomer units may not be uniform throughout the length of a copolymer molecule.

7-2.2 RUBBER COMPOUNDING

In most cases the base elastomer is not cross linked or is only lightly cross linked prior to compounding. Compounding promotes curing of the elastomer and increases the serviceability of the product. Compounding materials can be classified as follows:[75]

1. Elastomers (natural, synthetic, reclaimed rubbers)
2. Vulcanizing agents (sulfur, sulfur-bearing materials, oxidizing systems, metallic oxides, polyamines)
3. Accelerators
4. Accelerator activators and retarders
5. Age resisters (antioxidants, antiozonants, protective waxes, heat-aging retardants)
6. Processing aids (peptizers, plasticizers, softeners, tackifiers, lubricants)
7. Reinforcing pigments and resins
8. Inert fillers and diluents (inorganic and organic)
9. Coloring dyes and pigments
10. Special-purpose materials (blowing agents, abrasives, reodorants, etc.)

Representative recipes for gum- and reinforced-rubber compounds containing some of these ingredients are as follows:[3]

Gum rubber		Reinforced rubber	
Pigment (ingredient)	Parts by weight	Pigment (ingredient)	Parts by weight
Natural rubber	100	Natural rubber	100
Zinc oxide	5	Zinc oxide	5
Sulfur	2.5	Stearic acid	3
Stearic acid	1	Benzothiazyl disulfide	0.6
Benzothiazyl disulfide	1	Sulfur	2.5
Phenyl-beta-naphthyl-amine	1	Phenyl-beta-naphthyl-amine	1
		HAF carbon black	40

In these recipes the sulfur, the zinc oxide, and the stearic acid constitute the curing system; the benzothiazyl disulfide accelerates cure; the phenyl-beta-naphthylamine is the antioxidant; and the carbon black reinforces the rubber.

Rubber compounds are mixed to provide intimate, homogeneous physical mixtures of ingredients prior to molding and curing (or vulcanization). Vulcanization causes a chemical combination of elastomers and curing-system ingredients which produces cross links between elastomer molecules and general improvement in mechanical properties.

In a given rubber compound, one or more elastomers can be used; the choice depends upon service requirements and cost allowance. Usually a curing system rather than a single agent brings about the desired vulcanization, as with the two rubber recipes cited above. An accelerator is necessary because rubber and sulfur normally react very slowly.[67] Only the presence of naturally occurring accelerators in natural rubber made possible its vulcanization in the first place. The consensus with the two recipes is that zinc oxide, stearic acid, and benzothiazyl disulfide interact chemically to produce a reactive intermediate. The intermediate then accelerates cure. The mechanism is not precisely known. The zinc oxide and stearic acid are strictly designated as accelerator activators. Retarders serve to inhibit cure at processing temperatures without appreciably decreasing accelerator activity under curing conditions.

Age resisters have the collective function of protecting the vulcanized rubber from environmental attack, such as flex cracking, sun checking, and heat deterioration. They include antioxidants to prevent oxidation, antiozonants to inhibit ozone attack, and waxes to protect the surface against atmospheric cracking and sun checking.

Peptizers, plasticizers, and softeners all achieve the same initial function of aiding in the mechanical breakdown of raw elastomer. This breakdown or mastication aids in the dispersion or solution of the other ingredients in the rubber. Tackifiers, which increase self-adhesion, assist in adhering one rubber ply to another and so aid in the construction of rubber products. Lubricants reduce rubber friction and adhesion, thus facilitating milling and extrusion.

Reinforcing pigments or resins, such as the carbon blacks and the coal tar, styrene, and phenolic resins, improve such service properties as tensile strength, modulus, abrasion resistance, tear resistance, and resistance to compression set. The purposes of the remaining compounding materials in the list above are apparent.

A new category of ingredients, which is discussed in detail later, has assumed importance in the inhibition of radiation-induced deterioration of elastomers and rubber compounds. These additives, which bear a formal similarity to certain of the antioxidants and antiozonants, have been given the popular general designation "antirad" by their discoverers.[9,49] They are capable of providing specific protection against radiation damage to high polymers (see Refs. 5, 10, 36, and 41).

Elastomers are sometimes blended in a rubber compound to improve such properties as tensile strength, modulus, tear strength, ultimate elongation, solvent resistance, and tackiness.

7-2.3 VULCANIZATION OF ELASTOMERS

Except for cold vulcanization, i.e., vulcanization at room temperature using sulfur chloride and ultra-accelerators or catalysts, curing is accomplished conventionally by heating suitable rubber compounds. "Open" vulcanization may take place in steam, in hot water, or in hot air. However, curing in molds under pressure at elevated temperatures is much more common for industrial rubber products. Although it has not achieved any widespread usage, vulcanization by high-energy radiation holds some specialized interest and will be discussed later. It is another means of cold vulcanization but should be distinguished from conventional vulcanization since no chemical curing agents are used.

The degree of cure is important in rubber technology and is of special concern in radiation applications.[36] Four degrees of cure merit discussion: undercure, optimum cure, equivalent cure, and overcure. A base of reference is necessary to evaluate a state of cure. Usually a curing temperature is chosen on the basis of experience or by experiment, and samples of the compound are molded and cured at that temperature for a graduated series of times. Measurements of a critical physical property, such as modulus of elasticity, are then made. The results are plotted as a function of curing time. Such a curve appears in Fig. 7.1. An alternate stress–strain property, such as elongation, may also be measured and plotted for additional reference. Optimum cure for a particular property is the time at the chosen temperature which results in the optimum value for that property. There is usually a region of the curve which approximates optimum cure. The region prior to this represents undercure, in which the optimum value has not been reached. The subsequent region represents overcure, in which the optimum value has been passed.

Because of the subjective aspects of optimum cure in practice, the concept of equivalent cure is gaining acceptance. Equivalent cure represents the time at the curing temperature required to duplicate a given distinct point on the cure curve. It is the point just before the start of the plateau in Fig. 7.1. Reproducibility and reliability in rubber research depend directly upon the state of cure of rubber samples. The concept of equivalent cure[10] is especially useful in comparative studies involving recipe variations on a control rubber compound. A maximum value of the property of interest, such as 300% modulus of elasticity, may not exist. Hence it may be impossible to select an unequivocal optimum cure. Equivalent cure has fewer shortcomings in research, being more practicable and less subjective.

Other methods of characterizing state of cure exist besides the stress–strain family-of-cures procedures. One is the determination of the average molecular weight between cross links by measuring volume swell.[54] This

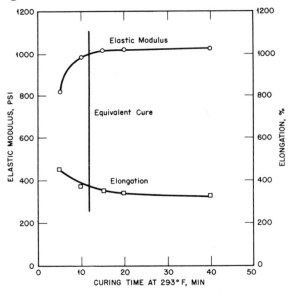

FIG. 7.1 Equivalent cure of rubber compounds.

approach, the least equivocal of all, can be rigorously applied only to solid polymers and gum rubbers; in practice, however, it has been applied to reinforced vulcanizates as well.[48] Another method in general use is the Mooney curing test. It employs the Mooney plastometer to measure both the time for scorching or incipient vulcanization and the rate at which vulcanization occurs after inception. These data are used in an empirical equation[74] to predict the approximate optimum cure time. For production goods, service requirements often dictate the technique of evaluation.

7-2.4 SIGNIFICANT PROPERTIES

Among the most important primary properties of an elastomer are its average molecular weight, its molecular-weight range, and its molecular-weight distribution. The utility of an elastomer depends critically on these and, after vulcanization, on the effective molecular weight between cross links. This cross-link density is the average weight of the segments of polymer chain between effective cross links.

The sizes of individual elastomer molecules vary widely.[74] For example, Hevea (natural) rubber ranges in molecular weight from 50,000 to over

3,000,000, with at least 60% being in excess of 1,300,000. Synthetic diene polymers generally possess a wider range of molecular weights, although the maximum is usually less than that of Hevea.

Polymers not cross linked dissolve in suitable liquids. As cross linking proceeds, the ability of polymer molecules to disentangle and separate (dissolve) becomes increasingly restricted until the gel point is reached. At this point the first insoluble polymer or gel fraction is formed. Thereafter, further cross linking diminishes the soluble or sol fraction and increases the gel fraction, decreasing the sol–gel ratio. In addition, this process increases the viscosity of the solution, at least up to the gel point. The gel, although insoluble, can still be swelled by the former solvent. As cross linking proceeds, however, the degree of swell decreases proportionately, and the polymer density increases. Cross linking affects all the service properties of rubber; in general, it increases the tensile strength (to its maximum), modulus (of elasticity), hardness, and density and decreases the plasticity, ultimate elongation, abrasion rate, and hysteresis.

Other important characteristics include dynamic mechanical properties, resistance to oxygen and ozone attack, resistance to thermal deterioration, and resistance to radiation-induced deterioration.

7-2.5 RUBBER TESTING

Experience dictates that standardized testing procedures be used whenever the results of rubber testing are to be of general interest. Methods[3] of the ASTM are thus widely used in this field. Table 7.1 lists the procedures referred to in this chapter.

In addition to those properties listed for the first method in Table 7.1, this stress–strain test measures modulus of elasticity as a function of elongation under tension. For more precise measurements of this property, many rubber research laboratories use equilibrium modulus tests in which a sample is stretched to a selected elongation (such as 100%), held for a given period (such as 1 min), and then subjected to modulus measurement while still elongated. This is not now an ASTM method, although it is quite useful.

Likewise, stress-relaxation measurements, another form of stress–strain testing, do not involve ASTM methods. Either intermittent or continuous stress can be employed in these tests. Whereas intermittent stress relaxation measures the net production (or destruction) of cross links without continuous stress, the alternate type of relaxation tests the net production of chain scissions.

Set, creep, and stress relaxation are all related and represent flow properties of elastomers and their vulcanizates.[74] When these effects result from continuous stress, they tend to be severe, especially at high temperatures or in strong radiation fields where chemical bonds may readily be broken.

Table 7.1 — STANDARD METHODS FOR TESTING RUBBER[a]

Property tested	ASTM Method[3]
Tensile stress, strength, ultimate elongation, and set	D 412-51T
Indentation	D 676-58T D 531-56
Abrasion resistance	D 394-47 (See also Pico method)[56]
Relative stiffening at low temperatures	D 1053-58T (Gehman torsion apparatus)
Impact resilience and penetration	D 1054-55
Resilience, static and dynamic modulus, kinetic energy, creep, and set	D 945-55 (Yerzley oscillograph)
Rate of heat generation and fatigue under compression	D 623-58 (Goodrich flexometer)

[a]Listed in approximate order of importance.

7-3 General Radiation Effects

7-3.1 RADIATION-INDUCED EFFECTS ON ELASTOMERS

Chapters 4 and 5 provide the general basis for understanding the effects that radiation induces in elastomers. Specific items in this special field are given here. References 14, 30, and 74 are particularly recommended for more complete descriptions.

As with all noncrystalline polymers, the main effect of any typical high-energy radiation is to ionize an elastomer or elastomeric compound. The transfer of energy from the radiation beam to the atoms of the polymer directly or indirectly causes the ejection of orbital electrons. These energetic electrons produce secondary ionizations. The physical and chemical aspects of this interaction are discussed in Chs. 2 and 3, respectively. Similar changes in an elastomeric material result from exposure to various types of high-energy radiation because of this common ionization effect. The radiations must achieve equivalent penetration to avoid surface effects and produce similar changes in physical properties (see Refs. 1, 39, 40, 58, 60, and 62).

A second point of importance is the effect of dose rate on elastomers and rubber compounds. Considerable experimentation[36,39,62] has shown that there is no dose-rate effect for elastomers and rubber compounds within the broad range of 10^4 through 10^7 rads/hr; i.e., at least over this range, any variation in dose rate does not significantly affect the change in physical properties of elastomeric solids. What does matter for a given radiation type is the total amount of radiation energy absorbed and the uniformity of absorption.

A final point is that ample experimentation has revealed no significant postirradiation effects in elastomers protected by age resisters. Measurements of hardness and elasticity have shown no change over periods ranging from three days to three months after irradiation.[39] It is thus apparent that the time of testing such materials after irradiation is not critical.

7-3.1.1 Basic Processes

The ions formed by ejection of orbital electrons recombine with free electrons to form energetic, unstable molecules.[61] The excited molecules quickly dissipate their excess energies, largely by bond scission, physical transfer, and possibly molecular rearrangement. The bond scissions produce free radicals and unsaturation, and most of the subsequent overt effects result from these.[63] Cross linking, chain scission, molecular rearrangement, and chemical reaction with environmental agents, especially oxidation and ozonization, occur and constitute the preponderant changes. Essentially all the changes in physical properties of elastomeric materials ensue from these basic processes. Although the primary and secondary ionization processes are obviously not temperature sensitive, the resultant chemical reactions are temperature dependent.[19]

7-3.1.2 Cross Linking

The radiation-induced attachment of side groups or branches to the main polymer chains (branching) and removal of such side groups are closely related to cross linking and chain scission, respectively. Graft copolymerization represents a special form of branching in which the comonomer is polymerized onto a base elastomer at radiation-induced free-radical sites. The graft polymer can be formed either by irradiating the base elastomer while it is immersed in the comonomer fluid or by immersing the polymer in the fluid after it has been irradiated. Such polymerization does not appear significantly dependent upon dose rate or rate of diffusion of comonomer after equilibrium has been reached.[20] The exclusion of air, such as by irradiation and immersion under vacuum, often aids in graft polymerization. At present no simple unified explanation of the mechanism is available.

Vulcanization of elastomers is one practical application of radiation-induced cross linking. This subject has drawn increasing interest over the years since 1948 (see Refs. 17, 25, 29, 38, 46, 55, 65, and 70). Irradiation permits vulcanizing quite readily many experimental polymers that resist cure by chemical means.[46] Although radiation cures closely resemble chemical ones in many respects, in most cases so far they provide aging characteristics, for example, in oils and hot air. The fact that radiation vulcanization requires neither heat nor chemical agents also distinguishes it from chemical cure.

The cross-linking process eventually produces gel, which is insoluble three-dimensional polymer as distinguished from soluble two-dimensional sol. The amount of gel produced by irradiation depends upon the initial molecular weight of the polymer, the molecular-weight distribution, the total radiation dose, and in a practical sense the effectiveness of the solvent. Increasing the radiation exposure in the case of a gel-forming polymer reduces the soluble fraction, asymptotically approaching an equilibrium value.[18] Those elastomers, such as polyisobutylene, which undergo chain scission predominantly during irradiation do not produce gel.

For a given polymer concentration, solutions prepared from an irradiated polymer that cross links predominantly will increase in viscosity with increasing radiation dose up to the gel point. [The gel point is that radiation dose at which the first insoluble material appears. It usually occurs when there is one cross link unit per weight-average molecule (see Ch. 5, Sect. 5-6.1.1)]. The converse holds for polymers that principally degrade. Therefore measurement of the solution viscosity of a polymer permits determination of the average cross-link density.[18,36]

7-3.2 Radiation-induced Effects on Rubber Compounds

7-3.2.1 Radiation Vulcanization

Section 7-2.3 describes conventional chemical vulcanization procedures for compounded rubber. Whereas curing agents are needed in chemical vulcanization, radiation vulcanization requires no curative, modifier, accelerator, or retarder. The elastomer still requires protective agents to withstand environmental aging (e.g., by heat, oxygen, or ozone) and usually a reinforcing filler (such as carbon black or silica) for good mechanical performance. Processing aids may be needed to ensure efficient mixing and satisfactory molding or shaping of the rubber stock. The basic aspects of a radiation-induced cure are the same as those described in Sect. 7-3.1 for rubber compounds. No heat is required, except possibly for the molding process.

An auxiliary aspect of radiation curing is the completion of vulcanization of rubber compounds. In radiation testing, certain physical properties may improve during the initial stage of irradiation. This is usually evidence that the chemical curing process did not reach its maximum effectiveness. It could also mean that the curing system is inadequate. In any event, tensile strength, ultimate elongation, and elastic modulus may all increase moderately. Some elastomers, such as polyisobutylene and polysulfide polymers, undergo predominant chain scission and so are degraded instead of vulcanized by radiation. Thus butyl rubber and polysulfide rubber compounds decrease in elastic modulus, hardness, and tensile strength with increasing radiation dose. The ultimate elongation loses meaning as the material becomes less a rubber and more a tar or a liquid.[42] Vulcanization of elastomers in general requires radiation exposures ranging from 10 to 40 megarads (i.e., million rads). Rubber compounds require a range of 10 to 40 megarads for optimum cure and 8 to 61 megarads to duplicate the molecular weights between cross links (M_c) which represent optimum chemical cure.[38]

7-3.2.2 Mechanisms of Radiation-induced Changes

One should clearly recognize that irradiation simultaneously induces cross linking and chain scission in an elastomer. The change in physical properties thus depends upon the dynamic balance between the rates of the two competing processes. Protection of an elastomeric material accordingly involves the concept of inhibiting one or both processes.

The combination of increasing elastic modulus and hardness on the one hand and decreasing tensile strength on the other appears anomalous. The explanation may lie in an increasing three-dimensional glasslike structure of the elastomeric material. Brittle fracture would contribute increasingly to gross tensile failure, with resultant decreased tensile strength.[66] Much remains to be learned about the mechanisms of cross linking and chain scission.

Polymer chemists and physicists have long recognized that heat accelerates oxidation of elastomers and rubber compounds. The thermal energy activates the bonds of the elastomer molecule and makes them more susceptible to attack by oxygen. Similarly, absorption of radiation energy excites the molecular bonds and promotes oxidation. There are experimental indications that ozone also attacks rubber during irradiation. First, the conversion of oxygen from the air by ionizing radiation generates ample amounts of ozone inside and around rubber samples. Second, radiation supplies the activation energy which usually results from stressing the sample and which appears necessary for ozonization.

7-3.2.3 Radiation-damage Inhibitors (Antirads)

Just as antioxidants and antiozonants inhibit oxidation and ozonization of polymers and vulcanizates during conventional environmental aging, they also provide appreciable protection during radiation aging in air. However, measurements of radiation damage in vacuum and in inert atmospheres have shown that the above two processes account for only a part of the total radiation effect. Important extensive damage occurs in the absence of oxygen and ozone.[9,13] This fact led to the search for and discovery of antirads, which are radiation-damage inhibitors for elastomeric and plastic materials (see Refs. 5, 9, 10, 11, 13, and 36). Subsequent research established that true antirads, as distinguished from fillers which protect simply by diluting the rubber compound, generally act specifically to inhibit either cross linking or chain scission; i.e., they inhibit one of the two processes to a greater extent than the other.[5,13] Initial attempts have been made to detail the mechanisms of antirad protection of elastomers, and this effort is continuing. Furthermore, it is recognized that, although antirads have considerable practical utility and merit, they also have certain inherent restrictions as physical admixtures. The ideal antirad would be a protective unit that is a strucural part of the polymer molecule itself. Directed efforts are being made to synthesize such polymers.[10,26,36]

As indicated, not all radiation-induced bonding to a polymer molecule results in a direct chain-to-chain cross link. There are two notable exceptions. In reinforced rubber compounds, irradiation bonds polymer molecules to the filler particles to produce a random three-dimensional network. Similarly, when the compound contains plasticizer, polymer and plasticizer may become joined during irradiation.

7-4 Specific Examples of Radiation-induced Effects

7-4.1 GRAFT COPOLYMERIZATION

Chen and Mesrobian[20] studied both the mechanism and the practical application of radiation-induced graft polymerization. Their sample system involved immersion of the polymer film in a large excess of the monomer inside a 1-in. by 12-in. Pyrex ampoule. The monomer that was used caused limited swelling of the polymer in each case. Air was evacuated from the system, nitrogen was admitted, and the ampoule was sealed. The sample system then underwent Co^{60} gamma irradiation at room temperature. In these studies the films were washed repeatedly after irradiation to remove residual monomer and any homopolymer formed from it. Then the researchers measured the extent of grafting by gravimetric techniques. They have subsequently obtained conclusive evidence of grafting by detailed fractional analysis. Minor modifications of this general procedure were employed in several cases and are described.

The mechanism of grafting was studied with a polyethylene film-styrene monomer system. Four possible variables were investigated: (1) temperature, (2) gamma-ray dose rate, (3) diffusion rate of monomer into polymer, and (4) variation of the solubility of monomer in polymer. Two polyethylene film thicknesses (4 mils and 10 mils) were immersed in styrene monomer and exposed to four dose rates, ranging from 20,000 to 300,000 rads/hr.

Four graft copolymers were next prepared in successful attempts to improve the service properties of the base polymers. Grafting acrylonitrile markedly increased the solvent resistance of vulcanized dimethyl-siloxane rubber. A radiation dose of 0.47 megarad transformed this elastic vulcanizate into a viscoelastic material having 33.7% grafted acrylonitrile. Its swelling indexes at 68°F were 1.17 in toluene and 1.10 in hexane compared with 2.33 and 2.64, respectively, before grafting. This ability to "armor" a given useful polymer or vulcanizate and so improve its utility in many different ways offers promising applications. It is a remarkable fact that the graft copolymer often combines desirable properties of both polymers.

7-4.2 VULCANIZATION

The most comprehensive report from the many workers (see Refs. 31, 46, 47, 57, and 71) on the vulcanization of elastomers and rubber compounds with nuclear radiation is that of Harmon.[38] To compare the properties of chemical and radiation vulcanizates, he prepared two sets of rubber compounds from the elastomers in Table 7.2. One set comprised

Table 7.2 — COMPARATIVE STRESS-STRAIN PROPERTIES
OF CHEMICAL AND RADIATION VULCANIZATES

Elastomer of the compound	Conditions of cure	Tensile strength, psi	Ultimate elongation, %
Natural rubber (NR)	50 min at 280°F[a]	2500	330
	4×10^7 rads[b]	2195	220
Styrene-butadiene rubber (SBR)	30 min at 300°F[a]	2840	395
	3×10^7 rads[b]	2020	300
Nitrile-butadiene rubber (NBR)	40 min at 300°F[a]	4600	340
	1×10^7 rads[b]	2760	185
Neoprene-W (CR-W)	40 min at 300°F[a]	3420	310
	1×10^7 rads[b]	2720	230
Kel-F 3700[c,d]	30 min at 230°F[a]	3000	180
	2.5×10^7 rads[b]	1900	330
Viton A[d]	30 min at 275°F[a]	1660	220
	1.2×10^7 rads[b]	1600	570

[a]Chemical vulcanization conditions.
[b]Radiation vulcanization exposure dose in air at room temperature at the Materials Testing Reactor gamma facility. [50]
[c]Radiation vulcanization occurred in vacuum at room temperature.
[d]The rubber compound also underwent subsequent oven curing at a higher temperature. [38]

compounds with chemical curing systems which were selected for good age resistance. Several different chemical curing systems were employed to obtain comparisons with more than one type of cure. The second set comprised recipes of the stocks to be cured by irradiation. In most cases these included only the elastomer plus the same amount and type of reinforcing agent as in the corresponding compound to be chemically cured. Separate but related studies determined the effect of the presence of age resister in one case and of potential cross-linking agents in another case on the quality and rate of radiation cure. Both main sets of compounds had the same mill mixing history. One set received optimum radiation cure in one series and equivalent cure in a second series. Equivalent cure was defined as that radiation cure which gave the same equivalent molecular weight between cross links, M_c, as the corresponding optimum chemical cure. The conditions of cure and the resulting optimum stress–strain values appear in Table 7.2.

The tests included a wide variety of static and dynamic measurements under different environmental conditions. The following conclusions were drawn:

1. Radiation cures have good high-temperature properties, comparable to peroxide cures.

2. The addition of an antioxidant that is not an antirad further improves the high-temperature properties of radiation vulcanizates.

3. The addition of an antioxidant results in an improvement in initial stress–strain values, probably by reducing the amount of oxidative chain scission that occurs at the same time as the cross linking.

4. The ozone resistance of radiation cures is neither better nor worse than that of chemical cures. Ozone resistance apparently is a function of the base polymer and any antiozonant materials introduced into the compound.

5. Oxidation rates are known to be dependent on curing systems, also on compounding ingredients, such as antioxidants. In general it would appear that radiation cures have oxidation rates comparable to protected chemical cures. The one exception is neoprene rubbers; with neoprene rubbers the radiation cures have much higher rates.

6. It is possible to increase the rate of radiation cross linking by incorporating materials into the compound which yield free radicals on irradiation.

7. Comparison of two or more different curing systems should be made at either equivalent 100% equilibrium modulus or equivalent molecular weight between cross links (M_c).

This research led directly to the first two automobile tires ever vulcanized with nuclear radiation alone.[69] Better abrasion resistance, heat-aging properties, and uniformity of tread vulcanization resulted from radiation curing than from conventional chemical cure.

7-4.3 Deterioration in Stress–Strain Properties

Figures 7.2 and 7.3 illustrate[13] the typical radiation-induced changes in stress–strain properties for two general classes of uncompounded elas-

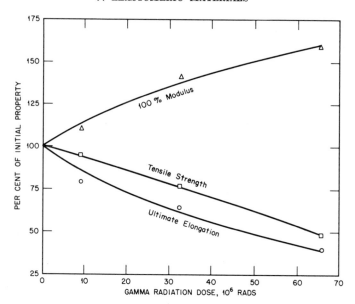

FIG. 7.2 Radiation damage to natural rubber (NR).

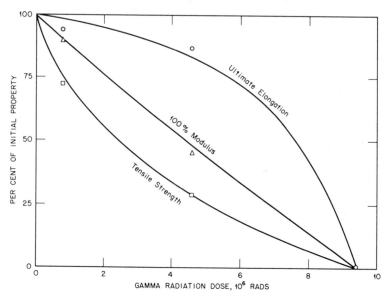

FIG. 7.3 Radiation damage to butyl rubber (IIR).

tomers. Natural rubber (NR) represents polymers that predominantly cross link during irradiation, and butyl rubber (isobutene-isoprene-IIR) represents polymers that undergo predominant chain scission.

Table 7.3 summarizes the changes induced in four standard ASTM rubber compounds.[13] All underwent cross linking.

In general, heating in the presence of radiation has a greater adverse effect on stressed than on unstressed rubber samples. The change in tensile strength of irradiated natural rubber and SBR vulcanizates has been reported[47] as a function of test temperatures ranging from 73 to 500°F.

Table 7.3 — RADIATION-INDUCED DETERIORATION
IN STRESS-STRAIN PROPERTIES[a,b]

Rubber black stock[c]	Physical properties[d]		Co[60] gamma-radiation exposure, megarads				
			0	9.25	32.4	64.8	92.5
NR	TS	(psi)	6080	5740	4670	3000	2200
	UE	(%)	340	290	220	140	60
	Mod	(psi)	469	519	659	726	793
SBR	TS	(psi)	4880	4800	4460	3660	2680
	UE	(%)	370	280	210	150	80
	Mod	(psi)	320	370	505	642	1000
CR-GN[e]	TS	(psi)	3210	2840	1740	Broke on bending[f]	
	UE	(%)	180	140	50		
	Mod	(psi)	508	622			
NBR	TS	(psi)	3980	4300	3700	3270	3320
	UE	(%)	300	200	140	70	40
	Mod	(psi)	395	652	1040		

[a] Exposures in air at room temperature.
[b] Electrographic test used to accommodate small samples. It gives consistently higher tensile strength and lower ultimate elongation than the usual Scott tester.
[c] See Sect. 7-2.1 regarding abbreviations.
[d] TS is tensile strength, UE is ultimate elongation, and Mod is 100% modulus.
[e] Neoprene GN.
[f] The sample is bent during electrographic testing.

Mooney measured the combined effects of heat and gamma radiation on eight factory rubber compounds.[10] The conditions[36] used in work at 158°F follow:

Experimental operation	Method and temperature, °F					
	I	II	III	IV	V	VI
Irradiation	Room	158	158	Room		
Heat aging					158	158
Testing	Room	Room	158	158	Room	158

In addition to the eight factory stocks, two variations of each recipe were compounded and given an equivalent chemical cure.[10] Each variation contained one of two potential antirads: either 35% *N,N'*-diphenylpara-phenylenediamine plus 65% phenyl-alpha-naphthylamine or quinhydrone. Figure 7.4 shows the effects that were noted. Method IV is illustrated, but the curves are similar in shape for the other methods involving irradiation both with and without the quinhydrone additive. The modest protection by

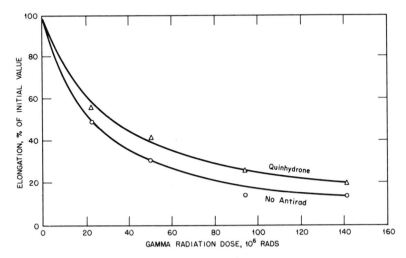

FIG. 7.4 Effect of radiolysis with and without quinhydrone antirad on rubber (NBR). Hycar fuel-cell liner stock irradiated at room temperature and tested at 158°F (Method IV).

the antirad probably indicates at least two things. First, the factory stock, which was already designed for good environmental aging, might have fortuitously already contained inhibitors of radiation damage. Second, quinhydrone, one of the first two of six to be tried, was not the most effective. Later results confirmed this.[36]

7-4.4 DETERIORATION IN COMPRESSION SET

Mooney verified that compression set is one of the most sensitive of rubber properties to radiation damage.[36] He studied changes in a set of samples that were kept compressed during gamma irradiation in oil and in air at room temperature. The test samples included the compounds of Sect. 7-4.3 and natural, polysulfide, polyacrylate, and highly fluorinated rubber vulcanizates. The oil was a heat- and radiation-resistant C_{14-16}-alkyl(diphenyl ether) fluid. Antirad variations of the basic recipes were investigated as before, but a wider variety of potential antirads was used.

The maximum improvement in radiation-induced compression set occurred in NBR (Hycar) bladder stock containing quinhydrone and immersed in alkyl(diphenyl ether). The antirad effected a 20% decrease in

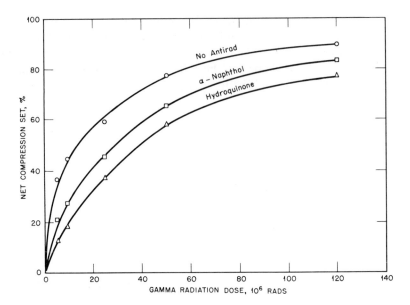

Fig. 7.5 Effect of radiolysis with and without antirads on rubber (NBR). Hycar fuel-cell liner stock irradiated and tested in air at room temperature.

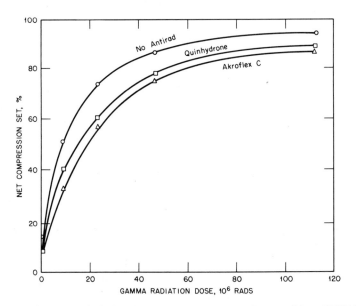

Fig. 7.6 Effect of radiolysis with and without antirads on rubber (NBR). Hycar fuel-cell liner stock irradiated and tested in alkyl(diphenyl ether) oil at room temperature.

compression set during irradiation. An antirad mixture of N-cyclohexyl-N'-phenylparaphenylenediamine (chain-scission inhibitor) and N,N'-dioctyl-paraphenylenediamine (cross-linking inhibitor) in an NBR (Hycar) fuel-cell liner compound resulted in 22% less compression set than with control stock. The protected stock required a 2.9-fold larger radiation dose to effect 50% compression set. Figures 7.5 and 7.6 show these results. Data from the control samples were used to correct all radiation test data for nonradiation-induced compression set.

Hycar PA-21 rubber has shown the most protection by additives thus far. The N-cyclohexyl-N'-phenylparaphenylenediamine and N,N'-dioctyl-paraphenylenediamine each separately reduced compression set by 26 and 29%, respectively. The dose required for 50% set was increased by factors of 4.1 and 4.4, respectively. These two antirads were among the most effective in the original screening study.

7-4.5 Changes in Mechanical Properties

Although mechanical tests do not accurately predict the performance of rubber components in complex service, they constitute a first step in that direction. The number of rubber compounds used in aircraft, for example, is large; and the compound recipes are often complex. Even in a single rubber product, there are likely to be several compounds. Therefore, for an initial investigation of radiation effects on dynamic mechanical properties, standard ASTM formulations of simple recipe were selected.[13] Radiation testing involved both gum-rubber- and carbon-black-reinforced vulcanizates of natural rubber, i.e., SBR, CR-GN (Neoprene GN), and NBR (Hycar 1002). The compounds were mixed and vulcanized according to standard ASTM methods. The optimum cures were determined and specified for all subsequent vulcanizations.

Ten mechanical properties were studied: dynamic modulus, hysteresis, permanent set, compression set, Yerzley resilience, dynamic resilience, deformation load, flexing compression, abrasion loss, and low-temperature modulus. This discussion will consider the results of seven of the tests. All data refer to carbon-black-reinforced stocks that were exposed to Co^{60} gamma radiation in air at room temperature. Figure 7.7 presents the data for natural rubber.

The dynamic modulus is the dynamically applied force per unit area required to produce a given distortion of the rubber (usually 20% as in this study). The SBR and natural rubber stocks underwent 101 and 84% increase in dynamic modulus, respectively. The Neoprene GN and Hycar 1002 samples became too stiff to test after radiation exposures of 9 and 33 megarads, respectively.

Dynamic resilience is the square of the ratio of the vertical height of the first rebound of a falling weight from the sample to the vertical height of the first fall. This property was measured to show the hysteresis of the rubber. Damping or hysteresis is proportional to 1 minus dynamic resilience. Neoprene GN and natural rubber samples showed almost no change in dynamic resilience, although the former was too stiff to test after the 33-megarad exposure. The SBR vulcanizate increased its dynamic

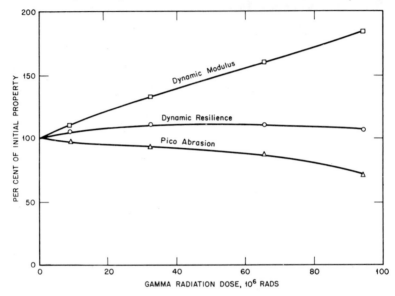

FIG. 7.7   Radiation effects on dynamic properties of natural rubber tread stock.

resilience by 230%. The Hycar 1002 nitrile samples had a sharp rate of increase but became too stiff to test after a 33-megarad exposure.

Abrasion measurements were made in a standardized manner with the Pico abrader.[56] The natural rubber and Neoprene GN samples decreased 30 and 45% in abrasion resistance, respectively. The SBR samples increased 28%. The Hycar 1002 stock exhibited a steady increase, reaching 244% of the initial value after the 93-megarad exposure.

Flexing compression is the percentage of decrease in sample height during flexure and was measured with the Goodrich flexometer (see Table 7.1). Radiation stiffened all the rubber compounds and thus generally decreased flexing compression. The natural rubber and SBR rubber samples showed decreases of 39 and 93% of their initial values, respectively. Neoprene GN and Hycar 1002 became too stiff to test after respective exposures of 33 and 65 megarads.

Natural rubber and Neoprene GN showed no significant change in Yerzley resilience over the entire dose range, whereas SBR and NBR samples showed marked increases. The increases were 38% for SBR and 23% for NBR.

In the radiation-induced change in permanent set, natural rubber was far superior to the other three elastomers. Although natural rubber showed small initial set and underwent relatively little change with irradiation, the SBR, CR-GN, and NBR vulcanizates all exhibited marked increases in permanent set.

If all these dynamic tests are considered together, the natural rubber stock is the most resistant to radiation damage followed, in order, by the SBR, NBR, and CR-GN stocks. Two critical hazards are connected with such a statement, however. First, it applies strictly only to the stated compounds of these elastomers. Second, it is based solely upon the tests employed. The hazards arise in extrapolating from such results without considerable experience in radiation testing.

The superiority of natural rubber was confirmed in tests on effects of gamma radiation on flex life of various vulcanizates.[46] Standard dumbbell strips of 0.100-in. thickness received a 46-megarad dose and were flexed from 0 to 75% elongation until rupture occurred. The average flexing time required to break the strips was recorded as flex life. The study involved reinforced vulcanizates of natural rubber, SBR, CR (neoprene), Acrylon EA-5, Silastic 401, Hypalon S-2, butyl rubber (isobutylene-isoprene, IIR), and polyurethane rubber. The natural rubber samples had flex lives of 12.5 hr before and 10.8 hr after irradiation. The SBR vulcanizate ruptured following 11.0 hr of flexing before and 1.5 hr of flexing after being irradiated. All remaining compounds had zero life after radiation exposure. The experimenters concluded that natural rubber vulcanizates offer the best over-all radiation service properties, even at elevated temperatures, especially in situations where good flex resistance is necessary.

7-4.6 CHANGES IN RATES OF STRESS RELAXATION

Both intermittent and continuous stress relaxation were measured to gain a better understanding of the roles that heat, oxygen, and ozone play in radiation-induced deterioration of rubber.[9,13] Ozone causes greater deterioration in stressed than in unstressed rubber. Therefore stress-relaxation studies[6] reveal ozonization and oxidation effects that would not be revealed by stress–strain measurements of rubber samples after irradiation in an unstressed state.

Standard ASTM gum and reinforced compounds of NR, SBR, CR, NBR, and isobutene-isoprene (IIR) elastomers were tested in air, vacuum, and nitrogen atmospheres at room temperature, 104°F, 122°F, 149°F, and 176°F. All samples had optimum cures, based on tensile strength and ultimate elongation; and stress relaxation took place during Co^{60} gamma irradiation. Radiation exposures ranged as high as 100 megarads, depending upon the sample and the test conditions. Concurrent measurements were made of duplicate sets of samples at 80% elongation: one unirradiated

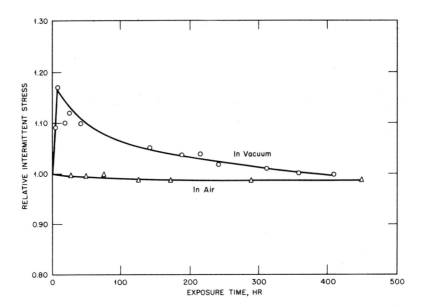

FIG. 7.8 Typical intermittent stress relaxation under irradiation. Pure gum natural rubber (elongation = 70%), gamma dose rate = 1.9×10^5 rads/hr, room temperature.

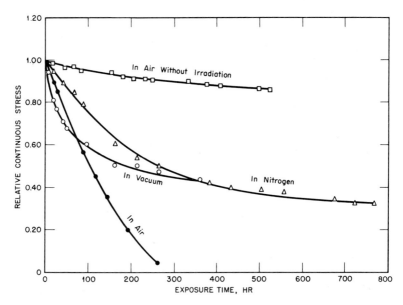

FIG. 7.9 Typical continuous stress relaxation under irradiation. Pure gum natural rubber (elongation = 70%), gamma dose rate = 1.9×10^5 rads/hr, room temperature.

control set and one irradiated test set. Typical results[9] appear in Figs. 7.8 and 7.9.

Figure 7.8 illustrates that vulcanized samples may undergo further cure during initial irradiation in vacuum. Air inhibits this effect (the stress–time curve in air without radiation follows closely the air curve of Fig. 7.8). Several typical comparative radiation effects are apparent in Fig. 7.9. First, irradiation greatly accelerates continuous stress relaxation in air. Second, the rate of stress relaxation during irradiation decreases somewhat more rapidly in a vacuum than in nitrogen and much more rapidly in a vacuum than in air. Exclusion of air (oxygen and ozone) thus reduces radiation damage of rubber materials under compressive or extensive stress.

An example of the influence of heat upon radiation-induced continuous stress relaxation is shown in Fig. 7.10. The rate of relaxation increases

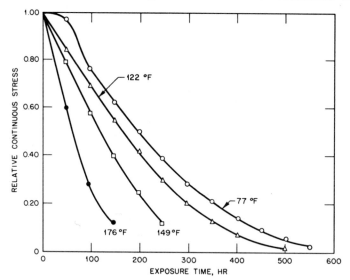

FIG. 7.10   Effect of heat on stress relaxation under irradiation. Natural rubber gum compound (elongation = 80%), gamma dose rate = 1.7×10^5 rads/hr, in air.

markedly with increasing temperature.[13] The effect seems to increase as the temperature exceeds about 125°F.

The order of increasing rate of relaxation is SBR < NBR < CR < NR < IIR for these particular gum-rubber compounds and SBR < NBR < NR < CR < IIR in the case of the carbon-black-reinforced vulcanizates. In general, the reinforced compounds have lower continuous stress relaxation rates than the gum-rubber compounds. The two butyl rubber (IIR) compounds softened rapidly during irradiation, thereby quickly failing.

It is interesting to conjecture that when a rubber experiences alternating application and removal of stresses, corresponding cycles of radiation-induced chain scission and cross linking should take place. Thus a much longer radiation service life should result from dynamic rather than static applications because of the two countereffects on the density of cross links in the elastomer.

7-4.7 A Mechanism of Antirad Action

Not only are antirads of interest from the practical standpoint of extending the radiation service life of rubber, but they offer an approach to a study of the mechanisms of radiation damage and protection.[5,6] Understanding the mechanism by which antirads inhibit radiation deterioration requires establishing (1) whether they prevent cross linking, chain scission, or both basic competing processes, (2) whether they act by an antioxidant type mechanism or are effective in the absence of oxygen, and (3) whether there are major differences in kind of mechanism from one antirad to the next or whether they vary only in degree of effectiveness. Continuous stress relaxation during irradiation was chosen as the means of determining the effects of antirads upon radiation-induced chain scission.

An ASTM standard carbon-black-reinforced natural rubber served as the base recipe for this study. It contained the customary sulfur curing system and antioxidant (phenyl-beta-naphthylamine). Five parts of each of ten selected antirads per hundred parts of elastomer (phr) were added separately to the base recipe to provide eleven rubber compounds, including the control. The compounds were mixed and cured to optimum stress–strain properties by ASTM procedures. Continuous stress-relaxation measurements were made with the Multilaxometer.[9] Testing took place in air and in nitrogen, with and without gamma irradiation. Antirads were selective in reducing stress relaxation as will be described.

An additional study of the rate of development of cross links as a function of radiation dose was also made.[6] The same ASTM base recipe was used, but the curing system was omitted; the antioxidant was retained. The same 10 antirads were used to provide the corresponding 11 stocks. The sample strips underwent gamma irradiation in air and in vacuum at room temperature. Testing involved the measurement of cross-link density in the rubber by volume-swelling techniques.[53] This method measures all effective cross links.

Table 7.4 lists some of the test results in terms of yields. The antirads inhibited chain scission during irradiation in air and decreased the rate of chain scission even in its absence. This must simply mean that the antirads reacted with R· and RO$_2$· radicals, having more effect on the latter.

All the antirads studied decreased the rate of cross linking by a factor of approximately 2 in the absence of air. In the presence of air, these antirads were less effective; and two of them actually increased the cross-linking rate.

Table 7.4 — EFFECT OF ANTIRADS ON SCISSION AND
CROSS-LINKING YIELDS IN NATURAL RUBBER[a]

Antirad additive (5 phr)	G, event/100 ev absorbed energy[b]			
	Cross links[c]		Scissions[d]	
	Vacuum	Air	Nitrogen	Air
No antirad (control)	1.9	0.29	2.7	13
N-Cyclohexyl-N'-phenylparaphenyl-enediamine	1.3	0.33	1.2	1.4
6-Phenyl-2,2,4-trimethyl-1,2-di-hydroquinoline	0.83	0.19	1.9	4.2
N,N'-Dioctylparaphenylenediamine	0.87	0.12	1.5	5.0
1,4-Naphthoquinone	1.1	0.48	2.0	5.6
Beta-naphthol	1.1	0.24	1.3	4.1

[a]From J. W. Born, *Materials Research and Standards.* Ref. 12.
[b]Samples underwent gamma irradiation at room temperature in the indicated environment.
[c]Rubber containing antioxidant.
[d]Rubber containing curing system and antioxidant.

The best antirads in each case are as follow: for preventing cross linking in vacuum, 6-phenyl-2,2,4-trimethyl-1,2-dihydroquinoline; for preventing cross linking in air, N,N'-dioctylparaphenylenediamine; and for preventing scission in nitrogen or air, N-cyclohexyl-N'-phenylparaphenyl-enediamine. Figure 7.11 illustrates some of these conclusions and provides an interesting comparison with Fig. 7.9.

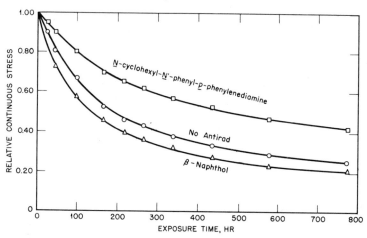

FIG. 7.11 Inhibition of continuous stress relaxation under irradiation. Carbon-black-reinforced natural rubber (elongation = 80%), gamma dose rate = 1.5×10^5 rads/hr, in air at room temperature.

7-4.8 CHANGES IN ELECTRICAL PROPERTIES

Little has been reported on radiation-induced changes in the electrical properties of elastomeric materials. This is particularly true of resistivity, loss tangent, and dielectric constant of elastomers used for electrical insulation.[76] There is an even more serious lack of data on changes in electrical properties during the actual course of irradiation.

Ionization and electron excitation in covalent organic compounds cause an instantaneous flow of electrons.[2] Nuclear radiation apparently causes a conductivity in electrical insulating polymers rather analogous to photoconductivity in semiconductors. Obviously, because of the instantaneous character of such radiation effects, changes in electrical properties should be measured during actual irradiation. The consensus is that as far as postirradiation behavior is concerned limiting changes in physical properties will precede permanent changes in electrical properties.

7-4.9 *Cis-Trans* ISOMERIZATION OF POLYBUTADIENE

A working understanding of the mechanisms of transfer of radiation energy to the polymer molecular system is important to the development of more effective antirads and radiation-resistant polymers. The study of isomerization has yielded information on this point.

Drawing on his experience in photochemistry and the photosensitized *cis–trans* isomerization of polybutadiene,[32] Golub studied the bromine-atom-sensitized, and subsequently the thiyl-radical-sensitized, isomerization of the polymer by gamma radiation.[33,34] The polybutadiene molecule contains repeating units that can exist in either of the *cis*- and *trans*-isomeric forms as follows:

Cis-polybutadiene   *Trans*-polybutadiene

Golub reasoned that the energy imparted to the polymer molecule from the nuclear radiation might excite the ethylenic double bonds in such a way as to permit rotation about the double bond. If so, an isomerization should occur from the higher energy *cis* form to the lower energy, and hence favored, *trans* form.

Cobalt-60 gamma irradiation of high (91%) *cis*-polybutadiene in sensitized benzene solution did indeed produce isomerization. Irradiation caused a transition from a 95/5 ratio of *cis*-to-*trans* forms to a 5/95 ratio at equilibrium. Golub derived a reaction mechanism for the interconversion of isomers and considered the kinetics of both sensitizer cases.[33,34]

The *cis*-to-*trans* ratios were determined by infrared absorption measurements on thin films of polymer cast from the irradiated solutions.[33] Figure 7.12 compares a bromine-atom-sensitized high *cis*-polybutadiene, before

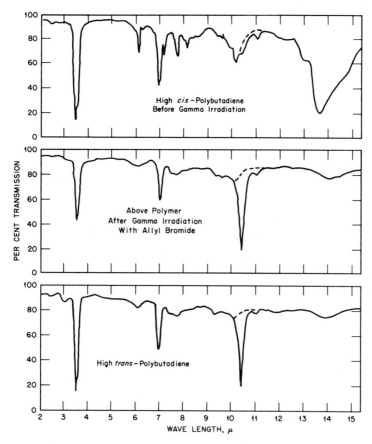

FIG. 7.12 Effect of irradiation on infrared absorption spectra of polybutadiene. (From M. A. Golub, *Journal of the American Chemical Society*, Ref. 33.)

and after irradiation, with a high *trans*-polybutadiene prepared by Zeigler catalysis. The irradiated polymer was essentially identical to the high *trans*-polybutadiene. Figure 7.13 illustrates how the rate of radiation-induced isomerization increases with greater sensitizer concentration.

7-5 Radiation-resistant Elastomers

The susceptibility of antirads to possible leaching or migration out of a rubber compound emphasizes the need for elastomers with outstanding inherent radiation resistance. Two main approaches exist for attaining

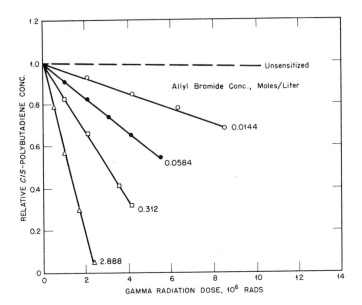

FIG. 7.13   Effect of sensitizer on radiation-induced isomerization. *Cis*-polybutadiene in benzene solution exposed in air at room temperature. (From M. A. Golub, *Journal of the American Chemical Society*, Ref. 33.)

such polymers: first, modification of present elastomers and, second, design and synthesis of new elastomers.

7-5.1 ELASTOMER MODIFICATION

The effect of varying the monomer combining ratios in two copolymer systems on the radiation stability of the resulting polymers has been determined.[10] Increasing the styrene content in a series of butadiene-styrene copolymers consistently increased resistance to radiation-induced cross linking. In a series of butadiene-acrylonitrile copolymers, the rate of cross linking during irradiation decreased with increasing acrylonitrile content up to 30 wt. % of the latter.

A promising new family of polymers based on diene elastomers, such as SBR, BR, and NR, has been produced and tested.[51,52] Diene elastomers, generally in latex form, were reacted with low-molecular-weight alkyl mercaptans as follows:

$$R-SH \;+\; \left[-CH_2-CH=CH-CH_2-\right]_n \;\longrightarrow\; \left[-CH_2-\overset{\displaystyle R}{\underset{\displaystyle |}{\overset{\displaystyle |}{\underset{\displaystyle S}{\overset{|}{C}}}}}H-CH_2-CH_2-\right]_n$$

Alkyl   Diene   Adduct

mercaptan   elastomer   elastomer

Mercaptan adducts,[51,52] principally of polybutadiene, were prepared having saturation values as high as 97%. In general, increasing saturation with the mercaptan resulted in improved resistance of the base elastomers to aging, ozone attack, heat, solvent swell, gas permeation, and deterioration by gamma radiation. After 10^8 rads the physical properties of an 89% adduct were altered less than were those of neoprene and of natural rubber. Varying the base elastomer, the mercaptan, and the extent of saturation produced a wide range of compositions and of static and dynamic physical properties.

Silicone elastomers with high concentrations of phenyl substituent possess outstanding radiation resistance combined with superior heat-aging properties.[73] However, although vulcanized compounds of the high phenyl silicone elastomer show very good retention of their initial physical properties during heating and irradiation, the initial property values were relatively low. This observation illustrates an important point in the evaluation of radiation resistance: the absolute magnitude of the property value before and after irradiation may be more revealing than the percentage of change or percentage of retention of the initial value.

Poly(ester-urethane) elastomers have been shown to be superior in radiation resistance.[40] Such polymers appear able to serve satisfactorily after radiation doses of 10^9 rads and above. They resist stress-cracking and retain great flexibility and general physical toughness, even after such large doses.

7-5.2 SYNTHESIS AND EVALUATION OF NEW ELASTOMERS

7-5.2.1 An Applied Approach

Polymers of low branching and unsaturation were synthesized in an effort to produce radiation-resistant elastomers.[27] Fifty homopolymers, copolymers, and block and sequential polymers were made from nineteen monomers. Radiation stabilities were evaluated by stress–strain measurements on rubber compounds from these materials. Gamma-radiation doses ranged from about 10^7 to 4×10^8 rads.

Certain experimental results were of particular interest:

1. Unlike polyolefins in general, polypropylene softened during irradiation.

2. Conjunctive (graft) polymers, such as butadiene-poly(alpha-methylstyrene) and butadiene-styrene-poly(alpha-methylstyrene), had about the same radiation stabilities as the corresponding copolymers with alpha-methylstyrene.

3. Natural rubber (cis-polyisoprene), poly(butadiene-co-alpha-methylstyrene), and poly(butadiene-co-ethylene) were three of the most radiation-resistant polymers in the study.

The backbone of a linear hydrocarbon elastomer is assumed to be plastomeric polyethylene; thus the data were interpreted in terms of the influence of substituent groups and structural features on the radiation stability of plastomeric polyethylene. Important general conclusions follow:

1. The presence of regular olefin linkages (as in polybutadiene) converts the polyethylene to an elastomer and improves the retention of tensile properties during irradiation.

2. The incorporation of methyl groups (as in ethylene-propylene elastomers) results in improved radiation stability with respect to hardness, ultimate elongation, and tensile strength but not to percentage of set at break.

3. The attachment of one methyl group to one of the unsaturated carbon atoms of each repeating unit in polybutadiene (as in natural rubber) improves radiation stability.

4. The incorporation of two such methyl groups, one on each of the two unsaturated carbon atoms of each repeating unit (as in the butadiene-dimethylbutadiene copolymer), leads to poor radiation resistance.

5. Phenyl groups introduced via styrene monomer (as in butadiene-styrene elastomers) improve the stability.

6. When phenyl-substituted fillers are physically mixed into elastomers, however, no specific inhibition of radiation effects occurs.

It must be remembered that these conclusions are based on stress–strain data for rubber compounds. Thus a number of factors besides polymer structural features can affect the evaluations of radiation stability.

7-5.2.2 A Basic Approach

Further research aimed at the development of elastomers and plastics with outstanding radiation stability has been conducted. Included were (1) studies of the mechanism of radiation damage, (2) synthesis of specially designed monomers, (3) preparation of quality polymers from such monomers, and (4) basic evaluation of radiation stabilities of the pure polymers.[11,36] Initially this study involved 22 monomers and over 40 polymers. Typical results are given in the following sections.

1. *Butadiene-Styrene Copolymer Series.* These copolymers, as well as physical mixtures of homopolymers of butadiene and styrene, were studied to determine the protective effect of an aromatic constituent (styrene) on the more radiation-susceptible portion of a polymer (butadiene). The upper curve of Fig. 7.14 illustrates that added polystyrene protects the polybutadiene in physical mixtures simply by dilution of the polymer system but provides no specific inhibition of radiation effects on the polybutadiene. In contrast, when the styrene is copolymerized with butadiene, it specifically protects the polymer system as the lower curve shows.

This difference in protection is ascribed to the relative efficiency of transfer of radiation energy from the butadiene units to the resonant styrene units, which can dissipate the energy nondestructively. In the copolymer system the styrene repeating units absorb and dissipate not only

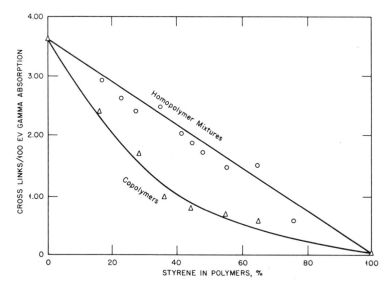

FIG. 7.14 Radiolytic cross linking of butadiene-styrene polymers. Exposures in air at room temperature.

the energy that they receive directly but also the energy that they acquire from neighboring butadiene groups by energy transfer. Thus for maximum effect the aromatic "energy sink" should be an integral part of the polymer molecule.

2. *Ethyl Acrylate-Maleic Anhydride Copolymer Series.* A group of these copolymers having various aromatic amine substituents was prepared for an examination of several variations of branch aromacity. Such substituents, attached to the maleic anhydride repeating units by condensation reactions, included aniline, 1-naphthylamine, and 4-aminobiphenyl. The resulting polymers received stepped gamma-radiation exposures in air at room temperature before molecular-property measurements were made.

Cross linking was the predominant radiation-induced effect. Therefore radiation damage was evaluated by determining the number of cross links produced per 100 ev of absorbed energy, G_x, and the ratio of the number of main chain bonds broken to the number of monomer units cross linked, β/α. Table 7.5 summarizes[11] the results. The incorporation of maleic anhydride units into the ethyl acrylate chain increased the G_x value and caused chain scission practically to disappear in the copolymer. Conversely, the aromatic amine substituents decreased G_x and increased the amount of chain scission. The G_x values decreased consistently with increasing resonance energy of the substituents.

Table 7.5 — RADIATION STABILITIES OF RELATED POLYMERS

Monomers polymerized	G_x [a]	β/α [b]	E, [c] ev
Ethyl acrylate (EA)	0.37	0.20	270
EA + maleic anhydride (MA) [d]	0.74	0.00	140
EA/MA + aniline	0.21	0.32	480
EA/MA + 4-aminobiphenyl	0.19	0.45	530
EA/MA + 1-naphthylamine	0.12	0.34	830
Phenyl acrylate	0.054	0.48	1800
N-Vinylcarbazole (NVC)	0.022		4500
EA + NVC (11.6 mole %) [e]	0.24	0.20	420
EA + NVC (22.2 mole %)	0.15	0.33	670
EA + NVC (33.5 mole %)	0.10	0.35	1000
EA + NVC (40.4 mole %)	0.071	0.36	1400
EA + NVC (51.6 mole %)	0.053	0.34	1900
Styrene	0.045	0.35	2200

[a] The number of cross links produced per 100 ev of gamma energy absorbed.
[b] Number of bonds broken per number of cross links produced.
[c] The net radiation energy (ev) required per cross link.
[d] The ethyl acrylate-maleic anhydride base copolymer.
[e] An ethyl acrylate-N-vinylcarbazole copolymer.

3. *Ethyl Acrylate-N-Vinylcarbazole Copolymer Series.* The radiation stability of poly(N-vinylcarbazole) was studied because of the high resonance energy of this homopolymer. The data in Table 7.5 show the material to be twice as resistant to cross linking as is polystyrene, which is generally recognized as one of the most radiation-resistant polymers.

This excellent performance of poly(N-vinylcarbazole) (NVC) led to its copolymerization with ethyl acrylate (EA), whose G_x value is good and whose homopolymer is elastomeric. Table 7.5 indicates the protection which the NVC units afford to the comonomer EA units. The polymer containing 11.6 mole % NVC appeared quite elastomeric. The polymer having 22.2 mole % NVC was a flexible, colorless, transparent plastic. Both polymers are quite interesting from an application standpoint.

4. *Correlation of Structure with Radiation Stability.* An important aspect here is the extent to which the distance of aromatic substituents from the main chain influences protection of a polymer (see Ch. 5, Sect. 5-7.2

for discussion). The phenyl group inhibits cross linking (Table 7.5) equally well in poly(phenyl acrylate) and polystyrene, which have similar structures. However, a more favorable β/α ratio results in the case of poly(phenyl acrylate).

7-6 Radiation-induced Deterioration in Service Performance

7-6.1 SPECIFIC RUBBER COMPOUNDS USED IN RUBBER PRODUCTS

Many research organizations have measured radiation damage to a large number of rubber compounds. Often the studies have originated from a pressing need for engineering information about the probable service life or functional threshold of damage of a rubber product for a particular radiation application. This has been true especially in the Aircraft Nuclear Propulsion Program. Several summaries are available to provide engineering guidance (see Refs. 4, 16, 21, and 22). Also recommended are Sisman and Bopp's pioneering work,[8,64] Bauman's design manual,[7] and Harrington's four articles.[39-44]

7-6.2 RUBBER PRODUCTS FOR MECHANICAL SERVICE

7-6.2.1 Aircraft Tires

A number of complete aircraft tire assemblies have been subjected to high-dose nuclear-radiation tests (see Refs. 10, 22, 23, 35, 36, and 45). For example, B-36 aircraft tire and tube assemblies were exposed in the Convair Ground Test Reactor Facility.[23,45] Some were fully inflated with nitrogen and some with air. A total dose of 6.9 to 12.2 megarads was received during a 50-hr irradiation period in air at room temperature. They then satisfactorily withstood 100 military landings plus 5 high-speed landings and passed minimum specifications in burst tests.

In a more definitive program[36] based on extensive research,[10] eight tubeless natural rubber aircraft tires were built for radiation test work. All were of identical design. Four tires contained Akroflex C, a rubber antioxidant which has been proved one of the best antirads for natural rubber. The other four tires had completely conventional composition, differing from the first four only in the absence of antirad. Both antirad and conventional tires achieved essentially the same state of chemical vulcanization before irradiation.

Four of the eight tires, two of each kind, served as unirradiated control specimens. The other two pairs were mounted on aircraft wheels for irradiation. Nominal exposures of 94 megarads from spent reactor fuel elements took place at the Materials Testing Reactor gamma facility.[50]

A watertight aluminum canister was specially manufactured to contain the tire undergoing irradiation.[36] Each tire remained fully inflated to the usual 210-psi service pressure during irradiation. Nitrogen instead of air served as the inflating gas to minimize oxidation and ozonization. Each tire–wheel assembly was irradiated in air at room temperature. The canister and its contents were rotated in a horizontal plane above the gamma source at 1 rpm throughout the irradiation. Figure 7.15 shows the loaded

FIG. 7.15   Tire canister in MTR gamma facility under water.

canister in place under water in the gamma facility. The canister and its contents were turned over midway through the total exposure. These two steps ensured maximum uniformity of radiation dose to all parts of the tire.

Landing tests took place on the dynamometer tester in the Aircraft Laboratory at Wright Air Development Division (see Fig. 7.16). The simulated service testing involved 25 high-speed (200 to 90 mph) tests followed by low-speed (90 to 0 mph) landings to failure. The testing basically duplicated the stringent regular procedure.[36]

Table 7.6 summarizes the resulting test data. All unirradiated tires "failed" because of ply separation. Each irradiated-tire test ended in a nearly bead-to-bead blowout (as seen in Fig. 7.16). The irradiated conventional tires apparently retained adequate landing capabilities for nuclear aircraft applications even though, as predicted, they underwent

FIG. 7.16 Dynamometer tester at aircraft laboratory.

severe deterioration. Tires made from rubber compounds containing the antirad had almost double the preirradiation service life of the conventional products. This marked improvement in performance was also retained after irradiation.

Several conclusions are apparent. First, tire failure resulted from

Table 7.6 — DYNAMOMETER TEST LIFE[a] OF
IRRADIATED AIRCRAFT TIRES

Tire type	Gamma dose,[b] 10^6 rads	Tire travel, miles of roll	
Standard[c]	0	154	206 av.
Standard[c]	0	258	
Antirad[d]	0	318	387 av.
Antirad[d]	0	456	
Standard[c]	77	26	32 av.
Standard[c]	75	38	
Antirad[d]	90	48	51 av.
Antirad[d]	89	54	

[a]Simulated landings (see Fig. 7.16).
[b]In air at room temperature.
[c]Type VII 26- by 6.6-in., 14-ply rating tubeless aircraft tire with nylon cord.
[d]Same as standard tire except for addition of 5 phr of antirad to each rubber compound.

radiation-induced deterioration in the tire cord as expected. Second, the tire rubber provided some protection to the tire cord. Third, since the cord was the weakest element and the antirad doubled radiation service life, the antirad may have partially permeated and secondarily protected the cord. This hypothesis further emphasizes the importance of the antirad protection of tire cords and strongly suggests that further improvement in tire radiation resistance is feasible.

7-6.2.2 *Aircraft Hose*

Hose must meet one or more of three requirements[22] of performance: flexibility, fluid and lubricant resistance, and resistance to high hydraulic pressure. Many typical aircraft hoses have undergone radiation tests.[22,24,37] Rubber compounds are used both in the hose tube and the flexible coupling. Irradiation generally causes eventual hardening or crumbling of the organic hose structure and reduction of tensile and compressive strength. Butyl hose should be avoided for applications involving high radiation doses because of the relatively rapid softening that irradiation induces.

Extensive work[37] was conducted on MIL-H-5511 base[72] and coupling assemblies.[48] The samples received gamma-radiation doses of 0.94 to 940 megarads in the Materials Testing Reactor gamma facility.[50] Impulse and burst tests were made on the irradiated and original materials according to the military specification.

The tests proved that the hose sections that received doses as high as 94 megarads still performed satisfactorily. As the radiation exposure exceeded about 100 megarads, rapid deterioration and failure of the hose occurred. The sections irradiated to a total dose of 280 megarads were too brittle to be used. Stress–strain measurements showed that irradiation increased tensile strength and decreased ultimate elongation. After exposure to about 28 megarads, the samples showed less loss of tensile strength from immersion in hydraulic oil and in an alcohol–water mixture and less volume increase during immersion in an alcohol–water mixture and in type III fuel.

The ability of the nylon 66 reinforcing cord to withstand high hydraulic impact and burst pressures after cumulative doses of 94 megarads is noteworthy. This dose is 10 times as high as that which the cord should withstand on the basis of radiation testing of the base cord since nylon oxidizes readily in air. The surrounding environment of the rubber and its age resister protected the cord. This information, obtained before the aircraft tire testing, encouraged the selection of the nominal 94-megarad exposure in the radiation testing of aircraft tires described in Sect. 7-6.2.1.

7-6.2.3 *Other Rubber Products for Mechanical Service*

Included among the remaining functional rubber products other than tires and hose are O-ring seals and backup rings, gasket and packing, shock and vibration isolators, sealants, structural adhesives, coatings, chemical fuel cells, electrical insulation, and electrical potting compounds. Some of these will be discussed here. References 16 and 22 give more detail on these and others.

Several organizations have tested O-ring seals and backup rings. Tentative conclusions were that Thiokol (LP) and Viton A seals resist radiation damage well (47 to 94 megarads), whereas silicone elastomers SE-551 and SE-371 have limited usefulness as seals in nuclear environments. Teflon was particularly unserviceable.[28] Radiation-induced deterioration of O-ring seals results especially in the evolution of corrosive gases and in improper sealing before mechanical failure.[22]

Leather, metal, and Teflon have been used in backup rings, which support the O-ring seals. Kel-F, Viton A, and the epoxies are candidates as backup-ring materials. So far all such materials have left much to be desired in radiation applications.

Kel-F, Hycar 1002 (nitrile rubber), Hycar PA-21 (polyacrylate rubber), and silicones 12602 and 12603 were investigated as gasket materials.[15] None of these materials was good beyond a dose of about 10 megarads. These results emphasize the relatively poor radiation stability of most highly halogenated elastomers as compared with nonhalogenated elastomers.

7-7 Thresholds of Radiation Damage

The concept of thresholds of radiation damage is important, particularly among nuclear engineers. A principal threshold used is defined as the nuclear radiation dose required to cause a 25% deterioration in a given physical property of an engineering material. It is also less commonly applied to the radiation service life of a component mechanical system. Figures other than 25% are occasionally used, but most are based on the fact that the radiation-induced property change reaches a specification limit at the chosen threshold dose. Thus the usefulness of a material beyond the threshold dose is limited.[16,22]

Although the threshold concept is very useful, there are several difficulties with its use. Threshold doses lack dependability and may prove inaccurate because of their variation with small changes in sample identity and size, operating conditions, and other factors. They are also related to a single, specific physical property generally, whose proper function is most critical. This is the weakest-link concept. These qualifying factors should be kept in mind when threshold doses are used.

Table 7.7 summarizes the 25% threshold-dose figures for a number of typical elastomeric and plastic materials for comparison.[16] Also included are ratios of equivalent threshold dosages of gamma photons to fast neutrons.

Information in Fig. 7.17 can also be used to compare radiation damage

Table 7.7 — FUNCTIONAL THRESHOLDS OF NUCLEAR
RADIATION DAMAGE

Compound polymer	25% damage dose,[a] 10^6 rads	Equivalent ratio γ/N[b]
Natural rubber (NR)	25	7.9
Styrene rubber (SBR)	10	7.2
Nitrile rubber (NBR)	7	6.4
Neoprene rubber (CR)	6	4.3
Silicone rubber (SE-450)	4	5.2
Butyl rubber (IIR)	4	9.1
Acrylate rubber (Hycar PA)	3	5.8
Polyethylene	90	9.0
Poly (vinyl chloride)	110	3.8
Poly (ethylene terephthalate)	120	3.6

[a]Based upon a particular stress-strain property, generally tensile strength.
[b]Ratio of the number of gamma photons to fast neutrons required per square centimeter to produce 25% damage.

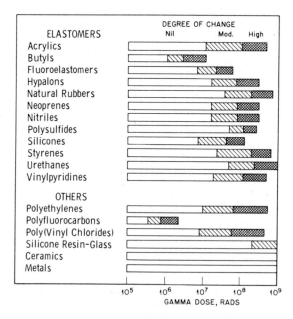

FIG. 7.17 Radiation resistance of materials. (From R. Harrington, *Rubber Age,*
N. Y., Ref. 42.)

to vulcanizates of various elastomers.[42] The initial bar section for each material represents incipient to mild damage (nearly always usable); the next section involves mild to moderate damage (often satisfactory); and the last section represents moderate to severe attack (limited use). These evaluations are based on changes in a number of physical properties.

Anyone intending to use the values cited in Table 7.7 and Fig. 7.17 should note that the relative ratings are general and may be based on retention of physical properties not particularly important to a specific application at hand. Accordingly, the most critical properties for the application must be considered, and a particular species within an elastomer class should be chosen for use because of its retention of those properties.

7-8 Principles of Application

Reduction of the information in this chapter to principles for rubber materials and components in nuclear radiation applications entails certain hazards. Both the formulation of rubber compounds and components and their special protection against radiation damage are as much an art as a science. For example, an antirad must be carefully matched to an elastomer, and the compatibility of the antirad with the pigments in the rubber compound must be considered. Furthermore, careful consideration of the end use of the rubber is necessary. Therefore important qualifications apply to most of the following principles:

1. At present, conventional rubber compounds exhibit about a 50-fold variation in their resistance to radiation-induced deterioration in tensile strength and ultimate elongation; i.e., the 25% damage threshold varies from about 1 megarad for butyl and polysulfide rubbers to about 50 megarads for natural rubber. In general, 100% modulus undergoes an even more rapid change. For compounds of rubbers which cross link predominantly during irradiation, this modulus will be approximately 200 to 300% of the initial value at a radiation exposure dose of 100 megarads. Exposure doses of 50 to 150 megarads produce 50% compression set during irradiation of practical rubber compounds. The presence of radiation-damage inhibitors in the rubber stocks will retard all these changes.

2. The observations regarding thresholds of damage for rubbers broadly resemble those for oil lubricants (see Ch. 9):

   a. Physical and dynamic mechanical postirradiation tests indicate no problems from nuclear radiation below 10^5 rads for butyl rubbers and 10^6 rads for the remaining rubbers.
   b. In the 10^5 to 5×10^6 rad range, the butyl rubbers lose practically all utility.
   c. In the 10^6 to 10^7 rad range, the other rubbers progressively lose from 5 to 25% of their original tensile strength and ultimate elongation.

d. In the 10^6 to 10^8 rad range, the rubbers in item c progressively lose from 25 to 75% of their original tensile and elongation values.

e. After a 5×10^8 rad dose, the rubbers in item c retain only about 10% or less of their original stress–strain values.

f. Experimental elastomers in the research and early laboratory development stages show promise of extending the 25% damage threshold (for tensile strength and ultimate elongation) to 10^9 rads. They will probably include highly aromatic poly(vinyl ester) and polycondensate rubbers. They also promise to have markedly improved thermal stability, a desirable property.

g. At present it appears that none of the conventional elastomers retain rubbery characteristics after radiation exposure exceeding 10^9 rads.

h. It is thus generally concluded that for the next five to ten years any rubber that would otherwise receive a radiation dose exceeding 10^8 to 10^9 rads must be shielded.

3. The eight preceding statements strictly apply only to rubbers that are irradiated in an essentially unstressed state in air at room temperature. Gross radiation damage is markedly less in the absence of oxygen (and ozone) but is accelerated by heating or stressing the elastomeric material.

4. In contrast to the statements for unstressed rubbers, the rate of change of stress–strain properties is roughly 10 times as fast for rubbers that are stressed during irradiation. For example, rubber samples lose 50% of their original property value in one-tenth the radiation exposure during continuous compression or elongation as when the samples are unstressed during irradiation.

5. The judicious selection and educated use of antirads in certain rubber compounds can give twofold to fivefold improvement in radiation resistance; in ideal cases a tenfold increase is possible.

6. Consideration of the combined results of various dynamic mechanical tests after irradiation indicates that the order of decreasing radiation resistance is natural rubber, butadiene-styrene rubber, butadiene-acrylonitrile rubber, and chloroprene rubber.

7. Present evidence indicates that in the case of rubbers that undergo compression during irradiation the order of decreasing resistance to radiation damage is chloroprene rubber, natural rubber, butadiene-styrene rubber, and nitrile-butadiene rubber. However, with the best antirad protection available, the nitrile-butadiene and polyacrylate rubbers become the most resistant, acquiring about 62% set during a 60-megarad dose as compared with 75 to 90% set for the other rubber compounds.

References

Several of the following were cited in the text as authority for statements made. Others were not quoted but are included because they contain pertinent information. All were consulted in the preparation of this chapter.

1. Alexander, P., *et al.*, Radiation-Induced Changes in the Structure of Polyisobutylene, *Proc. Roy. Soc. (London), A232*(1188): 31 (October 1955).
2. Alexander, P., Charlesby, A., and Ross, M., The Degradation of Solid Polymethylmethacrylate by Ionizing Radiation, *Proc. Roy. Soc. (London), A223*(1154): 392 (May 1954).
3. American Society for Testing Materials, *The 1958 Book of ASTM Standards, Part 9, Plastics, Electrical Insulation, Rubber, Carbon Black*, pp. 1155–1826, ASTM, Philadelphia, Pa., 1958.
4. Elastomers for Air Weapons, in *Proceedings, Joint USAF WADC–University of Dayton Conference, Mar. 27-28, 1957.*
5. Bauman, R. G., and Born, J. W, The Mechanism of Radiation Damage. I. Chain-Scission and Antirad Action, *J. Appl. Polymer Sci., 1*(3): 351 (May–June 1959).
6. Bauman, R. G., The Mechanism of Radiation Damage. II. Cross Linking and Antirad Action, *J. Appl. Polymer Sci., 2*(6): 328 (November–December 1959).
7. Bauman, R. G., *A Design Manual for Elastomers Used in Nuclear Environments*, Report WADC-TR-58-114, The B. F. Goodrich Co., June 1958.
8. Bopp, C. D., and Sisman, O., *Radiation Stability of Plastics and Elastomers*, USAEC Report ORNL-1373, Supplement to ORNL-928, Oak Ridge National Laboratory, July 1953.
9. Born, J. W., *A Study of the Effects of Nuclear Radiations on Elastomeric Compounds and Compounding Materials*, Report WADC-TR-55-58, Part II, The B. F. Goodrich Co., December 1955.
10. Born, J. W., *et al.*, *A Study of the Effects of Nuclear Radiations on Elastomeric Compounds and Compounding Materials*, Report WADC-TR-55-58, Part IV, The B. F. Goodrich Co., February 1958.
11. Born, J. W., *Nuclear Radiation Resistant Polymers and Polymeric Compounds*, Report WADC-TR-55-58, Part VI, October 1960.
12. Born, J. W., Effects of Nuclear Radiation on Rubber, *Materials Research and Standards, 1*(4): 280 (April 1961).
13. Born, J. W., Diller, D. E., and Rowe, E. H., *A Study of the Effects of Nuclear Radiations on Elastomeric Compounds and Compounding Materials*, Report WADC-TR-55-58, Part III, The B. F. Goodrich Co., December 1956.
14. Bovey, F. A., *The Effects of Ionizing Radiation on Natural and Synthetic High Polymers*, Interscience Publishers, Inc., New York, 1958.
15. Bresee, J. C., *et al.*, Damaging Effects of Radiation on Chemical Materials, *Nucleonics, 14*(9): 75 (September 1956).
16. Broadway, N. J., *et al.*, *The Effect of Nuclear Radiation on Elastomeric and Plastic Materials*, Report REIC-3, Battelle Memorial Institute, May 1958.
17. Charlesby, A., Cross Linking of Rubber by Pile Radiation, *Atomics and Atomic Technol., 5*(1): 12 (January 1954).
18. Charlesby, A., Beneficial Effects of Radiation on Polymers, *Nucleonics, 14*(9): 82 (September 1956).
19. Charlesby, A., and Bevington, J. C., *The Mechanisms of Radiation-Induced Changes in High Polymers*, British Report AERE M/M 85, November 1954.
20. Chen, W. K. W., and Mesrobian, R. B., Studies on Graft Copolymers Derived by Ionizing Radiation, *J. Polymer Sci., 23*(104): 903 (February 1957).
21. Collins, C. G., and Calkins, V. P., *Radiation Damage to Elastomers, Plastics, and Organic Liquids*, Report APEX-261, General Electric Company, September 1956.
22. Convair, *Radiation Effects—Methods and Data*, Report NARF-58-43T, October 1958.
23. Convair, *Effects of Reactor Radiation on B-36 Aircraft Systems, Addendum VII*, Report NARF-57-41T, August 1957. (Classified)

24. Convair, *Effects of Irradiation on Component Materials,* Report FGT-1718, December 1957.

25. Davidson, W. L., and Geib, I. G., Effects of Pile Bombardment on Uncured Elastomers, *J. Appl. Phy., 19*(5): 427 (May 1948).

26. Davis, P., et al., *Research and Development of Hi-Temperature Nuclear Radiation Resistant Elastomers,* Quarterly Progress Report 1, Burke Research Company, October 1957.

27. Davis, P., et al., *Research and Development of Hi-Temperature Nuclear Radiation Resistant Elastomers,* Quarterly Progress Report 1, Burke Research Company, October 1957.

28. De Zeih, C. J., *Effects of Nuclear Radiation on Cork, Leather, and Elastomers,* Report D2-1819, Boeing Airplane Co., June 1957.

29. Epstein, L. M., and Marans, N. S., Radiation Curing of Silicone Rubber, *Rubber Age, N. Y., 82*(5): 825 (February 1958).

30. Flory, P. J., *Principles of Polymer Chemistry,* Cornell University Press, Ithaca, N. Y., 1953.

31. Gehman, S. D., and Auerbach, I., Gamma Ray Vulcanization of Rubber, *Intern. J. Appl. Radiation and Isotopes, 1*(1 and 2): 102 (July 1956).

32. Golub, M. A., *Cis-Trans* Isomerization in Polybutadiene, *J. Polymer Sci., 25*(110): 373 (August 1957).

33. Golub, M. A., The Radiation Induced *Cis-Trans* Isomerization of Polybutadiene. I., *J. Am. Chem. Soc., 80*(8): 1794 (April 1958).

34. Golub, M. A., The Radiation Induced *Cis-Trans* Isomerization of Polybutadiene. II., *J. Am. Chem. Soc., 81*(1): 54 (January 1959).

35. Gregson, T. C., and Gehman, S. D., Radiation Damage of Airplane Tire Materials, in *Third Semiannual Radiation Effects Symposium October 28–30, 1958,* Vol. 3, Lockheed Nuclear Products.

36. Harmon, D. J., *A Study of the Effects of Nuclear Radiations on Elastomeric Compounds and Compounding Materials,* Report WADC-TR-55-58, Part V, pp. 8–31, The B. F. Goodrich Co., April 1959.

37. Harmon, D. J., *Effect of High Energy Gamma Radiation on the Physical Properties and Life of Type MIL-H-5511 Aircraft Hose,* Research Report, The B. F. Goodrich Co., April 1956.

38. Harmon, D. J., Radiation Vulcanization of Elastomers, *Rubber Age, N. Y., 86*(2): 351 (November 1959).

39. Harrington, R., Elastomers for Use in Radiation Fields, *Rubber Age, N. Y., 81*(6): 971 (September 1957).

40. Harrington, R., Elastomers for Use in Radiation Fields. Part II. Effect of Gamma Radiation on Heat-Resistant Elastomers, *Rubber Age, N. Y., 82*(3): 461 (December 1957).

41. Harrington, R., Elastomers for Use in Radiation Fields. Part III. Effects of Gamma Radiation on Elastomers, *Rubber Age, N. Y., 82*(6): 1003 (March 1958).

42. Harrington, R., Elastomers for Use in Radiation Fields. Part IV. Effects of Gamma Radiation on Miscellaneous Elastomers and Rubberlike Materials, *Rubber Age, N. Y., 83*(1): 472 (June 1958).

43. Harrington, R., Elastomers for Use in Radiation Fields. Part V. Effects of Gamma Radiation on Nitrile Elastomers, *Rubber Age, N. Y., 85*(6): 963 (September 1959).

44. Harrington, R., Elastomers for Use in Radiation Fields. Part VI. Radiation Resistance of the Neoprenes, *Rubber Age, N. Y., 86*(3): 819 (February 1960).

45. Heil, J. H., *Evaluation of an Aircraft Tire Irradiated in Systems Panel Test No. 2,* WADC-TN-58-86, Wright Air Development Center, March 1958.

46. Jackson, W. W., and Hale, D., Vulcanization of Rubber with High Intensity Gamma Radiation, *Rubber Age, N. Y.,* 77(6): 865 (September 1955).
47. Johnson, B. L., Adams, H. E., and Barzan, M. L., Radiation Effects in Elastomeric Vulcanizates, *Rubber World,* 137(1): 73 (October 1957).
48. Kraus, G., Degree of Cure in Filler-Reinforced Vulcanizates by the Swelling Method, Parts I and II, *Rubber World,* 135(1): 67 (October 1956) and 135(2): 254 (November 1956).
49. Loughborough, D. L., Juve, A. E., Beatty, J. R., and Born, J. W., *A Study of the Effects of Nuclear Radiations on Elastomeric Compounds and Compounding Materials,* Report WADC-TR-55-58, December 1954.
50. Martens, J. H., and Minuth, F. G., *Selected List of Neutron and Gamma Irradiation Facilities,* USAEC Report TID-7009, April 1957.
51. Meyer, G. E., *et al.,* A Versatile New Family of Elastomers. I., *Rubber World,* 136(4): 529 (July 1957).
52. Meyer, G. E., *et al.,* A Versatile New Family of Elastomers. II., *Rubber World,* 136(5): 695 (August 1957).
53. Moore, C. G., and Watson, W. F., Determination of Degree of Cross Linking in Natural Rubber Vulcanizates, Part II, *J. Polymer Sci.,* 19: 237 (February 1956).
54. Mullins, L., Determination of Degree of Cross Linking in Natural Rubber Vulcanizates, Parts I and II, *J. Polymer Sci.,* 19(92): 225, 237 (February 1956).
55. Newton, E. B., *Cross Linking of Hevea by Electrons,* U. S. Patent No. 1,906,402 (May 2, 1933).
56. Newton, E. B., and Sears, D. L., *Apparatus for Determining Abrasion Resistance,* U. S. Patent No. 2,799,155 (July 16, 1957).
57. Nikitina, T. S., *et al.,* Radiation Vulcanization of Rubber, in *A Portion of the Proceedings of the First All-Union Conference on Radiation Chemistry, Moscow, 1957* (English translation), Part VI, The Effect of Radiation on Polymers, p. 275, Consultants Bureau, Inc., New York, 1959.
58. Ossefort, Z. T., Gamma Radiation of Elastomers and Their Monomers, Report RIA-57-1002, Rock Island Arsenal Lab., April 1957.
59. Pauling, L., *The Nature of the Chemical Bond,* p. 53, Cornell University Press, Ithaca, New York, 1942.
60. Saldick, J., Analytical Evaluation of the Effects of Radiation on Organic Materials, in *Conference on Effects of Radiation on Dielectric Materials, Naval Research Laboratory, Washington, D. C., December 14–15, 1954,* ONR Symposium Report ACR-2.
61. Simha, R., and Wall, L. A., Mechanism of High Energy Radiation Effects in Polymers, *J. Phys. Chem.,* 61(5): 425 (April 1957).
62. Sisman, O., and Bopp, C. D., Radiation Stability of Plastics and Elastomers, *Nucleonics,* 13(7): 28 (July 1955).
63. Sisman, O., and Bopp, C. D., Radiation Stability of Polymers, in *Conference on Effects of Radiation on Dielectric Materials, Naval Research Laboratory, Washington, D. C., December 14–15, 1954,* p. 85, ONR Symposium Report ACR-2.
64. Sisman, O., and Bopp, C. D., *Physical Properties of Irradiated Plastics,* USAEC Report ORNL-928, Oak Ridge National Laboratory, June 1951.
65. Sisman, O., and Bopp, C. D., *Radiation Stability of Plastics and Elastomers,* USAEC Report ORNL-1373, Supplement to ORNL-928, Oak Ridge National Laboratory, July 1953.
66. Sisman, O., and Wilson, J. C., Engineering Use of Damage Data, *Nucleonics,* 14 (9): 58 (September 1956).

67. Stern, H. J., *Rubber: Natural and Synthetic*, p. 144, Maclaren & Sons, Ltd., London, 1954.

68. Stewart, J. R., *Stewart's Scientific Dictionary*, 4th ed., p. 257, Stewart Research Laboratory, Alexandria, Va., 1953.

69. Stockman, C. H., Harmon, D. J., and Neff, H. F., Radiation Makes Better, Longer Lasting Tires, *Nucleonics*, 15(11): 94 (November 1957).

70. Sun, K. H., Effects of Atomic Radiation on High Polymers, *Modern Plastics*, *32*(1): 141 (September 1954).

71. Tarasova, Z. N., *et al.*, The Structure and Properties of Vulcanizates Obtained by the Action of Nuclear Radiation, in *A Portion of the Proceedings of the First All-Union Conference on Radiation Chemistry, Moscow, 1957* (English translation), Part VI, The Effect of Radiation on Polymers, p. 283, Consultants Bureau, Inc., New York, 1959.

72. U. S. Department of Defense, *Hose: Aircraft, Hydraulic, Pneumatic, Fuel, and Oil Resistant*, USAF Military Specification MIL-H-5511, Dec. 24, 1951.

73. Warrick, E. L., Fischer, D. J., and Zack, J. F., Jr., Radiation Resistant Silicones, in *Third Semiannual Radiation Effects Symposium, October 28–30, 1958*, Vol. 5, Lockheed Nuclear Products.

74. Whitby, G. S., *Synthetic Rubber*, John Wiley & Sons, Inc., New York, 1954.

75. Winspear, G. G., *The Vanderbilt Rubber Handbook*, p. 158, R. T. Vanderbilt Co., Inc., New York, 1958.

76. Woodard, R. E., *Electrical Properties of Irradiated Polymers*, Report WADC-TR-56-465, Wright Air Development Center, June 1957.

CHAPTER 8

Coolants

By James G. Carroll, Robert O. Bolt, and Charles A. Trilling

8-1 Introduction

The idea of cooling a nuclear reactor with a hydrocarbon has great appeal. Certain classes of organic compounds have long and satisfactory histories in nonradiation fields as heat-transfer fluids in the temperature range of 400 to 700°F. Their advantages over other materials are well known (see Refs. 34, 48, 80, and 97). Their advantages and disadvantages as prospective coolants in nuclear reactors have been spelled out[45,59] and are summarized in Table 8.1.

Table 8.1 — ADVANTAGES AND DISADVANTAGES OF POLYPHENYL ORGANIC COOLANT–MODERATORS

Advantages	Disadvantages
1. Good moderating ability (permits small reactor core)	1. Instability at high temperatures and high radiation dosages
2. Reactor safety, i.e., high negative temperature coefficient of reactivity	2. Low thermal conductivity (20% that of water)
3. Low vapor pressure (permits thin containment shell)	3. Reactive with zirconium
4. Low radioactivity from neutron absorption	4. Tendency to leak through seals
5. Noncorrosive to carbon steel, aluminum, etc.	5. Small latent heat of vaporization
6. Nonreactive chemically with nuclear fuels or steam	
7. Relatively nonflammable and nontoxic	

Organic fluids were first proposed in 1942 as coolants for plutonium-production reactors. At that time, however, not enough was known about the radiation stability of organic compounds; hence water was used. Since that time much work has been performed on organics, mostly under AEC contract. The important power reactor systems utilizing organic coolants as of 1962 are as follows:

1. The concept of an organic-moderated and -cooled reactor coupled with a steam turbine has received the most attention. Here the heat energy of the organic fluid in the primary loop is transferred to water in a secondary loop where steam to drive the turbine is generated. This concept has the pressurized-water reactor plant as its counterpart in the all-water system. The Organic Moderated Reactor Experiment (OMRE) is the first reactor of this type to be built. This reactor is a 6-Mw(t) installation[116] that went critical in September 1957 at the National Reactor Testing Station in Idaho. Its operation is described more fully in later sections of this chapter. A net 11.4-Mw(e) power plant, based in part on the technology developed in the OMRE, is to be in operation[11,104] in 1962 at Piqua, Ohio. The Experimental Organic Cooled Reactor (EOCR)[11] is also to be operational at 40 Mw(t) in 1962 in Idaho. Experience to be gained in these plants is to lead to the Prototype Organic Power Reactor (POPR),[11] a 50-Mw(e) installation. Other similar power plants have been proposed for construction outside the United States.

2. A boiling organic fluid is involved in another type[99] of organic-moderated and -cooled reactor plant. It has the boiling-water reactor as its counterpart in the water system and thus is a direct-cycle arrangement that avoids the secondary loop. This new scheme, however, has received little attention.

3. An organic-cooled deuterium-moderated reactor plant has been proposed.[71,91,119] Heavy water is used for most of the neutron moderation, and the organic fluid conducts heat from the fuel elements to a secondary water system as it does with the pressurized-water and OMCR concepts. This scheme is being actively investigated by both Canadian and Euratom groups. The Organic Test Reactor for research built on this concept is to be in operation[9] at the Canadian Whiteshell Center by 1965. This is a 25-Mw(t) installation with provision for an increase to 60 Mw(t). A 300-Mw(e) central-station plant is being considered. An 80-Mw(t) process steam plant has also been proposed.

This chapter covers only a part of the extensive organic reactor field, namely, the effects of radiation on coolants. Specifically, it deals with the highly aromatic hydrocarbons, the only materials to receive serious attention as reactor coolants. No comments are made on such related items as (1) the merits of the organic-cooling concept, (2) dual-purpose reactors in which organics can be processed, (3) economics of installation and make-up considerations involving the organic coolant, and (4) comparisons of reactor types, efficiencies, operation, etc. The information on coolants is presented in several steps. First, as background, a brief review of the thermal stability of organic coolants is covered. Then radiation effects as observed in static irradiations are reviewed. The results from the operation of a number of in-pile loops comprise another large area. Operation of the OMRE, the first organic reactor, is also reviewed.

The reader should not gain the impression that research in the organic reactor field is moving slowly. Indeed, the opposite is true; the technology of nuclear reactor coolants is developing rapidly from many active research programs under United States, Canadian, and Euratom sponsorship. Fundamental work includes theoretical and experimental studies to determine thermodynamic properties and limits of stability of prospective coolants and experimental studies to determine the mechanism of radiolysis of such materials through a knowledge of the products formed. Research of a more applied nature includes studies of effects of various irradiation conditions on coolants, studies of methods of recovering radiolyzed coolants, work on species of low-cost coolants, and a wide investigation of reactor fuel-element fouling by organic materials.

8-2 Thermal Stability

Coolants must withstand high temperatures in nuclear power reactors. A logical first step in the choice of suitable fluids is to select the best compounds based on thermal stability alone. Several investigators studied the thermal stability of organic materials initially to determine (1) the upper temperature limits possible, (2) the best chemical structures, and (3) the degree of pyrolytic breakdown and the nature of the reaction products. These studies preceded work on the combined effects of temperature and radiation.

8-2.1 STATIC TESTS

8-2.1.1 *Exposures at 1000°F*

Biphenyl, Dowtherm A† (about 23.5 wt. % biphenyl in diphenyl ether), 1-methylnaphthalene, amylbiphenyl, and o-terphenyl were heated at 1000°F. All were almost completely converted[29] to coke after 28 hr. This coke was not carbon but was probably a highly condensed aromatic compound. Even under the most drastic pyrolytic conditions, less than 1 mole of hydrogen per mole of original compound was evolved. Theoretically, between 4 and 7 moles of hydrogen per mole of compound would evolve in the total destruction of most of the materials studied.

Figure 8.1 shows typical rates of gas evolution observed. The compounds with alkyl side chains were inferior; biphenyl showed the lowest gassing rate. After 28 hr a tightly packed solid formed with the alkylbiphenyl, methylnaphthalene, and Dowtherm. A less dense material formed

† Dow Chemical Co.

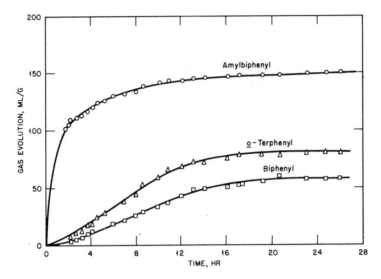

FIG. 8.1 Gassing of polyphenyls during pyrolysis at 1000°F. Initial nitrogen pressure of 15 psia; 316 stainless-steel vessels.

from biphenyl and *o*-terphenyl. In no instance did the residue burn or melt at red heat in a Bunsen flame.

Samples of biphenyl were recovered after exposure at 1000°F for varying times.[29] Pertinent data are given in Table 8.2. The nature of the

Table 8.2 — NATURE OF PRODUCTS FROM PYROLYZED BIPHENYL[a]

Time at 1000°F,[b] hr	Recovery	
	% liquid	% solid
0	0	100[c]
3.25	0	75
5.2	0	75
10.2	45	45
11.5	29	65
14.5	22	50
16.5		Residue

[a] Heated in 304 stainless-steel capsules.
[b] Initial nitrogen pressure was 200 psig.
[c] Recovery at room temperature; biphenyl melts at 158° F.

material recovered changed with continued exposure. The original solid product became a mixture of solid and liquid phases in the very short exposures and finally became a completely solid residue in the longer exposures. Thus volatile substances formed (cracking) first; coke formed ultimately.

Distillation data on the 11.5-hr sample showed the following: (1) about

15% of the biphenyl remained unchanged, (2) the lower-boiling fraction was almost entirely benzene, and (3) more than 60% of the material recovered boiled above the biphenyl fraction.

In spite of the high-boiling materials formed, no significant deposits were noted on the walls of the vessel after 14.5 hr at 1000°F. After 16.5 hr at this temperature, however, only an adherent residue remained. From these results[29] it is apparent that even in the absence of radiation the best of the organic materials has a life of only about 15 hr at 1000°F. The data also suggest that the useful life of a fluid working at high temperature may terminate suddenly.

8-2.1.2 *Exposures Below 1000°F*

Experiments were conducted at more practical temperatures for organics to aid in the selection of the best classes and to investigate their pyrolysis products. One study[31] involved 26 compounds. Included were condensed-ring compounds and polyphenyls and their halogenated derivatives, alkyl-polyphenyls, an aromatic silane, and an aromatic phosphate.

The observed gas phase consisted chiefly of hydrogen and methane, with decreasing amounts of other low-boiling paraffinic hydrocarbons. Unsaturated compounds were not detected in any appreciable quantity. The gaseous hydrocarbon-to-hydrogen ratio increased as coking increased. The individual ratios varied considerably, however, according to the chemical nature of the original aromatic compound. A comparison[31] of the thermal stability of some of the simplest polyphenyl and condensed-ring compounds is given in Table 8.3.

Table 8.3 — THERMAL STABILITY: POLYPHENYL VERSUS CONDENSED-RING COMPOUNDS[a]

| Compound | Gassing | | Residue (coke), per cent by distillation |
	Rate, ml/g	Hydrocarbon-to-hydrogen ratio	
Biphenyl	4	0.25	1.4
m – Terphenyl	5	0.61	35
p – Terphenyl	7	0.68	56
o – Terphenyl	9	2.0	39
p – Quaterphenyl	18	0.80	76
Naphthalene	3	0.49	0.1
Anthracene	121	8.8	79
Phenanthrene	101	2.9	78
Chrysene	93	2.6	90
Pyrene	111	0.65	87

[a]Conditions of test: 920 °F; 24 hr; initial nitrogen pressure of 300 psig; 304 stainless-steel capsules.

At 920°F naphthalene and biphenyl were outstandingly more stable than the other materials tested. These two were of comparable stability with respect to gas evolution, but a marked difference in effect on gas evolution was apparent with increasing temperature, as shown in Fig. 8.2.

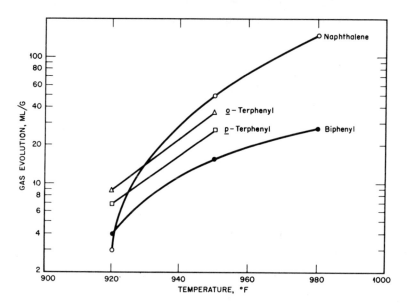

FIG. 8.2   Gas evolved during pyrolysis. Temperature maintained for 24 hr; initial nitrogen pressure of 300 psi; 304 stainless-steel vessels.

The evolution from naphthalene increased about five times faster than that from biphenyl in going from 920 to 980°F. No simple relation (e.g., of the Arrhenius type) is apparent between temperature and gas evolution.

With the exception of naphthalene, the polyphenyls as a class were more stable than the condensed-ring aromatics. The data on the polyphenyls illustrate the effect of decreasing stability with increasing molecular weight. On the basis of gas evolution alone, naphthalene appears to be superior in the 24-hr exposure at 920°F. This advantage was negated in longer exposures, as shown in Table 8.4.

A further difference was noted among all the members of the two classes in the character of the coke formed in the pyrolysis. Under the useful intermediate exposure conditions, the condensed-ring aromatics produced a hard, infusible residue that formed as a separate phase. The polyphenyls, on the other hand, formed "resins" that were relatively non-volatile but were still soluble in the reaction mixture. This difference in solubility favors the polyphenyls as a class.

Materials that showed no particular promise at 920°F included the aromatic derivatives of methane and ethane, aromatic silanes, and phos-

Table 8.4 — THERMAL STABILITY OF NAPHTHALENE
AND BIPHENYL[a]

	Exposure, hr	Gas evolution, ml/g	Residue,[28] %
Naphthalene	24	3	0.1
	72	121	63
Biphenyl	24	4	1.4
	72	21	41

[a]Conditions of test: 920 °F; initial nitrogen pressure of 300 psig;
304 stainless-steel capsules.

phates and aromatic compounds containing alkyl, chloro, or fluoro groups. Some comparative values of gassing and coke formation are given in Table 8.5.

The superiority of biphenyl over simple alkylbiphenyls was confirmed in studies of polymer† formation at various temperatures.[52,53,54] The alkyl-

Table 8.5 — EFFECT OF SUBSTITUENTS AND VARIATIONS
ON THERMAL STABILITY[a]

Compound	Gassing, ml/g	Per cent coke by manual recovery[31]
Naphthalene	3	0.1
Acenaphthene	155	
1-Methylnaphthalene	170	61
Stilbene	82	64
Triphenylmethane	59	70
Triphenylbenzylsilane	55	89
Triphenyl phosphate	40	74
Decalin[b]	233	45
Cetane[b]	136	86

[a]Conditions of test: 24 hr; 920 °F; initial nitrogen pressure of 300 psig;
304 stainless-steel capsules.

[b]Seven hours; 915°F.

biphenyls decreased in stability to pyrolysis with increasing complexity of the alkyl group. Figure 8.3 shows pertinent data.

Other extensive tests at 842 to 887°F also confirm the superior thermal stability of the highly aromatic compounds.[11] Various exposure times were used, and biphenyl, the terphenyls, naphthalene, and triphenylamine were found most promising. Similar results were obtained in studies of high-temperature lubricants through measurements of their vapor pressures at various temperatures in an isoteniscope.[24,85,102]

† Polymer is any material with a boiling point higher than that of the starting material.

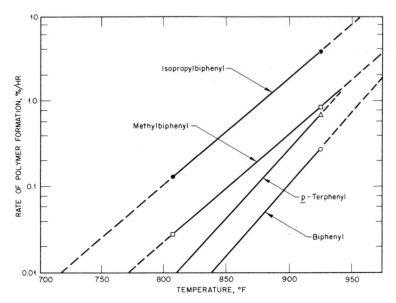

FIG. 8.3 Polymer formation with increasing temperature. Glass vessels; initial helium atmosphere.

8-2.1.3 *Role of Additives*

The kinetic nature of pyrolysis reactions suggests that thermal damage can be inhibited by suitable additives.[28] Several were tried in biphenyl and in naphthalene. As shown in Table 8.6, none had any beneficial effects on thermal stability.[31]

Table 8.6 — EFFECT OF ADDITIVES ON THE THERMAL
STABILITY OF BIPHENYL[a]

Additive		Per cent coke by manual recovery	Gassing, ml/g	Hydrocarbon-to-hydrogen ratio
Wt. %	Compound			
	None	41	21	0.47
1.5	Nitric oxide	81	23	0.90
2.4	Thianthrene	61	21	0.66
2.4	Triphenylmethane	77	113	0.9
2.4	Iodine	69	164	6.8

[a] Conditions of test: 920°F; 72 hr; initial nitrogen pressure of 300 psig; 304 stainless-steel capsules.

8-2.2 THERMAL LOOPS

Heat-transfer data on several polyphenyls, including biphenyl, Santowax R,† and Santowax OM,‡ were obtained over a range of temperature

† Monsanto Chemical Co., terphenyl mixture.
‡ Primarily *o*- and *m*-terphenyl with about 15 wt. % biphenyl.

and flow conditions.[105,118] The test fluid flowed in turbulence through an electrically heated thin-walled tube. Circulation was by a canned rotor pump at 60 psi and 5 gal/min. A center-tapped electrical resistance-heating circuit was used. The following conditions prevailed:

Fluid bulk temperatures, °F	480 to 770
Heater-surface temperatures, °F	565 to 875
Fluid velocities, ft/sec	5 to 25
Heat fluxes, Btu/hr/sq ft	40,000 to 290,000
Reynolds numbers	20,000 to 300,000
Nitrogen pressure, psig	300

Calculated heat-transfer coefficients showed a distinct deviation from the Sieder-Tate equation; the modified correlation[105] in Eq. 8.1, however, fitted the experimental data with a standard deviation of ±7.9%.

$$Nu = 0.015(Re)^{0.86}(Pr)^{0.27} \qquad (8.1)$$

where Nu = Nusselt number, $h(D/k)$, dimensionless
Pr = Prandtl number, $C_p(\mu/k)$, dimensionless
Re = Reynolds number, $Dv\rho/\mu$, dimensionless
h = heat-transfer coefficient, Btu/(hr)(sq ft)(°F)
D = inside diameter of test heater, ft
k = thermal conductivity of the organic, Btu/(hr)(sq ft)(°F/ft)
v = average fluid velocity, ft/sec
ρ = density of fluid, lb/cu ft
μ = viscosity of fluid, lb/(hr)(ft)
μ_s = viscosity of fluid at temperature s, lb/(hr)(ft)
C_p = specific heat of fluid, Btu/(lb)(°F)

Data on four fluids from four different laboratories were later included, and the equation took the following form:

$$Nu = 0.0243(Re)^{0.8}(Pr)^{0.4} \qquad (8.2)$$

When a consistent set of physical-property values was used, all experimental points agreed within ±20%. When data on irradiated fluids were included, the scatter increased to ±25%. Thus the correlation represents a good average of experimental results.

The modifications in Eqs. 8.1 and 8.2 eliminated the viscosity ratio term (μ/μ_s). In these tests scatter of the data was greater than the influence of viscosity ratio. As a result a negative exponent sometimes appeared for this term in the Sieder-Tate equation. McEwen[87] also found that the viscosity change caused a negligible effect on heat transfer. Ewing[56,111] confirmed that experimental heat-transfer data will correlate with a modified Sieder-Tate equation.

A series of high-temperature heat-transfer runs was made in the equipment described at the beginning of this section[105] to produce fouling of the heat-transfer surfaces. Fouling refers to the formation of cokelike deposits. During these runs the heated surfaces were held to temperatures between 850 and 1000°F. Bulk temperatures were approximately 750°F, and varying fluid velocities were 5 to 15 ft/sec for periods up to 100 hr.

The data for biphenyl, Santowax R, and a mixture of Santowax O and M showed that all heat-transfer-coefficient variations could be predicted from previous heat-transfer data for the same fluid. It was therefore concluded that fouling did not occur under these test conditions. Visual examination of the heat-transfer surfaces showed no evidence of fouling. Similar experiments with isopropylbiphenyl under 850°F surface temperature and 5 ft/sec flow conditions also showed no fouling.[56,111]

In previous work by Anderson,[2] tests were made on biphenyl in a circulating system. Operation was at bulk temperatures up to 585°F and at heat fluxes to 292,000 Btu/hr/sq ft; the surface temperature of the heater used was 788°F. No carbon deposits or fouling were observed on the heater ribbons after a maximum continuous operation of 145 hr. The heater in this case was a Nichrome ribbon 0.005 in. thick by 0.25 in. wide by 1 ft long. The ribbon was heated by current from a 10-kva transformer at potentials from 8 to 100 volts. A maximum of about 10 wt. % of the biphenyl was pyrolyzed to higher molecular weight material in these tests.

8-2.3 BURNOUT STUDIES

A series of 100 tests was conducted[47,101] to establish the maximum allowable transfer of heat to polyphenyl coolants before the occurrence of mechanical damage at the heat-transfer surface. The fluids studied included biphenyl, Santowax R, Santowax OM, and isopropylbiphenyl. The preheated fluid was passed through an electrically heated ½-in.-OD tube with an unheated rod inserted concentrically to form an annular passage. The power input to the tube was increased gradually until either the tube was damaged or film boiling occurred at the outside wall. Failure usually occurred in the manner shown in Fig. 8.4. Some tests were terminated before the conditions had become quite this drastic, and only pinhole leaks occurred below the flange.

Figure 8.5 is typical of the data obtained[47] for liquids below their critical pressures and temperatures. The nonboiling forced-convection region is the first mode encountered with increase in heat flux. Here, heat is transferred primarily by single-phase convection with laminar conduction in a very small region close to the wall (sublaminar boundary layer). The transition point into nucleate boiling is soon reached. Small vapor bubbles are first formed on the metal surface as the wall temperature exceeds the boiling point of the cooling fluid (saturation temperature). Since these

FIG. 8.4 Failure of test section in burnout studies. (Courtesy of Aerojet-General Corporation.)

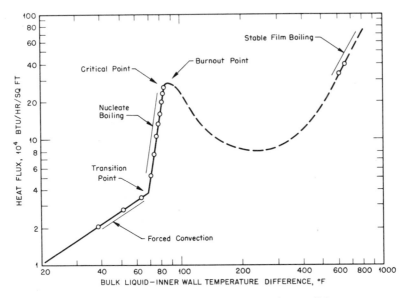

FIG. 8.5 Typical graph of various heat-transfer conditions.

vapor bubbles grow and collapse rapidly, they cause fluid agitation in the sublaminar boundary layer; this agitation increases the heat-transfer rates over those expected from nonboiling forced convection below the transition point. An increase of the heat flux causes only a slight increase in the film temperature difference. Nucleate boiling continues with increasing heat flux until the burnout point is reached. At this point a film of vapor insulates the liquid from the inner wall. The resultant rapid rise in the wall temperatures usually causes damage to test elements. The dashed portion of the curve (Fig. 8.5) was not obtained in these tests because the equipment was not suited for investigating the region beyond the burn-out point.[47]

Transition points and critical points were obtained for all fluids from curves similar to those of Fig. 8.5. The test variables ranged as follows: velocities of 0.5 to 17 ft/sec, pressures of 23 to 406 psia, subcooling of 0 to 328°F, and bulk temperatures of 510 to 831°F.

For a given coolant and system, the heat flux at either of these points depends upon fluid flow and applied pressure. The pressure has been shown to combine with bulk liquid temperature into a single variable,[47] the subcooling parameter (ΔT_{sub}). This is the difference between the saturation temperature (boiling point) and the bulk temperature. Typical data relating heat flux at the critical point $[(Q/A)_c]$ to ΔT_{sub} and fluid velocity are shown in Table 8.7.

Table 8.7 — CRITICAL HEAT FLUX FOR BIPHENYL

Critical heat flux $[(Q/A)_c]$, Btu/hr/sq ft	Velocity (V), ft/sec	Subcool temperature (ΔT_{sub}), °F
548,000	10.3	214
495,000	10.3	208
261,000	5.1	129
260,000	5.3	104
153,000	1.99	83
146,000	1.90	72

The interdependence of the quantities in Table 8.7 for biphenyl is expressed in the following equation. It is limited in application to velocities of 4.8 ft/sec and above.

$$(Q/A)_c = 454\Delta T_{sub}V^{0.63} + 116,000 \tag{8.3}$$

Similarly, the critical heat flux for Santowax R was correlated by the following equation:

$$(Q/A)_c = 552\Delta T_{sub}V^{0.667} + 152,000 \tag{8.4}$$

Thus the terphenyl mixture permits a higher critical heat flux than biphenyl for a given subcooling parameter. The higher boiling point for the terphenyls is also favorable.

8-3 Static Irradiations

8-3.1 TESTS WITH REACTOR FLUX

Irradiations were conducted (1) to determine the best types of organic compounds for a combined radiation and high-temperature environment and (2) to study temperature and radiation dependence. Highly aromatic compounds were generally involved, that is, those which showed good thermal stability. Exposures were in the absence of air to avoid the radiolytic oxidation phenomenon discussed in detail in Ch. 9 (Sect. 9-4.2).

The performance of an organic compound can be measured by the temperature it can withstand at a given radiation dose before becoming completely tarred or coked. Typical data[122] on temperature thresholds are shown in Table 8.8. The superiority of the polyphenyl class of aromatic

Table 8.8 — TYPICAL TEMPERATURE THRESHOLDS[a]
FOR AROMATIC COMPOUNDS IN A REACTOR[b]

Compound	Threshold temperature, °F
Fused ring:	
Naphthalene	815
Chrysene	810
Phenanthrene	780
Pyrene	750
Polyphenyl:	
Biphenyl	860
o – Terphenyl	855
p – Terphenyl	855
m – Terphenyl	840
p – Quaterphenyl	835
m – Quinquephenyl	800
Other:	
Dibenzothiophene	850
Dowtherm A	810
Diphenylacetylene	780
Carbazole	760
Amylbiphenyl	720

[a] Approximate point above which massive coking takes place at about 18×10^8 rads.

[b] Conditions of test: Brookhaven Graphite Research Reactor (BGRR); about 240 hr; 410 stainless-steel capsules; initial helium atmosphere.

hydrocarbons is evident. Also, biphenyl is better than naphthalene. There was little choice among the terphenyl isomers; greater differences are revealed by the data in Table 8.9, which show the *para* isomer to be the most stable of the three.[37,46]

The performance of dibenzothiophene shown in Table 8.8 is of particular interest. Unfortunately the radioactivity induced in the sulfur by

Table 8.9 — DECOMPOSITION OF TERPHENYLS[a]

	Polymer,[b] wt. %	Gas, ml/g
o-Terphenyl	38.3	2.04
m-Terphenyl	32.6	1.35
p-Terphenyl	25.4	0.38
4 wt. % *p*-terphenyl + 96 wt. % *m*-terphenyl	33.9	0.66

[a]Conditions of test: Materials Testing Reactor (MTR) dose of 90×10^{c} rads; stainless-steel capsules; 77 °F; initial helium atmosphere.

[b]Product boiling above starting material.

neutron capture is undesirable in a reactor coolant. The inherent stability of materials typified by this compound, however, suggests their use as stabilizing additives.

Figure 8.6 illustrates the temperature–damage curves[122] for some aro-

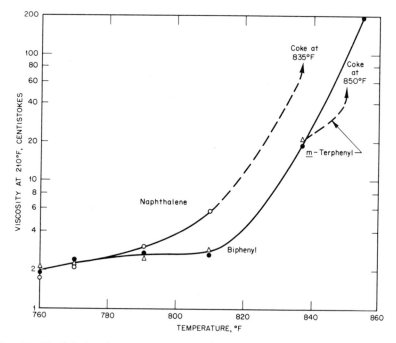

FIG. 8.6 Radiolysis of polynuclear aromatics at high temperature. BGRR reactor dose of 14×10^{8} rads; 410 stainless-steel capsules; initial helium atmosphere.

matic materials. Polymer formation, as indicated by viscosity change, remained small up to about 790 to 810°F. Beyond this range the fluids rapidly degraded. The temperature thresholds in Table 8.8 were taken at just below the coking point. Thus they are somewhat higher than those cited in Sect. 8-4.10 since the flat portion of the curve just before the sharp increase in damage was selected for them. This abrupt change found in the temperature–damage curve at a constant dose also occurred in the damage rate–temperature curve.[8]

Figure 8.7 shows the relationship[28,31] of temperature and dose in a differ-

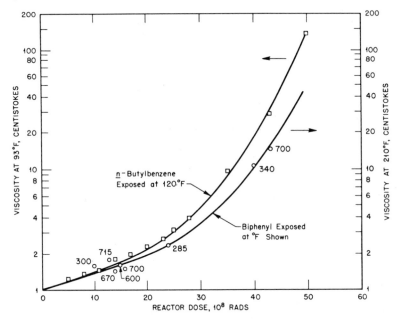

Fig. 8.7 Roles of temperature and dose in radiation damage. MTR and BGRR reactors; magnesium capsules; initial helium atmosphere.

ent profile for biphenyl. Data are also included for an organic fluid exposed at a given temperature below its threshold. The latter data illustrate the normal shape of the dose–damage curve, where temperature is not a factor. The difference in slope between n-butylbenzene and biphenyl reflects an expected stability difference in these materials. For biphenyl in Fig. 8.7, the temperature effect was negligible under the conditions shown.

Thus, in general, damage can be considered dependent on temperature only to a minor extent below the temperature threshold range. In the sensitive region (threshold range to below a pyrolysis range), which varies among compounds, temperature has an increasingly important effect. With mild temperature conditions, a reactor dose[28] of 1 to 5×10^{10} rads will substantially decompose almost all the organic material.

Contrary to the results from thermal-stability tests, certain chemical additives were found effective in reducing reactor-radiation damage to aromatic fluids at high temperatures.[122,128] Additives promise two important advantages in coolant technology: they may (1) permit base fluids to be used at higher, more desirable temperatures and (2) extend coolant life to yield lower make-up costs and decreased purification requirements.

The effect of thianthrene was analyzed statistically and shown to be beneficial.[122] Typical data are given in Table 8.10. Other additives, such

Table 8.10 — EFFECT OF THIANTHRENE ADDITIVE ON
RADIOLYSIS[a] OF m-TERPHENYL— BIPHENYL (50/50)

Radiation dose, 10^6 rads	Exposure temperature, °F	Additive, wt. %	Viscosity at 210°F, centistokes
12	760	0	2.70
12	760	5	2.08
10	840	0	22.0
10	840	5	17.9

[a]Conditions of test: BGRR; 410 stainless-steel capsules; initial helium atmosphere.

as dibenzyl selenide, naphthacene, phenazine, and phthalocyanine, were also effective in polyphenyls in certain cases.

Table 8.11 lists information[122] on gas evolution from aromatic materials

Table 8.11 — GAS EVOLUTION FROM POLYPHENYLS ON RADIOLYSIS

Exposure temperature,[a] °F	Gas evolved, ml/g					
	760	768	793	810	837	854
Biphenyl	7	11	11	13	20	27
With 5% thianthrene	9	9	11	13	16	20
With 50% m-terphenyl	9	7	8	14	21	27
m- Terphenyl	4	7	7	9	16	21
Naphthalene	10	20		46		

[a]Conditions of test: BGRR; 14×10^6 rads; 410 stainless-steel capsules; initial helium atmosphere.

radiolyzed at high temperature. These data are in accord with those given in Fig. 8.6 for polymer formation as measured by viscosity change.

8-3.2 TESTS WITH ELECTRONS AND GAMMA RAYS

Extensive static exposures to these radiation types were conducted on polyphenyl compounds, particularly the three terphenyl isomers, biphenyl, and p-quaterphenyl. Electron irradiations at various temperatures showed

p-terphenyl to be the most stable.[45] Later work[37] confirmed that p-terphenyl has superior stability and that biphenyl and m-terphenyl are somewhat less stable than the other polyphenyls. Figure 8.8 shows polymer formation for the terphenyl isomers.

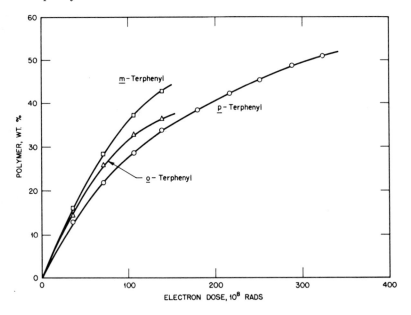

FIG. 8.8 Growth of polymer concentration. Temperature, 662°F; stainless-steel cells without oxygen.

In Fig. 8.8 the decrease in the rate of polymer yield[37] with increase in dose is noteworthy and appears to be a group property of polyphenyls. This indicates either that the products formed are more resistant to radiation than the starting material or that the rate of monomer polymerization drops off because of dilution of the monomer with polymer. The radiolysis products also have the very favorable effect of lowering the melting points of the original fluids.[28] This same decrease in polymer yield with dose was noted[37] in Fig. 4.12 in Ch. 4 for p-terphenyl at a higher exposure temperature. Pyrolysis in these exposures would be negligible.[37,66]

In the radiolysis of p-terphenyl with electrons, the composition of the gas evolved is dependent on both temperature and dose. The hydrogen percentage decreases with increasing temperature at constant dose and also with increasing dose at constant temperature.[37] Woodley[27] observed increasing amounts of hydrogen from biphenyl at increasing temperature up to 626°F. For methyl- and isopropylbiphenyl, however, relatively more light hydrocarbons (more than hydrogen) were formed with increasing temperature; this fact suggests the thermal decomposition of the polymers formed. This increase in hydrocarbon evolution rather than hydrogen evolution with increasing temperature in the 625 to 800°F range was observed for biphenyl and alkylbiphenyls in reactor work[122] and was confirmed by later studies.[37]

Colichman[45] showed in electron work that a mixture of p- and m-terphenyl had a stability between the stabilities of the two pure components. According to Burns et al.,[37] in reactor work Santowax R, a mixture of polyphenyls,† gave less gas than pure p-terphenyl. The constituents of Santowax R were concluded to be consumed by irradiation according to their initial proportions; no protection of the *ortho* and *meta* isomers was given by the *para* isomers. Atomics International personnel, however, showed that selected compounds retarded radiation damage in a terphenyl mixture at high temperature. Some 56 additives were investigated in Santowax OM; 9 were effective in reducing $G_{polymer}$ by at least 20% as shown in Table 8.12.

Table 8.12 — ADDITIVES[a] IN SANTOWAX OM

Additive (2 wt. %)	Reduction in $G_{polymer}$, %	Reduction in G_{gas}, %
1,1,4,4-Tetraphenylbutadiene	20	30
1,6-Diphenylhexatriene	25	30
Tetraphenylcyclopentadiene	25	35
Phenanthrene	20	55
Pyrene	25	15
3,4-Benzpyrene	50	50
α-Trixene	30	10
Triphenylmethane	30	15
1,2,3,4,5,6,7,8-Oxtahydrophenanthrene	30	10

[a]Conditions of test: gamma dose, 32×10^8 rads; 750°F.

The electron-dose values in Fig. 8.8 (and in Fig. 4.12) are large compared to the reactor doses cited in Sect. 8-3.1. Relatively low damage at similar high doses also has been observed with gamma rays as shown in Table 8.13. The inhibition provided by a selenide additive is also illustrated. Any differences in results from the reactor and the electron–gamma work could be caused by errors in dose measurement, particularly in the reactor effort, and/or by differences in the relative effects of neutrons and electrons. The latter explanation is likely the more important (see Ch. 3, Sect. 3-3).

8-3.3 EFFECT OF RADIATION TYPE

Burns et al.[37] reported that for equal energy absorbed in coolants fast neutrons had a greater effect than gamma rays (see Ch. 2, Sect. 2-4.3.2).

---

† About 1% biphenyl, 10% o-terphenyl, 53% m-terphenyl, and 36% p-terphenyl, plus small amounts of material of similar volatility.[37]

Table 8.13 — RADIOLYSIS OF POLYPHENYLS WITH GAMMA RAYS[a]

Compound	Exposure temperature, °F	Gamma dose, 10^e rads	Viscosity at 210 °F, centistokes
Biphenyl		0	1.00
	77	42[b]	1.12
	77	60[b]	1.13
Biphenyl-m-terphenyl (50/50)		0	2.00
	200	67[c]	2.78
	200	134[c]	5.84
Same with 5% dibenzyl selenide		0	1.70
	200	67[c]	2.38
	200	134[c]	3.67

[a] From Ref. 31 and unpublished information.
[b] Magnesium capsules; initial helium atmosphere.
[c] Vented aluminum vessels.

Polyphenyls were irradiated for successively higher doses to about 30×10^8 rads of reactor radiation and separately to about 200×10^8 rads of electron radiation. This produced up to 50 wt. % polymer content. Several different temperatures were also used. The initial consumption of polyphenyl (G_{-M} extrapolated to 0 dose) was from three to six times greater in the reactor, depending on temperature, as shown in Table 8.14. Initial gas yields also were consistently higher in the reactor exposures.

From the data of Table 8.14 and certain assumptions,[37] a possible set

Table 8.14 — INITIAL POLYMER YIELDS IN THE RADIOLYSIS
OF POLYPHENYLS

	Consumption of polyphenyl, G_{-M} at 0 dose					
Radiation type	1-Mev electrons			Graphite Reactor (BEPO)[a]		
Temperature, °F	572	662	752	572	662	752
Biphenyl	0.38	0.46		0.82	1.13	
o-Terphenyl	0.18	0.19	0.26	0.63	0.70	
m-Terphenyl	0.21	0.21	0.28	0.58	0.64	
p-Terphenyl	0.18	0.18	0.29	0.47	0.54	1.32
Santowax R	0.19	0.19	0.21	0.51	0.59	1.30

[a] British Experimental Pile Zero.

of fast-neutron yields was calculated[37] and is shown in Figure 8.9. The magnitude and temperature dependence of the fast-neutron effect are illustrated. The figures relate only to the particular fast-neutron spectrum prevailing in the BEPO core. It was estimated[37] that 70% of the energy

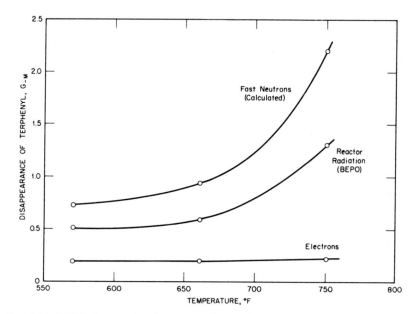

FIG. 8.9 Initial (extrapolated to zero dose) decomposition rates for terphenyls (Santowax R).

deposited by fast neutrons came from those of energy below 1 Mev in these experiments.

These results and those from several other programs relating to the fast-neutron effect in terphenyls were summarized and treated statistically.[66] The summary included data from the following sources:

Radiation source	Per cent of energy absorbed in coolant from fast neutrons
1-Mev electrons[42,45,46]	0
1-Mev electrons[37]	0
Curtiss-Wright Research Reactor[66]	65
Oak Ridge Graphite Reactor[66]	63 to 85
BEPO[37]	54.4
NAA-20 loop[25]	12

Although this work cannot be considered as conclusive because of various factors, it certainly indicates a fast-neutron effect. Figure 8.10 illustrates its dependence on polymer† content, and Fig. 8.11 shows its dependence on temperature. At 600°F and 30% polymer content, fast neutrons were found approximately 4.4 times more damaging than gamma rays for the same amount of energy absorbed.

† Material boiling above *p*-terphenyl.

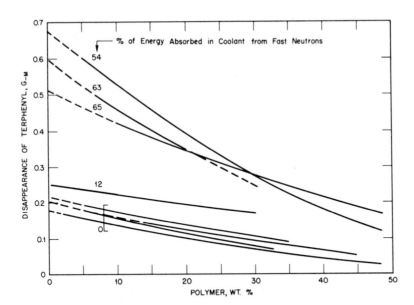

FIG. 8.10 Polymer content and the fast-neutron effect in terphenyl radiolysis. Various isomers; four reactors; two electron sources; 572 to 750°F.

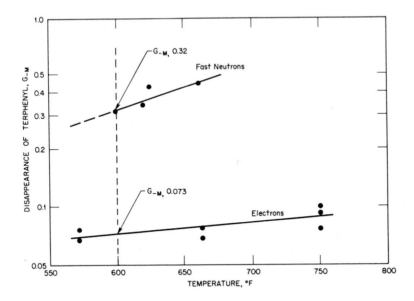

FIG. 8.11 Influence of temperature and radiation type on terphenyl radiolysis. Various isomers; four reactors; two electron sources; various doses.

The greater destructive power of energy from fast neutrons compared to that from gamma rays demands that caution be used in applying radiation-effects data obtained in one facility to another in which the neutron-to-gamma ratio is different. The data summarized here also suggest the following:

1. Organic-cooled reactors should work the coolant to the highest possible "polymer" content consistent with the retention of satisfactory engineering properties. This would allow advantage to be taken of the observed decrease in polyphenyl radiolysis rates with increasing polymer contents.

2. Polyphenyls might be used only as coolants. If other materials could be used as moderators, decomposition rates of the coolants would be reduced accordingly.

3. Because of the temperature sensitivity of the fast-neutron effect, it may not be feasible to utilize temperatures in the 750 to 800°F range without sacrifice in coolant damage.

8-4 Circulating In-pile Systems

8-4.1 INTRODUCTION

The static tests discussed in Sect. 8-3 highlighted the attractive features of organics as reactor coolants and pointed to the use of the polyphenyls. Broad limitations of temperature, dosage, and other environmental factors were outlined, as were the over-all effects of radiolysis on the physical properties of these materials. The work was inadequate, however, to allow the prediction of heat-transfer and engineering properties of the fluids. In particular, a need remained for data on polyphenyls containing high concentrations of their decomposition products. Any fluid used in a reactor would quickly become contaminated; it is not practical to operate continuously on pure material.

Several in-pile circulating loops were built and operated to investigate these items. Greenberg[70] reported on a loop that operated in the Experimental Breeder Reactor No. 1 (EBR-1). Specific damage, i.e., polyphenyl consumption per unit radiation, was fortuitously in good agreement with data from static tests. McEwen[87] reported that no fouling occurred with several fluids up to 585°F in a loop in the BGRR. De Halas[53] conducted rate studies in a loop in a Hanford reactor and produced threshold temperatures that were in good agreement with similar results from static irradiations. Nakazato and Gercke[96] observed no fouling with a polyphenyl mixture in a loop operated in a reflector position in the MTR.

This loop work justified an additional comprehensive study made by Atomics International. This integrated effort eclipses in significance and scope the earlier work. Results of the NAA-20 experiment are contained in two technical reports[25,82] and will serve as the basis for the discussion

Table 8.15 — COMPOSITION OF ORGANICS IRRADIATED
IN NAA-20 LOOP

| | Purity, wt. % | | | |
| | Biphenyl | Terphenyl | | |
		Ortho-	Meta-	Para-
Biphenyl	99.5			
Santowax R[a]	0.3	11.7	60.0	28.1
Santowax OM[a]	Trace	65.2	32.3	2.5
Isopropylbiphenyl (IPB):				
Meta-	55.4			
Para-	44.6			

[a] Monsanto Chemical Co.

to follow. Decomposition rates, heat-transfer rates, fouling characteristics, physical-property changes, induced radioactivity, and corrosion rates were studied for four different fluids. The composition of these materials is shown in Table 8.15.

8-4.2 DESCRIPTION OF EQUIPMENT

A sketch of the in-pile loop system[25] is shown in Fig. 8.12. The equipment had two sections that were connected at the reactor tank by means of an expansion bellows. The in-pile section was installed vertically in a

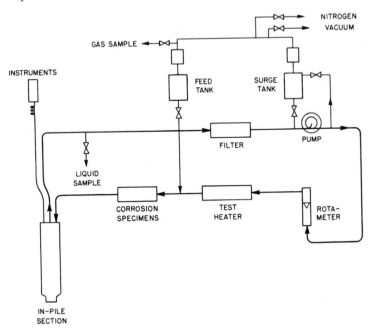

FIG. 8.12 Schematic flow diagram of NAA-20 loop.

high-flux region (A-13 reflector position) and was replaced in its entirety for each test. The permanent valve and pump console was at the reactor face.

Figure 8.13 shows[25] the in-pile section. It comprised an outer aluminum shell, an inner steel reservoir containing the organic fluid, and the in-pile

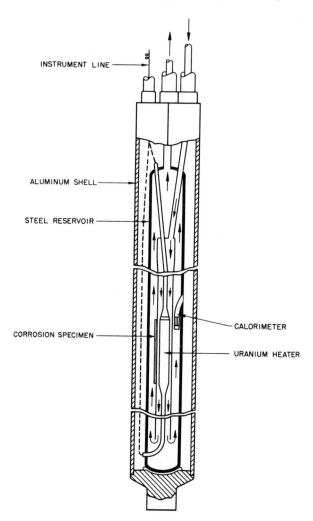

INSTRUMENT LINE

ALUMINUM SHELL

STEEL RESERVOIR

CORROSION SPECIMEN

CALORIMETER

URANIUM HEATER

FIG. 8.13 In-pile section of NAA-20 loop.

heater that contained auxiliary uranium. The uranium heater was located inside the reservoir and was enclosed in a stainless-steel tube. The annulus between the uranium metal and the stainless-steel enclosure was filled with NaK† to conduct away the fission heat generated by the uranium. The annular space surrounding this heater assembly carried the test fluid on its path through the in-pile section. Thermocouples were installed at strategic positions.

Radiation fluxes were monitored in the in-pile section of the loop. Slow-neutron flux was measured by cobalt–aluminum wires. Fast flux was monitored by nickel wires; gamma flux was measured by steel-rod calorimeters. Corrosion specimens of various metals were also placed in the in-pile assembly.

Heat transfer was measured in the (auxiliary) test heater shown in Fig. 8.12. It was designed for the same linear flow velocity and heat flux as the in-pile uranium heater. The test heater, however, was a stainless-steel tube through which the polyphenyl flowed. Alternating currents (up to 1000 amp at 8 volts) were passed through the tube to induce heat.

The organic fluid was circulated through the system by a canned rotor pump. The flow lines were provided with Nichrome trace heating wire and thermal insulation. The annular space between the concentric tubes of the in-pile section was pressurized to prevent in-leakage of reactor water. Mild steel was used throughout for construction of all system tanks and pipe. Stainless-steel components were limited to the bellows seal valves, the pump, the test heater, the uranium heater, and the rotameter.

Measurements of pressure, flow, and liquid level of the circulating organic fluid were made at the console. Precise measurements of the heat input to the resistance heater were made. The total volume of the system was about 8250 ml (approximately 0.29 cu ft). The in-pile volume was about 19.4% of the total.

8-4.3 PROCEDURE AND OPERATION

Each material listed in Table 8.14 was tested for one cycle in the MTR. Upon completion of the four single-cycle irradiations, biphenyl was irradiated for three consecutive cycles to evaluate long-term effects. For these experiments the operating time per cycle was 12 to 14 days for a total of about 11,000 to 14,000 Mwh (0.13 to 0.18 Mwh absorbed in coolant $\equiv 5.7$ to 7.8×10^9 rads). Over 98% of all dosage was under maximum reactor flux and power conditions of 40 Mw. Single-cycle exposures were sufficient to increase the polymer content of the coolant to approximately 30%.

The equipment was operated at nearly constant values of maximum bulk temperature and at a velocity of 13.5 ft/sec through the test heater and through the uranium heater. The heat fluxes for both heaters varied from about 130,000 to 180,000 Btu/hr/sq ft. A summary[25] of the tests is shown in Table 8.16.

† NaK is a sodium–potassium eutectic melting at approximately 60°F.

Table 8.16 — SUMMARY OF TESTS IN NAA-20 LOOP

Material	Average in-pile temperature, °F	Bulk temperature, °F	Pressure, psig	High boilers, wt. %	Maximum heater wall temperature, °F	
					Uranium heater	Test heater
Isopropylbiphenyl	641	600	350	27.6	700	780
Santowax R	645	600	110	29	750	800
Santowax OM	628	675	300	32.7	750	800
Biphenyl	676	670	310	35	780	800
	684	650[a]	300	33.3	758	800
	597	520[a]	300	36.1	650	800
	651	620[a]	300	39.8	710	800

[a] Three-cycle run.

8-4.4 COOLANT DECOMPOSITION

The index of coolant damage used in the NAA-20 work is the amount of product having lower volatility than the starting material. Such product is termed "high boilers" (HB) and was separated from the radiolyzed coolant by distillation.† Decomposition rate was computed on a weight basis:

$$G_{HB} = \frac{\text{Pounds of HB formed}}{\text{Mwh absorbed in the coolant} = (\text{Mwh})_a} \qquad (8.5)$$

In this work 12% of the energy absorbed in the coolant resulted from the moderation of neutrons. The remaining 88% came from the Compton scattering of gamma photons (if energies greater than 1.0 Mev are assumed‡).

$$G_{\text{polymer}} = \frac{\text{Number of polymer molecules formed}}{100 \text{ ev absorbed in coolant}}$$

For terphenyls

$$G_{HB} = 378 G_{\text{polymer}}$$

where the molecular weight of the polymer was taken as 460, about the value for the chief radiolysis product, hexaphenyl.

Figure 8.14 shows the build-up[25] of HB with increasing absorbed dose. Figure 8.15 gives the rate of HB formation[25] for all single-cycle irradiations summarized in Table 8.16. A semilog plot of data for a given run from Fig. 8.15 (log G_{HB}) yields a straight line. When bulk temperatures were varied by ±50°F from about 650°F, no change was noted in the marked dependence of the G_{HB} on HB content.

Only about 20% of the test fluid was exposed to radiation at any one time. If perfect mixing is assumed, this condition is equivalent to the entire fluid receiving 20% of the actual radiation flux. The entire fluid was exposed to heat continuously and thus was subject to thermal degradation. These effects were considered in determining G_{HB} values. The amount of HB generated thermally was found to be less than 1% of the total damage.

The NAA-20 system was not designed to measure gas generation. For the isopropylbiphenyl irradiation, however, about 15 ml of gas was generated per gram of residue formed. This confirms the value found by McEwen.[87] Gas generation rates for biphenyl, Santowax R, and Santowax OM were about equal and were estimated as a factor of 10 less than the rate measured for isopropylbiphenyl. McEwen's values were lower.[87]

---

† The radiolysis gas was ignored because it was but a minor weight fraction of the breakdown observed. With the Santowaxes the HB was taken as anything boiling above p-terphenyl.

‡ The G_{HB} is related to the G_{polymer} used in Sect. 8-3.2.

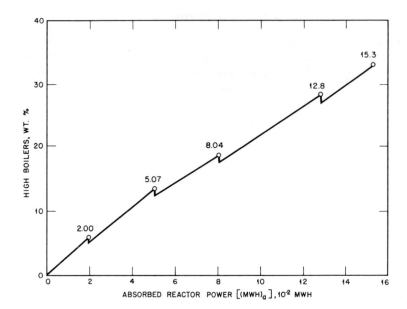

FIG. 8.14 High-boiler build-up in Santowax OM in NAA-20 loop. Zigs indicate fresh make-up.

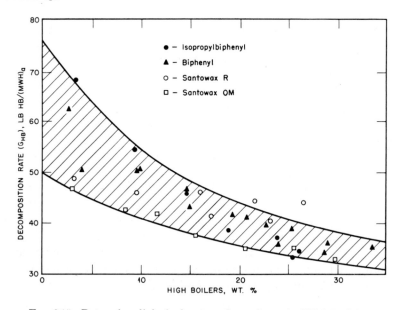

FIG. 8.15 Rate of radiolysis for organic coolants in NAA-20 loop.

8-4.5 HEAT TRANSFER

Heat-transfer determinations were made with both the test heater and the uranium heater under nearly identical conditions of bulk temperature, HB content, and fluid velocity. Corrections were made for the fact that flow in the uranium heater was annular and that in the test heater was tubular. This allowed a comparison of the effect of the reactor radiation field on the heat-transfer surface. There appeared to be none. The physical properties of the coolant were the same at each heater. In general, the heat-transfer coefficients decreases 15 to 20% for an increase to 30% HB. Typical changes[25] in the coefficient for biphenyl are shown in Fig. 8.16. The decreases are considered real. The curves presented, however, put a great deal of emphasis on single points.

The heat flux at the uranium heater was calculated by two methods: (1) from the monitored neutron dose and (2) from the observed radial temperature difference between the inside of the uranium heater and its outside wall. A careful consideration of the data showed no fouling effect or decrease in the heat-transfer coefficient at the uranium heater which was greater than the ±10% uncertainty prevailing in the determinations.

After irradiation the uranium heaters were examined visually in a hot laboratory. Care was taken to avoid overheating, contaminating, etc., the

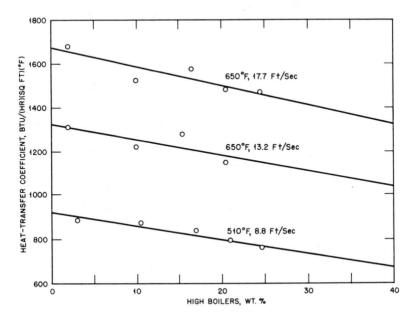

FIG. 8.16 Typical effect of radiolysis on heat-transfer coefficient for biphenyl, NAA-20 loop.

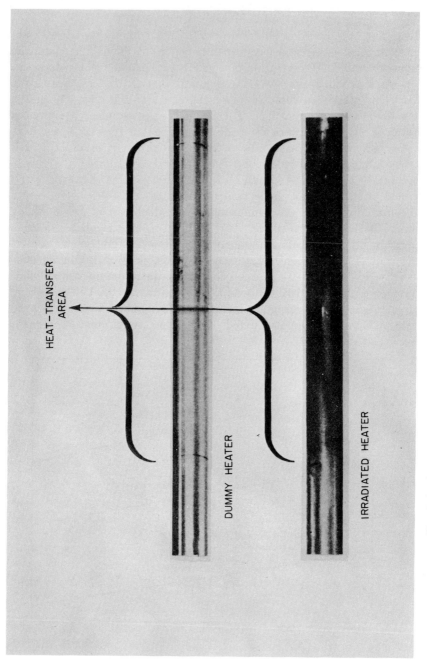

FIG. 8.17 Appearance of uranium heater after Suntowax R run, NAA-20 loop.

heaters before inspection. The heat-transfer area in all cases was covered with a very thin, hard, adherent film. It was not possible to remove the film by rubbing, nor could its thickness be measured. Figure 8.17 illustrates the appearance[25] of the film. No differences among fluids could be determined from this visual examination.

8-4.6 COOLANT ACTIVATION

One-gram portions of the samples removed from the NAA-20 loop for HB analysis were counted at four- to five-day intervals to detect active isotopes in the coolant. The over-all activation was very low, about 16 mr/hr/g, at contact. Levels decreased somewhat as irradiations progressed, possibly because of the removal of particles by the filter. The coolants charged to the loop were all of industrial grade. Prior to their use they were all given a neutron-activation test to indicate the level of impurities present. The radioisotopes resulting from the impurities were Na^{24}, Cl^{38}, Mn^{56}, and a trace amount of Co^{60}. All concentrations were only a few parts per million.

The activity of biphenyl after prolonged irradiation in the system increased by a factor of 10. This increase was generally caused by the appearance of Cu^{64}, Fe^{59}, Cr^{51}, and Zn^{65}. The copper and zinc might have come from silver solder in the system and the iron and chromium from rusting of the steel parts of the in-pile assemblies before their use.

Thus the final coolant activity was due primarily to impurities introduced with the charge fluid and to cleanup of the system for start-up. Activity in a reactor could be lower than that experienced in the NAA-20 loop. This would result from (1) a smaller surface-to-volume ratio in the reactor and (2) continuous purification.

8-4.7 CORROSION

Incidental to the NAA-20 runs, common structural metals were screened for compatibility with the circulating coolant.[25,68] Coupons of mild steel, aluminum, stainless steel, magnesium, and zirconium were exposed to the test fluid near the uranium heater and also in an out-of-pile position. The flow rate past the specimens was 0.5 ft/sec.

The stainless steel and aluminum exhibited excellent corrosion resistance. Although the mild-steel and alloy-steel coupons showed slightly greater weight changes and some discoloration, they were still considered as having showed good corrosion resistance. Magnesium and zirconium were unsatisfactory because of oxidizing and hydriding, respectively.

Magnesium oxide probably formed from trace amounts of water present in the system, estimated to be about 10 ppm. Zirconium hydride probably formed from reaction with radiolytic hydrogen. There were no indications of any radiation effect on the corrosion resistance of any of the materials tested.[82]

8-4.8 PHYSICAL-PROPERTY CHANGES

These changes were determined for samples from the NAA-20 loop. Densities and viscosities of the test materials increased with HB content, as typified by the data[25] for biphenyl in Figs. 8.18 and 8.19.

Specific-heat values for the polyphenyl mixtures were found to decrease with increase in HB content. Typical data[25] are shown in Fig. 8.20. Likewise, the melting points of the irradiated materials decreased with increasing HB content as the data[25] of Fig. 8.21 show.

The carbon-to-hydrogen ratio increased with an increase in HB content, as expected, because of the evolution of radiolytic hydrogen. The effect, however, was smaller than the increase in density; thus the volumetric hydrogen content (i.e., N_H, atoms of hydrogen/ml) actually increased. For biphenyl with 35 wt. % HB, N_H increased by about 2% over a wide temperature range.

8-4.9 EQUIPMENT EXAMINATION

Upon completion of the tests summarized in Table 8.15, the console was dismantled for examination. It had been in operation for about 130 days, during which irradiated polyphenyls were circulated continuously. The HB content in test samples was above 30 wt. % for approximately 50 of these days. In general, the parts were clean. The pump impeller housing showed the characteristic thin, hard, adherent film that was found in all portions of the loop containing polyphenyls exposed to high temperature in the absence or presence of radiation. The resistance heater was sectioned and examined for signs of fouling or scaling. No difference in appearance between the test heater and the other portions of the piping could be detected.

8-4.10 DECOMPOSITION RATES

De Halas conducted experiments (see Refs. 49, 52, 53, and 54) on prospective coolants in the absence of oxygen in an attempt to separate radiolytic and pyrolytic effects. The index of damage used was "tar" or polymer formation. Again, anything boiling above the starting material was considered polymer, and the two were separated by a single plate distillation under vacuum.

Polymerization both in pyrolysis and in radiolysis tests followed a first-order rate law; i.e., tar formation was directly proportional to the amount of the starting material remaining. Biphenyl was the most stable to pyrolytic damage only, followed by the three terphenyls and alkylated biphenyls, as already shown in Fig. 8.3. Similar results were obtained in

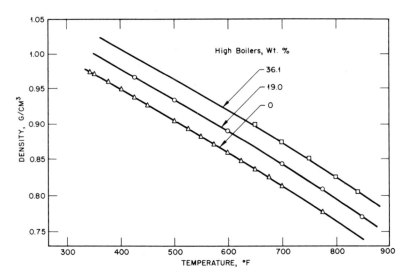

FIG. 8.18 Density of irradiated biphenyls, NAA-20 loop.

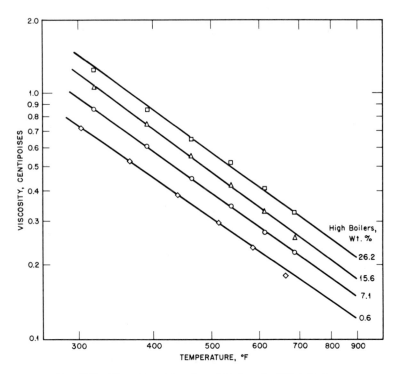

FIG. 8.19 Viscosity of irradiated biphenyls, NAA-20 loop.

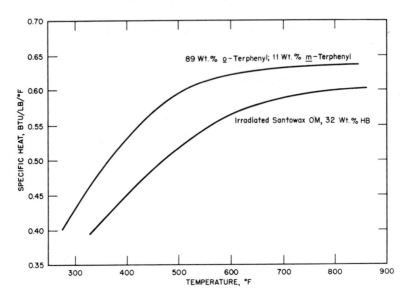

FIG. 8.20 Specific heat of polyphenyls, NAA-20 loop.

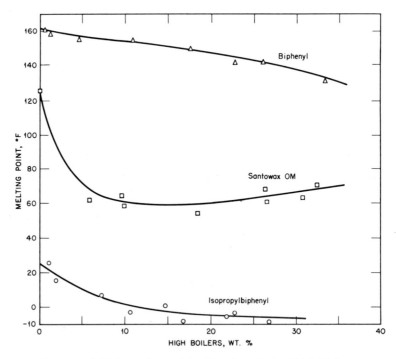

FIG. 8.21 Melting points of irradiated coolants, NAA-20 loop.

irradiations in a circulating loop in a Hanford pile. Temperatures below 200°F and doses of up to about 10^{10} rads† were used; isopropylbiphenyl, biphenyl, the terphenyl isomers, and a ternary eutectic (55 wt. % o-terphenyl, 20 wt. % m-terphenyl, and 25 wt. % biphenyl) were studied. There could have been essentially no pyrolytic damage to such materials at these temperatures. The rate constants varied less than 20% among the various fluids.

Some of the irradiated samples were subsequently heated in the absence of oxygen. This decreased the amount of tar in the coolant. The effect was further observed to occur at low temperatures, and it increased rapidly with increased time of exposure to heat.[49] Thus, during irradiation of any coolant at some temperature above the threshold temperature, part of the radiolytic tar will be destroyed by heat alone.

A difference in the nature of the radiolytic polymers from two types of starting materials was evident.[53] In the case of isopropylbiphenyl, a notable decrease in viscosity accompanied the reduced tar content,[49] as shown in Fig. 8.22. This was not true for the radiolyzed polyphenyl

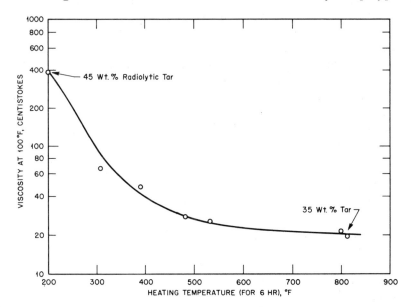

FIG. 8.22 Thermal destruction of the polymer in irradiated isopropylbiphenyl.

eutectic as shown in Table 8.17. This difference is expected. The point of major radiolytic attack with the alkylbiphenyl is the alkyl group (see Ch. 4, Sect. 4-7). This forms a styrene type monomer and subsequent polymer. This polymer would be less stable thermally than the polymer

† Effective total dose;[53] 20% gamma and 80% neutrons.

from the polyphenyl eutectic where the dominant radiolysis reaction forms higher polyphenyls.

De Halas concluded from his reactor and thermal-stability work that the decomposition rates resulting strictly from radiolysis are similar for the polyphenyls (only 20% variation).[53] The main stability differences as temperatures are raised during radiolysis are due to variations in resistance

Table 8.17 — THERMAL DESTRUCTION OF RADIOLYTIC
POLYMER FROM POLYPHENYL EUTECTIC[a]

Heating temperature (for 6 hr), °F	Tar, %	Viscosity at 100 °F, centistokes
Before heating	29	64
392	18	75
572	17	61

[a] 55 wt. % o-terphenyl, 20 wt. % m-terphenyl, and 25 wt. % biphenyl.

of individual compounds to pyrolysis. The polymerization rate for a polyphenyl in a reactor system remains only a minor function of temperature until a transition temperature is reached. At this point and beyond, the rate becomes much more dependent on temperature. These effects[53] are shown in Fig. 8.23. Because of the similarity of the radiolysis rates for all materials studied, only the curve for isopropylbiphenyl is given for radiolytic damage. The pyrolytic rates of all the other compounds studied fall between those shown for biphenyl and isopropylbiphenyl. The transition temperatures are indicated by breaks in the curves and are tabulated as follows:[50,53]

Compound	Transition temperature, °F
Biphenyl	805
Terphenyls	795
Methylbiphenyl	750
Isopropylated terphenyl	725
Isopropylbiphenyl	705

These transition temperatures correlate in a relative sense with the threshold numbers described in Sect. 8-3.1, although the latter are higher in absolute value. This results from differences in definition of thresholds, as noted previously. In any event these sets of data must be thought of as valid only for the exposure conditions under which they were determined. Thus an increase in dose rate would force an increase in the absolute values for transition temperature, or the point at which pyrolysis becomes predominant, as seen in Fig. 8.23. The reverse would also be true: a decrease in dose rate would decrease the transition temperature.

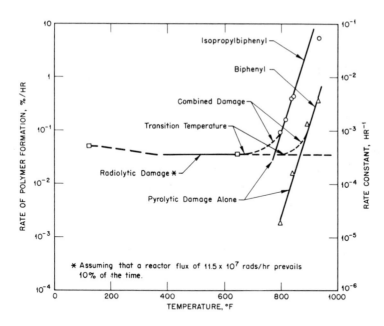

Fig. 8.23 Polymer formation from radiolysis and pyrolysis.

8-5 Organic Moderated Reactor Experiment

The OMRE was constructed to establish the feasibility of the concept of an organic-moderated and -cooled power reactor; it was to provide a conclusive demonstration of the behavior of the polyphenyls under conditions of temperature and neutron flux identical to those encountered in power-reactor applications.[116] Specifically, the OMRE was to demonstrate the following.

1. Technical feasibility: It was important to show whether the organic reactor could be operated continuously and reliably under steady-state conditions. Such operation had to be without any problems associated with possible deposition of organic materials on the heat-transfer surfaces in the system resulting from decomposition of the moderator–coolant.

2. Economic feasibility: It was essential to know the coolant make-up rate requirements resulting from hydrocarbon decomposition rates incurred in actual operation of such a power reactor. This would permit an accurate estimate of the effect of make-up cost on the cost of electric power from the organic reactor.

Additional objectives of the OMRE were to provide experience with the operation of the organic reactor and to provide a facility for testing fuel elements and system components associated with this reactor concept.

8-5.1 Design Criteria

The OMRE was designed to meet the following requirements:

1. An 800°F maximum fuel-element surface temperature. (This limitation was set by the lack of extended-time heat-transfer data at temperatures above 800°F.)

2. A 500 to 700°F bulk coolant temperature. (A temperature of 500°F was considered to be the lowest temperature of interest for power-reactor applications; the 700°F upper limit resulted from limitations of heat transfer from the fuel elements to the coolant.)

3. A 15 ft/sec maximum coolant velocity through the core. [This limitation was necessary to control the amount of erosion in the piping system and to keep a reasonable total coolant flow rate (9200 gal/min).]

Table 8.18 — COMPOSITION AND PHYSICAL PROPERTIES
OF INITIAL OMRE COOLANT

Composition, wt. %			
Biphenyl	16.0		
o-Terphenyl	46.1		
m-Terphenyl	31.8		
p-Terphenyl	6.1		
Physical properties			
	500°F	700°F	800°F
Specific gravity	0.89	0.80	0.75
Specific heat, Btu/(lb)(°F)	0.53	0.60	0.64
Viscosity, centipoises	0.46	0.22	0.18
Thermal conductivity, Btu/(hr)(sq ft)(°F/ft)	0.069	0.063	0.061
Vapor pressure, psia	5.3	42.9	94.5
Melting-point range	The mixture was a thick slurry (practically solid) at 70°F; it became completely liquid at slightly below 200°F		

The original design of the OMRE was based on the use of biphenyl as moderator, reflector, and coolant. This selection was made because of the existence of reliable information on its physical properties and because of its commercial availability and low cost. Its relatively low melting point minimized the preheating requirements for the system; its relatively high vapor pressure determined design requirements sufficiently stringent to allow for future use of any other similar hydrocarbons with a lower vapor pressure.

A considerable amount of information on the physical properties and behavior of the terphenyls had been obtained by the time construction of the OMRE was completed. It was then decided to use initially a commercial mixture of polyphenyls having a much lower vapor pressure than biphenyl. The composition and physical properties of this mixture are shown in Table 8.18.

8-5.2 System Description

A schematic flow diagram for the OMRE is shown in Fig. 8.24. The reactor core was located near the bottom of the reactor vessel and was covered by a 14-ft pool of hydrocarbon. A nitrogen blanket provided an inert atmosphere above the pool and maintained a 200-psig pressure on the system, corresponding to a saturation temperature of 920°F for the OMRE

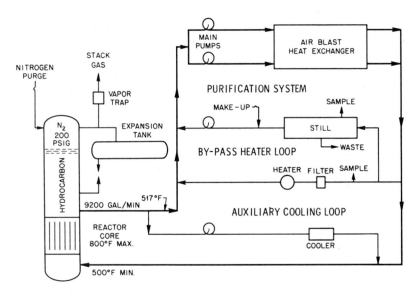

FIG. 8.24 Schematic flow diagram of the OMRE.

coolant. A continuous purge of nitrogen over the surface of the coolant prevented a build-up of radiolytic gases and swept them to the exhaust stack. An expansion tank was provided to take care of the large change in volume of the hydrocarbon during temperature transients.

The heat generated in the coolant in the core was rejected to the atmosphere by means of an air-blast heat exchanger. This device was preferred to a steam generator as a heat sink in this experiment because it simplified control of temperatures. The coolant was circulated by means of two 4600-gal/min centrifugal hot-oil pumps operating in parallel. The mechanical seals of these pumps were cooled by recirculation of a small stream of cooled hydrocarbon from the discharge side of the pumps; a small leakage of coolant was considered permissible and was collected in drums for disposal. An auxiliary coolant system rated at 100 kw was provided to remove afterglow heat from the reactor during shutdown when the main coolant loop was inoperative. A spray cooler was used as the heat sink for this loop.

The bypass heater loop provided continuous information on the change in heat-transfer properties of the hydrocarbon during reactor operation. The test section of this loop consisted of an electric heater and temperature and flow instrumentation. Thus the determination of heat-transfer coefficients of the coolant in the reactor as a function of irradiation time was possible. A convenient record was also provided of the effect of irradiation on the heat-transfer behavior of the coolant outside the reactor.

The purification system removed a small batch of damaged coolant from the main stream every day and purified it. The purified material, with additional fresh make-up, was returned to the reactor system, but high boilers resulting from radiation damage were rejected to waste storage. Purification was accomplished by means of low-pressure distillation (20 mm Hg, overhead cutoff temperature of 510°F). A batch system was used because it allowed the flexibility required by the large number of unknowns involved in such an experimental system. A continuous system would be used in a full-scale power plant.

With the exception of the reactor vessel, the whole system was made of carbon steel. All components were provided with preheating equipment to bring the temperature of the system above the melting point of the hydrocarbon and to maintain the coolant in a liquid state during extended shutdowns. Induction heating was used on the vessels and piping, the pumps and valves were traced with heating cable, and the air-blast heat exchanger was provided with an oil burner.

8-5.3 Performance Data and Operating History

Table 8.19 shows typical performance data from the OMRE. The conditions cited are identical to those proposed for full-scale organic-moderated and -cooled nuclear power plants. It should be emphasized that the OMRE generated no electricity. It was not a prototype of a nuclear power plant but, rather, a full-scale irradiation facility.

The initial operating history of the OMRE is summarized in Refs. 114, 116, and 117. The reactor was shut down in November 1958 for complete cleanup of the coolant and the system, as well as installation of the second core loading. A total of 958 megawatt-days (Mwd) of operation was accumulated on the first core. During this period tests were conducted at high-boiler concentrations of approximately 12, 30, and 40 wt. % and

Table 8.19 — TYPICAL OMRE PERFORMANCE DATA

High-boiler[a] concentration, %	30
Bulk coolant inlet temperature, °F	600
Maximum fuel-plate surface temperature, °F	750
Coolant velocity through core, ft/sec	15
Operating pressure, psig	200
Reactor power level, Mw	6
Average thermal-neutron flux, neutrons/cm^2/sec	1.8×10^{13}
Average heat flux, Btu/(hr)(sq ft)	31,000
Maximum heat flux, Btu/(hr)(sq ft)	116,000

[a]All compounds less volatile than p-terphenyl.

bulk coolant temperatures of 600 and 700°F. The maximum fuel-plate surface temperature was maintained at 750°F during the majority of the period. Over-all operation of the reactor was quite satisfactory.

8-5.4 COOLANT DECOMPOSITION RATES

The remaining discussion in Sect. 8.5 deals chiefly with results obtained in first core operation. The data presented have been supplemented and refined by operations with subsequent core loadings; however, the data shown accurately represent the radiation effects on coolants in the OMRE.

Figure 8.25 presents a summary[66] of information on polyphenyl decomposition rates obtained in initial OMRE work. These data are from core I and core II operation. They refine earlier OMRE data,[64] confirm the results previously obtained from the MTR in-pile loop experiment (Fig. 8.15), and are consistent with data from static irradiations (Fig. 8.8). Thus the decomposition rate decreases significantly with increasing concentration of decomposition products in the coolant (see also Fig. 8.10).

This may be chiefly a dilution effect; i.e., as starting material is consumed, less is available for subsequent radiolysis. In reporting data similar to those of Fig. 8.25 and Fig. 8.15, Mason[86] adjusts the results of in-pile loop tests to "constant terphenyl content." The resulting curves are relatively flat and indicate little protective effect from radiolysis products.

The decomposition-rate data in Fig. 8.25 are based on calculated values of total energy absorption in the OMRE moderator–coolant. These show the total amount of energy absorbed in the OMRE moderator–coolant to be 8.84 to 9.04% of the total power generated in the reactor.[66]

Of this absorbed energy approximately 25% can be attributed to the thermalization of fission neutrons and 75% to the attentuation of gammas from fission and neutron capture. In a full-scale power reactor, the amount of energy absorbed would be reduced to approximately 2.75% of the total power.[66] This would be due to the use of low-enrichment fuel instead of 93% U^{235}. Also, low absorption-cross-section cladding material (e.g., aluminum alloys) would be used in place of stainless steel, and a much lower moderator–coolant to metal volume ratio would be used in the core in place of the 10.4 of the OMRE.[79] Early OMRE data indicated that at

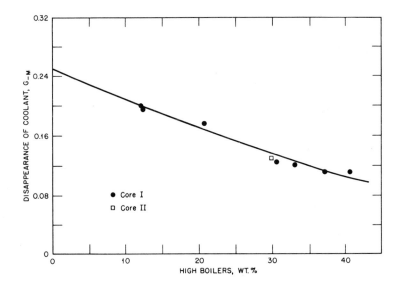

FIG. 8.25   Decomposition rate of OMRE coolant at 600°F (least-squares fit).

an HB concentration of 30 wt. % the decomposition rate of the coolant in a full-scale power reactor, i.e., 300 Mw(e), would amount to approximately 27 lb/Mwd(t) of reactor operation. Equivalence of the gross radiation-damage effects for the various types of radiation per unit of energy absorbed was assumed. Subsequent data[66] allow for the fast-neutron effect and indicate the revised decomposition rate to be 27 to 34 lb/Mwd(t).

The decomposition gases and low-boiler materials have not been included in this discussion. They amounted to only 1 to 2 wt. % of the total decomposition products observed.

8-5.5 PHYSICAL PROPERTIES OF COOLANT[10]

The density of the OMRE coolant was measured up to 700°F with a modified Lipkin[121] pycnometer mounted in a hot-air furnace. The pycnometer was pressurized with nitrogen to prevent boiling at the elevated temperatures. The absolute error of the measurements was estimated to be ±0.5%. Likewise, viscosity measurements were made under nitrogen pressure with a modification (Cannon-Manning[39]) of the Ostwald viscometer. Here, the relative error was estimated to be ±2%. The specific heat of the OMRE coolant was derived from experimentally obtained enthalpy data. A modified drop calorimeter[110] was used. Accuracy of the specific-heat measurement was estimated to be ±2%.

Figures 8.26, 8.27, and 8.28 show the density, viscosity, and specific

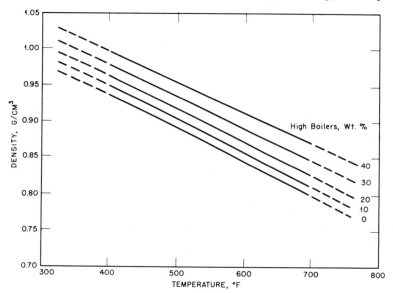

Fɪɢ. 8.26 Density of OMRE coolant.

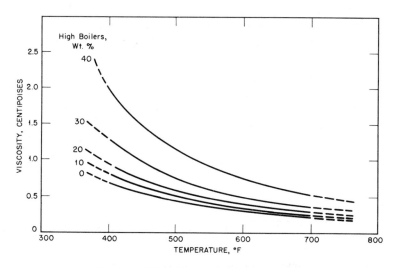

Fɪɢ. 8.27 Viscosity of OMRE coolant.

heat, respectively, of the OMRE coolant as a function of temperature for various HB concentrations. These figures are actually cross plots of 10, 9,

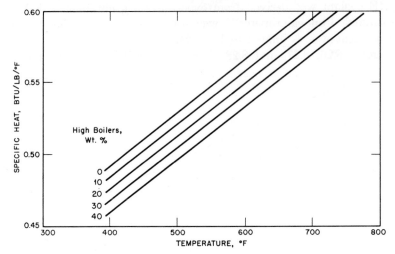

FIG. 8.28   Specific heat of OMRE coolant.

and 6 datum points, respectively, at each of four temperatures originally plotted against HB content. There was good agreement with the comparable loop data on biphenyl (see Sect. 8-4.8).

8-5.6 HEAT-TRANSFER RATES[98]

Heat-transfer coefficients for the irradiated OMRE coolant were measured in the bypass coolant loop at 500 and 600°F and 14.6 ft/sec flow throughout the period of operation of the reactor. The curves in Fig. 8.29 illustrate the slow and gradual decrease in heat-transfer coefficient as the

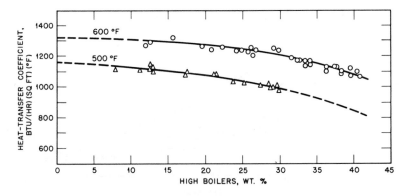

FIG. 8.29   Heat-transfer rates in the OMRE. Polyphenyl coolant velocity was 14.6 ft/sec.

HB content increased to 40%. This decrease is even smaller than expected from the measured changes in the viscosity of the coolant. The points in Fig. 8.29 were obtained both during build-up and during lowering of the HB content. The loss in heat-transfer properties of the coolant was perfectly reversible; this confirmed the absence of significant deposits on the heat-transfer surface.

Heat-transfer measurements in the core of the reactor did not permit as detailed an evaluation as those in the bypass heater. However, the two sets of data were in approximate agreement. It is therefore clear that no appreciable insulation of the reactor fuel-element surfaces took place as a result of deposits on these surfaces. Actual measurements on the fuel plates of an element examined in a hot cell after 549 Mwd of reactor operation showed the film left on the surface to range between 0.00012 and 0.00038 in. in thickness. Thus the fouling film was no great problem during the first 6 months of core I operation of the OMRE. Appreciable deposits were observed in later operation (see Sect. 8-6-3).

8-5.7 Coolant Activation

Most of the radioactivity observed in the OMRE coolant resulted from activation of impurities.[116] These were either originally present in the coolant or introduced into the coolant in the form of rust, welding slag, or metal filings from the OMRE piping and vessels. Most of these impurities were in a form less volatile than the OMRE coolant itself; therefore they were removed with the waste from the purification system. The most important of the activities observed were Mn^{56}, Mn^{54}, Fe^{59}, Co^{60}, Se^{75}, S^{35}, and P^{32}. The radiation measured near the surface of the 10-in. main coolant pipes was about 50 to 60 mr/hr during operation at 6.0 Mw (with a specific activity of the coolant of approximately 0.1 $\mu c/cm^3$). Radioactivity increased by an order of magnitude in the later days of operation of the reactor as a result of pickup of inorganic particulate matter by the coolant.

8-5.8 Corrosion Experience[68,98]

Mechanical test and corrosion specimens were loaded into two OMRE dummy-plug elements and into the bypass loop. Specimens of the in-pile dummy-plug element were removed for examination after exposure to 549 Mwd of reactor operation accumulated over a period of eight months. This corresponds to total measured integrated neutron fluxes of approximately 9×10^{19} neutrons/cm²/sec (thermal) and 3.5×10^{19} neutrons/cm²/sec (fast, energies greater than 1 Mev). The out-of-pile (bypass loop) specimens were removed after exposure to irradiated coolant for thirteen months. During this time the coolant temperature in the bypass loop was about 580°F (corresponding to a bulk coolant temperature of 600°F in the core during these exposures). Flow rates at both in-pile and out-of-pile specimen locations were estimated to have ranged from 0.3 to 0.5 ft/sec.

Evaluation of the corrosion data indicated the polyphenyl environment in the reactor to be relatively noncorrosive. No evidence of either stress corrosion or accelerated attack of bimetal couples was found. Corrosion rates were apparently unaffected by the presence of radiation. Types 410 and 304 stainless steels were only slightly darkened with weight changes of 0.10 to 0.85 mg/cm² and 0.00 to 0.01 mg/cm², respectively. Aluminum and 1020 and 4120 steels showed weight losses of the order of 0.3 to 0.4 mg/cm². The steel surfaces retained a thin gray to black film; the aluminum surfaces were relatively unaffected and were considered excellent. Magnesium experienced weight losses of the order of 9.5 mg/cm² accompanied by bad pitting.

Mechanical-property changes of the in-pile ferrous metals were attributed to direct radiation effects rather than to any influence of the coolant. Ultimate and yield strengths were increased and per cent elongation and reduction in area were decreased by the irradiation. Impact properties of type 410 stainless steel were lowered, whereas those of type 304 stainless steel remained unaffected. Out-of-pile specimens experienced no property changes other than those induced thermally. The polyphenyl environment showed no apparent effect on the property changes observed.

8-6 Nature of Radiolysis Products

Although coolant decomposition rates may be different for static vs. dynamic tests, the types of products formed are similar. These decomposition rates were discussed previously (see Sects. 8-3, 8-4, and 8-5). In this section the nature of the products formed chiefly from polyphenyl mixtures in loop and OMRE exposures are considered. Data for relatively pure polyphenyls were given in Ch. 4, Sect. 4-4.

The products from the radiolysis of polyphenyls can be divided into low-molecular-weight material and high boilers. The low-molecular-weight material is comprised of gases and "low boilers" that boil below the starting material. The low-molecular-weight material accounts for only 1 to 2 wt. % of the products formed. The remaining high boilers are high-molecular-weight polymers that boil above the starting material. The small concentration of low-boiling products indicates that the fracturing of aromatic rings plays only a small part in the radiolysis of polyphenyls as compared to polymerization reactions forming high boilers.

8-6.1 LOW-MOLECULAR-WEIGHT MATERIAL

In the NAA-20 loop experiment, samples of the gas phase were withdrawn periodically and analyzed for composition.[25] At the same time liquid samples were removed and dissolved gases were extracted from these by a Toepler pump for analysis. The gas phase from irradiated biphenyl comprised about 96 mole % of the following: hydrogen, methane, ethane, ethene, propane, and propene. Other products of four to eight carbon atoms were also detected in trace quantities. The dissolved gases from irradiated biphenyl contained relatively larger percentages of the higher molecular weight radiolytic gases. Benzene comprised the largest fraction. Typical data[25] for various coolants are given in Table 8.20. Ratios

Table 8.20 — GAS ANALYSES FROM NAA-20 LOOP SAMPLES

Coolant	Isopropylbiphenyl		Biphenyl		Santowax R	
HB content, wt. %	25		23		23	
Test temperature, °F	595		640		620	
Phase	Gas	Liquid	Gas	Liquid	Gas	Liquid
Gas solubility, cu ft (STP)/lb		0.095		0.042		0.012
Hydrogen, mole%	29.4	4.61	37.1	11.30	66.00	18.6
Methane	53.0	39.80	33.50	25.40	18.30	15.6
C_2-C_4	16.79	49.00	27.93	50.28	13.93	33.65
Benzene	0.29	2.88	0.24	7.44	0.64	21.9
Other	0.52	3.81	1.33	5.21	2.12	10.25

of the mole % in the gas phase to that in the liquid phase changed slightly; this indicates that the solubilities of various constituents changed as a function of HB content. These changes were small in relation to the changes in the gas composition.

Benzene in the liquid-phase products of biphenyl decreased with increasing HB content, e.g., 18.1 mole % benzene at 6 wt. % HB; 12.5 mole % benzene at 18 wt. % HB; and 7.4 mole % benzene at 23 wt. % HB. Likewise, in the NAA-20 loop composition of the gas phase varied with HB content,[25] as shown in Fig. 8.30. Hydrogen generation would arise from the formation of longer chain polyphenyls, whereas low-molecular-weight gases would be formed by opening the aromatic ring. Of particular significance is the absence of gases containing nitrogen. The system operated under nitrogen pressure.

In the OMRE the vent gases were analyzed by passing samples through a gas chromatograph running off the line from the reactor vessel to the stack.[67] Table 8.21 presents a typical analysis of the vent gases formed during the operation of the reactor. The data are given on a nitrogen-free basis. Because of the continuous nitrogen purge, the gas leaving the top of the reactor vessel contained approximately 85 vol. % nitrogen and 15 vol. % radiolysis products.

During the first year of OMRE operation, the low-boiler concentration

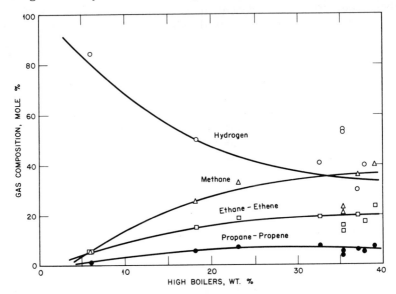

FIG. 8.30 Composition of radiolytic gas from biphenyl irradiated in NAA-20 loop.

in the irradiated coolant averaged 0.7 wt. % with a range of 0.0 to 1.0%. Essentially the same range of concentration was found during the second year (core II) of operation.[16] The nongaseous product boiling below the

Table 8.21 — TYPICAL COMPOSITION OF OMRE VENT GASES

Compound	Vol. % (nitrogen-free basis)
Hydrogen	65
Methane	11
Ethane and ethene	14
Propane and propene	8
Butane and butene	2
Total	100

starting material was analyzed by gas chromatographic and mass-spectrometric techniques. The most important constituents included benzene, toluene, ethylbenzene, p-ethyltoluene, m- and p-xylene, n-propylbenzene, n-butylbenzene, and indane. Traces of at least 14 others were detected.

During core II operation concentrations of 9 to 12 wt. % of intermediate boilers (volatility between that of biphenyl and of HB) were found[16] in the irradiated coolant. About 12 compounds were identified of which the most significant were fluorenone, phenanthrene, and 3-methylbiphenyl. The total concentration of these three was at least ten times that of the other compounds present.

8-6.2 HIGH BOILERS

In the radiolysis of terphenyls irrespective of the exposure facility, the average molecular weight of the separated polymers was found to be at least twice that of the parent.[37] The polymers were soluble in chloroform to about 98%. Such solutions were partially extracted with ether. The extracts showed average molecular weights in the range of 450 to 510. Analysis suggested a large (80%) proportion of hexaphenyls, probably formed by the union of two terphenyl units. The ether-insoluble material was of 760 to 825 molecular weight and was identified as octa- to nonaphenyls and some alkylpolyphenyls. Spectra suggested that there were more *para*-linked rings here than in the ether-soluble fraction.

Similar polymers recovered from the electron irradiation[37] of biphenyl had average molecular weights of 315 ±10 (quaterphenyl = 306). Fourteen runs were examined. None contained any of the isomeric terphenyls. These results substantiate the premise that the major decomposition mechanism for biphenyl is "doubling up" and that ring cleavage is a lesser reaction. These and similar data are inadequate for an understanding of the underlying chemistry of polyphenyl radiolysis, but they led to the following conclusions:[37]

1. Polymers obtained individually from pyrolysis, neutron exposure, and electron irradiation are not identical in all respects.
2. Rate laws from polymer yield vs. dose curves contribute little to the understanding of the mechanism of radiolysis. No less than three rate laws based on different assumptions could be fitted to a single set of data.

As expected, the high-boiler fraction of irradiated coolant from the OMRE was found to be a very complex chemical system. Clear-cut separations of individual components were extremely difficult. For this reason, low-voltage mass spectrometry was applied to the whole high-boiler fraction. Such low-voltage spectra from mixtures are relatively simple as compared with high-voltage spectra because of the lack of fragmentation in the spectrometer. Approximately 75% of the high boilers found (up to octaphenyl) in a typical irradiated OMRE coolant sample were substituted polyphenyls and triphenylenes in an approximate ratio of 3 to 1. These are shown[15] in Table 8.22. The analyses in Table 8.22 were made on the volatile fraction (distillate) of the high boilers. The nondistillable

Table 8.22 — TYPICAL COMPOSITION OF VOLATILE FRACTION
OF OMRE HIGH BOILERS

Substituted polyphenyls	Wt. %	Substituted triphenylenes	Wt. %
Alkylterphenyls	0.5	Triphenylene	9.1
Quaterphenyls	8.6	Alkyltriphenylenes	1.3
Alkylquaterphenyls	1.3	Phenyltriphenylenes	0.8
Quinquephenyls	16.8	Alkylphenyltriphenylenes	1.1
Alkylquinquephenyls	1.5	Diphenyltriphenylenes	1.5
Hexaphenyls	25.8	Alkyldiphenyltriphenylenes	1.4
Alkylhexaphenyls	1.1	Triphenyltriphenylenes	2.5
Heptaphenyls	1.6	Alkyltriphenyltriphenylenes	0.8
Alkylheptaphenyls	0.1	Tetraphenyltriphenylenes	0.1
Octaphenyls	0.8		
Totals	58.1		18.6

portion melts above 500°F, has an average molecular weight above 800, and has so far defied separation and identification by known methods.†

Estimates have been made[16] of the molecular-weight distribution in the total HB from core I operation. The average value was 535 and the range was from 228 (triphenylene) to 3000 (39 phenyl groups). About 8 wt. % was above 1500, and the largest single peak was at 458 (hexaphenyl). As with biphenyl the preponderance of the dimer indicates that the main reaction of the terphenyls is doubling up. In core II operation of the OMRE, the molecular weight of the total HB leveled off[16] at about 610 for 30% HB. This observation is significant and indicates that a steady-state condition is reached.

8-6.3 FILM FORMATION[16,17]

Shutdowns of the OMRE for fuel-element installation, removal, and rearrangement or for maintenance inside the reactor vessel resulted in exposure of the hot coolant to the ambient atmosphere. This introduced oxygen and water into the system and resulted in corrosion of the carbon-steel components either directly or through coolant-oxidation products. Particles from the corrosion were picked up by the circulating coolant and, together with radiolytic polymer, produced a fouling film on the fuel-element heat-transfer surfaces. The film was 14 to 26 wt. % iron [chiefly the carbide ($Fe_{20}C_9$) with about 10 wt. % Fe_3O_4], 60 to 78 wt. % carbon, and 3 to 4 wt. % hydrogen. It was insoluble in the coolant and common solvents and did not soften or melt at temperatures to 1020°F.

The mechanism of film formation is not completely understood, but

† An analysis similar in extent to that on irradiated OMRE coolant was conducted on the HB from the NAA-20 loop samples.[77]

it is evident that both inorganic and organic constituents are necessary in the evolution of the film particle. Iron oxides were probably the original inorganic constituents, but these were converted to carbides in the presence of organic compounds. These inorganic particles acted as nucleation sites for coolant radiolytic polymer and/or as catalysts for polymerization of coolant components. Thus inorganic-organic composite particles were formed. Such particles migrated to the heat-transfer surfaces, where some of them adhered and underwent radiolysis, pyrolysis, etc. Fuel-element constitution may have an effect on this adherence and subsequent reaction; some differences have been observed with various elements. For example, fouling took place with stainless-steel-clad highly enriched elements but not with aluminum-clad elements of low enrichment.

Films similar to those observed on fuel elements have been laid down on hot surfaces by pyrolyzing irradiated coolant. Both inorganic particles and organic polymer were necessary to produce the film. Filtration of the coolant before tests removed particles and substantially reduced the amount of film formed.

This information indicates that the fouling problem can be solved by eliminating the inorganic particulate matter and/or the organic polymer from the coolant. The polymer cannot be completely eliminated because it results inevitably from the radiolysis of the coolant. The inorganic material can, however, be limited by keeping air and water intrusion to a minimum and by efficient continuous purification of the coolant. The success of the purification approach in reducing fouling to acceptable levels was demonstrated[61] in the OMRE core IIIA operation.

The film-forming problem may be particularly severe with *para*-linked compounds because of solubility problems. The polyphenyls double up under radiation and yield, for example, from terphenyls, significant quantities of hexaphenyl and higher polyphenyls. These higher molecular weight materials include *ortho, meta,* and *para* isomers. *Para* isomers are notoriously insoluble, and even small amounts of such products might "plate out" on inorganic particles and thus contribute to film formation. Other organic species, e.g., alkyl aromatic compounds, may produce polymers with better solubility characteristics.

8-6.4 ALTERNATE COOLANTS

The possibilities of using low-cost refinery streams are being investigated. The mechanism of radiolysis or the nature of their radiolysis products might be markedly different from that of the polyphenyls. A survey[40] showed that thermal stability varied considerably among 140 specimens. The best were roughly equivalent in thermal stability at 750°F to polyphenyls at 900°F. Some capsule irradiations were made of selected cuts from refinery streams termed "alkylphenanthrenes." These fluids appear[16,17] promising relative to polyphenyls in preliminary tests.†

8-7 Application Principles

Certain conclusions can be drawn from the work on coolants reported in this chapter. That these conclusions have practical usefulness is being demonstrated by the successful and projected operation of organic-moderated and -cooled reactors. The principles on which coolant selection and operation are based are as follows:

1. Polyphenyls are the most stable organic materials to combined heat and radiation.

a. Polyphenyls [$C_6H_5(C_6H_4)_nC_6H_5$, where $n = 0$ or higher integer] are superior to fused-ring compounds.

b. *Para* isomers are more stable than *meta* or *ortho* variants.

c. Unsubstituted-ring materials are more stable than alkyl aromatic compounds.

2. Coolants are damaged by both heat and radiation. Without radiation polyphenyls will withstand up to 900°F for short times (less than 100 hr) in an inert atmosphere. At low temperatures polyphenyls will withstand about 400×10^8 rads. Under conditions prevailing in organic-cooled and -moderated reactors, damage to coolants would become critical at temperatures over 800°F.

3. Polyphenyls radiolyze at high temperature by forming some material of lower molecular weight and some of higher molecular weight than the original. Hydrogen and hydrocarbon fragments up to C_4 comprise about 1 wt. % of the total radiolysis products. The high-molecular-weight polymer comprises higher polyphenyls and triphenylene. These are predominantly unsubstituted but also contain innumerable alkyl variants.

4. Additives are not effective in reducing pyrolytic damage. They might, however, be useful in enhancing radiation stability.

5. The amount and composition of radiolysis products depend on both radiation dose and the temperature of exposure.

6. Irradiation of polyphenyls lowers the melting point and increases viscosity and density. Specific heat is lowered.

7. Radiation lowers the heat-transfer coefficient of polyphenyls about 15 to 20% for a 30 wt. % increase in high-molecular-weight polymer. This loss is recoverable by purifying the coolant. This level of degradation is equivalent to about 10^{10} rads at low temperature.

---

† A similar effort bearing on coolant costs has shown that high boilers from the radiolysis of polyphenyls can be converted by chemical techniques to lower molecular weight polyphenyls.[32,125] A catalytic hydrogenolysis process, applied to the OMRE high polymer, is believed technically feasible on a large scale.[74,127]

8. Fouling of heat-transfer surfaces by polyphenyls does not appear to be a serious problem provided the coolant is scrupulously clean:

a. Under thermal conditions alone to about 950°F.

b. In the presence of radiation to about 800°F.

9. During irradiation coolants do not become

a. Radioactive except by activation of contaminants or

b. Corrosive except to magnesium and zirconium to which organic coolants are corrosive before irradiation.

10. About 500,000 Btu/(hr)(sq ft) can be transferred into a polyphenyl coolant before burn-out occurs at incipient film boiling.

11. In a typical polyphenyl-cooled and -moderated reactor (OMRE), coolant decomposition rates decrease with increasing percentage of degradation products. At practical operating levels of polymer contaminants, the decomposition rates were as much as 50% below those shown initially.

12. According to OMRE experience about 27 to 34 lb of coolant would be consumed per megawatt-day (thermal) of operation for a power reactor using an organic coolant–moderator.

13. Data from capsule experiments, circulating loop tests, and the reactor experiment are in good agreement. Circulating in-pile loops are a vital intermediate step to full-scale reactor experiments.

14. Organic-cooled and -moderated nuclear power reactors are technically feasible.

8-8 Bibliography

This bibliography is extensive but is not intended to be exhaustive. The existence of several literature surveys will be helpful to the reader who needs to secure primary references. The two compilations by Smith[108,109] will be of interest to those wishing to review the early work on radiation effects on organic coolants. The searches by Meckly[92] and by Smith[107] serve as guides to related nonradiation technology on organic coolants. The monumental report by McEwen[88] has excellent coverage of the coolant literature and draws from 254 references on all phases of coolant technology.

References

Several of the following were cited in the text as authority for statements made. Others were not quoted but are included because they contain pertinent information. All were consulted in the preparation of this chapter.

1. Ablitt, J. F., Selecting the Reactor Coolant, *Atomics and Nuclear Energy*, 9(10): 355 (October 1958).

2. Anderson, W. K., *Pyrolytic Reactions of Diphenyl Under High Heat Flux Conditions*, USAEC Report ANL-5304, Argonne National Laboratory, August 1954.
3. Anderson, W. K., Organic Coolant Studies, in *Compilation of Organic Moderator and Coolant Technology*, USAEC Report TID-7007, Pt. 1, p. 35, January 1957.
4. Anderson, W. K., Melting Points and Viscosities of Mixtures of Diphenyl with Its Pyrolysis Products, in *Compilation of Organic Moderator and Coolant Technology*, USAEC Report TID-7007, Pt. 1, p. 129, January 1957.
5. Anderson, W. K., Thermal Stability of Diphenyl, in *Compilation of Organic Moderator and Coolant Technology*, USAEC Report TID-7007, Pt. 1, p. 196, January 1957.
6. Anderson, W. K., and Greenberg, S., Organic Coolant Moderator, in *Compilation of Organic Moderator and Coolant Technology*, USAEC Report TID-7007, Pt. 1, p. 171, January 1957.
7. Anon., Westinghouse Invents the OMFBR, *Nucleonics, 16*(11): 24 (November 1958), and *Nucleonics, 17*(4): 22 (April 1959); Martin to Build Pebble-Bed Critical, *Nucleonics, 17*(12): 25 (December 1959).
8. Anon., Radiolytic Decomposition Analysis, *Nuclear Eng., 5*(45): 59 (February 1960).
9. Anon., OTR to be Built at Whiteshell (Canada), *Nuclear News, 5*(2): 19 (February 1962).
10. Asanovich, G., *Thermo-Physical Properties of OMRE Circulating Coolant*, USAEC Report NAA-SR-MEMO-3843, Atomics International, May 1959.
11. Atomics International, Organic Materials as Reactor Coolants and Moderators, in *Compilation of Organic Moderator and Coolant Technology*, USAEC Report TID-7007, Pt. 1, p. 137, January 1957.
12. Atomics International, Engineering Development Program Supplementary to the OMRE and In-pile Loop Studies, in *Compilation of Organic Moderator and Coolant Technology*, USAEC Report TID-7007, Pt. 2(Del.), January 1957.
13. Atomics International, *Proceedings of the SRE–OMRE Forum, Held at Los Angeles, California, Nov. 8–9, 1956*, USAEC Report TID-7525, Jan. 15, 1957.
14. Atomics International, *OM Terphenyl Substitution for Diphenyl in the OMRE*, AI-1635, May 1957.
15. Atomics International, *Bimonthly Technical Progress Report—January–February 1959*, USAEC Report NAA-SR-3579, April 1959.
16. Atomics International, *Proceedings of the Organic Cooled Reactor Forum, Los Angeles, Oct. 6–7, 1960*, USAEC Report NAA-SR-5688, October 1960.
17. Atomics International, *Bimonthly Technical Progress Report—September–October 1960*, USAEC Report NAA-SR-5836, November 1960.
18. Barker, K. R., Cummings, H. E., and King, E. C., *Corrosion Testing in Isopropylbiphenyl*, Memo Report 126, Mine Safety Appliance Company, February 1957.
19. Baxter, R. A., and Keen, R. T., *High Temperature Gas Chromatography of Aromatic Hydrocarbons, Instrument Design and Exploration Studies at Temperatures up to 430°C*, USAEC Report NAA-SR-3154, Atomics International, June 1, 1959.
20. Bechtel Corporation and Atomics International, *Organic Cooled Reactor Study: 300 Mw Power Plant Conceptual Design*, USAEC Report TID-8501, Pt. 2, July 1959.
21. Beldecos, N. A., and Lokay, J. D., *Thermodynamic Investigation of the Benzene Turbine Cycle*, USAEC Report WIAP-M-24, Westinghouse Electric Corporation, July 5, 1953.

22. Bently, R., Brown, G., and Schlegel, R., *Physical Constants of Proposed (Pile) Coolants*, USAEC Report CP-3061, University of Chicago, June 23, 1945.
23. Blake, E. S., Edwards, J. W., Hammann, W. C., and Reichard, T., *High Temperature Hydraulic Fluids*, USAF Report WADC-TR-54-532, Pt. 3, April 1957.
24. Blake, E. S., Edwards, J. W., Hammann, W. C., and Reichard, T., *High Temperature Base Stock Fluids*, USAF Report WADC-TR-54-437, December 1957.
25. Bley, W. N., *An In-pile Loop Study of the Performance of Polyphenyl Reactor Coolants*, USAEC Report NAA-SR-2470, Atomics International, Sept.- 15, 1958.
26. Bolt, R. O., Some Effects of Temperature on the Radiation Stability of Aromatic Hydrocarbons, in *Compilation of Organic Moderator and Coolant Technology*, USAEC Report TID-7007, Pt. 1, p. 92, January 1957.
27. Bolt, R. O., and Carroll, J. G., *Summary Evaluation of Organics as Reactor Moderator-Coolants*, USAEC Report AECD-3711, California Research Corporation, Mar. 15, 1955.
28. Bolt, R. O., and Carroll, J. G., Organics as Reactor Moderator-Coolants: Some Aspects of Their Thermal and Radiation Stabilities, in *Proceedings of the First International Conference on the Peaceful Uses of Atomic Energy, Geneva, 1955*, Vol. 7, p. 546, United Nations, New York, 1956.
29. Bolt, R. O., and Carroll, J. G., Summary Report: Research on the Radiation Stability of Organic Fluids, in *Compilation of Organic Moderator and Coolant Technology*, USAEC Report TID-7007, Pt. 2(Del.), p. 1, January 1957.
30. Bolt, R. O., and Carroll, J. G., Research on the Radiation Stability of Organic Fluids, in *Compilation of Organic Moderator and Coolant Technology*, USAEC Report TID-7007, Pt. 2(Del.), p. 44, January 1957.
31. Bolt, R. O., Carroll, J. G., and Fontana, B. J., Research on the Radiation Stability of Organic Fluids, in *Compilation of Organic Moderator and Coolant Technology*, USAEC Report TID-7007, Pt. 2(Del.), p. 145, January 1957.
32. Bolt, R. O., Carroll, J. G., West, W. W., and Hanneman, W. W., *Some Possibilities for Reducing Organic Reactor Coolant Costs*, USAEC Report TID-11042, California Research Corporation, August 1960.
33. Bolt, R. O., Fontana, B. J., and Wright, J. R., *Inhibited Reactor Coolants and Use Thereof*, U. S. Patent No. 2,833,331, April 1959.
34. Brownlie, David, Biphenyl and Diphenyl Oxide for Power Generation, *Steam Engr.*, *1*(11): 477 (August 1932).
35. Brownlie, David, Diphenyl Oxide in Heat Technology, *Steam Engr.*, *2*(7): 306 (April 1933).
36. Brownlie, David, Developments with Dowtherm, *Steam Engr.*, *9*(100): 124 (January 1940).
37. Burns, W. G., Wild, W., and Williams, T. F., The Effect of Fast Electrons and Fast Neutrons on Polyphenyls at High Temperatures, in *Proceedings of the Second International Conference on the Peaceful Uses of Atomic Energy, Geneva, 1958*, Vol. 29, p. 266, United Nations, New York, 1959.
38. Calkins, V. P., *Radiation Damage to Nonmetallic Materials*, USAEC Report APEX-167, General Electric Company, August 1954.
39. Cannon, M. R., and Fenske, M. R., Viscosity Measurement, *Ind. Eng. Chem. Anal. Ed.*, *10*(6): 297 (June 1938).
40. Carroll, J. G., *Petroleum Refinery Streams as Prospective Reactor Coolants: Thermal Stability Investigations*, USAEC Report TID-6367, May 1960.
41. Carroll, J. G., and Bolt, R. O., Radiation Effects on Organic Materials, *Nucleonics*, *18*(9): 78 (September 1960).
42. Colichman, E. L., and Fish, R. F., *Pyrolytic and Radiolytic Decomposition Rate*

Studies on Ortho-, Meta-, and Para-Terphenyls, USAEC Report NAA-SR-1287, North American Aviation, Inc., May 15, 1955.

43. Colichman, E. L., and Fish, R. F., Resistance of Terphenyls to Heat and Radiation, *Nucleonics*, *15*(2): 72 (February 1957).

44. Colichman, E. L., and Gercke, R. H. J., *Radiation Stability of the Terphenyls and Other Polyphenyl Materials as Measured by Gas Evolution*, USAEC Report NAA-SR-1288, North American Aviation, Inc., June 15, 1955.

45. Colichman, E. L., and Gercke, R. H. J., Radiation Stability of Polyphenyls, *Nucleonics*, *14*(7): 50 (July 1956).

46. Colichman, E. L., and Gercke, R. H. J., *Selection of Organic Materials as Reactor Coolant-Moderators*, Am. Soc. Testing Materials, *Spec. Tech. Publ. No. 220*, p. 119, 1958.

47. Core, T. C., and Sato, K., *Determination of Burnout Limits of Polyphenyl Coolants*, USAEC Report IDO-28007, Aerojet-General Corp., Feb. 14, 1958.

48. Dean, D. K., Applications of Dowtherm Vapor Heating, *Ind. Eng. Chem.*, *31*(7): 797 (July 1939).

49. De Halas, D. R., *Irradiation of Organic Reactor Coolants in Dynamic Systems*, USAEC Report HW-53717, General Electric Company, Nov. 25, 1957.

50. De Halas, D. R., Radiolytic and Pyrolytic Decomposition of Organic Reactor Coolants, in *Proceedings of the Second International Conference on the Peaceful Uses of Atomic Energy, Geneva, 1958*, Vol. 29, p. 287, United Nations, New York, 1959.

51. De Halas, D. R., *Irradiation of the Biphenyl, Ortho-, Meta-Terphenyl Eutectic*, USAEC Report HW-54994, General Electric Company, Feb. 17, 1958.

52. De Halas, D. R., *Pyrolytic and Radiolytic Decomposition of Organic Reactor Coolants*, USAEC Report HW-53718, General Electric Company, May 1958.

53. De Halas, D. R., *Kinetics of the Decomposition of Organic Reactor Coolants*, USAEC Report HW-56769, General Electric Company, July 1958.

54. De Halas, D. R., *Preliminary Investigation of Isopropylated Terphenyl—A Potential Reactor Coolant*, USAEC Report HW-57400, General Electric Company, Sept. 9, 1958.

55. De Halas, D. R., Radiolytic and Pyrolytic Decomposition of Organic Reactor Coolants, *Nuclear Engineering—Part VI, Chemical Engineering Progress Symposium Series*, Vol. 55, No. 23, p. 7, American Institute of Chemical Engineers, New York, 1959.

56. Ewing, C. T., et al., *Heat-Transfer Studies on a Forced Convection Loop with Biphenyl and Biphenyl Polymers*, Report NRL 4990, Naval Research Laboratory, July 16, 1957.

57. Forest, H. O., Brugman, E. W., and Cummings, L. W. T., The Specific Heat of Diphenyl, *Ind. Eng. Chem.*, *23*(1): 37 (January 1931).

58. Francis, W. C., *The Organic Loop in the MTR Gamma Facility: Design and Preliminary Test*, USAEC Report IDO-16189, Phillips Petroleum Co., Aug. 11, 1954.

59. Freund, G. A., Organic Coolant-Moderators for Power Reactors, *Nucleonics*, *14* (8): 62 (August 1956).

60. Fricke, E. F., *A Preliminary Nuclear Design Study of Diphenyl Moderated and Cooled Reactors*, USAEC Report ANL-5457, Argonne National Laboratory, November 1955.

61. Gercke, R. H. J., Atomics International, personal communication, March 1962.

62. Gercke, R. H. J., *OMRE Research and Development Program*, in *Proceedings of the SRE–OMRE Forum, Held at Los Angeles, California, Feb. 12 and 13, 1958*, USAEC Report TID-7553, p. 151, May 1958.

63. Gercke, R. H. J., Silvey, F. C., and Asanovich, G., *The Properties of Santowax-R (Mixed Terphenyl Isomers) as Organic Moderator-Coolant,* USAEC Report NAA-SR-MEMO-3223, Atomics International, 1959.

64. Gercke, R. H. J., and Swanson, N. J., *Decomposition Rates of the OMRE Moderator-Coolant,* USAEC Report NAA-SR-3833, Atomics International (in preparation).

65. Gercke, R. H. J., and Trilling, C. A., *A Survey of Decomposition Rates of Organic Reactor Coolants,* USAEC Report NAA-SR-3835, Atomics International, June 1959.

66. Gercke, R. H. J., and Zack, J. F., Jr., *Coolant Decomposition Rates and Make-up Costs for Organic Reactors,* USAEC Report NAA-SR-6920 (in preparation).

67. Gilroy, H. M., *Analysis of OMRE Waste Gas,* USAEC Report NAA-SR-MEMO-4130, Atomics International, Jan. 26, 1960.

68. Gioseffi, N. J., and Kline, H. E., *Behavior of Structural Materials Exposed to an Organic Moderated Reactor Environment,* USAEC Report NAA-SR-2570, Atomics International, Oct. 1, 1959.

69. Gray, D. N., and Schmidt, J. J. E., *Determination of the Relationship Between Structure and Radiation Stability of Various Classes of Alkyl Aromatic Fluids,* Quarterly Progress Report No. 2, Project 7-(1-7331), Denver Research Institute, January 1958.

70. Greenberg, S., *Stability of Diphenyl Under Fast Flux Irradiation in a Dynamic System,* USAEC Report ANL-5305, Argonne National Laboratory, October 1954.

71. Hälg, W., and Schaub, T. H., *Diphenyl Cooled, Heavy Water Moderated Natural Uranium Reactor Prototype,* Swiss Report RAG-4, Reaktor A. G., Würenglingen, Switzerland, May 1958.

72. Hellman, M., *Ultraviolet Spectra of Polyphenyls,* Engine Fuels Section, Nat. Bur. Standards (*U. S.*) Report, July 1956.

73. Hellman, M., *Summary Report of Progress on the Analysis of Irradiated Organic Coolants,* Nat. Bur. Standards (U. S.) Report No. 5255, April 30, 1957.

74. Hillyer, J. C., Phillips Petroleum Co., personal communication, March 1962.

75. Holser, E. F., Heat Transmission with High Boiling Organic Compounds, *Ind. Eng. Chem.,* 28(6): 691 (June 1936).

76. Jordan, D. P., and Leppert, G., Nucleate Boiling Characteristics of Organic Reactor Coolants, *Nuclear Sci. and Eng.,* 5(6): 349 (June 1959).

77. Keen, R. T., *et al., Radiolysis Products of Polyphenyl Coolants. Part I: In-pile Loop Irradiations,* USAEC Report NAA-SR-4355, 1962.

78. Keshishian, V., *Effect of Temperature Upon the Energy Absorption in Organic Coolants in the OMRE,* USAEC Report NAA-SR-MEMO-2902, Atomics International, July 1958.

79. Keshishian, V., *Energy Absorption in the Coolant of a 555 Mw Thermal OMR,* USAEC Report NAA-SR-MEMO-3245, Atomics International, Nov. 13, 1958.

80. Killeffer, D. H., Stable Organic Compounds in Power Generation, *Ind. Eng. Chem.,* 27(1): 10 (January 1935).

81. Kirk, R., The Biphenyl Heat Engine, *Steam Engr., 4*(2): 53 (November 1934).

82. Kline, H. E., Gioseffi, N. J., and Bley, W. N., *Dynamic Corrosion in Polyphenyls Under Irradiation,* USAEC Report NAA-SR-2046, Atomics International, May 1958.

83. Loeb, W. A., and Held, K. M., Organic Coolants for Reactor Power Plant Use, in *Compilation of Organic Moderator and Coolant Technology,* USAEC Report TID-7007, Pt. 1, p. 179, January 1957.

84. Madison, J. J., and Roberts, R. M., Pyrolysis of Aromatics and Related Heterocyclics, *Ind. Eng. Chem.,* 50(2): 237 (February 1957).

85. Mahoney, C. L., *et al.*, *Engine Oil Development*, USAF Report WADC-TR-57-177(Pt. II), Shell Development Company, February 1958.
86. Mason, E. A., Massachusetts Institute of Technology, personal communication, March 1962.
87. McEwen, M., *Preliminary Engineering Study of Organic Nuclear Reactor Coolant-Moderators*, Report RE-CR-964, Monsanto Chemical Company, March 1956.
88. McEwen, M., *Organic Coolant Databook*, Technical Publication No. AT-1, Monsanto Chemical Company, July 1958.
89. McEwen, M., and Wiederhold, E. W., An In-Pile Study of Organics as Nuclear Reactor Coolants, *Nuclear Engineering—Part V, Chemical Engineering Progress Symposium Series*, Vol. 55, No. 22, American Institute of Chemical Engineers, New York, 1959.
90. McGoff, M. J., and Mausteller, J. W., *In-Pile Testing of Monoisopropylbiphenyl*, Technical Report 55, Mine Safety Appliances Company, February 1957.
91. McNelly, M. J., Some Aspects of the Use of an Organic Coolant in a Heavy-Water-Moderated Power Reactor, *Nuclear Engineering—Part VI, Chemical Engineering Progress Symposium Series*, Vol. 55, No. 23, p. 13, American Institute of Chemical Engineers, New York, 1959.
92. Meckly, E. P., *Literature Search in Organic Coolants—Part II*, Mine Safety Appliances Company, June 1956.
93. Milak, G. C., *Corrosion and Other Aspects Relative to the Use of Diphenyl as a Coolant-Moderator*, USAEC Report ANL-5587, Argonne National Laboratory, November 1956.
94. Milich, W., and King, E. C., Test Loop for Determining Burnout Heat Flux, *Nucleonics*, *16*(4): 109 (April 1958).
95. *Radiation Resistant Fluids*, brochure, Monsanto Chemical Company, 1959.
96. Nakazato, S., and Gercke, R. H. J., *Organic In-Pile Loop NAA-18*, USAEC Report NAA-SR-1592, Atomics International, July 1956.
97. Othmer, D. F., Trends in Heat Transfer, *Ind. Eng. Chem.*, *22*(9): 988 (September 1930).
98. Perlow, M. A., Heat Transfer and Fouling, in *Annual Technical Progress Report, AEC Unclassified Programs, Fiscal Year 1959*, USAEC Report NAA-SR-3850, Sect. III-A, p. 3-A-7, Atomics International, August 1959.
99. Purdy, D. C., Diphenyl as a Thermodynamic Fluid, *Nucleonics*, *14*(4): 109 (April 1957).
100. Rice, W. L. R., *The Effects of Gamma Radiation on Organic Fluids and Lubricants*, USAF Report WCLT-TM-58-18, p. 18, Wright Air Development Center, February 1958.
101. Sato, K., *Determination of Burnout Limits of Polyphenyl Coolants*, USAEC Report AGC-AE-32, Aerojet General Corp., February 1957.
102. Schmidt, J. J. E., Krimmel, J. A., and Farrell, T. J., *Chain-Type Polyphenyl and Polynuclear Aromatic Compounds as Base Materials for High Temperature Stable and Radiation Resistant Lubricants and Hydraulic Fluids*, USAF Report WADC-TR-56-207(Pt. III), Denver Research Institute, 1958.
103. Shimazaki, T. T., and Anderson, W. F., Heat Transfer Considerations in the Use of Organic Reactor Coolants, in *Advances in Nuclear Engineering*, Vol. 2, pp. 456–464, New York, Pergamon Press, Inc., New York, 1957.
104. Siegel, S., and Wilson, R. F., OMCR Power Plants: Their Status and Promise, *Nucleonics*, *17*(11): 118 (November 1959).
105. Silberberg, M., and Huber, D. A., Heat Transfer Characteristics of Polyphenyl Reactor Coolants, *Nuclear Engineering—Part VI, Chemical Engineering Progress*

Symposium Series, Vol. 55, No. 23, p. 43, American Institute of Chemical Engineers, New York, 1959.

106. Silverman, Louis, *et al., Chemistry of the Pyrolysis of p-Terphenyl,* USAEC Report NAA-SR-1203, North American Aviation, Inc., May 1955.

107. Smith, E. H., *Polyphenyls: Literature Search,* USAEC Report ER-8098, Martin Company, March 1956.

108. Smith, Harry P., *Compilation of Organic Moderator and Coolant Technology,* USAEC Report TID-7007, Pt. 1, January 1957.

109. Smith, Harry P., *Compilation of Organic Moderator and Coolant Technology,* USAEC Report TID-7007, Pt. 2(Del.), January 1957.

110. Southard, J. C., A Modified Calorimeter for High Temperatures, *J. Am. Chem. Soc., 63*(11): 3142 (November 1941).

111. Stone, J. P., *et al., Heat-Transfer Studies on a Forced Convection Loop with Monoisopropylbiphenyl,* USAEC Report NRL-5225, Naval Research Laboratory, November 1958.

112. Stone, J. P., Ewing, C. T., Blachly, C. H., Walker, B. G., and Miller, R. R., Heat Transfer Studies on a Forced Convection Loop with Biphenyl and Biphenyl Polymers, *Ind. Eng. Chem., 50*(6): 895 (June 1958).

113. Sugalski, A. A., *Organic Coolant Radiation Experiment No. 1,* USAEC Report KAPL-M-AAS-1, Knolls Atomic Power Laboratory, June 1957.

114. Swanson, N. J., and Muller, D. R., *OMRE Operating Experience,* Nuclear Engineering and Science Conference, Cleveland, April 1959, preprint V-121.

115. Trilling, C. A., *Organic Moderated Reactor Experiment Progress Report No. 1, October 1955–July 1956,* USAEC Report NAA-SR-1700, Atomics International, March 1957.

116. Trilling, C. A., The OMRE—A Test of the Organic Moderator–Coolant Concept, in *Proceedings of the Second International Conference on the Peaceful Uses of Atomic Energy, Geneva, 1958,* Vol. 9, p. 468, United Nations, New York, 1959.

117. Trilling, C. A., OMRE Operating Experience, *Nucleonics, 17*(11): 113 (November 1959).

118. Trilling, C. A., *et al.,* A Study of the Polyphenyls for Use as Moderators and Coolants in Nuclear Power Reactors, in *Proceedings of the Second International Conference on the Peaceful Uses of Atomic Energy, Geneva, 1958,* Vol. 29, p. 292, United Nations, New York, 1959.

119. Veras, A. F., *et al., 200 Megawatt Nuclear Power Station Using a National Uranium Organic Cooled Heavy Water Moderated Heterogeneous Power Reactor,* USAEC Report CF-57-8-15, Oak Ridge School of Reactor Technology, August 1957.

120. Weisner, E. F., *Organic Moderator Reactor Research and Development Program Quarterly Progress Report, January–March 1957,* USAEC Report NAA-SR-1936, Atomics International, September 1957.

121. Weissberger, A., *Physical Methods of Organic Chemistry,* Vol. 1, Pt. I, p. 334, Interscience Publishers, Inc., New York, 1949.

122. West, W. W., *The Radiolysis of Prospective Organic Reactor Coolants,* USAEC Report AECU-4295, March 1959.

123. Wetch, J. R., Analysis of the Use of Organic Moderator in Liquid Sodium-Cooled Power Reactor, in *Compilation of Organic Moderator and Coolant Technology,* USAEC Report TID-7007, Pt. 1, p. 108, January 1957.

124. Wheelock, C. W., Ed., *11,000 KW Nuclear Power Plant Employing an Organic Moderated Reactor,* USAEC Report NAA-SR-2558, Atomics International.

125. Wineman, R. J., Adams, J. S., and Scola, D. A., *Organic Coolant Reclamation,* USAEC Report AECU-4136, Monsanto Chemical Company, October 1959.
126. Wineman, R. J., Monsanto Chemical Co., personal communication, March 1962.
127. Woodley, R. E., *The Effect of Reactor Irradiation on Candidate Organic Coolants,* USAEC Report HW-52814, General Electric Company, September 1957.
128. Wright, J. R., and Bolt, R. O., *Reactor Coolant and Method of Use,* U. S. Pat. 2,915,567, December 1959.

CHAPTER 9

Lubricants

By James G. Carroll and Robert O. Bolt

9-1 Introduction

The advent of nuclear power has added nuclear radiation to the list of environmental factors under which lubricants must function. This new factor is significant because lubricants vary a thousandfold in their ability to survive the effects of neutrons and gamma rays. Base oils, as well as chemical additives used in lubricant practice, influence the radiation stability of the products. The interplay of radiation with the traditional enemies of lubricants, oxygen, heat, and mechanical shear, is of prime importance. Radiation accelerates the oxidation of a lubricant to degrade its physical and performance properties. The effect of temperature on radiolysis is more subtle, as will be described.

In and around nuclear reactors, lubricants find use in three general areas, as shown in Fig. 9.1.

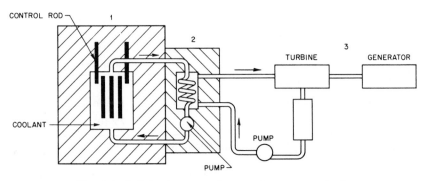

Fig. 9.1 Lubrication areas in a nuclear power plant.

1. Area 1 is inside the reactor where radiation and temperature are maximum.
2. Area 2 is the heat-exchange region in which temperature and radiation are moderate to low.
3. Area 3 is outside the shield where radiation levels are low and temperatures are those usually found in turbine generators.

High radiation levels may also prevail in reprocessing plants where spent uranium fuel is recovered and in "hot cells" where radioactive materials are handled.

In the absence of oxygen and at moderate temperature, 10^6 rads has little or no effect on lubricants; 10^7 to 10^8 rads begins to separate the good materials from the bad; and above 10^8 rads aromatic compounds are increasingly required for good radiation resistance. Only carefully selected aromatic materials such as poly(phenyl ethers) will survive 10^{10} rads. What concerns the lubrication specialist is a significant change in an important property of the lubricant, e.g., viscosity, consistency, acidity, or oxidation stability, as measured in standard tests.[2,98] These changes result from alterations in the chemical nature of the lubricant base oil and/or additives. Gas is evolved and molecules are dehydrogenated, cross linked, and polymerized on radiolysis. Continued exposure eventually turns all organic lubricants to hard, brittle solids.

For the Vallecitos prototype boiling-water reactor, Hausman[51] estimated that the radiation does not exceed 100 rads/hr at the turbine. Considering that only a small fraction of the turbine oil in the circulating system is exposed at a given time, this dose rate should create no lubrication problems with conventional fluids. Dose rates of 10^5 rads/hr prevail in control rods and fuel-handling drives. Here, radiation damage can be controlled by shielding, using stable oils, or adjusting relubrication periods.

In the Fermi reactor the radiation dose rates are high,[75] as noted in Table 9.1. This plant was designed so that oils would not be needed in

Table 9.1—APPROXIMATE YEARLY GAMMA DOSES
IN THE FERMI REACTOR

Area	Dose, rads/year
1. All areas close to primary sodium pipes	10^9
2. Rotating shield plug	10^2 to 6×10^{10}
3. Equipment compartment	7×10^7 to 7×10^8

[a]R. E. Mueller, personal communication, Ref. 75.

areas of high gamma flux. If, however, special oils[24] had been available, they probably could have been used safely.[75]

In gas-cooled reactors, such as those of the Calder Hall complex in England, lubricants must operate in an atmosphere of CO_2. Both oils and greases are required in gear trains and roller bearings of several components. These include[76] compressors, control drives, blowers, and fuel-charging mechanisms at temperatures up to 400°F. Tentative test schedules have been written for radiation-resistant lubricants for these uses.[3] In six months such materials receive 1.5×10^9 rads in charging mechanisms.

The applications just cited are in stationary power plants of the central-station type. Lubrication requirements also exist for naval vessels and proposed nuclear-powered aircraft, rockets, and locomotives. In some of these mobile plants, extra weight would impose penalties, and so shielding cannot be used to protect the lubricant. Thus the radiation doses exceed those in stationary plants. This consideration invites the development of lubricants of enhanced radiation resistance.

9-2 Base Oils

The base oil makes up 75 to 100% of most organic lubricants (including greases). This oil, in turn, may be a blend of several constituents designed to yield desired physical properties. The radiation stability of the finished lubricant is determined predominantly by the chemical nature of the base oil.

The most important determinant of radiation resistance in a base oil is aromatic content. Figure 9.2 shows the influence of aromatic content on

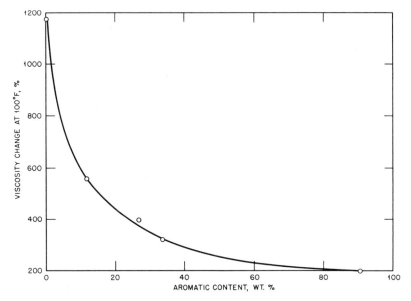

FIG. 9.2 Effect of aromatic content of mineral oils on radiation-induced viscosity change. Exposed to 8.2×10^8 rads in BEPO reactor. (From V. W. David and R. Irving, in *Proceedings of the Conference on Lubrication and Wear,* Institute of Mechanical Engineers, Ref. 39.)

radiation-induced viscosity change for a series of mineral oils.[39] All were naphthenic distillates of about 280 molecular weight with viscosities of about 15 centistokes at 100°F.

In general, any substituents on the aromatic nucleus reduce radiation stability. However, some substituents are usually necessary to provide desirable physical properties such as low melting point. With alkylaromatic hydrocarbons branched chains are more stable than straight chains.[16] Here, so that maximum chemical as well as radiation stability can be attained, a hydrogen atom present on the carbon adjacent to the ring should be avoided. This has been accomplished with alkylated poly(phenyl ethers) by the use of short-chain α-cumyl $[C(C_6H_5)(CH_3)_2—]$ or *tert*-butyl $[CH_3C(CH_3)_2—]$ groups.[65]

Selected alkyl-substituted poly(phenyl ethers) (*meta, para,* or mixed *meta-para* linked compounds) appear to have about the same resistance to radiation-induced viscosity change as do unsubstituted ethers of the same molecular size.[63] This was shown in gamma exposures at a maximum of 350°F and 53×10^8 rads. Longer exposures would very likely have brought the observations in line with those cited in Ch. 8, Sect. 8-3; i.e., unsubstituted aromatics are more stable than substituted aromatics.

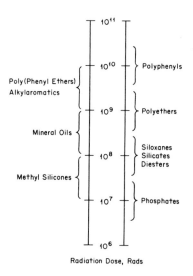

FIG. 9.3 Radiation resistance of base fluids.

With all base oils radiolysis results in the rupture of chemical bonds. Hydrogen or hydrocarbon fragments evolve from the parent molecule, and unsaturation occurs in the surviving species. This unsaturation or other reactive centers can cause decreased oxidation stability, can lead to cross linking, which increases viscosity, etc. If oxygen is present in the system, carbonyl and other oxygenated compounds form. With phosphates and the halocarbons, very corrosive acidic products result. The varying degrees to which these events occur determine the usability of lubricants in the presence of radiation. Subject to earlier remarks regarding molecular structure, the relative radiation resistance of the principal types of base oils is shown in Fig. 9.3.

9-2.1 PETROLEUM OILS

Petroleum oils are mostly of paraffinic and naphthenic (cyclic) structure. Aromatics are largely removed by refining because of their poor viscosity–temperature properties. Table 9.2 presents data[11] on the radiol-

Table 9.2—CHANGES IN A NAPHTHENIC WHITE OIL ON RADIOLYSIS

Gamma dose at 75°F, 10^8 rads in air	0	0.9	9.0
Viscosity:			
At 210°F, centistokes	7.44	8.59	41.2
At 100°F, centistokes	70.5	88.8	1010
Flash point, °F	435	400	395
Pour point, °F	-30	-30	-5
Neutralization No., mg KOH/g	Nil	Nil	
Vapor pressure, mm Hg at 400°F	2.1	7.7	10

ysis of a naphthenic white oil. Damage after about 10^8 rads was not significant; after 10^9 rads it was quite large. Because petroleum oils are mixtures, the effects of composition and structure are difficult to assess. However, Table 9.3 compares[26] four different types of petroleum oils commonly used in lubricant formulations.

Table 9.3— VISCOSITY CHANGE OF PETROLEUM OILS WITH IRRADIATION

	Viscosity at 100°F		
	Centistokes	Per cent increase	
Gamma dose at 75°F, 10^9 rads in air	0	0.8	5
25 V.I. naphthenic (pale)	101	10	74
85 V.I. paraffinic (bright stock)	924	11	75
85 V.I. paraffinic (neutral)	106	12	310
95 V.I. paraffinic (white)	96	10	480

9-2.2 ALKYLAROMATICS

Deficiencies, such as high melting points, poor volatility, inadequate lubricity, and poor viscosity index, in unsubstituted aromatic ring compounds can be offset to varying degrees by attaching alkyl substituents. Short-chain alkyl groups (C_1 to C_4) bring about some improvement in properties yet permit radiation stability approaching that of the parent. Longer alkyl chains (C_{10} to C_{20}) improve viscosity and viscosity index but at a large sacrifice in radiation resistance. When a radiation-resistant lubricant is developed, the eventual choice of alkyl chain length on the aromatic ring is necessarily a compromise.

Considerable work was done[11] with an alkylbiphenyl whose chain was a mixture of 16 and 18 carbon atoms (C_6H_5—C_6H_4—C_{16-18}). Significant properties and their change with irradiation are shown in Table 9.4.

Table 9.4 — RADIATION-INDUCED CHANGES IN AN ALKYLBIPHENYL

Gamma dose at 75 °F, 10^8 rads in helium	0.8	8.3
Viscosity change[a]:		
At 210°F, %	8	64
At 100°F, %	11	111
Pour point, °F	+5	+10
Flash point, °F	+15	+30
Gas, ml/g	1	

[a]Originally 36.5 centistokes at 100°F.

Alkylbenzenes (C_6H_5R) and diarylalkanes (C_6H_5—R—C_6H_5) are other types of compounds that offer a comparison. Several fluids of each type were made and were irradiated in screening tests with gamma rays under helium. The effect[11] on viscosity and gas evolution is shown in Table 9.5.

Table 9.5 — INFLUENCE OF IRRADIATION ON ALKYLAROMATICS

Gamma dose at 75°F, 10^6 rads in helium	Viscosity[a] change at 100°F, %		Gassing, ml/g	
	1	5	1	5
n-Nonylbenzene	3	23	1.2	4.2
Di-n-nonylbenzene		61		8.2
sec-Octyl-n-decylbenzene	1.3	20	1.3	5.8
1,6-Diphenylhexane	3.8	17	0.9	1.7
1,9-Diphenylnonane	5.3	25	0.9	2.4
1,10-Diphenyldecane	12.3	46	1.0	2.7

[a]Original viscosity of 3 to 11 centistokes at 100°F.

The "dumbbell" diarylalkane molecules are especially important because of their good viscosity–temperature characteristics as well as good chemical and radiation stability.

1,9-Bis(phenoxyphenyl)nonane, , is particularly interesting. After 2.6×10^8 rads of gamma radiation[11] (under helium at 75°F), the compound showed a 15% increase in kinematic viscosity at 100°F; gas evolution was 0.9 ml/g. This structure is of promise for use in lubricants requiring high radiation resistance.

9-2.3 ESTERS

9-2.3.1 Aliphatic

The synthetic esters of dicarboxylic acids are widely used as lubricant base stocks. They have good viscosity–temperature characteristics and good oxidation stability. Radiation stability, however, is fair to poor. A dialkyl sebacate, $ROOC(CH_2)_8COOR$, is typical of this class of fluids. Irradiation effects[87] on the di(2-ethylhexyl) derivative are shown in Table 9.6. A dose of 10^8 rads caused appreciable changes in this fluid. Di(2-

Table 9.6—INFLUENCE OF IRRADIATION ON DI(2-ETHYLHEXYL) SEBACATE

Gamma dose at 75 °F, 10^8 rads in air	0	0.4	1.0	7.2^b
Viscosity:				
At 210°F, centistokes	3.31	3.58	3.98	17.6
At 100°F, centistokes	12.7	14.1	16.6	132
Flash point, °F	415	400	255	
Neutralization No., mg KOH/g	0.01	3.1	6.9	

[a] Plexol 201, Rohm & Haas Co.
[b] Exposed in Oak Ridge Graphite Reactor, absence of air.

ethylhexyl) esters of adipic and of azelaic acid showed[71,87] similar changes in viscosity, flash point, and acid formation.

Oxidation at 347°F after about 10^8 rads was significantly worse as was coking for all aliphatic esters in a series of 12 studied.[71] Wear properties (Shell Four Ball at 400°F) were generally somewhat improved. The best of the series was a tridecyl carbonate, $ROC(O)OR$. It showed negligible viscosity change and an increase in neutralization number of only 0.4, probably because of the formation of CO_2 rather than a nonvolatile acid.

9-2.3.2 Aromatic

Aromatic esters are not widely used in conventional lubricants because of the poor viscosity–temperature characteristics that result from the aromatic ring. This group, however, imparts sufficient radiation resistance that these compounds have been considered for radiation-resistant lubricants. The dialkyl terephthalates, $RO_2C-p-C_6H_4CO_2R$, are typical candidates. Radiolytic changes[11] in diisooctyl terephthalate are shown in Table 9.7.

Table 9.7—RADIATION-INDUCED CHANGES IN
DIISOOCTYL TEREPHTHALATE

Gamma dose at 75 °F, 10^8 rads in air	0	0.8	9.0
Viscosity:			
At 210°F, centistokes	5.09	5.83	13.6
At 100°F, centistokes	31.7	40.0	153
Pour point, °F	-65	-55	-25
Flash point, °F	420	360	280

9-2.3.3 *Phosphates*

Organic phosphates are used in lubricants either as base fluids or as additives. In either use their radiation resistance is low. Several of these esters were damaged severely[67] at 10^8 rads, as shown in Table 9.8. At this

Table 9.8—RADIOLYTIC CHANGE IN PHOSPHATE ESTERS[a]

	Increase in viscosity at 100°F, %	Increase in neutralization No., mg KOH/g
Tricresyl	54	12.6
Diphenyl cresyl	46	13.9
Triisooctyl	32	9.2

[a]Gamma dose of 10^8 rads at 75 °F in nitrogen.

dose a large (about 20%) percentage of each compound was converted to acidic materials. Even when used in small concentrations to impart load-carrying capacity, the phosphates form appreciable amounts of strong acid during irradiation. In oil solution the presence of such acid leads to base-oil degradation and corrosion problems. This precludes the use of phosphates as base oils and limits their use as wear agents in lubricants for radiation environments.

9-2.3.4 *Silicates*

Organic silicates and silanes are used conventionally in hydraulic and heat-transfer fluids. As already shown in Fig. 9.3, these fluids have low radiation resistance. Typical effects are given in Table 9.9.

9-2.4 SILICONES

These fluids are polymers having the repeating structure $-Si(R)_2-O-$. Their principal virtue is in generally excellent viscosity–temperature and viscosity–volatility characteristics. These and other properties of silicones depend on the siloxane backbone and are modified by the organic (R) groups substituted on this chain. The best physical properties generally

Table 9.9 — RADIOLYTIC CHANGES IN SILICATE TYPE FLUIDS AT 75 °F

Fluid	Radiation			Increase in viscosity at 100 °F, %	Increase in neutralization No., mg KOH/g	Gassing, ml/g
	Type	Dose, 10^8 rads	Atm			
Tetra(isooctyl) silicate[67]	e⁻	1	N₂	29	0.4	
Tetrakis-n-dodecylsilane[67]	e⁻	1	N₂	35	0.0	
Hexa(2-ethylbutoxy)disiloxane[67]	γ	1	He	28		4.8
		5	He	410		14.8
Tetra(2-ethylhexyl) silicate[39]	n	11	Air	Solid		

result from methyl groups, but such polymers have notoriously poor radiation resistance.† However, the substitution of phenyl groups enhances radiation stability[11,38,67,101] at some sacrifice of physical properties. Radiation changes in commercial silicone fluids of increasing phenyl content are shown[11] in Table 9.10. Correlation is considered good and confirms the

Table 9.10 — INFLUENCE OF RADIATION ON SILICONES

Gamma dose at 75 °F, 10^8 rads in helium	Electron fraction aliphatic[92]	Increase in viscosity at 100 °F, %		Gas evolved, ml/g	
		5	9	5	9
Dow Corning 200/50	0.458	Gel		22	
Dow Corning 550	0.283	Gel		2.1	
Dow Corning 703	0.174	1000	Gel	1.9	2.7
Dow Corning 710	0.189	153	Gel		3.0
Dow Corning XF 4320	0.195	160	Gel	1.7	3.2

observations of Fischer[44] wherein G_{gas} was found to increase with increasing electron fraction aliphatic‡ of the silicone fluid. Thus optimum resistance is obtained with silicones of low molecular weight and high phenyl content.

The radiation dose required to gel a linear dimethyl silicone is reported by Currin[38] to depend directly on molecular weight:

$$\text{Gelation dose} = \frac{423 \times 10^3}{\text{mol. wt.}} \text{ rads}$$

† All factors, such as molecular weight or viscosity effects, must be considered when radiation resistances are compared. For example, a dimethylpolysiloxane of 10^6 centistokes will gel below 5 megarads; a 1 centistoke fluid will gel only above 1500 megarads.[44]

‡ Electron fraction aliphatic is the number of electrons associated with all the atoms of the aliphatic groups divided by the total number of electrons in the entire molecule.[44,92]

Although this relationship gives doses about twice as high as those reported by Charlesby,[30] they are consistent with the data of Mahoney.[67]

Silicones of both the dimethyl and the methyl phenyl series showed no decrease in their high level of oxidation stability after 10^8 rads. Coking also was not impaired. A chlorinated silicone† was shown[67] to gel after 0.9×10^8 rads at 75°F and to liberate large amounts of free hydrogen chloride during exposure.

9-2.5 HALOGENATED COMPOUNDS

In early work[12] certain of these materials were found to be resistant to reactor radiation. Poly(chlorotrifluoroethylene)‡ and dichlorobiphenyl§ ranked well with other organics on the basis of viscosity change. However, they corroded iron and copper when irradiated in the presence of these metals. Thus they were not considered practical for further development as components of radiation-resistant lubricants.

This appraisal has been confirmed[67] in more recent work. Various viscosity grades of poly(chlorotrifluorethylene) were exposed to 0.9×10^8 rads at 75°F under nitrogen. Viscosity increase at 100°F was only 8 to 15%, but an appreciable amount of strongly acidic material was liberated. Oxidation-corrosion tests showed that extensive metal corrosion was caused by these acidic compounds. Tris(perfluorobutyl)amine¶ and perfluoro(ethyl ether)¶ were also sensitive to irradiation and formed large amounts of acidic materials; i.e., neutralization numbers were about 5 to 6 after the exposure cited.

9-2.6 ETHERS

9-2.6.1 *Aliphatic*

Polyethers of this type are used successfully in conventional lubricants. In general, they have good low-temperature and viscosity–temperature properties and good lubricity. The Dow polyglycols†† and the UCON‡‡ series of polyethers are examples of these fluids. A typical compound is

$$\text{UCON DLB-144E, } RO\left[\begin{array}{c} CH_3 \\ | \\ -CHCH_2O- \end{array}\right]_n OR.$$

Table 9.11 shows some effects[11] of radiation on this material.

---

† General Electric Company, 81406.
‡ Fluorlube, Hooker Chemical Corp.
§ Arochlor 1232, Monsanto Chemical Co.
¶ Minnesota Mining and Manufacturing Company.
†† Dow Chemical Co.
‡‡ Union Carbide Chemicals Co.

Table 9.11 — RADIOLYTIC CHANGE IN UCON DLB-144E

Gamma dose at 75 °F, 10^8 rads in helium	0	1.0	5.0
Viscosity:			
At 210°F, centistokes	7.10	7.70	18.5
At 100°F, centistokes	30.5	36.6	120
Gassing, ml/g		0.9	17.1

In general, the polyethers show a low change in viscosity with radiation dose. Frequently a decrease is shown. This is due in part to radiolytic depolymerization and dilution of the base stock with the resulting fragments. Thus viscosity change alone is not a good index of radiation resistance for polyethers. Gas evolution is relatively high. These compounds respond peculiarly to inhibitors and are mentioned in the later section on additives.

9-2.6.2 Polyphenyl

As a class poly(phenyl ethers) $[C_6H_5(—OC_6H_4—)_nOC_6H_5]$ show great promise as high-temperature radiation-resistant lubricants. These materials have good inherent stability to oxidation, heat, and radiation. Their physical properties, however, are generally poorer than those needed. Melting points of many ethers are high, and viscosity–temperature properties are poor. However, eutectic mixtures of unsubstituted poly(phenyl ether) isomers can be made that show no tendency to crystallize. Such mixtures have viscous pour points of 5 to 40°F. These characteristics of poly(phenyl ethers) depend on structure and substituents, but types of substituents are severely limited if the excellent stability of the unsubstituted nucleus is to be retained. Only a small number of alkyl-containing groups, e.g., the tert-butyl or α-cumyl $[C(C_6H_5)(CH_3)_2—]$ groups, are tolerable. Considerable research[59,67] has been done on these poly(phenyl ethers).

Figure 9.4 illustrates some viscosity changes for certain poly(phenyl ethers) (some have melting points as high as 230°F).[65] The greatest change occurs at the lowest temperature. This is true with all compounds and indicates that the life of a lubricant in an application with a critical low-temperature requirement would be shorter than the life in an application at high-operating temperature.

Of the seven poly(phenyl ethers) for which averages are shown in Fig. 9.4, two were outstanding. For 11×10^8 rads, bis(p-phenoxyphenyl)ether

showed no change in evaporation at 500°F; the flash point decreased from 516 to 403°F. For the same dose bis(p-tert-butylphenoxy)phenyl ether,

$[(CH_3)_3C-p-C_6H_4O-pC_6H_4-]_2O$ (melting point 178°F), showed an increase in evaporation from 3 to 6%; the flash point was lowered from 572 to 554°F. Viscosity changes for these two compounds after irradiation

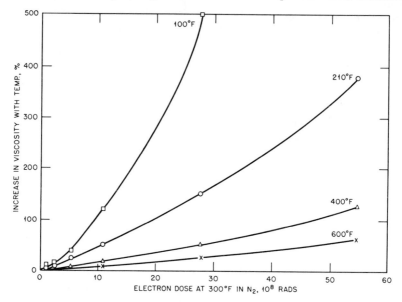

FIG. 9.4 Average radiation-induced viscosity increase of seven p-linked poly(phenyl ethers).

are shown[65] in Table 9.12. The lower melting-point *meta*-linked ethers and the liquid eutectic mixtures had resistance to radiation changes similar to the high-melting-point *para* compounds.[63]

Table 9.12 — CHANGE IN VISCOSITY OF POLY(PHENYL ETHERS) AFTER IRRADIATION

Electron dose at 300°F, 10^8 rads in nitrogen	Increase in viscosity, %				
	1.1	5.5	11	28	55
Bis(*p*-phenoxyphenyl) ether:					
At 400°F	2.5	12	19	40	79
At 300°F	3	12	23	57	116
Bis [*p*-(*p-tert*-butylphenoxy)-phenyl] ether:					
At 400°F	3	13	18	55	150
At 210°F	6	31	50	202	980

Table 9.13 notes the viscosity change with irradiation[11] for a diphenyl ether having an alkyl chain of mixed C_{14-16}. In a helium atmosphere the fluid evolved[11] about 2.4 ml of gas per gram of oil after 2.4×10^8 rads.

Table 9.13—CHANGE IN VISCOSITY OF A C_{14-16}-
ALKYL(DIPHENYL ETHER) AFTER IRRADIATION

Gamma dose at 75°F, 10^8 rads in air	Viscosity change, %		
	0.8	2.4	8.3
Temperature:			
At 400°F	-4	5	53
At 210°F	6	26	108
At 100°F	8	39	195

Considerable work was done on this fluid, and it is mentioned again in later sections.

9-2.7 SOLID FILMS

Dry lubricants of the solid-film type are used at extremely high or at very low temperatures or in applications where maintenance and regular relubrication are not possible. Solid-film lubrication is of particular interest for applications above 800°F, e.g., in spots in airborne nuclear power systems where both radiation and temperature are high. Solid films under consideration include the following:

1. Thin metal films such as titanium and chromium applied by electroplating.
2. Laminar solids such as graphite, mica, talc, and molybdenum disulfide and nonmetallic phthalocyanines.
3. Organic compounds such as metallic soaps, halogenated silicones, and halogenated plastics.
4. Ceramics.

Of these the laminar solids, particularly graphite and molybdenum disulfide, have received some attention for use in radiation fields.[6,52,58,83] Such materials can be applied as lubricants to machine parts in several ways:

1. As a dry powder.
2. By spraying a colloidal substance in water or organic solvent.
3. By metallic bonding through sintering with a bearing metal such as copper.
4. With an organic binder that is cured by heating.

The lubrication properties of the laminar solids are not appreciably altered by high-level radiation. These materials will probably retain their lubrication function up to about 10^{10} rads. The organic binder will suffer damage consistent with its chemical structure (see Chs. 5 and 6). The combination of binder and dispersed inorganic material will function as a lubricant for doses well above those that will degrade the organic alone.

Wear-test results were reported[83] on solid films irradiated with gammas and with neutrons. Although the film compositions were proprietary and not disclosed, they were of the bonded molybdenum sulfide and graphite type. The doses were about 2×10^9 rads for the organic portion of the material. Results were mixed, but, in general, this dose caused no impairment of wear properties. Resistance to corrosion by salt spray was similarly not affected.

A dry film for use in ball bearings has also been studied.[6] The film comprised 55% molybdenum disulfide, 6% graphite, and 39% sodium silicate binder. The material was sprayed onto metal parts and cured by heating. It outperformed films with organic binders, e.g., phenolics and epoxies, and permitted good bearing performances at 350°F after 5×10^9 rads of gamma radiation.

9-3 Additives

This term applies to chemical compounds that improve certain properties of a base oil. For the most part organic compounds are used, usually less than 5 wt. % and frequently less than 1 wt. %. The lubrication scientist works for synergism, i.e., an effect that is much greater than expected on the basis of relative per cent composition.

Additives are used for a variety of purposes: (1) to reduce radiation damage, (2) to retard oxidation, (3) to improve viscosity–temperature properties, (4) to form a gel or a grease, (5) to reduce wear and enhance load-carrying ability, and (6) to suppress foaming.

9-3.1 RADIATION-DAMAGE INHIBITORS

Selected materials can retard the changes in the physical properties of base oils which result from radiolysis. Many of these additives are also oxidation inhibitors, but others function whether or not oxygen is present in the system. For this reason this discussion is separated from that on antioxidants.

Radiation-damage inhibitors are "used up" during irradiation. Even so, the effect is frequently discernible above 10^9 rads, and the contribution of the additive at lower doses justifies its use in lubricants of low or intermediate radiation resistance. The underlying phenomena and mechanisms were reviewed in Chs. 2 and 3. Only the measurable effects on important properties are of concern here.

An early survey[12] with a dialkyl sebacate, an alkylbenzene, and a polyether showed that a dialkyl selenide† was effective in reducing radiolytic viscosity increase in all three oils. The experiments were conducted in the Oak Ridge Graphite Reactor at 175°F in capsules to which air had access. The selenide was increasingly effective for amounts up to 10%. Also

† OLOA 250, Oronite Division of California Chemical Co.

effective was a pinene-P_2S_5 product.† Ineffective were a phenol,‡ a zinc dialkyl dithiocarbamate, and an arylamine.

Another widely used antioxidant, phenothiazine, was effective[67] in reducing physical-property changes in a diester in the absence of air, as shown in Table 9.14. For the same conditions diarylamines were less effec-

Table 9.14 — EFFECT OF PHENOTHIAZINE IN DI(2-ETHYLHEXYL) SEBACATE[a]

Additive, wt. %	Increase in viscosity at 100°F, %	Increase in neutralization No., mg KOH/g
0.0	45	7.0
0.5	26	4.3
1.0	20	3.5
2.0	9	2.8

[a]Gamma dose of 0.9×10^8 rads at 75°F in nitrogen.

tive. With air present, selenium and sulfur-containing materials dramatically reduced[27] viscosity change in the diester, as shown in Fig. 9.5.

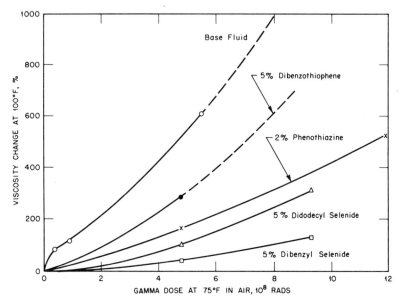

FIG. 9.5 Effects of additives on radiation-induced viscosity change in di(2-ethylhexyl) sebacate.

Generally, additives are most effective in radiation-sensitive fluids. Figure 9.6 illustrates this point[10] for a silicone and for an alkylbiphenyl.

† Santolube 394C, Monsanto Chemical Co.
‡ Paranox 441, Enjay Company, Inc.

Certain free-radical scavengers were also tried as radiation-damage inhibitors, even though they were not conventional antioxidants. Iodine and its compounds retarded viscosity change; iodobenzene was particularly beneficial.[12] The optimum concentration of iodobenzene in the dialkyl sebacate was about 5 wt. % for a reactor dose of 12×10^8 rads at 150°F. Other halogenated aromatic additives were much less effective than the aromatic iodides.

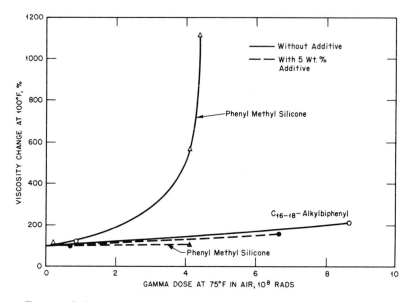

FIG. 9.6 Influence of didodecyl selenide on radiolytic viscosity change.

Infrared spectrometry disclosed that iodobenzene was consumed during irradiation. In alkylaromatic, diester, and polyether base oils, iodobenzene in 2 wt. % concentration disappeared after a reactor exposure of 2.5×10^8 rads at 160°F. The reaction products were not determined, although iodine remained in the sample.

Mahoney[67] confirmed that iodine compounds reduce viscosity changes in diesters during irradiation, although there was little reduction in the formation of acidic products. However, iodides usually caused other problems. Some iodine-containing compounds formed insolubles during irradiation. Iodopropane, iodobenzene, and iodoaniline destroyed the antioxidant effect of phenothiazine in dialkyl sebacate blends, even in the absence of radiation.

Diester oils can also be protected by selected aromatic materials,[67] as shown in Table 9.15. Other experiments indicated that physical mixtures of aromatics and aliphatic compounds were as effective as specially tailored alkylaromatics.[12] Octadecylbenzene was compared with a mixture of mineral oil and 1-methylnaphthalene in this regard; each fluid contained the same aromatic-carbon content. After irradiation[12] the viscosity change of the physical mixture was equivalent to that of the "chemical mixture." This illustrates that from a radiation-damage standpoint, exotic

Table 9.15 — PROTECTION OF DI(2-ETHYLHEXYL) SEBACATE FROM ELECTRON EFFECTS[a]

tert-Butylated naphthalene, wt. %	Increase in viscosity at 100°F, %	Increase in neutralization No., mg KOH/g
0	45	7.0
5	24	3.7
20	16	1.2

[a]Dose of 0.9×10^8 rads at 75°F in nitrogen.

synthetic compounds are not required; simple blends will do as well. In lubricant uses, however, this principle is limited by requirements such as volatility and viscosity–temperature characteristics of the finished blends. Highly aromatic materials degrade both of these properties in aliphatic oils.

9-3.2 ANTIOXIDANTS

This category covers the most important type of additive. Oxygen, even in minor amounts, is hostile to lubricants and hastens their degradation. The function of the antioxidant is to retard this degradation. This is generally accomplished by reaction with the free radicals generated in the oxidation process. Since radiation produces large quantities of free radicals from a base oil and accelerates oxidation, antioxidants are "used up" rapidly during radiolysis because of several factors, including (1) inactivation of the inhibitor through reaction with free radicals generated both by radiation and by oxidation, (2) the formation of oxygen-sensitive degradation products in the base oil, and (3) direct damage to the inhibitor.

The direct damage to inhibitors is small at low dosage. This was demonstrated by exposing aromatic inhibitors, such as phenothiazine and phenyl(α-naphthyl)amine, to gamma rays for about 10^8 rads in the solid state. Very little loss of antioxidant activity occurred (less than the 10% calculated).[67] In contrast, when the antioxidant was irradiated in oil solution for the same dose in the absence of oxygen, a large part of the additive underwent structural change. Activity was completely destroyed for phenothiazine and phenyl(α-naphthyl)amine in aliphatic hydrocarbon or diester blends. Thus the antioxidant reacted with the free radicals formed during exposure of the oil. Although this reaction with base-oil radicals minimizes damage to the oil, antioxidant activity is sacrificed[67] in the process.

Aliphatic hydrocarbons form considerable amounts of olefins during irradiation. Experiments were conducted[67] in which a synthetic olefin was added to an unirradiated base oil in the same percentage as that observed for olefins in an irradiated base oil. Certain inhibitors were sensitive to the presence of the synthetic olefin, as indicated by reduced antioxidant activity in oxidation tests. Neither stable free radicals nor peroxide contaminants were detected in irradiated aliphatic hydrocarbon oils. Thus the loss of inhibitor response was believed to result from the presence of olefins formed during irradiation.

The radiolysis products of diesters are even more harmful to oxidation stability than the olefins from hydrocarbons. Antioxidants were added to esters that had been preirradiated to about 10^8 rads; the blends showed[67] poor stability in oxidation tests. Analysis of the irradiated esters showed the presence of free acid. Stable free radicals could not be detected, and olefin and peroxide contents were low. Analytical methods for the determination of aldehydes and ketones were not conclusive. However, it was felt[67] that these components were the cause of the major loss of antioxidant activity.

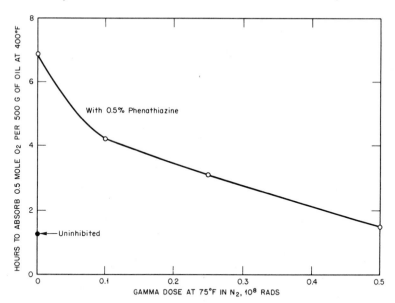

Fig 9.7 Reduction of antioxidant activity in di(2-ethylhexyl) sebacate with irradiation.

Mahoney calculated[67] that 13% phenothiazine would be needed to react with all radicals formed by about 10^8 rads in a diester blend. The rapid loss of activity of phenothiazine is shown in Fig. 9.7.

These considerations show that antioxidants of this type scavenge only a small portion of the radicals formed during the irradiation of oils. Thus, in concentrations normally employed (1 to 2% for phenothiazine), the inhibitor is destroyed below 10^8 rads.

In general, all classes of inhibitors and base fluids behave similarly: the antioxidant is used up during irradiation, and the rate of disappearance is accelerated by the presence of oxygen and by elevated temperature. Destruction of antioxidants and loss of oxidation stability are two of the more serious consequences of irradiation. The effect is of increasing concern if the lubricant is for use at high temperatures under oxidizing conditions.

9-3.3 VISCOSITY-INDEX IMPROVERS

In conventional lubricant practice high-molecular-weight polymers are frequently added to low-viscosity base oils to improve viscosity–tempera-

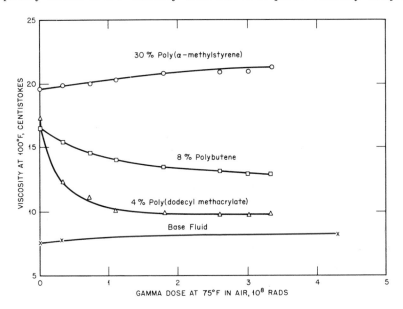

FIG. 9.8 Change of the viscosity of polymer solutions by irradiation. Base fluid: mixed alkylbenzenes (mole wt. ~250) containing 5% didodecyl selenide and 0.1% quinizarin. (From J. G. Carroll and R. O. Bolt, *American Society of Lubrication Engineers Transactions*, Ref. 24.)

ture properties (viscosity index) and also to raise viscosity. Polyesters [poly(dodecyl methacrylate)]† and hydrocarbons (polybutene)‡ of molecular weight 5000 to 15,000 are examples of these conventional improvers.

† Acryloid 855, Rohm & Haas Co.
‡ Polybutene 128, Oronite Division of California Chemical Co.

Other polymeric additives, such as poly(α-methylstyrene),[†] can increase viscosity and lower viscosity index or have little effect on it. Their effect on an alkylbenzene base oil[‡] having a low viscosity[24] and a viscosity index[14] of about 30 can be seen at the 0 dose points in Figs. 9.8 and 9.9.

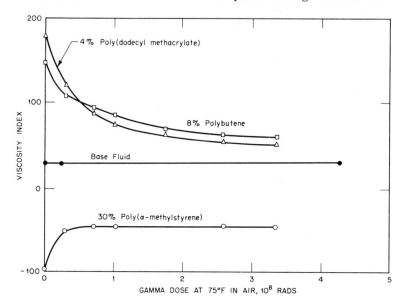

FIG. 9.9 Change of the viscosity index of polymer solutions by irradiation. Base fluid: mixed alkylbenzenes (mole wt. ~250) containing 5% didodecyl selenide and 0.1% quinizarin.

The polyester and polybutene scission rapidly[14] under irradiation. As a result the solution viscosity decreases as shown in Fig. 9.8. However, the polystyrene does not cleave; instead, it slowly cross links, and thus the viscosity of the solution is increased. The notion of a "constant-viscosity oil" is suggested[9,14] from a study of Fig. 9.8. Ingredients should include a low-viscosity oil, a polymer that scissions, and a second polymer that cross links. The reactions of the first polymer cause lowered viscosity; the reverse is true for the second polymer. As a result the viscosity of the solution remains relatively constant over a given radiation dose range.

The loss in thickening power of viscosity-index improvers stimulated research for more stable polymers. A series[11] of partially alkylated poly (α-methylstyrenes) (APAMS) was synthesized. Molecular weight governed their thickening power, that is, ability to raise viscosity index and viscosity; the APAMS were comparable to the polybutenes but less effective than the polyesters. Another variant was synthesized,[11] that is, a

† V-9 Resin, Dow Chemical Co.
‡ Alkane 56, Oronite Division of California Chemical Co.

series of poly(alkylphenoxyethyl methacrylates) (APEMS). Solutions were made of these polymers in an alkyl diphenyl ether base oil, and irradiations were conducted in a Co⁶⁰ gamma source in air at 75°F. The following is the observed order of radiation resistance and general suitability regarding retention of viscosity index and viscosity: APAM > APEM > isobutylene–styrene copolymer† > polybutene > polyesters.

9-3.4 Gelling Agents

A lubricating grease is a delicate gel formed by dispersing a solid in an oil. The solid or gelling agent, usually present in 10 to 25 wt. %, is likened to a sponge which acts as a storehouse for the oil. Many materials, organic and inorganic, are employed to form the particular structure desired. Most commonly the metallic soaps of fatty acids such as sodium stearate are used.

The effect‡ of gamma radiation on a paraffinic mineral oil gelled with sodium stearate is shown[53] in Fig. 9.10. The shape of the curve suggests a

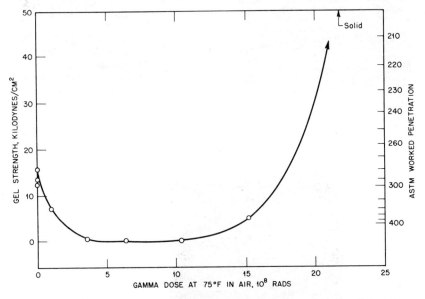

Fig. 9.10 Effect of radiation on consistency of sodium stearate–paraffinic oil grease. (From B. W. Hotten and J. G. Carroll, *Industrial and Engineering Chemistry*, Ref. 53.)

complex mechanism. The corresponding curve of radiolytic change for oils is continuously positive and with a paraffinic oil is shaped like that por-

† Parapol 50, Enjay Co., Inc.
‡ The units of gel strength were calculated by dividing the weight of the penetration cone by the final area of contact with the grease and multiplying by the acceleration due to gravity.

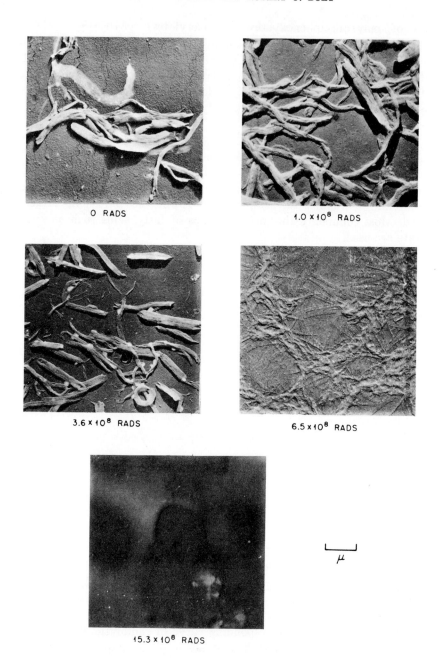

FIG. 9.11 Effect of radiation on crystallite structure of sodium stearate–paraffinic oil grease during gamma dose in air at 75°F. (From B. W. Hotten and J. G. Carroll, *Industrial and Engineering Chemistry*, Ref. 53.)

tion of Fig. 9.10 above 10^9 rads. Thus an attack on the gel structure and/or on the gelling agent may be responsible for the initial softening of the grease.

Electron micrography furnished evidence[53] for damage to soap crystallites during radiolysis, as shown in Fig. 9.11. At the two lowest dosages, the crystallites of the samples were slightly smaller than they were originally, and they were partly fractured; those at the higher dosage were increasingly eroded and were almost completely disintegrated at 15.3×10^8 rads. The consistencies of the samples of Fig. 9.11 follow:

Dose, 10^8 rads	ASTM worked penetration
0	289
1.0	342
3.6	452
6.5	500+
15.3	382

The fractured soap fibers cannot form a gel structure, and this explains the loss in consistency below about 10×10^8 rads. Beyond this dose the increasing stiffness must result from replacement of the soap lattice with cross-linked oil.

An attempt was made to reconstruct radiation-softened gels. Greases liquefied by irradiation were reheated to about 390°F. This temperature is above the original melting points of the lubricants. After cooling, a sodium stearate and a lithium–calcium soap grease recovered more than their original consistency. An aluminum stearate grease was only slightly reversible,[53] as shown in Table 9.16. It was hypothesized that radiation re-

Table 9.16—REHEATING IRRADIATED GREASES

Gelling agent[a]	Gamma dose at 75°F, 10^8 rads in air	ASTM worked penetration	
		Original	Regelled
Sodium stearate	0	310	
	3.5	Liq.	282
Lithium-calcium soap (3:1)	0	361	
	7.3	Liq.	250
Aluminum stearate	0	389	
	6.4	411	400

[a]In mineral oils.

duces metal ions to elements and carboxylate ions to radicals. Reheating in an environment containing some moisture and carbon dioxide could reverse the reaction[53] for sodium, lithium, and calcium, but not for the less reactive aluminum.

Three dry soaps were exposed separately to 2.4×10^8 rads gamma radiation at 75°F. They were then made into greases with a naphthenic mineral oil. Preirradiation caused the soaps to yield greases that compared with those made from unirradiated soaps as follows:

Lithium hydroxystearate was 30% softer.
Sodium stearate was 30% stiffer.
Sodium N-octadecylterephthamate was 10% softer.

The behavior of the sodium stearate is surprising. Greases from this gelling agent usually soften at this dosage. However, after irradiation the sodium stearate was a more effective gelling agent than before.

It is evident that the gelling agent is a radiation-susceptible component of a grease. Some effort has been devoted to making more stable materials. Improved radiation resistance resulted with the sodium N-octadecylterephthalamate $(C_{18}H_{37}N \overset{H}{} CO_2Na)$. Mixtures of this material with other more-aromatic salts such as sodium benzoate resulted in further improvement, as shown[20] in Fig. 9.12.

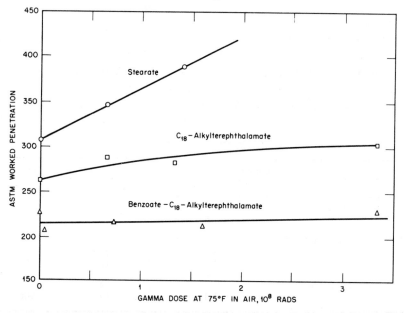

Fig. 9.12 Influence of sodium salt gelling agents on radiation-induced consistency change in naphthenic oil-base greases.

Some objections have been raised to partially metallic gelling agents in an environment of neutrons. Their activation creates a radiation source in intimate contact with the grease. This factor was considered for Na^{24}

(several beta and gamma emissions) and for Li^8 (13-Mev beta ray). The contribution from activation here is not large (about 5% by calculation) for the equivalent of 15×10^8 rads. Even so, this item has prompted the use of silica, organic dyes, and nonmetallic salts as grease thickeners. The actual performance of greases made from these and more conventional gelling agents is deferred to the discussion of lubricating greases in Sect. 9-5.3.

9-3.5 ANTIWEAR ADDITIVES

Antiwear additives are widely used in lubricants. They are most desirable for sliding surfaces and for surfaces where hydrodynamic film lubrication is marginal, i.e., where an oil film may only be intermittently present. Antiwear additives react with the surfaces and prevent metal-to-metal contact. Most used are the aryl phosphates, particularly tricresyl phosphate (TCP) in concentrations of 0.5 to 3 wt. %. As mentioned in Sect. 9-2.3.3, TCP decomposes at low radiation doses and gives off strong acids; it also adversely affects other properties, as will be shown in later sections.

Small samples of synthetic oils were irradiated[34] with reactor flux. The only significant damage, as shown in Table 9.17, was to diester-based oils

Table 9.17 — ACID PRODUCTION FROM AN INHIBITED DI(2-ETHYLHEXYL) SEBACATE[a]

Additive	Radiation type	Increase in viscosity at 100°F, %	Neutralization No., mg KOH/g
None	Reactor	0	0.4
	Co^{60}	4	0.2
1% phenothiazine	Reactor	2	0.1
	Co^{60}	1	0.4
1% phenothiazone	Reactor	4	2.6
5% tricresyl phosphate	Co^{60}	5	3.7
5% tricresyl phosphate	Reactor	6	2.8
	Co^{60}	7	6.7

[a]Dose of 6×10^6 rads at 75°F in nitrogen.

containing TCP. As noted, confirming irradiations with gamma rays also showed high acidity at this dose level for the blends containing the phosphate. Also of interest, the antioxidant activity decreased considerably, whereas the coking tendency increased for the phosphate blends. Similar behavior was observed with a diester engine-oil formulation of the MIL-L-7808 type[96] which contained TCP and phenothiazine.

The fatty acids or their salts, such as oleic acid or sodium oleate, constitute another class of antiwear additives. These are used as oiliness agents. No work is available specifically on the radiation stability of these materials in lubricants. However, they would probably not withstand above about 10^7 rads.

9-3.6 EXTREME-PRESSURE AGENTS

Extreme-pressure (EP) agents are used where machine parts to be lubricated are highly stressed so that film lubrication is infrequent and boundary lubrication prevails. Hypoid gear assemblies, differentials, planetary and reduction gearing of gas turbines, aircraft actuators, etc., require EP agents. They are usually organic compounds, such as paraffins, fats, and esters, containing sulfur or chlorine. The EP materials are themselves corrosive to many nonferrous metals; they react with the surface to form a protective chloride or sulfide, which permits a controlled rate of wear and prevents a catastrophic rate of wear.

In general, the radiation stability of an EP agent is governed by that of the basic molecule; for example, a sulfurized ester would behave much like an ester and a chlorinated biphenyl would behave like a polyphenyl. However, this stability is reduced somewhat by the sulfur or chlorine substituents. The materials become increasingly acidic on irradiation above the 10^7-rad level, particularly the chlorine-containing compounds, which evolve HCl. Such corrosive products, of course, are deleterious[26] to both metals and the lubricant.

9-3.7 FOAM INHIBITORS

Oils entrain air while lubricating bearings, gear chains, etc. If the trapped air tends to form a stable foam, this promotes excessive wear of machine parts. To retard foam formation and to promote foam collapse, small amounts (less than 0.01 wt. %) of a methyl silicone fluid are added in conventional practice to the lubricant.

Little information is available on effects of radiation on foaming; but, in general, it can be said that irradiation increases the foaming tendency of conventional lubricants. In particular, the tendency to form foam is increased[56] above 10^7 rads for mineral oils, although foam stability is not altered. Thus it has been shown that silicone-containing mineral oils were satisfactory before irradiation but unsatisfactory[56] after about 10^8 rads. Results indicated a complete loss of the silicone antifoam agent. However, a similar dose increased only slightly the foaming tendency of diester lubricants containing antifoam agents. This is not surprising because foaming of pure compounds (diesters), in general, is less than that of mixtures (mineral oils).

9-3.8 RUST INHIBITORS

These materials are used to prevent rusting of ferrous surfaces to which water has access during lubrication. One type employed in steam-turbine oils is nonemulsifying. Dodecyl acid maleate is a typical material in this class. Steam-turbine oils containing a compound of this sort were shown[56] to lose their rust resistance after gamma irradiation. The effect became pronounced at less than 10^8 rads, at which dose all fluids investigated failed the rust test. Interfacial tension of inhibited steam-turbine oils also increased with gamma dose. This became significant at 10^8 rads, where substantial damage to rust inhibitors would be expected.

A second type rust inhibitor, emulsifying in nature, is used in heavy-duty motor and diesel engine oils. Typical examples are petroleum sulfonates or their sodium, calcium, or nonmetallic salts. No data are available on oils containing these specific compounds, but they are expected to be superior in radiation stability to those fluids containing nonemulsifying additives. Serious damage to the emulsifying rust inhibitors is not expected below about 10^8 rads.

9-4 Environmental Factors

The relative rates of damage caused by different types and intensities of radiation are certainly important factors with lubricants. Unfortunately, there is little information available on this point. The reader is referred to Ch. 3, Sect. 3-1.1, to Ch. 4, Sect. 4-1.3, and to Ch. 8, Sect. 8-3.2, for a general discussion applicable to the lubricant field. The interrelation of radiation, heat, and oxidation effects on lubricants will be considered here. The added effects of mechanical stresses on radiolysis have not been separated; they are covered together in Sect. 9.5.

9-4.1 ROLE OF TEMPERATURE

Increasing the temperature always accelerates changes occurring in lubricants. This is just as true with radiation effects as with other environmental factors. With radiation, however, there is usually a threshold temperature below which heat causes only a small amount of the total damage. Above the threshold, thermal degradation becomes an increasingly important item.

Five lubricants were exposed[12] in a reactor in open capsules (i.e., air was present) at several temperatures ranging from 68 to 428°F. The dose was about 15 to 19 × 10^8 rads. An alkylbenzene, an alkyl terephthalate, a dialkyl sebacate, and a polyether contained inhibitors; an amylbiphenyl was tested neat. Temperature had little effect on radiation-induced viscosity change below 285°F. The effect became marked at 356°F, whereas at 428°F only the amylbiphenyl was still liquid. Thus about 285°F was found to be the temperature threshold of damage for inhibited lubricants.

The contribution of temperature to radiation damage depends upon the inherent stability of the base fluid. As illustrated in Table 9.18, at 400°F

Table 9.18—COMPARISON OF RADIATION DAMAGE AT TWO TEMPERATURES[a]

Temperature during irradiation, °F	Viscosity change at 100°F, %		Gassing, ml/g	
	75	400	75	400
Hexa(2-ethylbutoxy)disiloxane	400	151	15.3	31
Naphthenic white oil	168	440	5	33
C_{14-18}-alkyl(diphenyl ether)	50	48	5	5.5
C_{14}-alkyl(diphenyl ether)	47	38	4	6.5

[a]Gamma dose of 5×10^8 rads in helium.

irradiation markedly alters[11] the viscosity change and the gas evolution of a disiloxane and a mineral oil compared to changes at 75°F. The disiloxane actually suffered some cracking at the higher temperature. The diphenyl ethers, being inherently more stable to both temperature and radiation, suffered no appreciable additional effect at 400°F. In these exposures the presence of air would have imposed additional damage from oxidation.

Inhibitors influence the role of temperature in radiolysis,[11] as noted in Table 9.19. For a mineral oil the temperature effect on viscosity and on

Table 9.19—INFLUENCE OF TEMPERATURE AND INHIBITOR ON RADIOLYSIS OF A NAPHTHENIC WHITE OIL[a]

Irradiation temperture, °F	No inhibitor		2% didodecyl selenide	
	75	400	75	400
Increase in viscosity:				
At 210°F, %	74	229	72	78
At 100°F, %	168	440	127	128
Gassing, ml/g		32	25	23

[a]Gamma dose of 5×10^8 rads in helium.

gassing was not very great in the inhibited sample but was appreciable in the neat fluid.

9-4.2 INFLUENCE OF OXYGEN

Oxygen is the traditional enemy of lubricants. It attacks these materials to form new species that almost invariably have poorer properties as lubricants than the old species. Radiation speeds oxidation and hastens degradation. For example, even at 75°F the radiolytic viscosity increase of inhibited alkylaromatic oils exposed to air in open capsules was double[24] that of identical samples irradiated under helium. With neat fluids the observed differences would have been greater.

Doses that do not cause measurable changes in physical properties with inhibited oils can, however, lower oxidation stability. This was shown with two fluids irradiated[34] in open containers in a reactor. The base oil was a highly refined naphthenic mineral oil. In one case a dialkyl selenide was added, and in the other a phenolic inhibitor was present. Total doses were 10×10^6 rads and 5×10^6 rads, respectively. Physical-property changes were only slight, but oxidation resistance at 400°F after this exposure was significantly worsened. Here, viscosity change at 100°F was about 30% for the irradiated oils compared with 4% for the original materials; neutralization number was 3 to 3.7 compared with 0.03 to 0.5 for the unirradiated oils after oxidation.

Effects of radiation were shown graphically in experiments conducted[12] in an aluminum cell inside the Oak Ridge Graphite Reactor. Lubricants were placed in the cell, and oxygen was then bubbled through them. Typical results are shown in Fig. 9.13. The inhibited octadecylbenzene oil shown

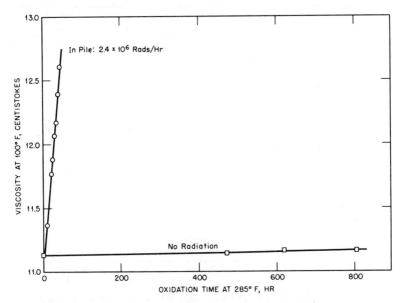

Fig. 9.13 Effect of reactor radiation on viscosity of octadecylbenzene containing 5% didodecyl selenide during oxidation. (From R. O. Bolt and J. G. Carroll, *Industrial and Engineering Chemistry,* Ref. 12.)

was the best of those tested. After a dose of about 1.2×10^8 rads at 285°F, oils containing optimum compounding yielded[12] the following percentage increase in viscosity at 100°F:

Octadecylbenzene	22–31
Dialkyl sebacate	40–42
Paraffinic mineral oil	153

Acidity also increased rapidly,[12] but similar values were obtained with all three oils.

Because of the great acceleration of oxidation by radiation, the size of the benefit derived from oxidation inhibitors is not clear. In one of the experiments conducted[12] in the Oak Ridge Graphite Reactor, an additional 4% didodecyl selenide was introduced midway in the test. The curves for acidity and viscosity showed discontinuity at this point and lower rates of change beyond it. This shows the effect of the additive. It is generally recognized that additives become less effective with continuing irradiation. Additives are also less effective in materials having a high inherent radiation stability.

Irradiation leaves a lubricant permanently damaged as far as oxidation susceptibility is concerned. Several lubricants were irradiated and then oxidized by bubbling oxygen through them. In all cases the preirradiated

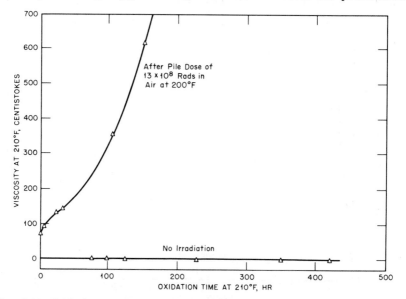

Fig. 9.14 Oxidation of preirradiated di(2-ethylhexyl) sebacate containing 5% didodecyl selenide. (From R. O. Bolt and J. G. Carroll, *Industrial and Engineering Chemistry*, Ref. 12.)

oils thickened more rapidly than the original unirradiated fluids.[12] Figure 9.14 illustrates the magnitude of this difference for a diester, one of the most susceptible fluids. The greater ease of oxidation of preirradiated oils testifies to the formation of more readily oxidized species and/or the destruction of the oxidation inhibitor as a result of irradiation. Those oils that were least affected by oxidation in the presence of radiation were also found to be the least susceptible to oxidation outside the reactor after preirradiation. Observations such as these prompted the intensive study[59,67] of poly(phenyl ethers) as lubricants.

As with other fluids, oxidation stability of the poly(phenyl ethers) is affected more by irradiation than are the other physical and performance properties. Although the stability loss from irradiation is much smaller with these highly aromatic fluids than with conventional lubricants, this property is still one of the most important factors governing service life.

Oxidation tests were conducted on poly(phenyl ethers) before and after electron irradiation. The tests were conducted at 500°F, where only the best materials survive oxidation even without radiation. The most resistant material tested was the high-melting *bis*(*p*-phenoxyphenyl) ether. The low-melting unsubstituted *meta* isomers and the liquid eutectic mixtures gave similar results.[60] The behavior of the *para* isomer is shown[67] in Fig. 9.15

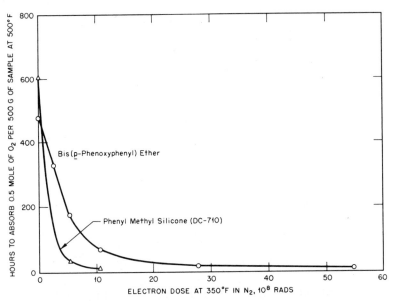

FIG. 9.15 Effect of preirradiation on oxidation stability at 500°F.

compared to a phenyl methyl silicone, which is itself quite stable to high-temperature oxidation in the absence of radiation. Irradiated samples absorbed oxygen rapidly for a short time, after which the absorption rate tended to become linear. *m*-Terphenyl showed approximately the same degree of sensitivity to radiation as the ether. Phenanthrene and an aromatic silane were moderately more resistant than the ether but were severely affected above 10^9 rads. A phenyl phthalate was considerably more susceptible to irradiation. The most stable alkyl[poly(phenyl ethers)], α-cumyl and *tert*-butyl compounds, were still considerably inferior[65] to the unsubstituted ethers. However, the highly irradiated poly-(phenyl ethers) were more resistant to oxidation than a typical unirradiated diester lubricant now used in jet engines.

Even with the inherently stable poly(phenyl ethers), increasing temperature severely degrades oxidation stability. The effect is devastating in the presence of radiation,[65] as shown in Fig. 9.16. The alkyl-substituted com-

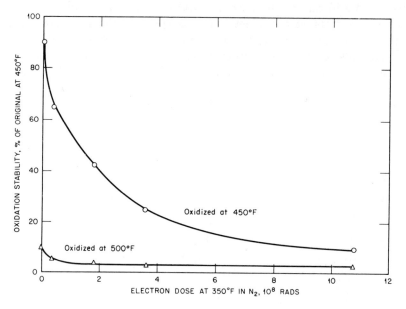

FIG. 9.16 Effect of temperature on the oxidation stability of a preirradiated fluid, p-(p-α-cumylphenoxy)-4-phenoxybenzene.

pound tested has a useful life of about 250 hr before irradiation. Either oxidation at 500°F or a small radiation dose drastically reduces[65] this useful life.

Below about 300°F the combined effects of oxidation and radiation vary less drastically with temperature. Diesters and similar lubricants can be considered for use at low doses. Even here, the temperature influence is significant,[12] as shown in Fig. 9.17 for acid formation in a diester.

According to a rule of thumb for a fluid saturated with oxygen, the oxidation rate doubles for each 18°F rise in temperature above 300°F. This means that an oil having a useful life of 1000 hr at 300°F could be useful for less than 3 hr at 450°F. Data[65] show that typical inhibited diester lubricants actually exceed this rate of decrease in stability with

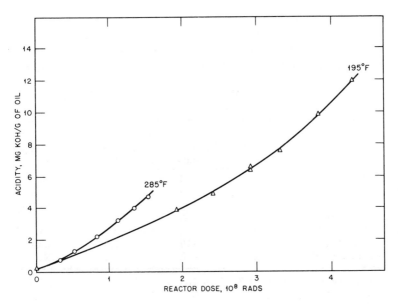

FIG. 9.17 Effect of temperature on oxidation of di(2-ethylhexyl) sebacate containing 5% didodecyl selenide in a reactor. (From R. O. Bolt and J. G. Carroll, *Industrial and Engineering Chemistry*, Ref. 12.)

increasing temperature. Concurrent irradiation merely hastens the demise of the fluids.

9-5 Finished Lubricants

9-5.1 COMMERCIAL OILS

9-5.1.1 *General*

Because nuclear radiation causes profound changes in lubricants, there arises the question of the useful limits of conventional materials: Are products that are commonly used in industrial practice completely useless in nuclear applications? This question prompted a survey[26] of the radiation resistance of commercial oils including several mineral oils typical of large refinery production. Common industrial, marine, and automotive oils were represented. All were off-the-shelf samples.

The oils were subjected to gamma radiation for doses of 10^8 rads to 7×10^8 rads. At the latter dose viscosity change at 100°F ranged from 60 to 600%. Typical results[26] at the 10^8 rad level are shown in Table 9.20. The general effects expected from the previous discussion were observed. All fluids darkened and acquired an acrid odor; all increased in viscosity except the auto-transmission fluid, which decreased in viscosity because of scission of the added polymer. Wear properties and load-carrying capacity of certain oils were enhanced by irradiation. Formation of radiolytic polymer improved the viscosity index of some of the materials. The effect of irradiation on compounding in the lubricants was particularly significant and may limit their application more than the effect on the base material.

Table 9.20 — CHANGES IN IRRADIATED MINERAL-
OIL-BASED PRODUCTS[a]

Fluid	Change in			
	Viscosity at 100°F, %	Viscosity index	Neutrality No., mg KOH/g	Copper corrosion
Turbine oil[b,c]	+15	+4	Nil	Nil
Machine oil[c]	+10	-3	+0.5	Increase
Steam-cylinder oil[c]	+23	0	Nil	Nil
Marine-engine oil[c]	+28	+3	Nil	Nil
Industrial gear[c]	+23	+1	Nil	Nil
MIL-L-2105 gear[c]	+18	-10	+0.15	Increase
Auto transmission[b,c]	-21	-18	+0.06	Nil

[a]Gamma dose of 10^8 rads at 75°F in air.
[b]Oxidation inhibited.
[c]Other compounding.

The release of strong acids from extreme-pressure agents (gear oils) and the breakdown of polymeric viscosity-index improvers (transmission fluids) illustrate this point. This survey[26] indicated that many commercial oils can be used in the presence of gamma radiation for doses of about 10^8 rads. This performance, however, may be restricted by factors not brought out, such as oxidizing conditions or unstable inhibitors.

9-5.1.2 Turbine Oils

Turbine oils are the principal lubricants used in conventional and nuclear steam power plants. They lubricate the turbine bearings and much of the accessory equipment. A modern turbine oil is made up of a well-refined mineral oil and various amounts of oxidation inhibitor, rust inhibitor, and foam preventive. In plants where the reactor coolant is also the working fluid, e.g., in the boiling-water reactor, the turbine must operate in a radiation field produced by the radioactive steam and impurities. Although early estimates[51] for a prototype indicate that radiation dose rates are negligible, large plants may impose a more stringent radiation environment. With this in mind the limits of performance of various turbine oils were investigated.

Ten fluids were studied[56] including fully formulated steam- and marine-turbine oils and the base stocks from which these were derived. Standard tests[2] were performed before and after gamma irradiation up to 2.7×10^8 rads. Of particular significance was the degradation of oxidation stability. This probably resulted from the direct destruction of the stabilizer and/or the formation of oxidizable entities in the oil. Finished oils lost 40% or more in oxidation life after a dose of 0.5×10^8 rads. The inhibitors were of only small benefit. These effects[56] are shown in Fig. 9.18.

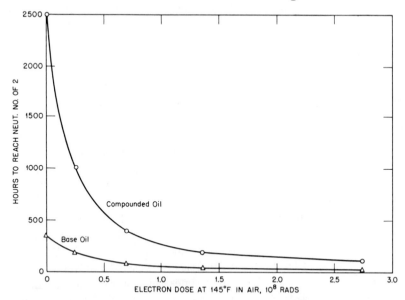

FIG. 9.18 Effect of irradiation on the oxidation stability of turbine oils. (From C. F. Kottcamp, R. P. Nejak, and R. T. Kern, *American Society of Lubrication Engineers Transactions*, Ref. 56.)

Other effects described previously were observed:

1. Foaming tendencies were increased for all oils after irradiation.

2. Rust resistance was impaired, probably owing to the degradation of the polar rust inhibitors. The addition of fresh rust inhibitor to the irradiated oils permitted them again to pass the rust test.

3. The load-carrying capacities of the compounded oils were adversely affected by the exposure. However, that of the base oils improved slightly. This effect again suggests the destruction of additives.

4. All the formulations studied evolved about 0.05 ml of gas per gram of oil per 10^6 rads. The gas was about 90% hydrogen with smaller quantities of methane, ethane, propane, and other hydrocarbons. Considering the over-all data[56] it appears that effects of radiation become limiting to the performance of turbine oils at dose levels of about 5×10^6 rads.

9-5.2 OILS OF ENHANCED RADIATION STABILITY

9-5.2.1 *Tests in the Oak Ridge Graphite Reactor*

In early experiments three oils were used[29] to lubricate miniaturized machinery operating in the reactor. The fluids, specially selected from previous static and oxidation test work, were di(2-ethylhexyl) sebacate, poly(propene oxide), and octadecylbenzene. All fluids contained iodobenzene, didodecyl selenide, and quinizarin. In addition, the diester contained 1-methylnaphthylene as a radiation-damage protector. Both low-speed (80 rpm) and high-speed (10,000 rpm) tests were made at 285°F. Identical runs were made outside the reactor for comparison with tests in the presence of radiation. For all tests the oils and the operating parts were examined.

The low-speed experiments involved a journal bearing operated for 55 to 105 hr. Thick lacquer coatings built up on the commutators and carbon brushes of the drive motors. This caused some early shutdowns. Both the wear data and the torque data indicated the lubricating ability of the poly(propene oxide) to be improved during irradiation, whereas the other two oils became poorer lubricants. Oil viscosity increased from 75 to 260% compared with increases of 16 to 41% in the reference out-of-pile tests. The in-pile dose was about 4×10^8 rads.

In the high-speed tests, air turbines supported by ball bearings were operated at 10,000 rpm both in the reactor and in the absence of radiation. These units ran for about 200 hr for a dose of 5×10^8 rads. Poly(propene oxide) was damaged least with an increase in viscosity of about 125%; the value for the diester was about four times this figure; that for the alkylbenzene was between these values. Damage to the oils[29] was roughly comparable to that in the low-speed tests for comparable doses.

The high-speed in-pile tests resulted in greater amounts of sludge and carbon formation than were observed in the reference tests. The deposits were noted on the wall and on the sides of the sumps and on the bearing housings. The bearings of the in-pile experiments were closer to failure at the completion of the tests. This resulted primarily from lacquer deposits on the bearings themselves rather than from mechanical damage.

On the basis of these limited tests at 285°F, it was concluded that the over-all lubrication process does not change under irradiation. Of the materials studied[29] the compounded poly(propene oxide) was the most satisfactory lubricant in the reactor. This was based on wear and torque data, cleanliness, and oil deterioration.

9-5.2.2 Fluids from Available Materials

Another investigation[24,25] had as its objective the development of oils of enhanced radiation stability from readily available ingredients. Oils in three viscosity grades were made from relatively radiation-resistant alkylbenzenes containing didodecyl selenide and quinizarin. Polybutene and polystyrene polymers were added to improve both viscosity and viscosity–temperature properties. The behavior of these polymers was described in Sect. 9-3.3. For reference standards 13 typical mineral oils meeting mili-

BASED ON ALKYL AROMATIC

0   10^9 5×10^9

GAMMA DOSAGE, RADS

BASED ON MINERAL OIL

0   10^9 5×10^9

GAMMA DOSAGE, RADS

Fig. 9.19 Radiolysis of lubricating oils following gamma dose at 75°F. (From J. G. Carroll and R. O. Bolt, *American Society of Lubrication Engineers Transactions*, Ref. 24.)

tary specifications were selected, three or more in each of the viscosity grades, light, medium, and heavy. The new radiation-resistant oils were first tested against the requirements in the conventional specifications. In general, the new materials were acceptable lubricants in these tests. The marginal properties, foaming, pour point, etc., were those which normally would be controlled or improved by additives.

All oils were exposed to gamma rays for nominal doses of up to about 70×10^8 rads. No mineral oils survived 40×10^8 rads. All were reduced to brittle, plastic solids.[24] Figure 9.19 shows their typical appearance. By contrast, all the special oils were still fluid and only slightly darkened after this dose. Figure 9.20 shows the radiation-induced viscosity change[24] for

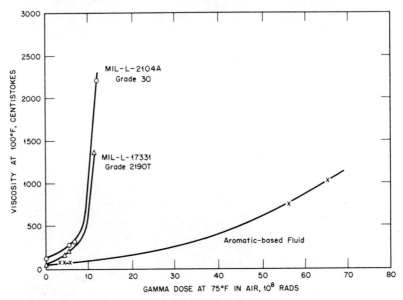

FIG. 9.20 Radiation-induced viscosity change of medium-grade oils. (From J. G. Carroll and R. O. Bolt, *American Society of Lubrication Engineers Transactions*, Ref. 24.)

medium-grade oils. Generally the higher the initial viscosity, the higher was the radiolytic viscosity increase. For all grades the aromatic-base lubricants were clearly superior. For noncritical uses (nonoxidizing conditions below 225°F), the new oils are probably usable to above 5×10^9 rads. This approaches the limits of radiation tolerance for fluid hydrocarbon lubricants. Two major oil companies have made available to industry a commercial line of radiation-resistant lubricants[5,54] made from readily available materials. The next step in producing further radiation stability is the use of completely aromatic compounds, i.e., materials with no substituents in the aromatic rings.

9-5.2.3 *Radiation-resistant High-temperature Lubricants*

Poly(phenyl ethers) are very promising materials for further and perhaps ultimate development for high-temperature use. The outstanding stability properties of these unsubstituted compounds were first discussed in Sect. 9-2.7. Characteristics of two such materials[64] are listed in Table 9.21 together with those of a diester for comparison.

Table 9.21 — PROPERTIES OF PROMISING POLY(PHENYL ETHERS)

	Bis(m-phen-oxyphenyl) ether	m- Bis (m-phen-oxyphenoxy)-benzene	Di(2-ethylhexyl) sebacate-based MIL-L-7808C lubricant
Pour point, °F	5	40	-75
Viscosity:			
At 100°F, centistokes	60.9	332	12.6
At 400°F, centistokes	1.34	2.04	1.07
At 700°F, centistokes	0.47	0.63	
Flash point, °F	465	540	458
Evaporation loss, wt. % at 500°F	33.3	3.62	96
Small-scale panel coke, at 800°F, mg	0.5	0.2	37
Initial thermal-decomposition temperature, °F	835	870	575
Oxidation stability, hours at 500°F to absorb 0.5 ml of oxygen/500 g of oil	280	330	0.3

The viscosity–temperature properties of poly(phenyl ethers) are good considering their highly aromatic structure. They are also quite stable to radiation-induced viscosity change, as discussed previously. The volatility of these compounds depends on their molecular weight and is also influenced by the molecular configuration. Flash points and fire points likewise depend on volatility. The ether linkage imparts good wear properties,[63] which approach those obtained with dialkyl sebacates. In general, *meta*-linked ethers have lower pour points than those with *para* linkages; however, mixed *para*- and *meta*-linked compounds are acceptable.

The over-all stability of poly(phenyl ethers) in preliminary work justified a program[17] to determine their performance in functional tests with and without radiation. Three fluids were tested:

1. Mixed-*bis*(mixed-phenoxyphenoxy)benzene, predominantly with *meta* linkages and termed 5P4E (5-phenyl-4-ether).
2. *Bis*(mixed-phenoxyphenyl) ether, predominantly *meta* linkages and termed 4P3E.
3. MIL-L-9236A, a military specification lubricant[101] for high-temperature use. (The formulation is proprietary, but the base fluid is a substituted ester.)

The fluids were evaluated for oxidation, for panel coking,† and for film strength in gear and bearing rigs. Radiation was provided during test by a 3-Mev Van de Graaff generator.

In oxidation-corrosion tests at 500°F, the poly(phenyl ethers) were more stable to viscosity increase, acid formation, and over-all decomposition[17] than the reference fluid, as shown in Table **9.22**. Metal corrosion for all three fluids was small.

Table 9.22 — OXIDATION STABILITY OF POLY(PHENYL ETHERS)[a]

	5P4E		4P3E		MIL-L-9236A[b]	
Electron dose, 10^8 rads	0	1	0	1	0	1
Viscosity increase:						
At 100°F, %	19.8	68	9.8	43	1220	1180
At 210°F, %	8.5	27	5.0	20	425	448
Neutralization No., mg KOH/g	1.2	2.2	0.9	2.2	0.9	13.5
Decomposition, % unchanged	87	94	75	71	37	24

[a]Forty-eight hours at 500°F, 5 liters of air per hour, 100 ml of oil.
[b]Not a poly(phenyl ether); typically a substituted ester base oil.

Panel coking tests without radiation showed that the poly(phenyl ethers) produced less coke at temperatures at least 200°F higher than the reference oil. Tests with concurrent electron irradiation were unsuccessful. The oil droplets were repelled from the heated plate by an electrostatic effect. Careful observation of this effect indicated that it was real,[17] although not understood.

The three fluids were tested in a closed circuit[17] (four square) gear rig. An air flow of 40 ml per gram of lubricant per hour was used. The gears were run at no load because for all fluids the viscosity above 400°F was low enough that scoring occurred immediately if a load of 288 lb per inch of face was applied.

After all tests the gears were in excellent condition. Interestingly enough gear performance was not impaired by the extensive lubricant degradation;

† The test oil is splashed against a hot metal plate, and the deposited carbonaceous residue is weighed and reported in milligrams at the temperature of the plate.

Table 9.23 — DEGRADATION OF LUBRICANTS IN GEAR TESTS [a,b]

	5P4E				4P3E	MIL-L-9236A	
Temperature, °F	600		800		700	500	
Electron dose, 10^8 rads	0	10	0	1	10	0	5
Viscosity increase:							
At 100°F, %	23	4150	443	2320	14,315	28.6	42,400
At 210°F, %	8	327	107	253	861	18.1	6,310
Neutralization No., mg KOH/g	2.4	19.5	2.5	2.2	4.4	4.0	17.4
Decomposition, % unchanged	99.5	62	83	63	49	78	19
Load-carrying capacity at end of test, lb/in.	860	860	860	860	568	568	1.132

[a]Spur gears, 6 DP, SAE 2212 steel, Rockwell hardness C60, 20 μin.
[b]Twelve-hour test, no load, 3200 rpm.

Table 9.24— DEGRADATION OF LUBRICANTS IN BEARING TESTS[a,b]

	5P4E			4P3E		MIL-L-9236A	
Temperature, °F	600	600	800	600	600	500	500
Electron dose, 10^8 rads	0	10	1	0	10	0	5
Viscosity increase:							
At 100°F, %	20	5076		1970	11	60	3163
At 210°F, %	9	406		312	5	17	1100
Neutralization No., mg KOH/g	0.2	9.5		12.3	3.8	2.8	17.9
Decomposition, % unchanged	99	61	42	69	94	88	22
Bearing condition:							
Wear	Very light	Light	Very heavy	Light	Nil	Very light	Light
Deposits	Nil			Med.	Nil	Nil	Heavy
Increase in case pressure (friction), psi	1	0.3	>10	>10	0	0.1	>10

[a] Twelve-hour test, 200-lb axial load, 40,000 rpm.
[b] Twenty-five millimeter ball bearings.

this illustrates the tolerance that some systems have for large lubricant property changes. Representative data[17] are given in Table 9.23.

The three fluids were tested[17] in ball bearings. An oil jet impinged 70 g of oil per minute on the bearing through which oxidizing air flowed at a rate of 40 ml of air per gram of oil per hour. The five-ring ether effectively lubricated the bearing at 800°F and 10^8 rads. The four-ring ether was satisfactory at 600°F and 5×10^8 rads. However, at 600°F and 10^9 rads, bearing friction became excessive in two runs owing to viscosity increase and to deposits in the bearing. Thus the heavier 5P4E was clearly superior for use in high-temperature bearings in the presence of radiation. The reference oil was satisfactory at 500°F with no radiation and was still acceptable after 10^8 rads. However, a dose of 5×10^8 rads brought on excessive decomposition and bearing friction. Representative data[17] are shown in Table 9.24.

9-5.3 LUBRICATING GREASES

As discussed in Sect. 9-3.4, the following changes occur in greases as a result of exposure to ionizing radiation:

1. Initial attack on the gelling agent and structure to cause softening below about 10^8 rads.
2. Later cross linking and polymerization of the oil to cause hardening above about 10^8 rads.

The 10^8-rad level is arbitrary; actually, it may be as low as 10^7 rads for silicone oils or as high as 10^{10} rads for inorganic gelling agents. Each oil, gelling agent, and inhibitor is a separate case. These components have all been reviewed individually in earlier sections. Here, radiation effects for several typical greases are reported in terms of the properties that control actual performance.

9-5.3.1 *General Effects*

Effects of gelling-agent identity on consistency changes in the radiolysis of greases have already been discussed in Sect. 9-3.4. In an investigation of effects of the base-oil component,[13] several experimental greases were made from a sodium terephthalamate. These, together with several commercial greases, with and without inhibitors, were irradiated and subjected to standard tests.[98] Consistency change for several products after irradiation[13] is shown in Table 9.25. The type of oil exerts a large influence. The aromatic and the polyether fluids were best. However, with the polyether, changes in properties other than consistency were less satisfactory.

The performance of all greases in standard bearing tests[93,98] was shortened markedly by irradiation.[13,28] Typical changes[28] are shown in Fig. 9.21. Initial points are averages; other points are individual runs. For the three

Table 9.25 — RADIOLYTIC CHANGE IN CONSISTENCY
FOR TEREPHTHALAMATE GREASES

Oil[a]	Gamma dose, 10^8 rads	Change in ASTM worked penetration[b]
Mineral oil	6	+7
	22	Hard[c]
Polyether	5	-34
	19	+8
	52	Hard[c]
Diester	5	+2
	17	Hard[c]
Alkylnaphthalene	12	+76
	27	+116

[a] Oxidation inhibited.
[b] + = softer, - = harder.
[c] Too hard for measurement.

greases in Fig. 9.21, the percentage of initial bearing life remaining after 5.5×10^8 rads was

     6% for the polyether–terephthalamate at 250°F
     36% for the mineral oil–sodium soap at 300°F
     62% for the alkylnaphthalene–terephthalamate at 300°F

(All formulations contained 5 wt. % didodecyl selenide.)

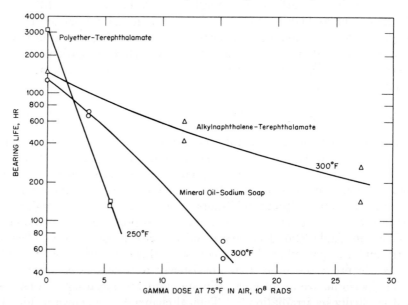

FIG. 9.21 Impairment of grease performance by irradiation. Greases inhibited with 5% didodecyl selenide; 204 ball bearings at 10,000 rpm. (From J. G. Carroll, R. O. Bolt, and B. W. Hotten, *Lubrication Engineering*, Ref. 28.)

Other standard tests[98] were run on these irradiated greases. At the 5×10^8-rad level, the following general observations[28] were made:

1. Low-temperature torque was impaired to a minor degree.
2. Copper corrosivity, evaporation at 300°F, and wear properties were not greatly altered.
3. Oxidation stability was sharply impaired.

These general observations were supported by results[90] from the irradiation of some 50 greases conforming to various military specifications. Gamma doses were around 10^8 rads at 75°F.

9-5.3.2 Commercial Greases

As with oils the question arises: just how much radiation can be withstood by off-the-shelf products? For an answer to this question, several commercial greases have been tested before and after irradiation at up to 7×10^8 rads. Changes[26] in consistency and dropping point are shown in Table 9.26.

Table 9.26 — RADIOLYTIC CHANGES IN COMMERCIAL GREASES[a]

Gelling agent	Wt. %	Viscosity of mineral oil at 100°F, Saybolt Seconds (Universal)	Change in ASTM		Dropping point
			Penetration[b]		
			Unworked	Worked	
Sodium soap[c]	28	490	-10	+62	+6
Calcium soap[d]	18	600	+27	+67	0
Aluminum soap	11	1175	+77	+14	
Lithium-calcium soap[c,d]	16	140	+32	+45	+5
Sodium salt[c,d,e]	12	628	-7	+1	0

[a] Gamma dose of 10^8 rads at 75°F in air.
[b] + = softer, - = harder.
[c] Oxidation inhibited.
[d] Other compounding.
[e] Sodium N-octadecylterephthalamate.

The similarity of base stocks affords another comparison of the gelling agents. The aromatic-salt grease was clearly superior in consistency change. Those greases with a pronounced change in physical properties also showed drastic changes in fiber structure of the gelling agent (see Fig. 9.11). The sodium-salt grease and the lithium–calcium grease lost 80 and 55%, respectively, of their preirradiation bearing performance after 10^8 rads. At the higher dose of 7×10^8 rads, all greases continued to soften.[26]

9-5.3.3 Greases for Enhanced Radiation Resistance

Both radiation-stable oils and gelling agents are needed for greases in this category. The improved oil postpones eventual hardening, whereas the improved gelling agent reduces the magnitude of initial softening. Aromatic compounds, with their superior resistance to radiolysis, can be used in both portions of the grease. One example of this approach is an alkyl-biphenyl oil gelled with a sodium N-octadecylterephthalamate, available commercially as NRRG 159.[†]

This material has been tested considerably. For example, a series of tests was made[11] on a sample exposed to 7×10^8 rads of gamma radiation at 75°F. Worked penetration increased from 261 to 330, but work stability[‡] actually improved. Oxidation stability at 250°F worsened. However, bearing performance at 300 and 350°F was 25 and 50%, respectively, of original values. The product was also soft and smooth after a reactor dose of 16×10^8 rads. In further work NRRG 159 was tested[23] with 0.6-in.-bore ball bearings at 6500 rpm in special motors operating in the Materials Testing Reactor. Bearing temperatures were about 150°F. In helium two tests reached 14×10^8 rads (1450 hr of running time) without failure; a third failed at 34×10^8 rads (3470 hr of running time).

The use of inorganic gelling agents practically eliminates concern for the welfare of this grease component. In one series of experiments, several inorganic gelling agents were tried in various base oils. On the basis of bearing tests, an alkylbenzene–silica[§] grease[¶] was most attractive.[13] In other work, greases were made in four consistency grades from 233 to 366 worked penetration and tested before and after gamma irradiation. All materials were reduced to viscous fluids by working after a dose of 40×10^8 rads in air or in helium.[14] This apparently anomalous softening can be explained in one of two ways:

1. Damage to the silica, possibly agglomeration because the initial particle size was about 0.01 μ.
2. Attack on the gel structure, probably via surface adsorption on the silica of radiolysis products in the oil.

The latter explanation is more acceptable because silica greases display similar behavior after exposure to oxidation or heat. Even so, the silica–alkylbenzene greases can be used successfully in very high radiation fields as long as temperature remains below about 225°F and rotation speeds do not exceed about 4000 rpm. Similar results were observed for silica-thickened mineral oil greases in which the oil was rich in naphthenes and aromatics (APL 700 and 701, Shell Oil Co.).

Dyestuffs, another type of nonsoap gelling agent, have been used in radiation-resistant greases. Some success was found with a mineral oil

[†] Standard Oil Co. of California.
[‡] Penetration after 100,000 strokes.
[§] Estersil, E. I. du Pont de Nemours and Co., Inc.
[¶] NRRG-300, Standard Oil Co. of California.

gelled with Indanthrene Blue.† After an electron exposure[49] of 8×10^8 rads, the grease performed in postirradiation tests as follows:

ASTM worked penetration, % decrease	3
Oxidation: psi O_2 uptake, % increase	
At 100 hr	200
At 200 hr	125
Bearing test: hours at 300°F, % decrease	60

9-5.3.4 Dynamic Tests

There is a good case for subjecting lubricants to radiation, thermal, oxidation, and mechanical stresses simultaneously, i.e., so-called "dynamic testing." Sometimes such tests are more severe than irradiating the lubricant separately and then determining its performance in functional tests.

These considerations led to the idea of conducting standard lubricant bench tests in a radiation environment. In one such grease evaluation,[20] electric motors were operated at 3350 rpm in a gamma source. The ball bearings of one unit were lubricated with a sodium soap–mineral oil grease‡ and operated for 1058 hr with a bearing temperature of about 300°F. The lubricant accumulated a total dose of 35×10^8 rads. Interestingly this product performed better than would have been predicted from static irradiation results. The static sample of the grease exposed adjacent to the bearings was hard, rubbery, and no longer a lubricant. The material was too hard either to work or to show an unworked penetration. In previous static irradiations this grease was similarly too hard after 21×10^8 rads but was still fluid in postirradiation tests after 15×10^8 rads. This dynamic test showed that the shear action of the operating bearing extended the radiation threshold slightly for this particular grease.

The progressive degradation of greases under combined irradiation, oxidation, and mechanical working was evaluated[49] in other experiments. A Shell roll tester was modified and operated in a gamma source. The apparatus permitted periodic examination of the grease under dynamic irradiation conditions; work stability is the parameter most sensitive to irradiation.

The apparatus was used with a series of greases prepared by thickening an alkylated naphthalene with representative nonsoap gelling agents. Three of these, indanthrene, hydrophobic silica, and a clay, exhibited little change in consistency at 4×10^8 rads. The alkylated naphthalene, however, was limited by volatility to applications not exceeding 200°F. Therefore a carefully selected aromatic mineral oil fraction was substituted, and addi-

---

† N,N'-Dihydro-1,2,2',1'-anthroquinoneazine, General Aniline & Film Corp.
‡ Chevron OHT Grease, Standard Oil Co. of California.

tional tests were performed. Several of the modified greases were exposed to 8×10^8 rads with 3-Mev electrons. The grease made with indanthrene proved markedly superior. It was concluded[49] that these greases would provide satisfactory performance at temperatures up to 300°F and at radiation doses up to about 10^8 rads. The dyestuff indanthrene was considered sufficiently radiation resistant that greases based on it would be limited in performance only by the stability of the base oil.

9-5.4 ENGINE OILS

Aircraft gas turbines impose severe thermal, oxidative, and mechanical stresses on a lubricant. If nuclear radiation is added to this environment, the lubricant requirements indeed become severe. Poly(phenyl ethers) are likely candidates for this use but are not completely compatible with present engine systems. Presently used engine oils[96] are basically diesters that contain an antioxidant (e.g., phenothiazine) and sometimes a wear additive (e.g., tricresyl phosphate).

The film strength of this type lubricant was found not to be impaired[65,87] by gamma irradiation up to about 2.5×10^8 rads. Indeed the 10^8-rad level improved load-carrying ability.[65] At 2.5×10^8 rads, coking at 600°F was worsened by a factor of 20. These and other data[65] on a typical engine oil are given in Table 9.27.

Table 9.27 — TEST RESULTS ON TYPICAL IRRADIATED
MIL-L-7808 LUBRICANT

Gamma dose at 75°F, 10^8 rads in air	0	0.25	0.8	2.5
Viscosity:				
At 210°F, centistokes	3.27	3.43	3.60	4.30
At 100°F, centistokes	12.7	13.1	14.0	17.7
At -65°F, centistokes	10,120	9,760	13,930	17,980
Flash point, °F	460	460	455	460
Evaporation, wt. % (6 1/2 hr at 400°F)	7.7	10.8	11.2	15.0
Coking at 600°F, mg	5	13	74	91
Gear test, lb/in. of face	2,180	2,210	2,090	2,250
Oxidation at 347°F:				
Change in 100°F viscosity, %	2.6	1.3	13.2	22.1
Change in neutralization No., mg KOH/g	0.2	1.9	3.6	3.8

Irradiation lowered coking at 600°F for several neat diesters, mineral oils, and alkyl polyethers. Several inhibitors also reduced coking. However, the presence of more than one additive usually caused coking to increase[27,65] with gamma irradiation at the 10^8-rad level. Most combinations showed markedly worse coking at 700°F after irradiation.

An engine oil based on an alkyl(diphenyl ether) showed good stability in most properties to about 10^9 rads. Coking of the base oil, however, was comparatively high at 700°F. An alternate alkylbiphenyl base fluid also showed high coking values at 700°F. For both fluids coking was reduced appreciably by inclusion of an alkyl selenide antioxidant and also certain high-boiling-point materials, such as a petroleum bright stock.[11]

The poly(phenyl ethers) and their selected alkyl derivatives showed comparatively small increases in coking at 700 and 800°F after irradiation for 5 to 10×10^8 rads. Coking at 800°F was two or three times[65] that obtained with the unirradiated materials. However, the coking values for these materials were still very much lower than values of most ordinary lubricants even before irradiation (see Sect. 9-5.2.3).

Droegemueller and Clark report[40] sudden and drastic changes in the physical properties of lubricants during dynamic tests. These experiments were conducted in an oil coker and also in a high-temperature bearing rig in which gamma radiation input during a test was at the rate of about 2×10^6 rads/hr. Doses totaled about 10^7 rads. This exposure under static conditions normally brings about only small changes in the physical properties of these lubricants. In similar dynamic test work,[42,57] 41 engine oils were investigated with the following conclusions.

1. Static irradiation causes changes in some properties at doses as low as 10^6 rads, but gross changes in many materials occur only above 10^8 rads.
2. Mechanical tests can evaluate gross differences in performance between different lubricants as well as ascertain the effects of additives.
3. Preirradiation of the materials affect behavior in the test machines, either improving or impairing performance.
4. Mechanical evaluation in an irradiation environment is more severe than preirradiation followed by tests in the absence of radiation.

9-5.5 HYDRAULIC FLUIDS

These materials must generally operate over the widest range of temperatures of any lubricants. In practice typical hydraulic fluid formulations are based on a low-viscosity base oil. To this is added a high-molecular-weight polymer for improvement of both viscosity and viscosity–temperature characteristics. Wear additives may also be present. The effects of radiation on these components were reviewed in previous sections. This section covers briefly (1) radiation effects on typical commercially available hydraulic-fluid formulations and (2) available test work in dynamic systems.

9-5.5.1 *Fluid Types*

The classic mineral-oil hydraulic fluid[94] is defined by Military Specification MIL-O-5606. The fluid typically contains a polyester and tricresyl phosphate. In general, the behavior of the fluid on irradiation follows patterns suggested by foregoing discussions. The early destruction of the polyester reduces viscosity to about that of the base oil. Radiolysis products of the aryl phosphate contribute to the degradation of the fluid. These effects become measurable at about 5×10^6 rads and become excessive at about ten times this dose.

Two silicate-based fluids[95] are currently being used extensively at temperatures up to about 400°F: HTHF 8200† is based on a disiloxane fluid, and OS-45‡ is an ortho silicate fluid. Summaries[88] of radiation effects on each of these fluids are given in Tables 9.28 and 9.29, respectively. On the

Table 9.28 — TEST RESULTS ON IRRADIATED HTHF 8200 HYDRAULIC FLUID

Gamma dose at 75°F, 10^8 rads in air	0	0.8	4	8.3[a]
Viscosity: At 210°F, centistokes At 100°F, centistokes	12.1 34.0	9.85 29.9	20.7 74.3	97.3 425
Flash point, °F	405	235	170	120
Neutralization No., mg KOH/g	0.01	0.03	0.2	0.3
Evaporation, wt. % (6 1/2 hr at 400°F)	22	17	17	16
Gas evolution, ml/g	0	2.8	12.9	

[a] Solidified at 10^9 rads.

basis of physical-property changes, both can be used to about 10^8 rads. The changes in the physical properties of these fluids can be explained entirely on the basis of previous discussions. The initial viscosity decreases reflect depolymerization of the viscosity-index improver. The lowering of the flash point indicates formation of low-molecular-weight radiolysis products in both fluids. Gas evolution may become a problem above 10^8 rads because it is involved with the compressibility[80] of the fluids, an

† Available from Oronite Division of California Chemical Company.
‡ Available from Monsanto Chemical Co.

Table 9.29 — TEST RESULTS ON IRRADIATED OS 45 HYDRAULIC FLUID

Gamma dose at 75°F, 10^8 rads in air	0	0.1	2.5	8.3
Viscosity: At 210°F, centistokes At 100°F, centistokes	3.92 12.0	3.16 10.5	3.83 14.1	8.02 36
Flash point, °F	375	230	165	110
Evaporation, wt. % (6 1/2 hr at 400°F)	19	33	33	31
Gas evolution, ml/g	0	2.5	8	22

important property for hydraulic fluids. Oxidation stability becomes impaired below the 10^8-rad level.

Alkylaromatic materials have been utilized to develop high-temperature radiation-resistant hydraulic fluids. These base oils were discussed previously. The radiation effects[11] on a typical finished fluid† are shown in Table 9.30. This aromatic product can probably be used to about 10×10^8 rads.

Table 9.30 — TEST RESULTS ON AN ALKYLAROMATIC HYDRAULIC FLUID[a]

Gamma dose at 75°F, 10^8 rads in air	0	1	5	11
Viscosity: At 210°F, centistokes At 100°F, centistokes	12.0 85.3	9.84 70.2	10.2 82.6	13.4 122
Flash point, °F	480	460	430	280
Neutralization No., mg KOH/g	0.17	0.01	Nil	1.3
Gas evolution, ml/g	0	1.1	7.5	11.4

[a] NRRO-216.

9-5.5.2 Circulating Tests

Tests in a pumping system are a necessary part of hydraulic fluid evaluations. Typical experiments of this sort were conducted on HTHF 8200 (disiloxane base) and Fluid 0-1A‡ (alkylbenzene base) to investigate the effects of irradiation. Operation of the aircraft piston type pump was at 3000 psi for 150 hr at 160°F followed by 100 hr at 275°F. Pump performance[47] in terms of efficiency and delivery was satisfactory on both fluids before and after irradiation to 4 to 7×10^8 rads.

† NRRO-216, Standard Oil Co. of California.
‡ NRRO-358, Standard Oil Co. of California.

For irradiated 8200 fluid the lowered flash point and impaired oxidation stability did not reduce pump performance; the relatively high viscosity (see Table 9.28) probably helped to reduce wear rates below those for the original material. The fluid based on an alkylbenzene showed somewhat higher wear after irradiation, probably due in part to the hostility to copper of radiolytic derivatives of the selenide inhibitor used. After irradiation the aromatic fluid also showed some lacquer and sludge formation. This doubtless resulted[47] in large part from the low thermal stability of the polymer additive. The pump tests were in a nitrogen atmosphere, which, of course, mitigated oxidative damage to the fluids.

A problem peculiar to high-performance hydraulic systems pertains to gas entrained in the fluid. If the gas exceeds saturation and becomes a separate phase, the response characteristics of the system become spongy. This is untenable. Irradiation, of course, causes hydraulic fluids to evolve gas. For a gamma dose of 2.5×10^8 rads, gas evolution of 13.4, 12.2, and 3.2 ml/g was reported[80] for MIL-0-5606, HTHF 8200, and for an alkyl (diphenyl ether), respectively. For all three fluids the gas was about 90% hydrogen.

The effects of this gas were determined by measuring the bulk modulus or isothermal compressibility of the fluids with hydrogen present for both one- and two-phase systems up to 5000 psi and 300°F. A large reduction in bulk modulus was noted when the gas was present in sufficient quantity to form a separate phase. Dissolved hydrogen caused only a small reduction. In effect, this means that the pressure on a hydraulic system must be kept above the saturation pressure of the quantity of gas anticipated. For operation in a radiation field, two solutions must be considered:

1. Use of aromatic fluids that evolve less gas than other types of fluids.
2. Bleeding of the dissolved hydrogen from the system.

The effect of radiolytic gas upon the response characteristics of a hydraulic system was investigated[74] further. A typical flight-control system was operated with HTHF 8200 at 200°F and 3000 psi in a gamma radiation field of about 1.5×10^5 rads/hr. The sensitive system operated successfully for more than 120 hr through a gamma dose of 1.8×10^7 rads with no perceptible effect. Mechanical malfunction not related to irradiation precluded further observations. From static irradiations gas evolution of about 0.5 ml per gram of oil would be predicted for this dose.

9-6 Principles

The following may be helpful to the reader in reducing the information in this chapter to the practice of lubrication in the presence of nuclear radiation:

1. The identity of the organic base fluid is the most important factor in resistance to irradiation; base materials vary a thousandfold in their

susceptibility to radiolysis. An approximate order of stability is this: polyphenyls > poly(phenyl ethers) > alkylaromatics > aliphatic ethers > mineral oils > aromatic esters > aliphatic esters > silicones > aromatic phosphates.

2. Oil lubricants, in general, can be classified according to dose ranges as follows:

a. 10^6 rads or below; no unusual problem from radiation.

b. 10^6 to 10^7 rads; methyl silicones, aliphatic diesters, and phosphate esters become affected; polymers in solution degrade. For most other cases other environmental factors are controlling.

c. 10^7 to 10^8 rads; radiation effects on physical properties render diesters and certain mineral oils marginal in performance. Oxidation stability and thermal stability are adversely affected for all fluids. Some lubricants are usable; some are marginal in this range.

d. 10^8 to 10^9 rads; oxidation and thermal stability of most lubricants are seriously impaired. Major changes occur in most physical properties. Aliphatic ethers, aromatic esters, and certain mineral oils (carefully selected) may be used.

e. 10^9 to 10^{10} rads; polyphenyls, poly(phenyl ethers), or alkylaromatics are recommended.

f. 10^{10} rads or above; radiation becomes extremely limiting. Lubrication with even the best organic oils is very restricted, and laminar solids should be considered for use.

3. Additives normally used in lubricants, e.g., antioxidants, antiwear agents, EP agents, and antifoam agents, suffer radiation damage. Their depletion during irradiation, or their radiolysis products, can cause complications below radiation levels at which the base oil degrades.

4. Selected additives reduce radiation damage in base oils. They are most effective in the least stable fluids. However, greater gains can be made by choosing base stocks judiciously than by attempting to improve unstable fluids by the use of additives.

5. Oxidation drastically reduces the life of a lubricant; radiation accelerates oxidation.

6. The role of temperature is interrelated to that of oxygen, additives, and radiation dose. Radiation damage is generally a minor function of temperature below about 300°F.

7. Under irradiation, greases first soften because of damage to the gel structure and then harden because of cross linking of the oil. Conventional greases are usable to about 10^7 rads. Special products are available for use from 10^9 to 5×10^9 rads.

8. Many machine elements have some tolerance for degraded lubri-

cants. In some cases (see Chap. 9, Sects. 9-5.3.4 and 9-5.5.2), a system will function for a higher radiation dose than would be predicted from the static radiolytic changes in a critical physical property.

References

Several of the following were cited in the text as authority for statements made. Others were not quoted but are included because they contain pertinent information. All were consulted in the preparation of this chapter.

1. Albrecht, T. W., Radiation Effects on Organo-Silicons, in *Third Semiannual Radiation Effects Symposium, October 28-30, 1958,* Vol. 5, Lockheed Nuclear Products.

2. American Society for Testing Materials, *The 1958 Book of ASTM Standards, Part 7, Petroleum Products, Lubricants, Tank Measurements, Engine Tests,* Philadelphia, Pa., 1959.

3. Andrew, A., *Test Schedules for Radiation-Resistant Lubricants,* British Report AERE-JCJ-TM-O1D, published in 1958.

4. Anon., Radiation-Resistant Greases—Gamma Test Rig at Harwell, *Nuclear Power, 5*(55): 111 (November 1960).

5. Anon., Radiation-Resistant Oils and Greases, *Nucleonics, 18*(4): 124 (April 1960).

6. Anon., Dry Film Good Lubricant, *Chem. Eng. News, 37*(38): 25 (September 1959).

7. Anon., Dynamic Tests Spark Nuclear Program, *Lubrication Eng., 13*(7): 380 (July 1957).

8. Anon., Atomic Experiments Develop Radiation-Resistant Lubricants, *Oil Gas J., 55*(34): 97 (August 1957).

9. Bolt, R. O., and Carroll, J. G., Constant Viscosity Radiation-Resistant Lubricant and Method of Using Same, U. S. Patent No. 2,943,056, June 28, 1960.

10. Bolt, R. O., Carroll, J. G., Harrington, R., and Giberson, R. C., Organic Lubricants and Polymers for Nuclear Power Plants, in *Proceedings of the Second International Conference on the Peaceful Uses of Atomic Energy, Geneva 1958,* Vol. 29, p. 276, United Nations, New York, 1959.

11. Bolt, R. O., and Carroll, J. G., *Effects of Radiation on Aircraft Lubricants and Fuels,* Report WADC-TR-56-646 (Part II), April 1958.

12. Bolt, R. O., and Carroll, J. G., The Radiolysis and Radiolytic Oxidation of Lubricants, *Ind. Eng. Chem., 50*(2): 221 (February 1958).

13. Bolt, R. O., Carroll, J. G., Hotten, B. W., and Calish, S. R., *Radiation-resistant Greases,* USAEC Report AECU-3148, California Research Corp., June 1956.

14. Bolt, R. O., Carroll, J. G., and Wright, J. R., *Radiation-resistant Lubricants— Their Development and Status,* USAEC Report TID-5186 (Del.), California Research Corp., June 1954.

15. Bolt, R. O., Carroll, J. G., and Fontana, B. J., *Research on the Radiation Stability of Organic Fluids,* USAEC Report TID-5148 (Del.), California Research Corp., October 1953.

16. Bolt, R. O., and Carroll, J. G., *Research on the Radiation Stability of Organic Fluids,* USAEC Report TID-5094 (Del.), California Research Corp., July 1952.

17. Borsoff, V. N., Beaubien, S. J., and Kerlin, W. W., *High Temperature Lubrication in the Presence of Nuclear Radiation,* Report WADD-TR-60-424, Shell Development Co., June 1960.

18. Bremer, Allen F., *Basic Lubrication Practice,* Reinhold Publishing Corp., New York, 1955.

19. Brooks, H. B., Cedel, A. E., and Haley, F. A., *The Effects of Radiation on Selected Materials—Insulators, Lubricants, Fluids, Metals,* Report NARF-59-26T, Convair, July 1959.
20. California Research Corporation, *Effects of Radiation on Aircraft Lubricants and Fuels,* Quarterly Progress Report, p. 10, February 1957.
21. Calish, S. R., Pino, M. A., and Wilgus, D. R., *Development of Nuclear Radiation-resistant Hydraulic Fluids,* WADC-TR-59-252, California Research Corp., April 1959.
22. Calkins, V. P., and Collins, C. G., General Radiation Damage Problems for Lubricant and Bearing Type Materials, *Am. Soc. Lubrication Engrs. Trans., 1* (1): 87 (April 1958).
23. Carroll, J. G., Bolt, R. O., Cunniff, C. E., and Heyl, P. T., Field Tests on a Radiation-Resistant Grease, *Lubrication Eng., 18*(2): (February 1962).
24. Carroll, J. G., and Bolt, R. O., Development of Radiation-Resistant Oils, *Am. Soc. Lubrication Engrs. Trans., 2*(1): 1–6 (April 1959).
25. Carroll, J. G., and Bolt, R. O., *Development of Radiation Resistant Oils,* USAEC Report AECU-3764, California Research Corp., June 1958.
26. Carroll, J. G., and Calish, S. R., Some Effects of Gamma Radiation on Commercial Lubricants, *Lubrication Eng., 13*(7): 338 (July 1957).
27. Carroll, J. G., Organic Selenides and Coking of Irradiated Gas Turbine Oils, in *First Semiannual Radiation Effects Symposium, Fort Worth, Texas, May 22–23, 1957,* Report NARF-57-19T, Vol. 1, Convair 1957.
28. Carroll, J. G., Bolt, R. O., and Hotten, B. W., Radiation Resistant Greases, *Lubrication Eng., 13*(3): 136 (March 1957).
29. Carroll, J. G., and Bolt, R. O., Lubrication in the Presence of Nuclear Radiation, *Lubrication Eng., 12*(5): 305 (September 1956).
30. Charlesby, A., Effect of Molecular Weight on the Crosslinking of Siloxanes by High Energy Radiation, *Nature, 173*(4406): 679 (April 1954).
31. Clark, J. M., and Lawrason, G. C., The Behavior of Radiation Resistant ANP Turbine Lubricants, *S.A.E. Journal, 66*(12): 77 (December 1958).
32. Colichman, E. L., and Fish, R. F., Resistance of Terphenyls to Heat and Radiation, *Nucleonics, 15*(2): 72 (February 1957).
33. Collins, C. G., and Calkins, V. P., *Radiation Damage to Elastomers, Plastics, and Organic Liquids,* USAEC Report APEX-261, General Electric Company, September 1956.
34. Convair Div., Gen. Dynamics Corp., *Results of System Panels Test Number 2, Addendum 5,* Report NARF-58-IT (Add. 5), Convair, September 1958.
35. Cooper, L. A., and Davies, B. R., Lubrication Problems at Nuclear Power Stations, *Sci. Lubrication (London), 9*(8): 31 (August 1957).
36. Cosgrove, S. L., *The Effect of Radiation on Lubricants and Hydraulic Fluids,* Report REIC 4, Battelle Memorial Institute, April 1958.
37. Cosgrove, S. L., The Effect of Radiation on Lubricants and Hydraulic Fluids, Report REIC 4 (2nd Add.) Battelle Memorial Institute, March 1960.
38. Currin, C. G., *Effects of Gamma Radiation on Silicone Dielectrics, Am. Inst. Elec. Engrs.* Conference Paper 58-289, February 1958.
39. David, V. W., and Irving, R., Shell Research Ltd., Chester, England, Effect of Nuclear Radiation on Hydrocarbon Oils, Greases, and Some Synthetic Fluids, in *Proceedings of the Conference on Lubrication and Wear,* Institute of Mechanical Engineers, London, 1957.
40. Droegemueller, E. A., and Clark, J. M., Dynamic Radiation Effects on Hydro-

carbon Fluids Under Thermal, Oxidative, and Mechanical Stress, in *Second Radiation Effects Symposium*, October 1957, Vol. 4, Battelle Memorial Institute.

41. Dvorak, H. R., Weakest-Link Method Helps System Design for Radiation Environments, *Space/Aeronautics*, *30*(6): 20–21 (December 1958).

42. Fainman, M. Z., Reynolds, O. P., Wolford, O. C., and Kaufman, E. D., *The Behavior of Fuels and Lubricants in Dynamic Test Equipment Operating in the Presence of Gamma Radiation*, Inland Testing Laboratories, July 1958.

43. Fainman, M. Z., The Behavior of Fuels and Lubricants in Dynamic Test Equipment Operating in the Presence of Gamma Radiation in *Third Semiannual Radiation Effects Symposium, October 28–30*, Vol. 5, Lockheed Nuclear Products.

44. Fischer, D. J., Zack, J. F., Jr., and Warrick, E. L., Radiation Stability of Silicone Greases, *Lubrication Eng.*, *15*(10): 407 (October 1959).

45. Frewing, J. J., and Scarlett, N. A., Lubrication Requirements of Nuclear Power Plants, in *Proceedings of the Fifth World Petroleum Congress, New York, June 1959*, World Petroleum Publications, New York, Sect. X, p. 163, 1959.

46. Frewing, J. J., *Radiation Resistant Lubrications*, paper presented at the Royal Dutch Institute for Engineers in Utrecht, November 1958.

47. Furby, N. W., Operation of Hydraulic Pumps in Irradiated Fluids, *in First Semiannual 125A Radiation Effects Symposium, May 22–23, 1957*, Report NARF-57-19T, Vol. 4, Convair, May 1957.

48. Gray, D. N., *Determination of the Relationship Between Structure and Radiation Stability of Various Classes of Alkyl Aromatic Fluids*, Denver Research Institute Quarterly Progress Report, January 1958.

49. Handschy, J. R. A., Armstrong, J. W., and Gordon, B. E., Greases Stable to Radiation under Dynamic Conditions, *Lubrication Eng.*, *14*(7): 292 (July 1958).

50. Haley, F. A., Intereffects Between Reactor Radiation and MIL-L-7808C Aircraft Turbine Oil in *Third Semiannual Radiation Effects Symposium, October 28–30, 1958*, Vol. 5, Lockheed Nuclear Products.

51. Hausman, R. F., and Booser, E. R., Application Problems with Petroleum Lubricants in Nuclear Power Plants, *Lubrication Eng.*, *13*(4): 199 (April 1957).

52. Horwedel, L. C., Electrofilm, Inc., personal communication, October 1960.

53. Hotten, B. W., and Carroll, J. G., Radiation Damage in Lubricating Greases, *Ind. Eng. Chem.*, *50*(2): 217 (February 1958).

54. Irving, R., The Development of Radiation Resistant Lubricants, *Shell Aviation News*, No. 238: 14–15 (April 1958).

55. King, J. A., and Rice, W. L. R., The Effects of Nuclear Radiation on Lubricants, *Lubrication Eng.*, *13*(5): 279 (May 1957).

56. Kottcamp, C. F., Nejak, R. P., and Kern, R. T., The Effects of High Energy Ionizing Radiation on Turbine Oil Performance Characteristics, *Am. Soc. Lubrication Engrs. Trans.*, *2*(1): 7 (April 1959).

57. Krasnow, M. E., Reynolds, O. P., and Wolford, O. C., *The Behavior of Fuels and Lubricants in Dynamic Test Equipment Operating in the Presence of Gamma Radiation*, Report WADC-TR 58-264, Inland Testing Laboratories, March 1958.

58. Lavik, M. T., *High Temperature Solid Dry Film Lubricants*, Report WADC-TR-57-455, February 1958.

59. Mahoney, C. L., Barnum, E. R., Kerlin, W. W., Sax, K. J., and Saari, W. S., Polyphenyl Ethers as High Temperature Nuclear Radiation Resistant Lubricants, *J. Chem. Eng. Data*, *5*(2): 172 (April 1960).

60. Mahoney, C. L., Barnum, E. R., Kerlin, W. W., and Sax, K. J., *Meta-Linked Polyphenyl Ethers as High Temperature Radiation-Resistant Lubricants, Am. Soc. Lubrication Engrs. Trans.*, *3*(1): 83 (April 1960).

61. Mahoney, C. L., Barnum, E. R., Kerlin, W. W., Sax, K. J., and Saari, W. S., Effect of Radiation on the Stability of Synthetic Lubricants, in *Proceedings of the Fifth World Petroleum Congress, New York, June 1959*, World Petroleum Publications, New York, Sect. X, p. 147, 1959.

62. Mahoney, C. L., Barnum, E. R., Kerlin, W. W., Sax, K. J., and Saari, W. S., Polyphenyl Ethers as High Temperature Radiation-Resistant Lubricants, *Preprints of General Papers, Am. Chem. Soc. Div. Petrol. Chem.*, Vol. 4, No. 1, March 1959.

63. Mahoney, C. L., Barnum, E. R., Saari, W. S., Sax, K. J., and Kerlin, W. W., *Nuclear Radiation-Resistant High Temperature Lubricants*, Report WADC-TR-59-173, Shell Development Co., December 1958.

64. Mahoney, C. L., Saari, W. S., Sax, K. J., Kerlin, W. W., Barnum, E. R., and Williams, P. H., Development of Radiation-Resistant High Temperature Lubricants, in *Third Semiannual Radiation Effects Symposium, October 28–30, 1958*, Vol. 5, Lockheed Nuclear Products.

65. Mahoney, C. L., Kerlin, W. W., Barnum, E. R., Sax, K. J., Saari, W. S., and Williams, P. H., *Engine Oil Development*, Report WADC-TR-57-177 (Pt. II), August 1958.

66. Mahoney, C. L., Sax, K. J., Kerlin, W. W., and Barnum, E. R., Development of Radiation-Resistant High Temperature Lubricants, in *Second Semiannual Radiation Effects Symposium, October 1957*, Vol. 4, Battelle Memorial Institute.

67. Mahoney, C. L., et al., *Engine Oil Development*, Report WADC-TR-57-177, July 1957.

68. Manley, L. W., Pukkila, A. O., and Barry, E. G., Lubricants Suffer When Subjected to Nuclear Radiation, *S.A.E. Journal*, 66(8): 50 (August 1958).

69. Matuszak, A. H., *Nuclear Radiation-Resistant Turbine Engine Lubricants*, Report WADC-TR-57-255 (Pt. 2), Esso Research and Engineering Company, April 1958.

70. Matuszak, A. H., The Development of Nuclear Radiation Resistant Turbine Engine Lubricants, in *Second Semiannual Radiation Effects Symposium, October 1957*, Vol. 4, Battelle Memorial Institute.

71. Matuszak, A. H., *Nuclear Radiation Resistant Turbine Engine Lubricants*, Report WADC-TR-57-255, September 1957.

72. Maughan, G. J., and Chaffin, E., *Bibliography on Effects of Radiation on Lubricants*, British Report DEGIS 149(R), March 1960.

73. Midland Silicones, Ltd., *Effects of Radiation on Organo Polysiloxanes*, Technical Data Sheet A8-2, July 1958.

74. Miller, R. N., and Bennett, W. C., The Effect of Radiation on the Response Characteristics of a Flight Control System, (Unclassified) in *Second Semiannual Radiation Effects Symposium*, October 1957, Vol. 2, Battelle Memorial Institute. (Classified).

75. Mueller, R. E., Atomic Power Development Associates, personal communication, 1958.

76. Nailor, C. H., Petroleum Lubricants—Their Application in Nuclear Plants, *Nuclear Eng.*, 3(26): 203 (May 1958).

77. Neely, R. J., Comparison of Dynamic and Static Irradiation Tests of Aircraft Fluids, *Lubrication Eng.*, 15(8): 325 (August 1959).

78. O'Connor, H. C., Developing Radiation-Resistant Lubricants, *Nuclear Power*, 4(40): 88 (August 1957).

79. Okrent, E. H., The Lubrication Requirement of Nuclear Powered Surface Vessels, *Lubrication Eng.*, 17(5): 218 (May 1961).

80. Peeler, R. L., and Yaplee, H. S., Isothermal Bulk Modulus of Hydraulic Fluid-

Hydrogen Mixtures (Unclassified), in *Second Semiannual Radiation Effects Symposium, October 1957*, Vol. 2, Battelle Memorial Institute. (Classified).

81. Pino, M. A., and Wilgus, D. R., Nuclear Radiation Resistant Hydraulic Fluids, in *Proceedings of Air Force–Navy–Industry Lubrication Conference*, Report WADC-TR-59-244, p. 623, Wright Air Development Center, October 1959.

82. Reinsmith, G., Nuclear Radiation Effects on Materials, *ASTM Bull. No. 232*, September 1958.

83. Rice, W. L. R., Kirk, D. A., and Cheney, W. B., Radiation-Resistant Fluids and Lubricants, *Nucleonics, 18*(2): 67 (February 1960).

84. Rice, W. L. R., and Cox, W. L., *The Effects of Nuclear Radiation on Solid Film Lubricants*, Report WADC-TR-58-499, Wright Air Development Center, September 1958.

85. Rice, W. L. R., and Cox, W. L., The Development of Nuclear Radiation Resistant Solid Film Lubricants, in *Third Semiannual Radiation Effects Symposium, October 28–30, 1958*, Vol. 5, Lockheed Nuclear Products.

86. Rice, W. L. R., and Way, J. H., *Effects of Nuclear Radiation on Organic Fluids*, Report WADC-TR-57-266 (Pt. 2), Wright Air Development Center, May 1958.

87. Rice, W. L. R., *Effects of Nuclear Radiation on Organic Fluids, Part I, Gamma Radiation Stability of Certain Mineral Oils and Diester Fluids*, Report WADC-TR-57-266 (Pt. 1), May 1957.

88. Rice, W. L. R., *Gamma Radiation Stability of OS-45 and OS-45-1 Hydraulic Fluids*, Report WADC-TR-57-573, Wright Air Development Center, November 1957.

89. Rice, W. L. R., *Nuclear Radiation Resistant Lubricants*, Report WADC-TR-57-299, Wright Air Development Center, May 1957.

90. Rice, W. L. R., *The Effect of Nuclear Radiation on Military Specification Greases*, Report WADC-TR-56-430 (Pt. 1), Wright Air Development Center, December 1956.

91. Scarlett, N. A., and Cliffe, J. O., Radiation Resistant Greases, *Nuclear Eng., 5* (44): 23 (January 1960).

92. Schiefer, H., Dow Corning Corp., personal communication, September 1961.

93. U. S. Department of Defense, *Grease, Ball, and Roller Bearing, Extreme High Temperature*, Military Specification MIL-G-25013A (USAF), February 1955.

94. U. S. Department of Defense, *Hydraulic Fluid, Petroleum Base, Aircraft and Ordnance*, Military Specification MIL-H-5606A, February 1957.

95. U. S. Department of Defense, *Hydraulic Fluid, Nonpetroleum Base, Aircraft*, Military Specification MIL-H-8446 (USAF), June 1955.

96. U. S. Department of Defense, *Lubricating Oil, Aircraft Turbine Engine, Synthetic Base*, Military Specifications MIL-L-7808C, November 1955, and MIL-L-7808D, November 1959.

97. U. S. Department of Defense, *Lubricating Oil, Aircraft Turbine Engine, 400°F*, Military Specification MIL-L-9236B (USAF), March 1960.

98. U. S. General Services Administration, *Lubricants, Liquid Fuels, and Related Products; Methods of Testing*, Federal Test Method Standard 791, December 1955.

99. Warrick, E. L., Fischer, D. J., and Zack, J. F., Jr., Radiation Resistant Silicones in *Third Semiannual Radiation Effects Symposium, October 28–30, 1958*, Vol. 5, Lockheed Nuclear Products.

100. Warrick, E. L., Effects of Radiation on Organopolysiloxanes, *Ind. Eng. Chem., 47*(11): 2388 (November 1955).

101. Williams, C. G., Lubricants Under Radiation, *Engineering, 187*(4864): 715 (May 1959).

CHAPTER 10

Adhesives

By Robert Y. Mixer

10-1 Introduction

Adhesives have come a long way from the glue pots of the furniture makers' guild to the present-day applications as pressure-sensitive tapes and temperature-resistant bonding materials. Adhesives now are important structural materials, their progress being largely stimulated by the demands of modern high-speed aircraft and missiles. The use of nuclear power has added a new dimension for these materials, radiation resistance.

Only the metal-to-metal adhesives now used in structural members of aircraft and missiles have received attention in irradiation studies. They are predominantly organic polymers and are susceptible to radiation damage, as discussed in Ch. 5. The adhesives used for bonding paper, leather, glass, fibers, cloth, plastics, and wood have not yet been studied.

In the work with adhesives, the irradiation environments have been static rather than dynamic in nature. Exposures were generally carried out in air at ambient temperatures with no load applied to test specimens. Various destructive tests were then performed: tensile, shear, bend, and fatigue. Ideally, adhesives should be irradiated at both high and low temperatures while being subjected to shearing, bending, and peeling stresses. In this way the combined effects of radiation and mechanical stresses can be accurately determined. Stress relaxation is very important in the degradation of adhesives and other polymeric materials. The extent to which radiation accelerates this process is not known for adhesives. (See Ch. 7, Sect. 7-4.7, for discussion pertaining to elastomeric materials.)

In this chapter radiation-effects data for adhesives are correlated with those for model compounds and for analogous organic materials. Aspects discussed include the effect of temperature, type of radiation, fillers, and protectors. Some possible damage mechanisms are also presented.

10-2 Background Information

Several general references (see Refs. 1, 8, 9, 10, and 16) on the subjects of adhesion and adhesives have appeared in recent years. They cover the theory and use of adhesives with particular attention to modern structural applications. The formulation and general chemistry of the various classes of adhesives are also presented. Manufacturers' product bulletins are good sources for specific information not relating to radiation effects.

10-2.1 Types of Adhesives

Many current structural adhesives are based upon phenolic or epoxy resins. Frequently, a vinyl or diene polymer is added as a modifier. The phenolic- or epoxy-based adhesives listed in Table 10.1 are the only ones that have received radiation-effects studies. The exact chemical composi-

Table 10.1—ADHESIVES THAT WERE IRRADIATED

Adhesive	General chemical type
FM-47 tape[a]	Vinyl-phenolic
Cycleweld A-Z[b] (liquid)	Acrylonitrile rubber-phenolic
Cycleweld 55-9[b] (liquid)	Vinyl-phenolic
Cycleweld C-3[b] (liquid)	Neoprene rubber-phenolic
Cycleweld C-6[b] (liquid)	Modified nylon-phenolic
Cycleweld C-14[b] (paste)	Modified epoxy
AF-6[c,d]	Acrylonitrile rubber-phenolic
Epon VIII[e] (paste)	Epoxy
422 tape[e]	Epoxy-phenolic[f]
Epon 820[e]	Diglycidyl ether of Bisphenol-A

[a]Bloomingdale Rubber Company.
[b]Chrylser Corporation, Cycleweld Cement Products Div.
[c]Minnesota Mining and Manufacturing Company.
[d]Unsupported calendered tape.
[e]Shell Chemical Company.
[f]Epon 1001, 33 parts; Plyophen 5023, 67 parts; dicyandiamide, 6 parts; aluminum, 100 parts; and copper 8-quinolinoleate, 1 part.

tion of these adhesives is unavailable (except where indicated) because they are proprietary formulations. The vinyl polymer in the formulations can be a polyvinyl formal or butyral. The phenolic resins can be represented by phenol-ended chain polymers (Formula 10.1) in which the

$$(10.1)$$

phenolic nuclei are joined by methylene bridges located *ortho-ortho* or *ortho-para* to the phenolic hydroxyl groups.

The epoxy resins (Formula 10.2, where n may vary from 0 to 7) used in the adhesives are, in all probability, condensation products of epichloro-

$$\overset{O}{\overset{\diagdown}{CH_2}}CHCH_2O\left[\langle\!\!\!\bigcirc\!\!\!\rangle C(CH_3)_2\langle\!\!\!\bigcirc\!\!\!\rangle OCH_2\overset{OH}{\overset{|}{CH}}CH_2O\right]_n\langle\!\!\!\bigcirc\!\!\!\rangle C(CH_3)_2\langle\!\!\!\bigcirc\!\!\!\rangle OCH_2\overset{O}{\overset{\diagdown}{CH}}CH_2$$

(10.2)

hydrin and Bisphenol-A. The curing agents for the epoxy resins are compounds with chemically active hydrogens, such as polyamines, polybasic acids, polyhydric phenols, and polyamides. The adhesives in Table 10.1, except for the 422 tape, which contains approximately 50 wt. % aluminum dust, contain little or no inorganic filler. The effect of fillers is covered in Sect. 10-3.

These adhesives, which were developed primarily for metal-to-metal bonding in aircraft structures, allow reduced stress concentrations and withstand fatigue better than riveted structures. "Honeycomb" sandwich construction with its high strength-to-weight ratio depends almost entirely upon adhesive bonds. Adhesives are also used in other laminar constructions. These materials are generally evaluated in destructive tests (tensile shear, bend, and fatigue) which are set forth in military specifications.[19] Nondestructive test methods using ultrasonic probes[3] also have been used in radiation-damage correlations.

10-2.2 IRRADIATIONS

In most of the environmental studies discussed in this chapter,† only electron and gamma radiations were used.[2,13,14] These produce equivalent changes for equivalent energy absorbed. This is expected from the discussion in Ch. 3, Sect. 3-3.2 and has been confirmed[15,20,21] in a number of studies. For example, methyl methacrylate exposed to 40×10^6 rads from a Co^{60} source suffered the same decrease in molecular weight as a sample receiving 42×10^6 rads from 1-Mev electrons.[15] Also, electrons and gamma rays gave an equivalent reduction in tensile shear strength as a function of dosage for two adhesives, Epon VIII and FM-47, bonded to aluminum.[13] These data are shown in Fig. 10.1.

Standard tensile shear specimens[19] involved two pieces of 64-mil aluminum bonded with the adhesive under test. These were used in gamma exposures where attenuation of the incident radiation was small. The specimens, however, were changed in electron exposures where beam attenuation was a problem. Here, 20-mil aluminum was used for one member of the

† This research was largely supported by the USAF Materials Central, Directorate of Laboratories, ASD, Wright-Patterson Air Force Base, Ohio.

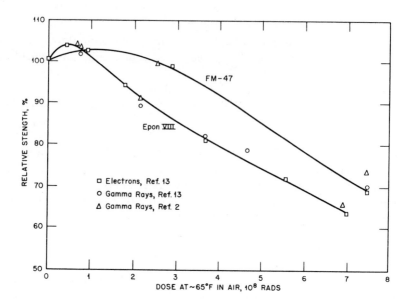

FIG. 10.1   Effect of radiation type on the tensile strength at room temperature.

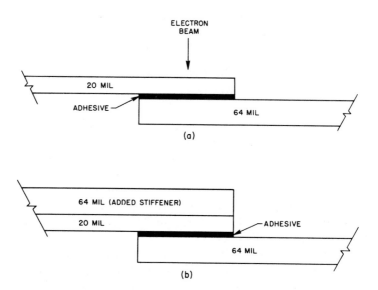

FIG. 10.2   Aluminum tensile shear specimen for exposure and subsequent testing of an adhesive. (a) Specimen for exposure. (b) Specimen (a) for destructive testing after exposure.

joint; and the adhesive was irradiated through this member,[13] as shown in Fig. 10.2.

The electron irradiation studies on adhesives required special dosimetry. Cellophane containing a radiation-sensitive dye (dimethoxydiphenyldiazo-bis-8-amino-1-naphthol-5,7-disulfonic acid) was selected because of its sensitivity and simple analysis.[13]

10-3 Radiation Effects

10-3.1 TENSILE SHEAR STRENGTH

Electron and gamma irradiation generally deteriorates the tensile shear strength of adhesives. The magnitude of the effect for a given dose varies with each adhesive. The data for this discussion were selected from the work of Arlook and Harvey.[2] The adhesives studied (see Table 10.1) were developed for optimum performance in the absence of radiation, not for radiation resistance.

Figures 10.1 and 10.3 show the effect of irradiation at room temperature. The tensile shear strength relative to the original is an average of five values. At low doses (around 0.9×10^8 rads), some adhesives show an improvement in strength. This indicates that the radiation provided additional cure toward optimum strength and suggests that adhesives might be designed with such an increase in mind, i.e., final curing in use. One adhesive, AF-6, showed increased strength over the entire dose range (up to 7×10^8 rads).

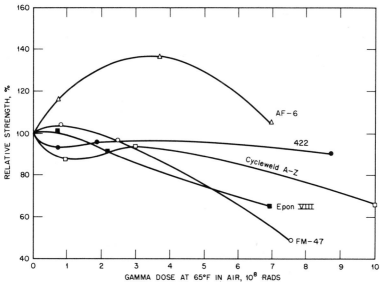

FIG. 10.3 Effect of radiation on tensile shear strength at room temperature.

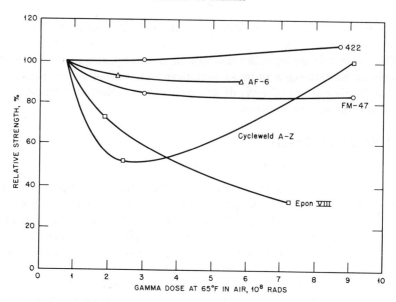

FIG. 10.4 Effect of radiation on tensile shear strength at 260°F. Tested at 260°F after one-half hour soak at 260°F.

Increasing the temperature during testing (subsequent to radiolysis) appears to increase the change in tensile shear strength for a given dose. The effect of elevating the test temperature is shown in Figs. 10.4 and 10.5. In these experiments the control samples were not run at elevated temperatures. Consequently, the samples irradiated at the lowest dose became the

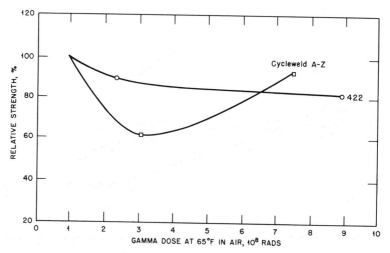

FIG. 10.5 Effect of radiation on tensile shear strength at 500°F. Tested at 500°F after one-half hour soak at 500°F.

control samples; i.e., the values for other doses were related to those at the lowest dose. This upgraded the performance of adhesives that had poor low-dose values, e.g., Cycleweld A-Z. At a test temperature of 260°F, FM-47 and 422 showed relative strengths of greater than 80% over the entire dose range. Adhesives 422 and Cycleweld A-Z were the only ones tested at 500°F; however, only 422 gave consistently high relative values, retaining 82% of its strength after a dose of 8.6×10^8 rads.

Several organic metal-to-metal adhesives from Germany (Agomet R, Agomet E, Agomet PV 456L, Metallon KP, Araldit 123B, and Sichel PRL 36) were exposed[12] to doses of gamma radiation from 0.93×10^6 to 3.7×10^6 rads. There was little change in tensile shear strengths at these low dosages. Two of the adhesives (Agomet R and VP-456L) were irradiated during the age hardening (conditions not given) of the cured adhesives. Agomet R specimens had substantially improved strengths compared to specimens irradiated after age hardening. Agomet E and Metallon KP showed typical decreases in tensile strengths when the irradiated specimens were tested at higher temperatures, 104°F and 140°F.

Limited studies have been made on the effect of mixed radiation at relatively low doses on the physical properties of lap-shear specimens and honeycomb panels. Lap-shear specimens made with Plastilock 620-626 (phenolic-modified synthetic rubber), 422, and Metalbond Mn3C-M3C (Buna N-nylon-phenolic) adhesives showed no deleterious effects when irradiated[11] at ambient temperature with a mixed field† of approximately 1.7×10^7 rads. This applied to clad and unclad aluminum and magnesium specimens tested at room temperature and 260°F. Further irradiations of Plastilock 620-626 and 422 clad aluminum specimens while the samples were immersed in six fluids (water, salt water, antiicing fluid, hydraulic oil, JP-4 fuel, and hydrocarbon type III fuel) had no effect.

Sandwich panels made from clad aluminum skin, either aluminum or glass fiber honeycomb, and 422 adhesives were irradiated[11] in a mixed field of approximately 1.7×10^7 rads and then subjected to simple-beam, column-creep, shear-modulus, and shear-stress tests. There was no adverse effect except for a small decrease in the column creep and shear stress of the glass honeycomb panels. This decrease is questionable since the glass honeycomb showed excellent radiation resistance to mixed fields in this study.

One might expect a shift from an adhesive failure to a cohesive failure as a result of irradiation. This might result from the embrittlement of the organic portion of the bond. The type of failure observed, however, varied considerably and showed no trend.

Available data show that the addition of a filler can markedly improve the radiation resistance of an adhesive. This was true[14] for the highly filled glass-reinforced plastics, which showed complete resistance at 10^9

† Including 6×10^{14} fast neutrons/cm² and 6×10^{13} thermal neutrons/cm².

rads, and a phenolic-glass laminate, which showed complete resistance to 10^{10} rads. A study was made to determine the comparative effectiveness of various fillers.[14] The filler contents were carried to high levels in order to approximate those in the 422 adhesive and in resin-glass laminates. The data obtained are shown in Table 10.2. Powdered tin was better than titanium dioxide as a protective filler. The adhesive with 67 wt. % tin retained 90% of its strength when subjected to a dose of 8.6×10^8 rads.

Table 10.2 — EFFECT OF FILLERS ON STABILITY TO
ELECTRON IRRADIATION OF EPON 820 ADHESIVE[a] FOR ALUMINUM

Filler	Weight %	Dose, 10^8 rads	Tensile shear strength	
			Psi	Relative, %
None	0	0	2390	100
		2.4	1840	77
		8.6	1670	69
Powdered tin	10	0	2210	100
		2.4	2640	120
		8.6	1890	86
	67	0	2310	100
		2.4	2760	121
		8.6	2060	90
Titanium dioxide[b]	10	0	2420	100
		2.4	2290	95
		8.6	1980	82
	33	0	2250	100
		2.4	2340	104
		8.6	1960	81
	50	0	2090	100
		2.4	1970	94
		8.6	1700	81

[a] Low-viscosity Epon 828 cured with diethylaminopropylamine.
[b] Du Pont R-610.

There might be an opportunity for additional improvement in filler action if the filler were coated with a sizing agent similar or identical to those used on the glass cloth in resin-glass laminates. The coating of abrasive grits prior to adhesive bonding has been quite successful.

The addition to adhesives of antirads or of scintillators as protectors generally gave little or no improvement[13,14] in radiation resistance. A list of the materials tested is given in Table 10.3. These materials were selected from the work of Born[4] on elastomers (see Ch. 7, Sect. 7-3.2.3) and from materials known to be highly efficient scintillators. They were added separately to Epon VIII at concentrations of 1 and 10 wt. %. The adhesives were then irradiated to doses of 2.4×10^8 and 8.6×10^8 rads.

The only material tested that proved beneficial was 2,5-diphenyloxazole. At 10 wt. % concentration and at 7.4×10^8 rads, the observed relative tensile shear strength was 89% as compared to 60% for the control.

Table 10.3 — RADIATION PROTECTORS EVALUATED
FOR ADHESIVES[13,14]

Antirads	Scintillators
N,N'-Di-α-naphthyl-p-phenylenediamine	Carbazole
Diphenyl selenide	Dibenzofuran
Dibenzothiophene	p-Terphenyl
Triphenyl phosphate	Poly(N-vinylcarbazole)
2,2'-Dithiobis(benzothiazole)	N-Vinylcarbazole
2,2'-Dihydroxy-6,6'-dinaphthyl disulfide	2,5-Diphenyloxazole
2-Amino-4-(4-biphenylyl) thiazole	
4,4'-Thiobis(6-$tert$-butyl-3-methylphenol)	

In some preliminary experiments, tetra-2-ethylhexyl titanate was applied to the aluminum surface of tensile shear specimens before bonding; after being bonded in the normal manner, the specimens were irradiated. Compared to the control specimens, the titanate produced a striking improvement in shear strengths.[6] Unfortunately, these initial experiments were never repeated or expanded.

10-3.2 BEND STRENGTH

The effect of radiation on bend strengths was measured for a number of structural adhesives.[2] The same adhesives that were covered in the previous section (see Table 10.1) will be discussed. Specimens identical to those for tensile shear tests were irradiated at about 65°F in the discharged fuel-element gamma facility at the Materials Testing Reactor in Idaho. They were then tested[19] at room temperature, 180°F, 260°F, and 500°F after one-half hour at the respective elevated temperatures. Figures 10.6 and 10.7 show representative data. There were no controls tested as 500°F (Fig. 10.7); thus the relative bend strengths are based on the strengths at the lowest dose (around 0.9×10^8 rads). This has the effect of making adhesives with lower strengths at low doses look better at higher doses.

Increasing the test temperature appeared to increase the damage for a given dose as with the tensile shear strength tests. At room temperature, FM-47 showed over 80% retention of its original bend strength at 8.8×10^8 rads, and 422 showed more than 95% at 6×10^8 rads. At 500°F, 422 retained about 94% of its strength, thus indicating very good radiation resistance.

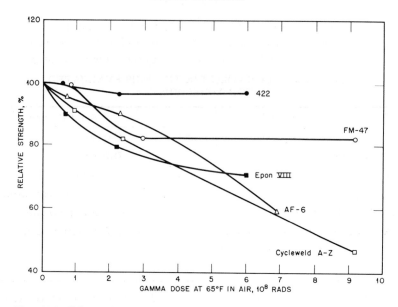

FIG. 10.6 Effect of radiation on bend strength at room temperature.

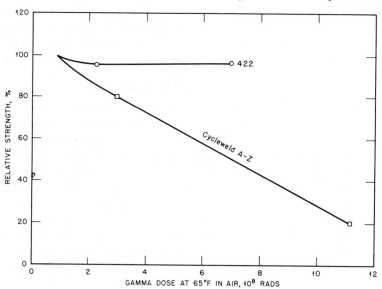

FIG. 10.7 Effect of radiation on bend strength at 500°F. Tested at 500°F after one-half hour soak at 500°F.

The bend strengths did not increase for the initial small dose of radiation as did tensile shear strengths. This can be explained as follows: the adhesive is under a fairly uniform shear across most of the area of the bond in the tensile shear test (the areas near the end of the bond may be under tension due to the bending moment). In the bend test the adhesive is under compression near one end of the lap joint and under tension over the rest of the bond. Irradiation causes cross linking and an increase in elastic modulus, which give rise to an increase in tensile shear strengths for small doses; further irradiation leads to a decrease because of embrittlement. In the bend test there is a more rapid concentration of tension forces once a break has started. This is similar to crack propagation. In the bend test elongation is far more important as a method of equalizing the stresses; therefore the bend strength should not show any initial increase because irradiation reduces the elongation due to cross linking.

10-3.3 FATIGUE

Arlook and Harvey[2] also studied the effects of radiation on structural adhesive bonds in fatigue. In the fatigue test the desired axial load on the irradiated samples was applied at room temperature at a rate of 3600 cycles/min. Figures 10.8 and 10.9 present the pertinent data obtained.

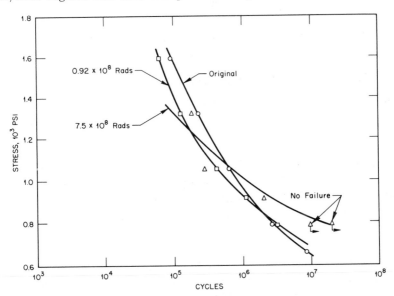

Fig. 10.8   Effect of gamma radiation on fatigue strength of FM-47 at room temperature.

The radiation effect is not as marked as in the case of tensile shear and bend strengths. Indeed, the change in fatigue strength was probably within the limits of experimental error. FM-47 appeared to have somewhat improved fatigue properties at low stresses and high doses. Adhesive 422 (also Epon VIII) withstood greater stresses in fatigue and were only slightly degraded by high doses.

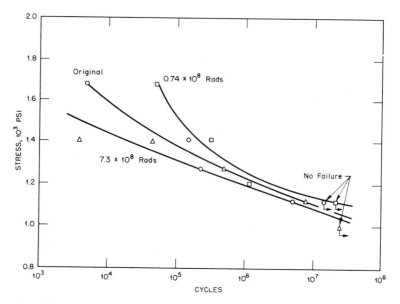

Fig. 10.9   Effect of gamma radiation on fatigue strength of 422 at room temperature.

10-4 Mechanism of Radiation Damage

Mechanism studies can provide valuable information on radiolysis processes and information that may lead to materials having greater radiation stability. Meaningful work on commercial adhesives would be a difficult task because the formulations are proprietary. Also, the interaction or influence of various adhesive components on each other during the irradiation process is unknown. A good approach has been to study the effect of irradiation on the individual components or on the simplest chemical structures (model compounds) which performed the intended functions.

10-4.1 EPOXY POLYMERS

The damage-mechanism studies began with epoxy polymers[13] because adhesives based on these materials enjoy a good reputation in structural uses and radiation resistance. The model compound approach was chosen because of the difficulty of handling (in an analytical sense) cross-linked epoxy polymers. The selected model compounds were prepared by reacting the low-molecular-weight epoxy polymer with an excess of an amine, phenol, or alcohol. The polymers used for study were diglycidyl ether of Bisphenol-A (DEBA) (see Formula 10.2, where $n = 0$), Epon 1001 (see Formula 10.2, where $n = 2$ to 3), and Epon X-131 [nominally, the tetraglycidyl ether of tetrakis(hydroxyphenyl)ethane]. Primary aliphatic, secondary aliphatic, and primary aromatic amine cures were each used as were a phenol and an aliphatic alcohol, as shown in Table 10.4. Thus the model compounds represented the resin molecule either between and including the cross-linking moieties or between cross links.

Table 10.4 — EFFECT OF IRRADIATION ON EPOXY MODEL COMPOUNDS

Model compounds	Electron dose, 10^8 rads	G_{gas} [a]	
		Total	H_2
DEBA + $BuNH_2$	4.5	0.52	0.47
+ Et_2NH	6.6	0.22	0.18
+ $C_6H_5NH_2$	5.2	0.10	0.10
	6.6	0.092	0.090
Epon 1001 + $BuNH_2$	4.7	0.46	0.37
+ Et_2NH	4.2	0.45	0.33
+ $C_6H_5NH_2$	4.2	0.041	0.041
Epon X-131 + $BuNH_2$	6.6	0.33	0.28
+ $C_6H_5NH_2$	6.6	0.085	0.076

[a] Molecules of gas formed per 100 ev absorbed.

These model compounds were irradiated with electrons for doses ranging from 0.93×10^8 to 6.6×10^8 rads. After irradiation, the compounds were analyzed, and reduced viscosities† were determined. The gases resulting from the irradiation were analyzed. These results provided information on the radiation stability of the components as to cross linking and cleavage.

The gas yields of the model compounds are shown in Table 10.4. With aliphatic amines the epoxy polymers showed increasing stability in the order: DEBA < Epon 1001 < Epon X-131. As expected, the aromatic amine product was far more stable than aliphatic amine products. Chain scission occurred in the epoxy polymers, as indicated by the data in Table 10.5 on the nitrogen content before and after irradiation. These data, coupled with infrared absorption information, showed that the cleavage was in the aliphatic portion, i.e., in the glycidyl group, rather than in the aromatic part of the molecule. This was expected in view of the tendency of aliphatic materials to scission and aromatic materials to cross link in radiolysis.[5]

The predominant effect of irradiation of epoxy polymers was cross linking. This was shown by the increase in reduced viscosity of the model compounds shown in Fig. 10.10. These viscosities were run in dichloroethane at 77°F. The model compounds from Epon X-131 plus n-butylamine or aniline became insoluble upon irradiation. All the compounds increased in viscosity, regardless of whether they were prepared from amines, phenol, or alcohol; however, those containing amine groups generally showed a greater increase in viscosity.

† Specific viscosity/concentration.

Cross linking of p,p'-methylenedianiline-cured epoxy polymers by gamma irradiation was shown[7] by an increase in hardness for doses up to 10^8 rads. The heat distortion temperature remained constant, and the

Table 10.5 — NITROGEN ANALYSES OF EPOXY MODEL COMPOUNDS

Model compounds	Electron dose, 10^8 rads	Nitrogen, %
DEBA Et_2NH	0	5.91
	0.93	5.60
	6.6	5.29
	6.6^a	8.78
Epon X-131 + $BuNH_2$	0	4.71
	6.6	4.71
	6.6^a	10.8

[a]Liquid was found on the cell diaphragm.

compression strength increased only slightly over this dose range. Irradiation of the same polymer cured with m-phenylenediamine resulted in a slight loss in hardness and compression strength and a marked loss in heat

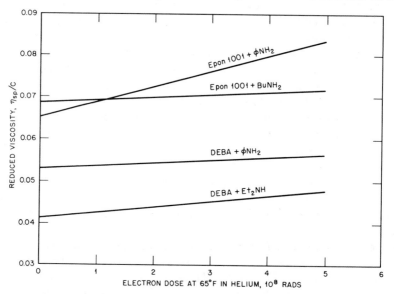

FIG. 10.10   Effect of radiation on model epoxy compounds.

distortion temperature. These doses were almost tenfold less than those received by the adhesives and model compounds in the studies by Arlook and Harvey[2] and by Mixer and Parkinson.[13] With doses of 10^9 rads, more marked effects would have been noticed.

Epoxy adhesive systems cured with anhydrides have not been studied; however, one investigation[7] of cast polymers indicated that pyromellitic dianhydride was between p,p'-methylenedianiline and m-phenylenediamine in radiation resistance. This is not surprising in view of the similar aromatic content and structure. No information is available on the radiation resistance of either epoxy (Bisphenol-A) polymers cured with other agents, such as polyamides, or other epoxy polymers.

10-4.2 PHENOLIC POLYMERS

No study has been made of the mechanism of radiolysis of phenolic-based adhesives or other model compounds. This is quite surprising in view of the outstanding thermal and radiation resistance of glass-reinforced phenolic laminates and phenolic-based adhesives. One investigation by Sisman and Bopp[18] on unfilled and unreinforced phenolic resins placed them much lower than other polymers in comparative stability than would have been expected from their high aromatic content. The damage resulted primarily from scission. One might conclude that phenolics depend upon inert fillers for high radiation performance.

10-4.3 VINYL POLYMERS

The radiolysis of the vinyl components of adhesives would be expected to be similar to that for vinyl polymers[5] (see Ch. 5, Sect. 5-6). Adhesives containing vinyl polymers that cross link upon irradiation (e.g., polyvinyl acetate or polyvinyl butyral) would degrade by embrittlement, whereas

Table 10.6 — GASEOUS PRODUCTS FROM ELECTRON
IRRADIATION OF POLYVINYL BUTYRAL

Gas	G_{gas} [a]
H_2	3.50
CO	0.73
CO_2	0.22
H_2O	0.15
Methane	0.11
Ethane	0.033
Propane	0.40
Propylene	0.018
Hexane	0.022
Total	5.2

[a] Molecules formed per 100 ev absorbed.

those formulations containing vinyl polymers that undergo chain scission (e.g., polyisobutene as a tackifier) would degrade by becoming more fluid.

In a preliminary study,[14] polyvinyl butyral (Bakelite's XYHL), which is representative of the vinyl component of a vinyl-phenolic adhesive, was irradiated under helium with electrons for a dose of 5.4×10^8 rads. The butyral was sufficiently cross linked at this dosage that it became insoluble and infusible. The yields listed in Table 10.6 were calculated from the analysis of the gases given off in this irradiation. Cross linking was the predominant reaction during irradiation; however, scission of the pendent side chain was demonstrated by the relatively large yields of CO, CO_2, and propane. This side-chain scission accounts for 10 to 20% of the radiation damage.

10-5 Summary

Adhesives upon irradiation behave quite like the corresponding plastics or reinforced plastics. For example, epoxy- and vinyl-based adhesives degrade by embrittlement in the same manner as the filled or unfilled plastics. The phenolic-based adhesives may be assumed to behave similarly. How-

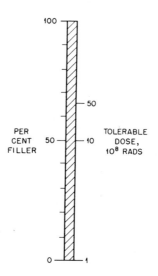

Fɪɢ. 10.11 Effect of filler on maximum tolerable radiation dose for adhesives.

ever, the comparison with phenolic plastics is not as straightforward; it will not be until some basic studies are completed. The combination of vinyl and phenolic polymers in an adhesive behaves as one would expect based on studies of the individual plastics.

Adhesives and reinforced plastics that have high thermal stability generally show high radiation resistance. Epoxy-based adhesives and laminates show good thermal stability and good radiation stability. Phenolic-based adhesives (e.g., 422) and laminates (e.g., CTL 91-LD) have excellent thermal stability and the best radiation resistance.

Both the inorganic filler in the adhesive and the glass fiber in the reinforced plastic laminate offer substantial radiation protection. The order of magnitude of this protection is portrayed in Fig. 10.11, where the maximum tolerable dosage is given for various filler contents. Most unfilled adhesives and plastics have good retention of properties up to a maximum dose of 10^8 rads. As shown, increases in filler content increase performance. This marked effect of filler offers a potentially fertile field for study to determine adhesives having the greatest resistance to radiation effects.

References

Several of the following were cited in the text as authority for statements made. Others were not quoted but are included because they contain pertinent information. All were consulted in the preparation of this chapter.

1. Aero Research, Ltd., *Structural Adhesives*, Lange, Maxwell, and Springer, Ltd., London, 1951.
2. Arlook, R. S., and Harvey, D. G., *Effects of Nuclear Radiation on Structural Adhesive Bonds*, Report WADC-TR-56-467, Wright Air Development Center, August 1956.
3. Arnold, J. S., *An Ultrasonic Technique for Nondestructive Evaluation of Metal-to-Metal Adhesive Bonds*, Stanford Research Institute, 1956.
4. Born, J. W., *A Study of the Effects of Nuclear Radiations on Elastomeric Compounds and Compounding Materials*, Report WADC-TR-55-58, Part II, The B. F. Goodrich Company, September 1956.
5. Bovey, F. A., *The Effects of Ionizing Radiation on Natural and Synthetic High Polymers*, p. 50, Interscience Publishers, Inc., New York, 1958.
6. Coles, H. W., U. S. Army Quartermaster Research and Development Command, Natick, Mass., private communication, 1958.
7. Colichman, E. L., and Strong, J. D., Effect of Gamma Radiation of Epoxy Plastics, *Modern Plastics*, *35*(2): 180 (February 1957).
8. de Bruyne, N. A., and Houwink, R. (Eds.), *Adhesion and Adhesives*, Elsevier Press, Houston, Texas, 1951.
9. Delmonte, J., *The Technology of Adhesives*, Reinhold Publishing Corporation, New York, 1947.
10. Epstein, G., *Adhesive Bonding of Metals*, Reinhold Publishing Corporation, New York, 1957.
11. Johnson, R. E., and Sicilio, F., *Radiation Damage to Metal Bonded and Sandwich Panels-I*, Report NARF-57-53-T, Convair, November 1957.
12. Matting, Von A., and Hahn, K. F., Die Wirkung Energiereicher Strahlen auf Metallkleber, *Atomkernenergie*, *4*(2): 64 (February 1959).
13. Mixer, R. Y., and Parkinson, D. B., *Nuclear Radiation Effects on Structural Plastics and Adhesives. Part III: Experimental Research*, Report WADC-TR-56-534, Stanford Research Institute, August 1957.
14. Mixer, R. Y., *The Effect of Nuclear Radiation on Structural Adhesives and Plastics*, Bimonthly Progress Report 2, SRI Project SU-1726, Stanford Research Institute, October 1957.
15. Morgan, P., *Plastic Progress, 1955*, p. 16, Iliffe & Sons, Ltd., London, 1956.

16. Rutzler, J. E., and Savage, R. L. (Eds.), *Adhesion and Adhesives, Fundamentals and Practice,* John Wiley & Sons, Inc., New York, 1954.
17. Sangster, R. C., and Irvine, J. W., Jr., Study of Organic Scintillators, *J. Chem. Phys., 24*(4): 670 (April 1956).
18. Sisman, O., and Bopp, C. D., *Physical Properties of Irradiated Plastics,* USAEC Report ORNL-928, Oak Ridge National Laboratory, June 1951.
19. U. S. Department of Defense, *Adhesive; Airframe Structural, Metal-to-Metal,* Military Specification MIL-A-5090B, July 1954, and Amendment 1, March 1955.
20. Wagner, R. M., and Towle, L. H., *Effects of High Energy, High Intensity Electro-magnetic Radiation on Organic Liquids,* Report WADC-TR-58-683, Stanford Research Institute, February 1959.
21. Zebroski, E. L., and Kinderman, E. M., *A Comparison of High-energy Electron and Gamma Irradiation Effects on Organic Liquids,* Report WADC-TR-57-141, Stanford Research Institute, February 1957.

CHAPTER 11

Textiles

By Henry A. Rutherford

11-1 Introduction

11-1.1 Classification

Textile fibers can be broadly classified into natural and man-made fibers. The latter can be subdivided into regenerated and true synthetic fibers. The natural fibers of prominence are cotton, wool, silk, and several of the bast materials. The commercially important fibers in the regenerated group are rayon and acetate. Certain selected polyamides, polyesters, and polyacrylics are at present the only fiber-forming polymeric substances that have achieved success as true synthetic textiles; and only a small percentage of the total fiber consumption can be attributed to these. The natural and the regenerated types account for approximately 95% of the total fiber consumption in the United States today.

The following is a chemical classification of textile fibers, including examples of each type in common use:

1. *Cellulosic:*

   (a) Cotton
   (b) Rayon
   (c) Cupra
   (d) Fortisan†
   (e) Bast fibers

2. *Cellulose ester:*

   (a) Acetate (degree of substitution 2.3); same chemical structure as Item 1, except the —OH groups are randomly replaced by —O—C—CH$_3$ to give an average substitution per glucose unit

   $$\overset{\|}{\underset{O}{}}$$

   of 2.3.

   (b) Arnel† (cellulose triacetate); same chemical structure as Item 1, except complete substitution of acetate groups for —OH.

† Celanese Corporation of America.

3. *Protein:*

   (a) Wool

$$-\overset{\text{H}}{\underset{\text{O}}{C}}-\overset{}{\underset{\text{R}}{C}}-NH-\overset{\text{R}}{\underset{\text{O}}{C}}-\overset{}{\underset{\text{H}}{C}}-NH-\overset{\text{H}}{\underset{\text{O}}{C}}-\overset{}{\underset{\text{CH}_2}{C}}-NH-\overset{\text{H}}{\underset{\text{O}}{C}}-\overset{}{\underset{\text{R}}{C}}-NH-\overset{\text{R}}{\underset{\text{O}}{C}}-\overset{}{\underset{\text{H}}{C}}-NH-$$

$$\text{S}$$
$$\text{S}$$

$$-\overset{\text{H}}{\underset{\text{O}}{C}}-\overset{}{\underset{\text{R}}{C}}-NH-\overset{\text{R}}{\underset{\text{O}}{C}}-\overset{}{\underset{\text{H}}{C}}-NH-\overset{\text{CH}_2}{\underset{\text{O}}{C}}-\overset{}{\underset{\text{H}}{C}}NH-\overset{\text{H}}{\underset{\text{O}}{C}}-\overset{}{\underset{\text{R}}{C}}-NH-\overset{\text{R}}{\underset{\text{O}}{C}}-\overset{}{\underset{\text{H}}{C}}-NH-$$

   (showing cystine cross linkage)

   (b) Silk (chemical structure represented by the main chain in the wool structure without cross linkages).

4. *Polyamide:*

   (a) Nylon 66 [poly(hexamethyleneadipamide)]

$$\left[-\underset{\text{H}}{N}-(CH_2)_6-\underset{\text{H}}{N}-\underset{\text{O}}{\overset{}{C}}-(CH_2)_4-\underset{\text{O}}{\overset{}{C}}- \right]_n$$

   (b) Nylon 6 [poly(caprolactam)]

$$\left[-\underset{\text{H}}{N}-(CH_2)_5-\underset{\text{O}}{\overset{}{C}}- \right]_n .$$

5. *Polyester:*

   (a) Dacron† [poly(ethylene terephthalate)]

$$\left[-O-(CH_2)_2-O-\underset{\text{O}}{\overset{}{C}}-\overset{\overset{\text{H}\ \text{H}}{C=C}}{\underset{\underset{\text{H}\ \text{H}}{C-C}}{}}-\underset{\text{O}}{\overset{}{C}}- \right]_n$$

   (b) Kodel‡ (composition unknown)

† E. I. du Pont de Nemours & Co., Inc.
‡ Tennessee Eastman Company.

6. *Polyacrylic:*

   (a) Orlon†

   (b) Acrilan‡

   (c) Creslan§

   (d) Verel¶

   (e) Zefran††

$$\left[-CH_2-\underset{CN}{CH}-CH_2-\underset{CN}{CH}-CH_2-\underset{R}{CH}-CH_2-\underset{CN}{CH}- \right]_n$$

Copolymers of acrylonitrile and other vinyl compounds

7. *Vinyl and Vinylidine:*

   (a) Dynel‡‡

   (b) Darvan§§   Copolymers of vinyl and vinylidine compounds

   (c) Saran††

8. *Inorganic:*

   (a) Glass fiber

   (b) Asbestos

Consideration of the effects of radiation on textiles in this chapter is limited largely to cotton, rayon, acetate, wool, nylon, Dacron, and Orlon since these textiles embrace the important chemical types in use today. Except for wool and Orlon, the formulae shown represent the chemical structure of the repeating units in the various fibers. Wool is a condensation product of α-amino acids, and the presence of cystine results in cross linkages between the main protein chains wherever this amino acid occurs in the chain. Other amino acid residues are merely designated by R. Orlon and the other polyacrylics are addition copolymers with acrylonitrile as one of the monomers; the other monomers are designated as $-CH_2-CH-$ and may occur at random along the chain. R

11-1.2 RADIATION AND TEXTILES

There are more than 500 end uses of textile materials, primarily in fabric form;[12] these may be broadly classified as apparel, household, surgical, military, special protective, and industrial textiles. Under normal conditions radiation does not present a hazard to textiles. Only military materiel is normally expected to suffer exposure to abnormal amounts of radiation and even it only under unusual conditions. Parachutes, webbings, cords, or other items used for braking and recovery of high-speed aircraft

† E. I. du Pont de Nemours and Co., Inc.

‡ Chemstrand Corp.

§ American Cyanamid Co.

¶ Tennessee Eastman Company.

†† Dow Chemical Co.

‡‡ Union Carbide Chemicals Company.

§§ Celanese Corporation of America.

and missiles, and tents and tarpaulins present some of the possibilities. Nylon and some Dacron are used in the first category; specially treated cotton fabrics are principally used for tentage and other heavy items. Military goods stored in areas contaminated by radiation from fall-out or from the explosion of atomic devices could possibly be subjected to radiation over long periods of time, with the result that the utility of the items would be decreased.

Aside from the military aspect, the effect of radiation on textile fibers is of interest from other points of view. One is in the realm of the industrial application of radiation, either by itself or in adjunct with chemical compounds, as a means of fiber modification and the production of new and more useful products. Another deals with the use of textiles in the manufacturing of such items as flexible hose, membranes, belting, etc., in turn, used in the construction and operation of nuclear reactors and radiation sources. In any such practical application, the effect of radiation on fiber and fabric properties must be considered. Active research is now being carried on in this area.

11-1.3 FINE STRUCTURE OF FIBERS

All the organic fibers are polymers and have certain structural features in common. Our present theory of fiber structure is that the polymer molecules are of the long-chain type, i.e., linear; and in the fiber these molecules lie more or less parallel to the long axis. The degree of orientation that describes this alignment has a marked influence on such fiber properties as strength. In general, the higher the degree of orientation, the higher the strength. Molecular length is also important; fibers of good strength are not achieved below an average length of 1000 A. Any treatment that lowers the average molecular length has an adverse effect on physical properties. Molecular symmetry of the linear molecule enhances the possibility of the formation of crystalline areas within the fiber structure, a factor that is desirable when high strength is required. There are areas where the molecules may not be tightly packed or aligned and where no crystallinity exists. Such parts are referred to as amorphous areas. Elongation characteristics are primarily associated with this part of the fiber structure. A schematic representation[15] of possible distribution arrangements of crystalline and amorphous areas which can influence mechanical properties is shown in Fig. 11.1. (See Ch. 5, Sect. 5-4.3 for a discussion of crystallinity and orientation.)

When structures containing both crystalline and amorphous areas are subjected to agents that cause deterioration, the attack usually takes place first in the disorganized portions. Thus the rate of attack, as well as the nature of the degraded product, may be influenced by the amount and distribution of the amorphous areas. High-energy radiation, because of its penetrating ability, would not be expected to show a preference for any particular portion of the fiber; and there is evidence that the attack in this case is a random one.

As discussed in Ch. 5, the chemical nature of the molecule has an influence on crystallite formation. Symmetrical structures, such as in linear polyethylene or cellulose, form highly crystalline fibers; polymers

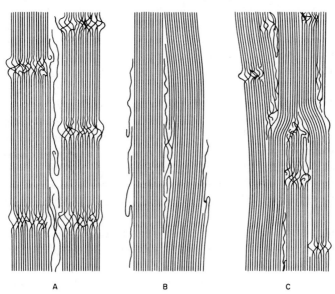

A   B   C

FIG. 11.1 Several possible arrangements (A, B, C) of crystalline (regular) and amorphous (irregular) areas in fibrous materials.

containing bulky side chains form materials of low crystallinity. Symmetrical molecules make better fibers when the polymer contains the kinds of chemical groups that lead to high intermolecular forces. For example, hydroxyl groups or amide groups that are capable of forming hydrogen bonds between chain molecules contribute considerably toward the strength of a material.

There are other important properties of textiles dependent upon the chemical and physical structure of the fiber. Some of these are toughness, modulus of elasticity, recovery from deformation, abrasion resistance, and softening point. Excellent discussions of fiber properties as related to structure and end-use requirements can be found elsewhere.[8,12]

11-1.4 SIMILARITY OF FIBER AND BASE POLYMER BEHAVIOR

The effects of high-energy radiation on polymers are well covered in the literature, which has been reviewed in Ch. 5. Chemical structure has the predominating influence on the behavior of fibrous materials toward radiation;[3,17] and, except in minor detail, the behavior of a fiber is not very different from the base polymer in some other form. The rather remarkable effects that have been observed with some materials during irradiation, e.g., polyethylene, have stimulated research toward improved fibers for textile applications. This trend is reflected in much of the literature dealing with radiation effects on fibrous materials.

Widely different radiation stabilities exist among the various types of polymers used in textiles. Those containing only hydrogen and carbon are the most stable. The gross effects of radiation are at least twofold; cross linking may occur or the long-chain molecules may undergo scission. Hydrocarbon long-chain polymers, as such, or those bearing no side chains other than phenyl groups are predominantly cross linked. Materials such as polystyrene and polyethylene show great stability toward radiation, and the changes in physical properties durings irradiation suggest cross linking. Cellulose, which is of special interest in the field of textiles, and materials that contain fluorine or chlorine on long hydrocarbon chains show little resistance to chain cleavage and are near the bottom of the radiation stability scale.[3] Polyesters and polyamides show intermediate orders of stability. Wall[28] has correlated heats of polymerization of the monomer with the tendency of the polymer either to cross link or degrade during irradiation. High heats of polymerization tend to produce cross linking in the polymer; low heats of polymerization tend to produce chain scission or degradation.

Changes in mechanical properties of polymers during irradiation have been studied by a number of investigators. Although films have largely been used for this work, the gross changes in properties of a fiber from a particular polymer are similar to those occurring in the film. The direction of change in properties is governed by whether cross linking or cleavage is the predominating reaction. Cross linking increases strength and modulus but decreases elongation. Cleavage of long-chain molecules, referred to as "degradation," produces decreases in strength, elongation, and, generally, in modulus of elasticity.

11-1.5 Determination of Effects on Textile Materials

Radiation effects on fibers can be determined in several ways. For the most part tensile strength,† elongation at break, and modulus are used as the critical physical properties. Decreases in strength are indicative of a decrease in average molecular length or of chain scission; increases in modulus are regarded as evidence of cross linking. Measurements of viscosity of the fibrous material in a suitable solvent are also useful. With some materials, particularly the cellulosics, factors have been deter-

---

† As used here, "tensile strength" denotes only that the materials broke under tension; it does not necessarily mean the strength per unit of cross-sectional area.

mined to convert viscosity to molecular weight or to degree of polymerization. A decrease in degree of polymerization indicates degradation.

The effect of high-energy radiation is not limited to cross linking or chain scission. Oxidation reactions that can profoundly influence fiber properties can also occur. This effect is particularly pronounced in the instances of cellulosic fibers and of wool. Whether the oxidation arises from the radiation per se or from the presence of ozone or hydrogen peroxide in the system is not clear. In any case the detection of organic chemical groups not present in the original material may also indicate the kinds of changes that have taken place.

Since 1952 a number of papers describing the effect of high-energy radiation on textiles have appeared. The fiber behavior observed in these studies parallels quite closely the general behavior of polymers in other forms; where differences occur, they are minor. It matters little whether the effects of radiation are determined on individual fibers, on staple yarns, on filament yarns, or on fabrics. The gross behavior of the material is an inherent property of the fiber itself and is not dependent upon the physical form in which the material is exposed. In the following discussion, therefore, it may be assumed that where stability characteristics of individual fibers are presented essentially the same behavior applies to yarns or fabrics and vice versa. Moreover, these terms are used interchangeably throughout the chapter.

11-2 Cellulose and Cellulose Derivatives

Under the influence of high-energy radiation, cotton, rayon, and acetate have low orders of stability and are degraded rather rapidly in comparison with other fibers. Table 11.1 is a compilation of data obtained by various

Table 11.1 — EFFECT OF RADIATION ON THE TENSILE STRENGTH OF CELLULOSIC FIBERS AND YARNS AT ROOM TEMPERATURE

Source of radiation	Dose, 10^6 rads	Material	Condition of exposure	Loss in strength, %
2-Mev Van de Graaff[6]	4.2	30/1 cotton yarn	Air	27
			Vacuum	29
Fission products	4.4	Purified cotton fiber	O_2	23
			N_2	24
Spent MTR fuel elements[2]	8.5		O_2	45
			N_2	37
Co[60]	4.4	30/1 cotton yarn	Air	25
Reactor[21]	26.0		Air	45
Co[60] (Ref. 7)	8.5	HT rayon cord	Air	40
			Vacuum	37

workers (see Refs. 2, 6, 7, and 21). Although different sources of radiation were used, the magnitude of degradation measured by change in strength for any given fiber at any given dose was approximately the same in each case.[†] The presence or absence of oxygen made little difference in the rate of degradation. Thus approximately the same decrease in strength was obtained whether the sample was exposed in oxygen, in nitrogen, or in vacuum. In this respect the cellulosics behave differently from some of the other textile fibers. The possibility of postirradiation effects and the possibility that samples exposed in vacuum or nitrogen might subsequently undergo a change when exposed to air are recognized, but these factors have not been considered. They could possibly influence the conclusions reached with respect to the comparative behavior of cellulosic fibers when exposed in the presence and absence of oxygen.

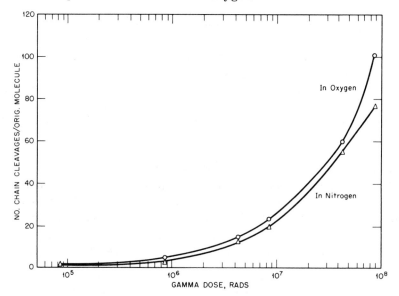

Fɪɢ. 11.2   Effect of irradiation on cellulose at about 75°F. (From F. A. Blouin and J. C. Arthur, Jr., *Textile Research Journal*, Ref. 2.)

When measurements more sensitive than tensile strength were used to evaluate degradation, a slightly greater effect was noted between exposure in an oxygen atmosphere and in a nitrogen atmosphere.[2]

Figure 11.2 shows[2] the rate of chain cleavage in cotton as determined by viscosity change.

The major structural changes that occur in cotton cellulose during

[†] Reactor exposures referred to in Table 11.1 were conducted in a water-cooled port, hole W-52, of the Brookhaven Research Reactor. The conversion factor used, regardless of textile composition, was 1 rad = 1.14×10^9 slow neutrons/cm² (cadmium-covered cobalt).

gamma irradiation, in addition to the chain cleavage shown in Fig. 11.2, are the formation of carbonyl groups and the formation of carboxyl groups. The dose curves for these changes are all similar in shape. Thus the cellulose chain is not significantly affected chemically until it receives a dose greater than 1 megarad. After this, the number of depolymerizations, the number of carboxyl groups formed, and the number of carbonyl groups formed increase rapidly with further increases in dose. The formation of carbonyl groups is by far the most predominant chemical change that occurs. This is borne out by the appearance of infrared absorption bands at 5.75 μ for samples having fairly high doses of radiation (45 megarads and above).[2] (The C=O of both carbonyl and carboxyl groups show absorption in the 5.45- to 6.5-μ range.)

Approximately twenty times more carbonyl-group formations occur in radiolysis than carboxyl-group formations or chain cleavages. Numerically, the formation of carboxyl groups at the various dosage levels is about the same as the chain cleavages that occur at the same level. This suggests that each chain cleavage causes the formation of one carboxyl group. At 87 megarads the number of depolymerization actions per gram of cellulose is 0.95×10^{20} in an oxygen atmosphere. (For nitrogen-atmosphere irradiations, a value of 0.66×10^{20} was obtained.) This compared to 1.02×10^{20} depolymerizations found at 87 megarads by Saeman et al.[16] for cotton linters irradiated with high-energy cathode rays.

For cellulosics irradiation always produces losses in strength (or tenacity), in elongation, and in modulus. Cotton and rayon become water soluble and extremely sensitive to alkalies as measured by solubility or by swelling characteristics.[20] Cotton that has been exposed to about 100 megarads is approximately 75% soluble in 1% boiling sodium hydroxide solution. At the same level of exposure, cotton dissolves to the extent of about 10% in water.[2] This behavior reflects unusual changes in the structure of the irradiated material. This solubility behavior is independent of whether the materials are exposed in air or in nitrogen. Small changes are observed in the moisture regain of cotton; this would suggest that there is no marked alteration of the submicroscopic structure. It must also be concluded that the observed chemical changes do not markedly affect the regain values.[2]

11-2.1 EVIDENCE OF OXIDATION

Oxidation in cotton and rayon during exposure to radiation has been clearly established by several workers.[5,6,25] However, neither the mechanism of formation nor the location of new groups in the cellulose molecule has been determined. It was concluded that the degradation products were mainly oxidized celluloses of the acidic type; the formation of a cellulose peroxide was also suggested.[6] The irradiated cotton had a lower than normal affinity for direct dyes and a greater than normal affinity for basic dyes. Substantive dyes of known behavior toward degraded celluloses have been used to show evidence of oxidation in cotton and rayon after exposure to gamma rays and to reactor radiation.[25]

The formation of the acid groups on oxidation was also demonstrated by changes in base exchange properties using radioactive-tracer techniques.[5] These groups can be detected in cotton at a dose level as low as 10^4 rads. The relative order of affinity of the cations investigated for the binding sites on irradiated cotton was calcium > cobalt > sodium.

11-2.2 RELATIVE RATES OF DEGRADATION AS DETERMINED BY PHYSICAL-PROPERTY CHANGES

At equal calculated radiation doses, reactor radiation and gamma rays alone have no apparent difference in effect on any given fiber (cotton, rayon, or acetate). The changes in strength, elongation, modulus, or viscosity (degree of polymerization) are identical at a given dose level. Moreover, with textile fibers the dose rate makes little difference, and, as in the case of different sources of radiation, the ultimate effect on the fiber is a function of the total dose only.[21]

The rates of degradation of cotton, rayon, and acetate differ somewhat. The number of chain scissions after any period of irradiation can be calculated by

$$L = 100 \left(\frac{1}{DP} - \frac{1}{DP_0} \right) \tag{11.1}$$

where L is the percentage of linkages broken, DP indicates the degree of polymerization after irradiation, and DP_0 indicates the initial value. Such treatment leads to the curves in Fig. 11.3. For any given amount of radiation, the number of chain scissions is greatest in cotton and least in acetate. Treatment of the data by Sippel's equation[17,18] leads to the same conclusion, namely, that the order of stability is acetate > rayon > cotton.

The relations between degree of polymerization and tenacity of cotton, rayon, and acetate after irradiation for different periods of time in a Co^{60} source are given in Fig. 11.4, where T indicates the tenacity (expressed in grams per denier) after exposure and T_0 indicates the initial value. The minimum dose was 4.3×10^4 rads and corresponds to the first points on the curve in Fig. 11.3. The last points were obtained at a dose of about 2.6×10^7 rads. The degree of polymerization of cotton is lowered rapidly without significant changes in tenacity, a characteristic that is also observed when this fiber is degraded by acid hydrolysis (chain scission). Both acetate and rayon decrease in tenacity (and viscosity) more slowly than cotton. It appears that the fibers are resistant to chain cleavage in the same order as cited above, i.e., acetate > rayon > cotton.

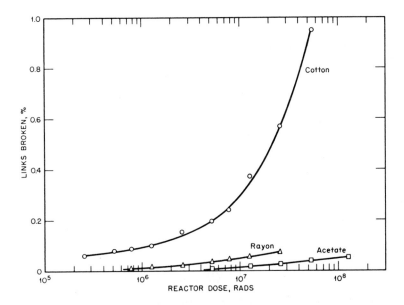

FIG. 11.3 Relation of chain scission in cellulosics to total dose in air at temperatures below 95°F.

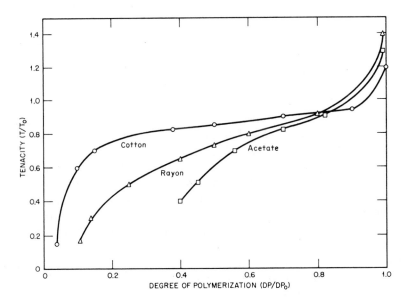

FIG. 11.4 Relation of tenacity to degree of polymerization in cellulose fibers. Gamma dose in air: 4.3×10^4 to 2.6×10^7 rads.

From these studies there appear to be linkages in the native cellulose chain molecule which are susceptible to radiolysis and which are not present in the regenerated materials. This is not surprising since the regenerated materials are native cellulose or its derivative treated to reduce the degree of polymerization. The different behaviors, however, may result from dissimilarities in degrees of crystallinity and/or orientation of the fibers between the native and regenerated cellulosics.

11-2.3 MECHANISM OF DEGRADATION

Much attention has been given to the mechanism of degradation of cellulose and its derivatives by radiation (see Refs. 1, 4, 16, 17, 18, and 29). Saeman, Millett, and Lawton[16] studied the effect of high-energy cathode rays on cotton linters using degree of polymerization as the criterion for degradation. Charlesby[4] used their data, assuming that the effect of radiation was to cause random fracture of the main chains, to verify a theoretical relationship:

$$\log [\eta] = - \log (R + R_0) + \text{constant} \tag{11.2}$$

where $[\eta]$ is intrinsic viscosity, R is the radiation dose, and R_0 is the "virtual" radiation dose needed to produce the initial number-average molecular weight (see Ch. 5, Sect. 5-2.4) from a chain of infinite molecular weight. Charlesby calculated that about 1 megarad produced 1.6 fractures per thousand glucose units in the cellulose chain. Arthur[1] also derived a similar expression relating the changes produced in several molecular properties of purified cotton to radiation dose. He found that his data conformed to

$$\ln P = k' \ln N_n + K' \tag{11.3}$$

where P is the molecular property and N_n is the total dose of gamma radiation measured experimentally. Typical data are shown[1] in Fig. 11.5.

The linear plot obtained by Charlesby (Eq. 11.2) shows that the crystalline and the amorphous regions in cotton are equally subject to chain scission by irradiation. If these two regions were not equally susceptible, the rate of radiolysis would decrease as the number of more readily scissioned centers became smaller relative to the number of more stable centers. The decrease in crystallinity on irradiation has further substantiation; both gamma- and cathode-ray irradiated cotton is hydrolyzed more readily than the original.[2,16] On the other hand, it is reported that the radial X-ray spectrometer tracings of the irradiated cotton show the crystallinity to be unchanged.[2]

When cellulose acetate yarn is exposed to X rays, structural changes can be found;[18,24] and the change in strength is a function of time of exposure (dose). The presence of 3% titanium dioxide delustrant had no influence on the rate of degradation. X-ray diffraction patterns indicate that the irradiation decreases the crystallinity of the cellulose acetate. A film of unplasticized cellulose acetate exposed to X rays was delustered in phenol. This also indicates that X rays have an effect on the crystallinity of the material.

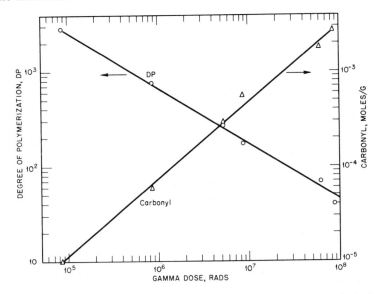

FIG. 11.5 Change in the molecular properties of cotton with radiolysis in oxygen at about 75°F.

From the evidence at hand, the question of the effect of high-energy radiation on the crystallinity of cellulose and its derivatives cannot be completely answered. A random attack is favored in which linkages in both the crystalline and amorphous regions are equally susceptible. This results in a decreased degree of crystallinity.

11-3 Protein Fibers

11-3.1 WOOL

The use of radiation for sterilizing woolen fabrics has been suggested[14] as a way to minimize the shrinkage and felting that occur during the conventional methods of sterilization. The effects of radiation on the fiber, therefore, are a matter of considerable importance. O'Connell and Walden[14] have studied the important single-fiber properties of wools irradiated with several types of high-energy radiation. These included soft X rays, gamma rays from Co[60], cathode rays from both a linear accelerator and a Van de Graaff generator, and ultraviolet light. Kirby and Rutherford[9] investigated the effects of reactor radiation and gamma rays from a Co[60] source.

11-3.1.1 *Radiation Effects on Physical Properties*

When wool is subjected to reactor radiation, the first noticeable change in properties is its susceptibility to damage by alkalies.[9] If the radiation dose is increased above a level of 10 megarads, the increase in susceptibility toward alkalies is accompanied by a decrease in the 30% index. This index is defined as the ratio of the work necessary to extend a single treated fiber 30% in water to the work necessary to extend an untreated fiber. Thus a number less than 1 indicates damage to the fiber.[19] At a 100-megarad dose level (a point at which the wool is completely soluble in alkali solution but fibrous characteristics still remain), only one-third as much energy is required to extend the fiber after exposure as before exposure (30% index, 0.33). The shape of the stress–strain curve of the exposed fiber, however, is identical with that of the unexposed; and the long-range elastic recovery is not lost. This indicates that irradiation does not disrupt the folded-chain configuration of the keratin molecule that is believed to account for the long-range recovery properties of wool. Moreover, the change in the 30% index brought about by nuclear radiation is independent of fiber diameter. Identical 30% indexes have been obtained on fibers of different deniers at given levels of irradiation.

Table 11.2 shows some of the physical properties of single undyed wool

Table 11.2 — EFFECT OF DIFFERENT RADIATION ON THE PROPERTIES OF SINGLE UNDYED WOOL FIBERS IN AIR AT ROOM TEMPERATURE [14]

Radiation source	Dose, 10^6 rads	Property[a]			
		Wet		Dry	
		Str. 30	YM	Str. 30	YM
X ray	0	0.46	10.9	0.95	18.7
	0.9	0.44	9.2	0.92	17.2
	2.8	0.41	9.4	0.92	18.2
	8.1	0.35	7.8	0.85	17.6
Co^{60} gamma rays	0	0.48	11.1	0.97	18.7
	1.8	0.44	8.8	0.90	15.8
	8.7	0.40	8.3	0.88	15.8
	22.4	0.39	7.6	0.87	15.3
Van de Graaff electrons	0	0.46	10.9		
	3.6				
	7.1	0.43	9.6		
Linear accelerator electrons	0	0.46	10.9		
	0.06	0.46	11.1		
	0.21	0.47	11.4		
	2.8	0.46	10.5		
	22.4	0.34	8.9		

[a]Str. 30 is the stress to extend the fiber 30%; YM is the initial modulus.

fibers after exposure to different kinds of radiation. Low doses of radiation do not appreciably damage the fiber, and about 5 megarads is required to produce a perceptible change. Fibers dyed with Rhodamine B are somewhat more resistant to irradiation. Moreover, this dye, which is recognized as having poor wash fastness, became more difficult to remove from the fiber by washing as the time of irradiation of the dyed fiber increased.

11-3.1.2 *Mechanism of Degradation*

As the level of reactor irradiation increases, a decrease in acid-combining capacity and in cystine content is observed.[10] This behavior is characteristic of wool fiber at progressive stages of oxidation by hydrogen peroxide solutions. Another parallel with the latter is that the reactor exposure does not appreciably change the total nitrogen, sulfur, or tyrosine content. If hydrolysis of the protein chains took place, the acid-combining capacity, which is a measure of free amino groups, would be increased, while the nitrogen, sulfur, and tyrosine would remain the same as in unhydrolyzed wool. Thus it is believed that the predominating effect of nuclear radiation on wool when exposed in an atmosphere containing oxygen and water is one of oxidation of cystine. The possibility of some cleavage of amide linkages is not excluded, but there is no experimental evidence for this mechanism of degradation. Finally, O'Connell and Walden[14] concluded that no new cross linkages were developed in wool as a result of irradiation.

There seems to be little question that the cystine in wool is oxidized during irradiation in the presence of oxygen and water. Such oxidation causes the wool to become increasingly sensitive toward alkalies, and the solubility in alkalies can be used to detect the first traces of damage. Because this oxidation constitutes an irreversible change in the chemical structure of the fiber, it is expected that the effect of the irradiation that might be used in sterilization would be cumulative. Although one or two treatments might not appreciably affect the physical properties of the fiber, frequent sterilization would lead to excessive damage.

11-3.2 SILK

There is little published literature dealing with the influence of radiation on silk. It is less stable than wool under the same conditions of exposure, as evidenced by changes in strength, but it is slightly more stable than the cellulosic fibers. There is evidence that some molecular change other than chain scission does occur because, whether the radiation is reactor radiation or gamma rays alone, exposed fibers are insoluble in zinc chloride solution under conditions where the unexposed fibers are soluble.[23] The nature of the modified structure is not understood.

11-4 Polyamide, Polyester, and Polyacrylic Fibers

Nylon 66 and 6, Dacron, and Orlon are characteristic, respectively, of this group. They have been examined rather extensively for their behavior toward radiation. The tendency of these polymers to cross link has been well established and is discussed in Ch. 5. Upon prolonged exposure, the materials deteriorate; and any desirable effect that might be produced· by cross linking, such as increase in modulus, is ultimately lost.

11-4.1 COMPARISONS

A comparison of the behavior of tire cords made from nylon, Dacron, and Orlon after exposure to a Co^{60} source in air and in vacuum is shown in Table 11.3. There is a marked difference in the effects of these two condi-

Table 11.3 — CHANGE IN STRENGTH OF TIRE CORDS WITH GAMMA IRRADIATION AT ROOM TEMPERATURE

Type cord	Atm.	Tensile strength in pounds for given dose in megarads					Change in strength after
		0	0.09	0.9	2.6	8.7	10×10^6 rads, %
Nylon 66 {	Air	26.5	23.7	19.7	16.2	12.7	-59
	Vac		20.9	25.0	20.6	23.1	-15
Nylon 6 {	Air	24.2	21.1	20.5	17.9	10.7	-62
	Vac.		22.4	21.0	22.4	21.4	-13
Nylon 66 HT {	Air	23.6	22.3	20.2	17.2	11.7	-57
	Vac.		23.0	22.1	20.2	21.4	-10
Dacron {	Air	35.0	37.3	33.6	34.7	31.7	-17
	Vac.		35.7	36.4	35.1	37.2	+7
Orlon {	Air	13.2	12.8	11.8	11.4	10.8	-20
	Vac.		13.0	12.2	11.4	11.9	-11

tions in contrast to the situation with the cellulosic fibers. The most noticeable offender is nylon. Loss of strength in air is approximately five times that in vacuum. When their performances in vacuum are compared, there are no great differences between these polymers, except possibly in the case of Dacron, which appears to be highly resistant. This is expected in view of the high aromatic content of the polymer. Although the performance of nylon from a strength standpoint after exposure in air and vacuum is quite different, certain other properties do not reveal this behavior. For example, the melting points of both nylon and Dacron are unchanged at the highest dosage indicated in Table 11.3.

Irradiation in air lowers the elongation at break and the flex fatigue. Irradiation does not improve the high-temperature stress–strain properties of the tire cords. Shrinkage tension at elevated temperatures of the polyamides is reduced by about 50% at an exposure level of 10 megarads. Dacron at a similar level of exposure increases[7] in shrinkage tension by about 17%.

A further comparison of the radiation stabilities of these materials is shown in Fig. 11.6. These data were obtained from parachute fabrics

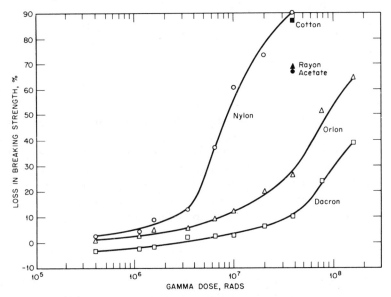

Fig. 11.6 Radiation-induced change in strength of synthetic fabrics (cotton shown for comparison).[13] Exposures in air at less than 95°F.

(nylon).[26] Both nylon and Dacron exhibited slightly better stability to irradiation when they were dyed olive drab or orange.[27] The data in Fig. 11.6 conform very closely to the data shown in Table 11.3 for the exposure of tire cords of nylon, Dacron, and Orlon to gamma radiation.

11-4.2 Cross Linking as Influenced by Draw Ratio†

There is no evidence that beneficial effects through cross linking are obtained by the exposure of nylon, Dacron, or Orlon textiles to levels of radiation above 10 megarads. Nevertheless, at levels below this value, benefits may be obtained. On exposure to small radiation doses, Dacron was shown to increase in modulus of elasticity; other physical properties were not deteriorated.[23,24] Filaments of different draw ratios did not act the same either initially or as the radiation dose was increased. Undrawn

† Draw ratio is the ratio of the stretched length of a filament to its original length.

Dacron and filaments drawn to the ratios of 2.5 to 1 and 3 to 1 increased in modulus continuously between the radiation doses of 0.1 to 10 megarads. Filaments drawn to a ratio of 3.5 to 1, although exhibiting an increase in modulus at the beginning of the exposure, i.e., at a level of 0.1 megarad, decreased in modulus as the irradiation continued.

At a draw ratio of 3.5 to 1, there is no difference between the effects of radiation on a crystalline Dacron filament and on an amorphous filament. Regardless of draw ratio the behavior of a bright filament and a dull filament do not differ. This indicates the absence of any specific effect of titanium dioxide, the dulling agent normally used in synthetic textile fibers.

Cross linking in nylon and Orlon, as evidenced by an increase in modulus, is also obtained at low levels of exposure. The degree of cross linking in these materials is also a function of draw ratio. Generally, the effect shows up more quickly in the undrawn filaments, i.e., the ones not highly oriented. At the levels of exposure where there are no adverse effects on fiber properties, melting point and solubility remain unchanged. As the radiation dose is increased beyond about 50 megarads, nylon is no longer soluble in phenol but forms a gel. It remains soluble, however, in formic acid. Orlon loses its complete solubility in dimethyl formamide.[23]

From this work,[23] it may be concluded that the degree of orientation of filaments from nylon (6 or 66), Dacron, and Orlon has some influence on the tendency of the polymer to cross link during exposure to radiation. On the other hand, it might be concluded that cross linking of unoriented polymers is more easily detected in terms of a change in modulus than is cross linking in oriented polymers. In any event this change in structure at low levels of exposure is of a low order of magnitude and is not sufficient to elevate the melting point of the polymers. As the radiation dose is increased above 10 megarads, the materials acquire abnormal solubility characteristics. This indicates molecular changes concomitant with cross linking. However, other radiation effects predominate over those of cross linking to deteriorate the filaments.

11-5 Radiation Tolerance of Textiles

Textile fibers can be divided into two broad categories with respect to their behavior toward radiation. One group is predominantly degraded no matter what criterion is used to establish the effect; the other group is significantly more resistant to radiation and at low dose levels may show an increase in modulus, indicating cross linking, without significant changes in other properties. Cotton, rayon, acetate, and wool are in the first category. Nylon, Orlon, and Dacron are in the second group. Nylon is a borderline case since it is relatively unstable when exposed in air. Neither the type of radiation nor the source seems to be important; the measured effect is a function only of the total energy absorbed by the material.

The over-all radiation tolerance of textiles is noted in Table 11.4. Three criteria are shown:

1. Strength has been considered more than anything else in evaluating the effects. While strength is not by any means the only important property in textile materials, it is common to think of this factor in determining the stability toward environments other than radiation and under various conditions.

2. Viscosity is used to evaluate molecular properties as an indication of the first significant change in fiber structure, which, in turn, influences properties.

3. The level of radiation that causes the first complete destruction in fibrous characteristics of the various materials is of interest. However, it can only be estimated and is of limited significance, as noted in Table 11.4. It is obvious that these values change as the conditions are varied.

Table 11.4 — RADIATION TOLERANCE OF TEXTILES
IN AIR BELOW 95 °F

	Dose, megarads		
	Where loss in strength becomes significant	Where viscosity is changed significantly	First complete destruction of fibrous properties[a]
Group I			
Cotton	0.1	0.055	30
Rayon	0.8	0.5	80
Acetate	1	1.3	100
Wool	5		100
Group II			
Nylon 6 or 66	2	1.1	100
Dynel	4		
Orlon	8		1,000
Dacron	25		10,000

[a]Estimates by extrapolation; values may not be realistic.

The modification of textile-fiber properties by radiation per se to produce improved products does not appear promising. Even though at low levels of radiation the modulus of nylon, Orlon, and Dacron is increased, the observation is without any practical significance; the use of radiation to improve the fibers in this respect is not justified. As a gross effect, the properties of all textile materials are harmed by exposure to radiation under ordinary conditions. The possibility exists, however, that textile fibers may be changed for the better by the in situ polymerization of monomers or by graft polymerization in a radiation environment. In any practical work of this nature for the industrial application of radiation in the field of textiles, the dosages would necessarily need to be limited to those that do not have a serious effect on fiber properties.

It is suggested that the highest practical level of exposure for the fibers in common use should not exceed the following:

Nylon, cotton: 1 megarad

Rayon, acetate, silk, wool: 20 megarads

Orlon, Dacron: 50 megarads

References

Several of the following were cited in the text as authority for statements made. Others were not quoted but are included because they contain pertinent information. All were consulted in the preparation of this chapter.

1. Arthur, J. C., Jr., The Effects of Gamma Radiation on Cotton. Part II: Proposed Mechanism of the Effects of High Energy Gamma Radiation on Some of the Molecular Properties of Purified Cotton, *Textile Research J., 28*(3): 204 (March 1958).

2. Blouin, F. A., and Arthur, J. C., Jr., The Effects of Gamma Radiation on Cotton. Part I: Some of the Properties of Purified Cotton Irradiated in Oxygen and Nitrogen Atmospheres, *Textile Research J., 28*(3): 198 (March 1958).

3. Bopp, C. D., and Sisman, O., How Radiation Changes Polymer Mechanical Properties, *Nucleonics, 13*(10): 51 (October 1955); see also USAEC Report ORNL-928, p. 225, 1951 and ORNL-1373, p. 81, 1954, Oak Ridge National Laboratory.

4. Charlesby, A., The Degradation of Cellulose by Ionizing Radiation, *J. Polymer Sci., 15*(79): 263 (January 1955).

5. Demint, R. J., and Arthur, J. C., Jr., The Effects of Gamma Radiation on Cotton. Part III: Base Exchange Properties of Irradiated Cotton, *Textile Research J., 29*(3): 276 (March 1959).

6. Gilfillan, E. S., and Linden, L., Effects of Nuclear Radiation on the Strength of Yarns, *Textile Research J., 25*(9): 773 (September 1955); Some Effects of Nuclear Irradiations on Cotton Yarn, *Textile Research J., 27*(2): 87 (February 1957).

7. Harmon, D. J., Effects of Cobalt-60 Gamma Radiation on the Physical Properties of Textile Cords, *Textile Research J., 27*(4): 318 (April 1957).

8. Kaswell, E. R., *Textile Fibers, Yarns and Fabrics,* Reinhold Publishing Corp., New York, 1953.

9. Kirby, R. D., and Rutherford, H. A., The Effect of Nuclear Radiation on Wool Fiber, *Textile Research J., 25*(6): 569 (June 1955).

10. Kirby, R. D., and Rutherford, H. A., Effect of Nuclear Radiation on Wool Fiber, to be published in *Textile Research Journal.*

11. Lawton, E. J., Bueche, A. M., and Balwit, J. S., Irradiation of Polymers by High Energy Electrons, *Nature, 172*(4367): 76 (July 1953).

12. McFarlane, Samuel B., *Technology of Synthetic Fibers,* Chap. 10, p. 255, Fairchild Publications, Inc., New York, 1953.

13. McGrath, J., and Johnson, R. H., *The Effects of Gamma Radiation on Textile Materials,* Report WADC-TR-56-15, Wright Air Development Center, February 1956.

14. O'Connell, R. A., and Walden, M. K., Influence of Ionizing Radiations on Wool Fiber Properties, *Textile Research J., 27*(7): 516 (July 1957).

15. Orr, R. S., DeLuca, L. B., Burgis, A. W., and Grant, J. N., Fiber Structure and Mechanical Properties of Untreated and Modified Cottons, *Textile Research J., 29* (2): 144 (February 1959).

16. Saeman, J. F., Millett, M. A., and Lawton, E. J., Effect of High Energy Cathode Rays on Cellulose, *Ind. Eng. Chem., 44*(12): 2848 (December 1952).
17. Sippel, A., Regularity of the Degradation of Textile Fibers with High Energy Radiations and Heat, *Melliand Texilber, 38:* 898 (August 1957).
18. Sippel, A., Changing the Tensile Strength and Degree of Polymerization of Artificial Fibers by Irradiation and the Relation of These Phenomena to the Molecular Fine Structure, Especially of Cellulose, *Kolloid-Z., 112:* 80 (February–March 1949).
19. Sookne, A. M., and Harris, M., Stress–Strain Characteristics of Wool as Related to its Chemical Constitution, *J. Research NBS, 19*(5): 535 (November 1937).
20. Teszler, O., and Hefti, H., A Method for the Determination of Cotton Degradation After Radioactive Irradiation, *Textil-Rundschau, 13:* 61 (February 1958).
21. Teszler, O., Kiser, L. H., Campbell, P. W., and Rutherford, H. A., The Effect of Nuclear Radiation on Fibrous Materials. Part III: Relative Order of Stability of Cellulosic Fibers, *Textile Research J., 28*(6): 456 (June 1958).
22. Teszler, O., and Rutherford, H. A., North Carolina State College, Raleigh, unpublished data, 1958.
23. Teszler, O., and Rutherford, H. A., The Effect of Nuclear Radiation on Fibrous Materials, in *Proceedings of the Second International Conference on Peaceful Uses of Atomic Energy, Geneva, 1958,* Vol. 29, p. 228, United Nations, New York, 1959.
24. Teszler, O., and Rutherford, H. A., The Effect of Nuclear Radiation on Fibrous Materials. Part I: Dacron Polyester Fiber, *Textile Research J., 26*(10): 796 (October 1956).
25. Teszler, O., Wiehart, H., and Rutherford, H. A., The Effect of Nuclear Radiation on Fibrous Materials. Part II: Dyeing Characteristics of Cotton and Rayon, *Textile Research J., 28*(2): 131 (February 1958).
26. U. S. Department of Defense, *Cloth, Nylon Parachute,* U. S. Air Force, Military Specification MIL-C-7020C (ASG), August 1958.
27. U. S. Department of Defense, *Cloth, Nylon Parachute Drag,* U. S. Air Force, Military Specification MIL-C-8021B, February 1958.
28. Wall, L. A., Factors Influencing the Behavior of Polymers Exposed to High Energy Radiation, *J. Polymer Sci., 17*(83): 141 (May 1955).
29. Winogradoff, N. N., X-Ray Irradiation of Cellulose Acetate, *Nature, 165*(4185): 72 (January 1950).

CHAPTER 12

Coatings and Films

By James G. Carroll and Robert O. Bolt

12-1 Introduction

This chapter is concerned mainly with protective coatings, most of which are applied in the liquid phase by brush, dip, or spray. Following application, these coatings form a thin, tough film (about 1 mil or 0.001 in. thick) by solvent evaporation, oxidation of the vehicle, and/or polymerization of unsaturates. Films that are preformed, e.g., poly(vinyl chloride) and cellophane, as in packaging, are also considered here.

Perhaps the most commonly used coatings are paints, mechanical mixtures of inorganic pigments and varnish. The varnish, or vehicle portion, is composed of the following:

1. The oil, which, with the resin, forms a tough film by oxidation and polymerization. (Linseed oil† is the most used; other unsaturated oils employed include fish oil, castor oil, soybean oil, tung oil, and oiticica oil.)

2. The resin, which speeds up drying and imparts hardness, gloss, resistance, and adhesion to the film. (Alkyd, e.g., glyceryl phthalate, and phenolic, e.g., phenol-formaldehyde, resins are most used; chlorinated rubber and silicone types are also used.)

3. The thinner, which adjusts the consistency of the mixture. (Turpentine and petroleum materials are the most used.)

4. The drier, which catalyzes hardening of the film. (Driers are metal soaps of organic acids, chiefly cobalt naphthenate but also metal linoleates and resinates.)

Any ratio of ingredients is possible; that chosen depends upon the application. Pigments are optional.

Lacquers differ from paints because lacquers form a film from the nonvolatile constituents after evaporation of the solvent. The ingredients of lacquers include:

1. Cellulosic polymers, which form the film. (Cellulose nitrate is most commonly used.)

---

† Linseed oil is a triglyceride of C_{18} unsaturated fatty acids, approximately 15% oleic, 45% linoleic, 35% linolenic, and 5% other.

2. Plasticizers, which impart flexibility to the film. (They may be vegetable oils, e.g., linseed, polymeric resins, e.g., alkyds, or monomeric chemicals, e.g., esters of dibasic acids. The last group, especially phthalates and sebacates, is widely used.)
3. Resins, which are added to impart specific properties to the film as in paints.
4. Solvents used are mostly acetates and ketones.

As with paints a wide range in the ratio and types of ingredients, including pigments, is possible; the choice depends upon the intended use.

Of particular interest is the wide variety of synthetic resins that may be added to paints or lacquers or used alone. Some of these resins are listed in Table 12.1.

Table 12.1—RESINS USED IN COATINGS

Resin type	Chemical type
Varnish:	
Alkyd	Glyceryl phthalates
Rosin	Abietic acid
Phenolic	Phenol-formaldehyde
Terpene	Cyclic hydrocarbons
Coumarone-indene	Polymers and copolymers
Petroleum	Unsaturated hydrocarbons
Epon[a]	Condensation products of epichlorohydrin and bisphenol
Amino	Urea-formaldehyde
Melamine	Triazines
Rubber	Rubber and chlorinated rubber
Vinyl	Poly(vinyl chloride); vinylidene chloride-acrylonitrile copolymer
Acrylic	Polymers of acrylic acid
Silicone	Silicone polymers
Cellulosics	Cellulose nitrate
Cellophane[b]	Cellulose plasticized with glycerol

[a] Shell Chemical Corporation.
[b] E. I. du Pont de Nemours & Co., Inc.

Protective coatings are used most frequently in radiation fields to prevent corrosion of equipment and to facilitate decontamination of equipment that comes in contact with radioactive debris, as in hot cells. Less important uses include coating the inside of food containers with baked-resin lacquers, packaging food with plastics for irradiation, lining storage basins with asphalts for radioactive wastes, applying wax coatings for containers, and using paints for liners of radiochemical processing tanks. In general, the following properties[21] are desirable in the application of films:

1. Resistance to

    a. Acid, alkali, grease, solvents
    b. Water immersion and permeation
    c. Discoloration with heat or aging
    d. Oxidative decomposition

2. Adhesion, hardness
3. Flexibility, impact resistance
4. Abrasion resistance
5. Tensile strength, elongation
6. Flow and leveling

12-2 General Effects of Irradiation

Chemically, coatings and films are polymers that behave, in general, as described in Ch. 5 (Sect. 5-6, 5-7, and 5-8). During radiolysis covalent bonds in the polymer molecule break, and thus changes occur throughout the coating. In an end-of-chain break, the smaller fragment may diffuse through the material to the surface (or to an imperfection) and emerge as a gas molecule at that point. The same effect would probably result from the detachment of small side chains. A reactive center, i.e., an ion fragment or a free radical, is created at the point of the break. This reactive center can then polymerize or cross link. Only a few of these cross links are needed to change the properties of the polymer significantly, i.e., to cause a rigid structure. Scission in the main polymer chain would bring about the opposite effects, i.e., decreased rigidity.

Important effects on the radiolysis of coatings result from the presence of the plasticizer. For example, degradation products from the plasticizer can be poorer solvents than the parent. Their generation can cause desolvation of polymer molecules to increase both crystallinity and rigidity of the structure. Similarly, increased cross linking of the polymer shrinks the structure and can squeeze out liquid plasticizer from the matrix. Thus the plasticizer can become segregated in droplets throughout the sample. Both the cross linking and the separation of plasticizer cause an increase in the rigidity of the irradiated sample.

The influence of other ingredients on radiation stability is probably less important. Driers are present only in small amounts and have little effect on radiolysis. With pigments, inorganic species suffer relatively little damage compared to organic species. Significant proportions of certain inorganic pigments reduce the total damage per unit volume of the specimen. On the other hand, finely divided metallic pigments can catalyze radiation damage.

Generally, ionizing radiation can damage organic coatings in several ways:

1. Blistering, from the separation of liquid or gas phases within the polymer.
2. Cracking, from shrinking of the polymer framework.
3. Peeling, from failure in adhesion.
4. Permeability, from increased porosity due to gassing.
5. Appearance, from discoloration.
6. Strength, from changes due to scission or cross linking.

Whether a coating is acceptable or not, after undergoing radiation-induced changes, depends upon the requirements set for its use. For example, an organic coating that becomes quite rigid during gamma irradiation might be quite satisfactory on concrete. The same coating would be useless on a flexible surface. The effects of radiation on a given coating are often difficult to predict because of the individual contributions of various ingredients whose identities frequently are not known. For this reason, most of the studies of radiation effects described here have been on specific commercial formulas and have been conducted under selected test conditions.

12-3 Coatings

12-3.1 GENERAL TYPES

Six different organic coatings applied to AZ-31 magnesium alloy that had been treated with a zinc chromate primer† were tested.[15,16] The specimens were irradiated for a range of doses up to 44×10^8 rads at 75°F. Following gamma exposure, some specimens were baked for 50 hr at 250 and 500°F. The coatings were then tested for adhesion, abrasion resistance,

Table 12.2—RELATIVE STABILITY OF ORGANIC COATING[15]

Coating	Approximate maximum gamma-radiation resistance, 10^8 rads
Phenolic (phenol-formaldehyde)	44
Silicone-alkyd enamel	9 to 44
Alkyd enamels:	
40% phthalic anhydride	9 to 44
32% phthalic anhydride	6 to 9
Epoxy	4 to 9
Fluorinated vinyl[a]	4 to 9
Nitrocellulose (white lacquer)	4 to 6

[a] Trifluorochloroethylene-vinylidene chloride polymer.

humidity resistance, and flexibility. In general, all coatings showed a resistance sufficiently high to make them useful in radiation environments,

† Dow No. 7, Dow Chemical Co.

as shown in Table 12.2. In most cases baking upgraded the properties of the irradiated materials.

After 9×10^8 rads and 50 hr at 500°F, the phenolic coatings retained their properties better than any of the other coatings tested. They had good abrasion resistance and adhesion and were little affected by exposure to 100% relative humidity for 28 days at 120°F. Silicone-alkyd enamel actually showed improved properties at 9×10^8 rads but became powdery and brittle at 44×10^8 rads. The epoxy and the fluorinated vinyl were degraded after 9×10^8 rads. There was, however, no reported attack on the magnesium by off-products of the fluorinated material. The nitrocellulose lacquer showed the least resistance of the coatings tested.

12-3.2 INFLUENCE OF PIGMENTS

Considerable differences in the effects of different pigments in the same resin were reported[16] after exposure to 8×10^8 rads. White titanium dioxide appeared to accelerate radiation damage in a nitrocellulose lacquer; toluidine red showed little effect; and carbon black inhibited radiation damage.

Similar paint films with and without various pigments were exposed[26] on aluminum panels to 1.5×10^7 rads of gamma radiation. The base vehicles were vinyl chloride, chlorinated rubber, and an oil paint. Pigments used included white lead, titanium dioxide, antimony oxide, calcium carbonate, barium sulfate, talc, iron oxide, chromium oxide, carbon black, Hansa yellow, and toluidine red. The pigmented samples contained 30 wt. % pigment to 100 wt. % vehicle. Regardless of the pigmentation the paints all behaved as expected from the stability of the base coatings; i.e., pigments exerted little effect at this low dose. At higher doses (or elevated temperature), catalytic action of the pigment might occur.

12-3.3 EFFECT OF SURFACE

The type of material coated is important. Porous material, such as concrete, and readily corroded material, such as iron, are easily made radioactive by contamination. Therefore a protective paint for use over these materials must have a smooth, nonporous film to facilitate decontamination. Polyethylene sheet is excellent; a stripable paint would be advantageous.

Bresee et al.[4] irradiated 23 commercial coatings comprising 11 different polymer bases. These coatings were applied to several different surfaces, including aluminum, steel, and concrete. Table 12.3 shows the gamma dose at which the coating failed or the maximum dose applied to the coating without failure. The influence of the surface to which the coating was applied is evident. The differences are significant; e.g., a vinyl coating (Amercoat-33) which failed on the aluminum panel after 2×10^8 rads did not fail on a concrete panel until 10×10^8 rads, about five times the gamma dose.

Coatings on concrete were generally more stable. This is attributed to (1) the greater chemical resistance of concrete to attack by gases and liquid decomposition products from the coating degradation and (2) the

Table 12.3—THE RADIOLYSIS OF MOUNTED PROTECTIVE COATINGS[4]

Polymer base	Trade name	Surface	Gamma dose (air), 10^8 rads	Appearance[a]
Furan	Alkaloy-550[b]	Concrete	9.4	No failure
		Steel rod	8.4	No failure
Modified phenolic	Amphesive-801[b]	Concrete	9.4	No failure
		Steel rod	8.7	Drastically embrittled
Silicone alkyd	Solar Silicone[c]	Concrete	6.7	No failure
	Alkyd	Steel	6.7	No failure
Epoxy	Epon-395[d]	Steel	6.7	No failure
Vinyl chloride	Amercoat-33[e]	Aluminum	2.1	Failed; blistered
		Concrete	10.5	Failed; blistered
		Steel	8.7	Failed; blistered
Styrene	Prufcoat[f]	Concrete	8.7	Failed; brittle
		Steel	8.7	Failed; cracked
		Steel (wet)	0.8	Failed; cracked
Vinyl	Corrosite-22[g]	Aluminum	2.1	Failed; blistered
		Concrete	11.0	Borderline failure

[a] Examined for blisters, cracking, hardening, tackiness, etc.
[b] Atlas Mineral Products Co.
[c] Solar Division, Gamble Skogmo, Inc.
[d] The Glidden Co.
[e] Amercoat Corp.
[f] Prufcoat Laboratories, Inc.
[g] Corrosite Corp.

absorption of these products in the porous concrete structure. In the case of vinyl coatings, the chemical attack would be from the halogen acids. Of the coatings tested only four polymer-base types did not fail at the maximum dose of about 10^9 rads. These were the furans, the epoxies, the silicone alkyds, and one modified phenolic specimen.

A second phase of this work[4] involved the chemical resistance and ease of decontamination of the protective coatings after gamma irradiation. Chemical resistance was determined by applying the paint to a 3/8-in. steel rod, irradiating specimens, and then immersing them in various reagents, including nitric, sulfuric, and hydrochloric acids; sodium hydroxide; and methyl isobutyl ketone. Additional specimens were prepared by painting panels of aluminum, steel, and concrete. After gamma irradiation of 1 to

10×10^8 rads, the panels were contaminated with fission products, which were removed by subsequent scrubbing.

Several of the irradiated coatings showed poor resistance to the chemical reagents. Two vinyl materials were easily decontaminated at 10^8 rads but failed at twice this dose. The silicone alkyd was difficult to decontaminate on concrete, and the coating failed on steel during scrubbing. One each of a furan-base and an epoxy-base coating (Alkaloy-550 and Epon-395) showed excellent chemical resistance and were easily decontaminated.

The suitability of coatings for a processing plant was investigated.[28] Fourteen commercial paints were applied to concrete panels and irradiated. All hardened after 10^9 rads, but results favored a furan-base coating (Alkaloy-550 or Durolon-36). After irradiation this type resisted chemical attack and was easily decontaminated of fission products.

Amercoat-35 was recommended[9] for use in low-level cells to 4.5×10^8 rads. Alkaloy-550 (available only in black) with a coating of white Zerox was recommended for high-level cells to 10^9 rads. Coatings of this type were judged[11] suitable for the Materials Testing Reactor underwater gamma facility to 10^9 rads in places where dose rates do not exceed about 10^5 rads/hr.

12-3.4 COATINGS MADE BY IRRADIATION

Gotoda[12,13] irradiated castor oil in a hydrogen atmosphere and found that the oil polymerized and could be used as a coating material. Linseed oil, cuttle fish oil, and soybean oil were irradiated under hydrogen, nitrogen, and air atmospheres and were found to be transformed into higher polymer oils. The cuttle fish oil was transformed into a coating that was anti-corrosive, but no water-resistant coatings were formed.

Radiation was used[2] to form coatings that were found to protect against chemical agents. Suspensions of 300-mesh metal powders, e.g., lead, antimony, and iron, in solutions of plastics and suitable solvents, such as vinyl polymers in chloroform or ethyl acetate, were irradiated. Useful mixtures contained as much as 97 wt. % metal powder in a plastic-solvent solution.

12-4 Packaging Film

Several samples of commercial packaging films were irradiated[18] with electrons to about 10^8 rads. Polyethylene,† polyester,‡ cellulose acetate,§ cellophane,¶ and polystyrene†† were placed on a conveyor belt and passed

† Alathon 10 and Alathon 14, E. I. du Pont de Nemours & Co., Inc.
‡ Mylar, E. I. du Pont de Nemours & Co., Inc.
§ Type CA-43 and Type CA-48, E. I. du Pont de Nemours & Co., Inc.
¶ Type CD and Type K-202, E. I. du Pont de Nemours & Co., Inc.
†† Plax Corp.

under an electron beam. Since the samples were in polyethylene bags, they were in contact with a minimum amount of oxygen.

The mechanical properties of most films deteriorated on exposure. There was, however, a wide variation among films as follows:

1. Polystyrene showed very little change[18] in mechanical properties (see Fig. 12.1); electrical properties were not changed markedly.

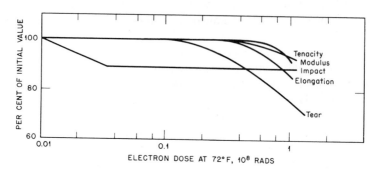

Fig. 12.1 Effect of irradiation on the mechanical properties of polystyrene. (From H. G. LeClair and W. H. Cobbs, Jr., *Industrial and Engineering Chemistry*, Ref. 18.)

2. Cellulosic films were seriously degraded[18] in mechanical properties, as shown in Fig. 12.2 for K-202 cellophane. (The K-202 cellophane has a coating of vinylidene chloride copolymer for moisture proofness which liberated large amounts of chlorides.) Gas permeabilities appeared to increase, although the brittleness of the irradiated specimen precluded accurate measurement. The permeability and strength characteristics were degraded enough to impair the use of cellophane as a packaging film at about 5×10^6 rads.

3. The polyester suffered slight impairment of mechanical properties similar in degree to that for polystyrene. The reduction in electrical resistivity was more marked and could be due to either cleavage of glycol end groups from the polymer chain or preferential degradation of the low-molecular-weight fractions of the material. Thin films of Mylar (polyethylene terephthalate) were less damaged than thick films.

4. Vinylidene chloride copolymer film liberated chlorides; this caused a lowering of pH.

5. Polyethylene film acted like limp cellophane after 10^7 rads. This was due to a sharp increase in impact strength; i.e., it became difficult to cause an initial break, but once broken, the film tore easily.

At a food-sterilization exposure level (1 to 3×10^6 rads), the properties of all films tested were essentially unaffected by irradiation. Meyers[19] confirmed that radiation reduced the permeability of polyethylene film (about 50% after 10^8 rads). Based on elongation and tear, packaging films rank as follows in their stability to 10^8 rads: polystyrene, Mylar polyester, cellulose acetate, polyethylene, and cellophane.

The order is changed somewhat if gassing is used as the sole criterion. Based on total gas evolution and change in chemical structure (gamma irradiations at 5.8×10^6 rads), the decreasing order of stability of a series

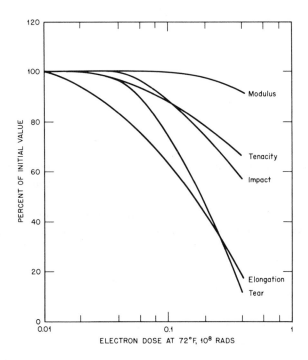

Fig. 12.2 Influence of irradiation on the mechanical properties of cellophane. (From H. G. LeClair and W. H. Cobbs, Jr., *Industrial and Engineering Chemistry*, Ref. 18.)

of 3.5-mil films was polystyrene, rubber hydrochloride and poly(chloro-trifluoroethylenes), polyesters, poly(vinylidene chlorides), polyethylene-coated polyester, high-density polyethylene, and low-density polyethylene.

The nature and amount of the major decomposition products from typical films are given in Table 12.4.

The gaseous products and their effects on tastes and odors are important in the use of such films in packaging food for preservation by irradiation. Gassing alone is an inadequate criterion of performance, particularly in extrapolating to higher doses; it is, however, sometimes useful as a rough index of stability for unknown materials. Ryan[22] irradiated a number of insulating materials and varnishes and developed an empirical equation for predicting gas evolution.

Table 12.4—GASEOUS PRODUCTS FROM IRRADIATED[a] FILMS

Material	Atmosphere	Product, μmole/g	
		Total	Major constituent
Low-density polyethylene	Vacuum	18.52	17.72 H_2
	Air	36.96	31.53 H_2
Polyester	Vacuum	1.48	1.22 CO_2
	Air	3.18	1.53 CO_2
Polystyrene	Vacuum	0.34	0.18 N_2
	Air	1.96	0.89 CO_2
Poly(vinylidene chloride)	Vacuum	11.97	10.33 HCl
	Air	5.97	4.84 CO_2

[a] 5.6×10^6 rads gamma dose.

12-5 Asphalts[4,14,27]

Structurally, asphalts are chiefly naphthenic and aromatic-ring compounds with aliphatic side chains. Approximate composition is expressed by $C_{85}H_{10}S_3NO$. These materials are derived from the nondestructive distillation of crude oil and can be further processed by air blowing or blending. Asphalts have been proposed as liners for radiochemical waste storage basins. Radioactive wastes vary in activity level from 10^{-4} to 10^2 curies/liter. Storage times may vary from a few years to possibly centuries. As a rough generalization a liner would receive a dose of 10^9 rads in something over 25 years.

Radiation causes asphalts to harden, i.e., increase in softening point and decrease in penetration, as shown in Table 12.5 for sprayable membranes.

Table 12.5—RADIATION-INDUCED HARDENING OF
ASPHALTIC MATERIALS[14]
(Gamma irradiation with 4.4×10^8 rads, 72°F)

Material	Number samples	Increase in softening point, °F/10^8 rads	Decrease in penetration at 77°F, 0.1 mm/10^8 rads
Asphalts	9	2.3	1.7
Below 45 penetration	4	2.6	0.8
Above 45 penetration	5	1.8	2.4
Blends			
10 to 20% Microwax	4	2.7	1.0
1% GRS rubber	1	3.1	2.9
25% mineral filler	2	5.9	5.3
Gilsonites	2	13.0	
Tars	4	2.7	1.0

In general, the physical properties of prefabricated asphaltic membranes were altered similarly to those of the sprayable membranes. Two types of prefabricated liners were irradiated as follows:

1. A 0.5-in.-thick plank† composed of a sandwich of an organic filler–asphalt mixture between layers of felt was unaffected at 4.5×10^8 rads but was embrittled and useless at 87×10^8 rads. The rate of gas evolution from this material is shown[14] in Fig. 12.3.

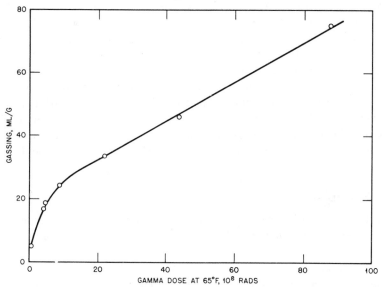

FIG. 12.3 Radiation-induced gassing from prefabricated asphalt plank.

2. An asphalt-coated asbestos-saturated prefabricated lining‡ showed "negative" gassing up to 3.5×10^8 rads, probably because of absorptive effects of the porous filler. Gas was formed at a very low rate (about 0.1 ml/g/10^8 rads) at 4.4×10^8 rads.

Hoiberg[14] concluded that asphaltic membranes are practical as liners for earthen basins in which to store radioactive wastes providing: (1) the wastes are neutralized, (2) temperatures do not exceed 150°F, and (3) the time for the asphalt to absorb 10^9 rads exceeds 25 years.

12-6 Waxes

Paper impregnated with paraffin wax is widely used in packaging. Although little work has been done with waxed paper, there is some information on its components. Paraffins tend to cross link on irradiation and thus increase their molecular weight.[6] Initially, the melting point de-

† Asphalt lining, Gulf States Asphalt Company.
‡ Asbestos liner, Johns Mansville Research Center.

creases owing to the formation of fragments; eventually gelation occurs. The gelation dose is 60-fold more for a heptane (C_7) normal paraffin than for a 3500 molecular weight wax.[6] About 8×10^8 rads gels[17] a paraffin wax. A 65% polymer yield was reported[25] for C_{27} solid paraffins irradiated to 8.6×10^8 rads in nitrogen. The formation of olefins was regarded as an intermediate in the cross-linking process.

Cellulose, the major constituent of paper, is quite unstable to radiation; about 10^8 rads causes 16% decomposition. Details on cellulose are given in Ch. 15, Sect. 15-2.3.

Several waxes, waxed papers, and blends of wax with oil and polyethylene were irradiated[10] up to 7×10^8 rads. In all cases melting points decreased and refractive indexes increased. Some irradiated wax samples became crumbly. These were similar in texture to wax to which oil had been added and suggested the formation of oil-like degradation products. However, cross linking predominated over degradation and crystallinity decreased. Some oxidation occurred when air was present during irradiation. Waxed-paper samples were too brittle for observation after about 5×10^7 rads.

12-7 Principles

Certain guide lines can be laid down for the use of coatings and films in the presence of ionizing radiation. These principles are summarized as follows:

1. The best types of coatings for up to 10^9 rads are the phenolics, silicone alkyd enamels, and alkyds and epoxy formulations. Halide-containing materials are not satisfactory because of the direct attack of the halo degradation products upon the coating and the surface.

2. Coatings containing aromatic compounds, e.g., polymer bases, plasticizers, and dyes are, in general, more resistant to radiation than those containing nonaromatics.

3. It is possible to enhance slightly the radiation stability of coatings by including certain organic dyes or a combination of inorganic pigments and carbon. Below 10^6 rads, however, the effect of ionizing radiation on pigmented coatings is much the same as on the corresponding unpigmented ones.

4. Below about 10^5 rads and with temperatures not in excess of 100°F, weather probably has more effect on a coating than does radiation.

5. The effect of radiation depends not only upon the coating per se but also upon the surface underneath the coating. In particular, coatings on concrete are more resistant than those on metal or wood.

6. Certain asphalts are radiolytically resistant to a dose of 10^9 rads and can be used below 150°F for membrane coatings on earthen basins to be used for storing neutralized radioactive wastes.

7. Packaging films can be irradiated with no damage to the film at the food-sterilization dosage of about 10^6 rads. The maximum decrease in the mechanical properties of cellulosic films (the worst case) is only about 10% at the sterilization exposure.

References

Several of the following were cited in the text as authority for statements made. Others were not quoted but are included because they contain pertinent information. All were consulted in the preparation of this chapter.

1. Bersch, C. F., Stromberg, R. R., and Achhammer, B. G., Effect of Radiation on Plastic Films, *Modern Packaging, 32*(12): 117 (August 1959).
2. Bouchereau, P. E., and Bonis, J. A. J., Protective Coatings, French Patent 1,005,033, Apr. 7, 1952.
3. Bragdon, C. R. (Ed.), *Film Formation, Film Properties, and Film Deterioration*, Interscience Publishers, Inc., New York, 1958.
4. Bresee, J. C., Watson, C. D., and Watson, J. S., *Gamma Radiation Damage Studies of Organic Protective Coatings and Gaskets*, USAEC Report ORNL-2174, Oak Ridge National Laboratory, November 1956.
5. Bresee, J. C., Flanary, J. R., Goode, J. H., Watson, C. D., and Watson, J. S., Damaging Effects of Radiation on Chemical Materials, *Nucleonics, 14*(9): 75 (September 1956).
6. Charlesby, A., The Cross Linking and Degradation of Paraffin Chains by High Energy Radiation, *Proc. Royal Soc. (London), A222*(1148): 60 (February 1954).
7. Charlesby, A., The Degradation of Cellulose by Ionizing Radiation, *J. Polymer Sci., 15*(79): 263 (January 1955).
8. Clayton, N. J., *Effects of Radiation and Contamination on a Polyester Resin Protective Coating*, USAEC Report WAPD-CTA-(EC)-305, Westinghouse Electric Corporation, February 1957.
9. Culler, F. L., *Selection of Organic Coating for Cell Walls in the Idaho Chemical Processing Plant*, USAEC Report CF-52-1-60 (Del.), Oak Ridge National Laboratory, January 1952.
10. Fox, R. C., California Research Corporation, Richmond, California, unpublished data, 1957.
11. Francis, W. C., *Radiation Damage to Certain Water Resistant Paints Used as Protective Coatings in Gamma Facilities*, USAEC Report IDO-16344, Phillips Petroleum Co., January 1956.
12. Gotoda, M., Polymerization of Castor Oil by Silent Electric Discharge, *J. Electrochem. Soc. Japan, 24*:177 (1956).
13. Gotoda, M., Amelioration of Drying Oil by Silent Electric Discharge. II. In Air and N₂, *J. Electrochem. Soc. Japan, 24*:313 (1956).
14. Hoiberg, A. J., Watson, C. D., and West, G. A., *An Evaluation of Asphalt and Other Materials for Lining Radiochemical Waste Storage Basins*, USAEC Report ORNL-2508, Oak Ridge National Laboratory, September 1958.
15. Horrocks, L. A., How Radiation Affects Six Organic Coatings, *Matls. in Design Eng., 47*(1): 120 (January 1958).
16. Horrocks, L. A., *The Effects of Nuclear Radiation on Military Specification Paints*, Report WADC-TR-57-186, Wright Air Development Center, March 1957.
17. Lawton, E. J., Bueche, A. M., and Balwit, J. S., Irradiation of Polymers by High Energy Electrons, *Nature, 172*(4367): 76 (July 1953).
18. LeClair, H. G., and Cobbs, W. H., Jr., Effect of Radiation on Plastic Packaging Films, *Ind. Eng. Chem., 50*(3): 323 (March 1958).

19. Meyers, A. W., Rogers, C. E., Stannett, V., and Szwarc, M., Permeability of Polyethylene to Gases and Vapors, *Modern Plastics, 34*(9): 157 (May 1957).
20. Minden, B. M., *The Effect of Nuclear Radiation on Protective Coatings,* Report NARF-58-39T, Convair, September 1958.
21. Payne, H. F., *Organic Coating Technology,* Vol. I, John Wiley & Sons, Inc., New York, 1954.
22. Ryan, J. W., *Effects of Radiation on Organic Materials,* USAEC Report GEL-57, General Electric Laboratories, December, 1952.
23. Simerl, L. E., *Testing Program for Irradiated Packaging Film,* Quartermaster Corps., U. S. Army, Report S-551 (Report No. 5), June 1957.
24. Singer, E., *Fundamentals of Paint, Varnish, and Lacquer Technology,* The American Paint Journal Co., Inc., St. Louis, Mo., 1957.
25. Snow, A. I., and Moyer, H. C., Radiation Chemistry of Solid Paraffins, *J. Chem. Phys., 27*(5): 1222 (November 1957).
26. Terai, I., Damage to Various Films by Gamma Irradiations, *Paint, Oil, and Chem. Rev., 121*(2): 6 (January 1958).
27. Watson, C. D., Hoiberg, A. J., and West, G. A., Asphalt Lining of Radiochemical Waste Storage Basins, *Ind. Eng. Chem., 50*(8): 87A (August 1958).
28. Watson, C. D., Tyner, N., Guinn, G. R., and Rogers, F. L., *Radiation Damage Studies—Paints, Plastics, Insulators, and Stainless Steels,* USAEC Report CF-51-11-144, Oak Ridge National Laboratory, November 1951.

CHAPTER 13

Dielectric Fluids

By Raymond S. Alger

13-1 Introduction

Liquid dielectric materials include the vegetable oils, mineral oils, halogenated hydrocarbons, and silicones. These are employed as insulating and cooling liquids in electrical equipment, e.g., transformers, capacitors, and switchgear. When such equipment is used in and around nuclear reactors, the life of the dielectric in the radiation field becomes one of the design parameters. Thus effects of radiation on dielectric fluids are of importance. For example, in the vicinity of the reactor core of the nuclear power plant shown in Fig. 9.1 of Ch. 9, a liquid dielectric would function for perhaps an hour owing to the high flux. Inside the primary shield the life might be 100 hr. Outside the primary shield neutrons are less of a problem, and the useful life of the dielectric would be extended; outside the biological shield the radiation effect would be negligible.

The effects of radiation on the chemical and physical properties of general types of organic materials are discussed in Ch. 9 (Sect. 9-2). This information must be considered in studies of dielectrics because changes in electrical properties are associated with chemical reactions, which, in turn, influence physical properties. Frequently the chemical and physical changes resulting from radiolysis terminate the useful life of a dielectric before electrical failure.

In Fig. 13.1 several common dielectrics are compared[11-13,30] on the basis of tolerance to γ or electron radiation. The shaded region begins at the dose where approximately a 25% change has been induced in one property of the material. Generally with liquids this is a physical property, such as viscosity. Plastics, ceramics, and metals have been included to assist in establishing a scale for comparison.

The discussion in this chapter starts with the structure and dielectric behavior of simple molecules. Although these simple materials seldom find use in electrical devices, a knowledge of radiation effects on liquid dielectrics depends largely on studies of pure compounds. The discussion is then extended to available insulating oils and their engineering applications. Some comparisons to pure compounds can usually be made although the exact composition of these oils frequently is not known. Finally, the effects

461

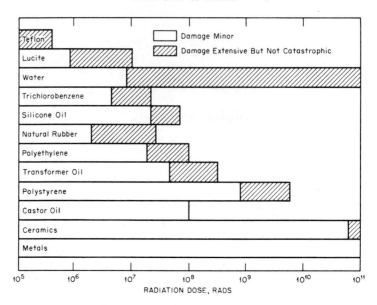

FIG. 13.1 Approximate tolerance of dielectric materials to static irradiation.

of radiation are considered in terms of both the effect on definite molecules and the influence on engineering applications.

For convenience the radiation effects on liquid dielectrics have been considered under three categories.

1. *Transient effects:* During irradiation the electrons and ions released in the ionization process may increase the electrical conductivity and dielectric loss.

2. *Gas evolution:* The gas liberated during irradiation may lead directly to mechanical damage, or it may promote destructive electrochemical activity when trapped at suitable interfaces, such as in impregnated paper insulation.

3. *Solid and liquid reaction products:* These products permanently change the dielectric properties, e.g., through the formation of sludge or acid in transformer oil.

13-2 Dielectric Properties

Dielectric materials perform two electrical functions in the systems considered here: (a) they insulate the conductors and (b) they increase the energy that can be stored in the electrical field between conductors. Different types of organic compounds show considerable variation in these electrical characteristics. Generally the best insulators allow the least energy to be stored. Their pertinent electrical properties can be described by the dielectric constant, loss, conductivity, and breakdown strength.

These parameters are normally defined and measured on a macroscopic scale; e.g., they can be determined from measurements of current and voltage in a simple capacitor containing the dielectric. In contrast, radiation phenomena involve the much smaller scale of atoms and molecules. The dielectric properties should be described in these same atomic and molecular terms for a clear understanding of radiation effects. In the following definitions and discussion, the engineering description is given first; then the properties are related to molecular phenomena and considered in the light of possible radiation effects.

The *dielectric constant* (ϵ') can be described either in terms of energy or force. The ability of a dielectric to increase the energy that can be stored in an electric field or to reduce the force between charges in the medium is measured by ϵ'.

The *relative dielectric constant* (ϵ'/ϵ_0) used throughout this chapter is the ratio of the electric-field strength in vacuum to the field in the dielectric resulting from a fixed charge distribution. Here ϵ_0 is the permittivity of free space.

The *static dielectric constant* is observed at low frequencies when the dielectric is in equilibrium with the applied field. Typical values for organic liquids range from 2 to 30. Both polar and nonpolar liquids with adequate insulating properties seldom exceed a ϵ'/ϵ_0 of 6.

The dielectric constant, ϵ', is related to molecular properties through the polarizability, which represents the electrical pliability of a medium. In an electric field the atoms and molecules of the dielectric are distorted or polarized and form an assembly of dipoles aligned with the applied field. These dipoles are responsible for the storage of energy and the reduction of force between charges. Conventionally, this polarization is divided into four components:

1. *Electronic polarization* results from the displacement of electrons relative to the positive nuclei of the atoms. This induced dipole moment is the main component in nonpolar materials.
2. *Atomic polarization,* normally a small effect in liquids, arises from the displacement of atoms relative to one another within a molecule.
3. *Orientation polarization* occurs in molecules with a permanent dipole moment which arises from an asymmetrical distribution of charge within the molecule.
4. *Space-charge polarization* involves the migration and trapping of charge carriers, chiefly in solids or at interfaces in nonuniform materials.

Electronic and atomic polarizations occur in times corresponding to optical and infrared frequencies. Thus their contribution to ϵ' is independent of frequency throughout the frequency range of electrical devices.

Furthermore, temperature and molecular structure have little effect on electronic and atomic polarization at these frequencies. In contrast, orientation and space-charge polarization are strongly temperature dependent, are determined by molecular structure, and show a pronounced frequency dependence in the electrical frequency range. In liquids and solids the permanent dipoles encounter many collisions and are hindered in their attempt to align with the applied field. This friction factor is temperature and structure dependent.

When the applied electric field is alternating, a frequency can always be found at which the permanent dipoles can no longer remain in equilibrium with the electric field and the polarization acquires a component out of phase with the driving field. At still higher frequencies the permanent dipoles make no contribution to the polarization and ϵ' decreases. This frequency dependence of ϵ' is characteristic of a relaxation spectrum.

The *dielectric relaxation time* (τ) describes the speed with which the permanent dipoles can adjust to the applied electric field. It is defined as the time for the polarization to decay by a factor of $1/e$ after the applied field is removed. Molecular structure, size, and temperature have a strong influence on τ.

Irradiation products include charged species, such as ions and electrons, and new molecular structures. Consequently on irradiation the components of polarization most sensitive to these species will show the most change. Thus orientation and space-charge polarization are primarily affected by irradiation, whereas electronic and atomic polarizations are relatively unaffected.

The units chosen to describe a dielectric's insulating characteristics depend on the frequency of the applied electric field. In a static field the d-c conductivity (σ_{dc}) defines the proportionality between the current flowing in the dielectric and the applied voltage. This current depends on the number and mobility of the charge carriers. In most commercial insulating liquids, these charge carriers arise from impurities such as water, solid particles, or gas bubbles. Although careful purification can remove these impurities, a residual conductivity always remains. Sources of charge that have been suggested to account for this residual current include: (a) ionization by natural radioactivity or cosmic rays, (b) thermal or field emission of electrons, and (c) molecular dissociation. Unfortunately the experimental results fail to specify the source beyond all doubt.[14,16]

A wide range of values for σ_{dc} are encountered in the various dielectric liquids, e.g., from 10^{-6} to 10^{-20} (ohm-cm)$^{-1}$. Insulating liquids are generally limited to d-c conductivities less than 10^{-12} (ohm-cm)$^{-1}$. The resistivity (ρ) is the reciprocal of σ. During irradiation the ions and electrons produced will contribute to the d-c conductivity and the ohmic losses.

In the alternating-electric-field case, energy is dissipated in the dielectric by both charge migration and the friction losses associated with the polarization of permanent dipoles. In the frequency range characterized by the relaxation spectrum, the friction loss predominates. Several related quantities are normally used to measure the a-c losses. When an alternating voltage is applied to a simple capacitor, the total current flowing can be divided into a charging current 90° out of phase with the applied field and a loss current in phase with the voltage as shown vectorally in Fig. 13.2. The loss current is related to the applied field by the a-c dielectric

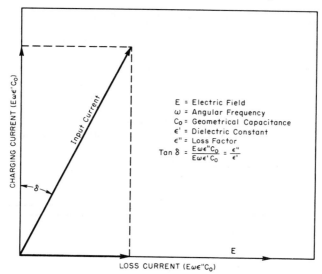

FIG. 13.2 Current vector diagram of a capacitor with loss.

conductivity $(\sigma_{ac} = \omega\epsilon'')$, where ϵ'' is defined as the *loss factor* and ω is the angular frequency. The ratio of the loss current to the charging current defined by tan δ is the dissipation factor or *loss tangent*. The parameters ϵ'', tan δ, and σ_{ac} are all sensitive to molecular structure and can show a strong dependence on temperature and frequency when the dielectric contains permanent dipoles.

As in the case of ϵ', the effects of irradiation are confined primarily to the production of permanent dipoles and space charge. The situation can become quite complicated depending on whether the irradiation products are more dipoles or are cross linkages that impede orientation. In either event the a-c losses would be increased at some but not necessarily all frequencies.

The *dielectric strength* defines the ability of a material to withstand an electrical field without breakdown or electrical puncture. The search for an intrinsic dielectric-strength characteristic of molecular structure is well documented in the literature.[14,28] The theories agree that puncture results from an electronic mechanism, the time periods involved being too short for appreciable ionic motion. Presumably space charge builds up through impact ionization, and cascading results in puncture. Despite the uncertainty in the theory, the measurement of dielectric strength provides one of the common tests for the quality of insulating oils. Breakdown voltages normally range from 100 to 550 volts/mil for liquid dielectrics.

It may be anticipated that the dielectric strength will be affected by radiation primarily through the production of gas, free electrons, and ions.

13-3 Molecular Structure and Dielectric Behavior

Because of the almost unlimited variety of organic molecules, generalizations regarding the influence of molecular structure on dielectric behavior must be used with caution. Interest is centered primarily in factors controlling the electrical permittivity, conductivity, and breakdown; the chemical stability; and the viscosity. As already pointed out, the polar molecules have permanent dipole moments accompanied by relatively large dielectric constants, whereas nonpolar molecules do not. Insulating

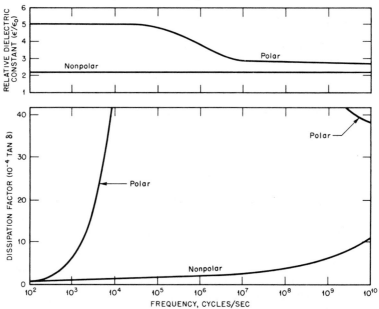

FIG. 13.3 Effect of frequency on dielectric properties of nonpolar and polar oils. Nonpolar = Primol-D (mineral oil, 49.4% paraffins and 50.6% naphthenes). Polar = Pyranol-1476 (isomeric penthachlorobiphenyls). [From A. R. Von Hippel (Ed.), *Dielectric Materials and Applications*, Technology Press of Massachusetts Institute of Technology in collaboration with John Wiley & Sons, Inc., Ref. 29.]

oils obtained from petroleum generally contain a mixture of nonpolar aliphatic (paraffinic) and alicyclic (naphthenic) compounds. If pure, these hydrocarbons have low relative dielectric constants and tan δ. When hydrogen atoms in these molecules are replaced with electronegative atoms such as oxygen, nitrogen, or halogens, a permanent dipole moment develops if the substitution is unbalanced or unsymmetrical. Figure 13.3 emphasizes[29] the flat frequency response of a typical nonpolar liquid compared to the relaxation spectrum of a highly polar compound.

Typical dielectric properties of a group of polar and nonpolar compounds are listed in Table 13.1. The examples include a six-carbon molecule from each of the main chemical classes of interest—aliphatic, alicyclic, and aromatic molecules. Although the pure compounds are used infrequently as insulating liquids, they demonstrate the influence of molecular structure on the dielectric constant.

Table 13.1 — ELECTRICAL PROPERTIES OF PURE COMPOUNDS

Compound	Polarity	Relative dielectric constant[a] (ϵ'/ϵ_0)	Resistivity (ρ_{dc}), ohm-cm	Dielectric strength, volts/mil
n-Hexane	NP	1.9	10^{18}	3300
n-Hexanol	P	13.3		
Cyclohexane	NP	2.0		
Cyclohexanol	P	15.0		
Benzene	NP	2.3	10^{18}	2800
Nitrobenzene	P	36.5		685

[a] At 1 kc.

The rules relating molecular structure to chemical stability have been only partially resolved. In a radiation field the relation becomes even more obscure as the reactive irradiation products dominate the chemical activity. Stabilizing structures such as the benzene ring are well known, but most structures must be studied on an individual basis.

The relation between molecular structure and physical characteristics is much clearer qualitatively. Factors that hinder molecular motion, such as length, branching, and attraction between molecules, tend to increase the viscosity and the melting and boiling points.

13-4 Commercial Formulations and Applications

13-4.1 GENERAL REQUIREMENTS AND THE IDEAL DIELECTRIC

Electrical devices, such as transformers, capacitors, cables, switchgear, etc., have a composite structure usually consisting of metal conductors and containers, solid dielectric materials and varnishes, and a liquid or gaseous impregnating dielectric. Obviously, electrical, chemical, and physical compatibility between the liquid dielectric and these other components is es-

Table 13.2 — ELECTRICAL PROPERTIES OF COMMERCIAL DIELECTRICS

Dielectric	Polarity	Relative dielectric constant (ϵ'/ϵ_0)	Loss factor (ϵ'') at ~1 kc	Resistivity (ρ_{dc}), ohm-cm	Dielectric strength, volts mil
Castor oil, plain	P	4.2	0.2100		500
Castor oil, hydrogenated[a]	P	10.2	<0.0001		300
Paraffin mineral oil[b]	NP	2.1	<0.00008		350
Naphthenic mineral oil	NP	2.2	0.0006	10^{13} to 10^{15}	350
Pentachlorobiphenyl[c]	P	5.0	0.0006	$>10^{12}$	
Trichlorobenzene[d]	P	4.5	0.0014		
$C_8F_{16}O$[e]	NP	1.8	0.053	$>10^{14}$	400
$(C_4F_9)_3N$[e]	NP	1.9	0.0095	$>10^{14}$	400
Methyl silicone[f]	NP	2.5	<0.0004	10^{14}	350

[a] Opalwax, Baker Castor Oil Co. [29]
[b] Bayol D, Esso Standard Oil Co. [29]
[c] Pyranol 1476, General Electric Co. [29]
[d] Pyranol 1478, General Electric Co. [29]
[e] Fluorochemicals FC-43 and FC-75, Minnesota Mining and Manufacturing Company.
[f] Dow Corning 200, Dow Corning Corporation.

sential. The ideal liquid would have an infinite dielectric strength, zero loss or conductivity, and a dielectric constant that could be adjusted as desired. These properties would be independent of frequency and temperature. Chemically, the liquid would be completely stable, both in its normal complex environment and in the presence of ionizing agents. Physically, the viscosity and thermal conductivity would be controllable and generally independent of temperature. Finally, this ideal fluid would be plentiful and economical to produce.

Since this ideal material does not exist, the available formulations must represent a compromise between the desired properties, the operating conditions, and costs. Typical electrical properties, measured according to American Society for Testing Materials specifications, are listed in Table 13.2 for the major types of commercial insulating liquids. Under the prescribed electrode arrangements, dielectric strengths of 10^5 volts/cm, resistivities of 10^{14} to 10^{15} ohm-cm, and a tan δ of 0.001 generally suffice for electrical equipment.

13-4.2 TYPICAL INSULATING OILS

Vegetable oils that contain high-molecular-weight polar molecules have been used extensively where a sizable dielectric constant is of primary concern. Castor oil, the principal example, is chemically stable despite an abundance of oxygen. Its relative dielectric constant of 4.2 can be increased by hydrogenation. This also produces a solid at room temperature.

Mineral oils are suited for use over a wide frequency range because they are composed of nonpolar molecules. Their relative dielectric constants of about 2 are low and independent of frequency up to 10^{10} cycles/sec (see Fig. 13.3); they have the lowest tan δ over this frequency range of any of the oil types. Although the mineral oils are quite stable chemically, oxidation increases the acidity of the oil, increases the losses, decreases the breakdown strength, and forms a sludge in the oil. When decomposition occurs under corona or in the presence of an arc, the gases formed (about 80 to 90% hydrogen) constitute a fire hazard. This gas formation is responsible for the strict electrical code governing the use of these oils in electrical equipment.

Halogenated hydrocarbons are used because of their high dielectric constants and nonflammability. For stability chlorinated aromatics are preferred to chlorinated paraffinic compounds. Commercial mixtures, called "askarels," are generally composed of chlorinated benzene, biphenyls, terphenyls, and naphthalenes. These molecules are polar and exhibit a relaxation in the loss curve as shown in Fig. 13.3. The gaseous products from the electric-arc decomposition[5] of pentachlorobiphenyl are 99 to 100% HCl. Stabilizers, such as anthraquinone and azobenzene, are added to the fluid to neutralize the corrosive HCl. Fluorochemical liquids combine excellent heat-transfer properties with chemical inertness and good dielectric characteristics (Table 13.2). Corona and arc discharges, as well as radiation, produce fluorides that have deleterious effects on metals and insulators; however, some of the fluorochemicals have been successfully used in circuit-breaker tests.

Silicone oils derive their outstanding advantage from unusual physical properties coupled with good chemical stability. Methyl silicones are the principal dielectric liquids in use, but phenyl methyl silicones have been studied and are attractive because of their superior stability. Silicones show relatively small viscosity variations with temperature and have low pour points. Electrically, their relative dielectric constants of about 2.5 are maintained[29] up to a frequency of 10^{10} cycles/sec.[28] Below 10^6 cycles the dissipation (tan δ) for the silicones is slightly lower than for the petroleum oils; at higher frequencies it rises to intermediate levels. Ionizing radiation liberates hydrogen, methane, and ethane gases from the silicones.

Polyphenyls have not been used as dielectrics, but these hydrocarbons are being used as nuclear reactor coolants (see Ch. 8). The trend toward higher operating temperature might make these highly stable compounds of interest for dielectric materials. No work has been published on the effects of radiation on the dielectric properties of polyphenyls. However, the electrical properties of Santowax R† have been measured[26] before irradiation. For 1, 10, and 100 kc, the dielectric constant (ϵ') varies linearly with temperature (t) over the range of 375 to 675°F as follows:

$$\epsilon' = -7.7 \times 10^{-4}t + 2.83 \pm 1.2\% \qquad (13.1)$$

The dipole moments of the terphenyl isomers are approximately zero, and the induced polarizability is high. The dielectric constant for the terphenyl mixture was calculated with acceptable accuracy from values for the pure isomers. It was concluded that changes in the composition of the terphenyl mixture would be very difficult to detect by changes in dielectric constant unless the changes were caused by impurities having very high dielectric constants.

The dissipation factor (tan δ) for Santowax R varied exponentially with temperature from 375 to 675°F and was inversely proportional to the frequency at 1, 10, and 100 kc. At 500°F values were 0.1, 0.01, and 0.001 ± 100% at 100, 10, and 1 kc, respectively. The large spread in the data precludes their use to detect changes in the mixture. However, the dissipation factor should be very sensitive to impurities such as water or ions.

The volume resistivity (ρ, reciprocal of σ) of Santowax R decreased from 10^{14} to 10^{11} ohm-cm through the fusion region (154 to 336°F). A further decrease from 3×10^{10} to 1×10^{10} ohm-cm resulted from increasing

† Mixture of terphenyls, Monsanto Chemical Co.

the liquid temperature from 400 to 600°F. The high resistivity indicates a low concentration of conductive contaminants. However, in an ionizing field such as occurs in a reactor, large changes in resistivity are expected.

13-4.3 APPLICATIONS AND SPECIAL REQUIREMENTS

In transformers a liquid dielectric provides electrical insulation and cools the windings and core. The electrical properties of characteristic transformer oils are described in Table 13.2. Chemically, an oil treated to resist sludging and oxidation is desirable. Physically, a low viscosity is needed. Petroleum oils are used in most installations where fire is not a problem. Chlorinated compounds, or askarels, are used in transformers primarily as protection against fires. Silicones are suitable but are more economical in the form of varnishes in dry or air type applications than in the form of liquid dielectrics.

Organic liquids are used as impregnating compounds in a wide variety of capacitors. Paper capacitors, both for power and for radio frequencies, use oil-impregnated cellulose as the dielectric. Tunable metal-plate and high-voltage mica capacitors are frequently oil immersed. Even electrolytic capacitors, both the wet and the so-called "dry" types, have organic compounds such as the polyhydric alcohols in their electrolytes.

In capacitors the dielectric provides electrical insulation and stores energy in the electric field. Maximum capacitance per unit volume can be approached through the use of a dielectric with a large polarizability and a minimum thickness. Frequently fields in excess of 10^3 volts/mil are maintained over areas of numerous square feet. Capacitors usually fail because of electrochemical reactions promoted by the high electric field. Electrically, the impregnating fluid should have a high dielectric constant, a low loss factor, and a high breakdown strength; chemical stability, when in contact with extensive metal surfaces, is essential. The physical requirements permit considerable latitude, and compounds ranging from oils to solid waxes are encountered.

The hydrogenated vegetable oils and chlorinated compounds are attractive capacitor dielectrics because of their high dielectric constants. Where stability of the capacitor under changing temperature and frequency outweighs the economy of minimum size, the nonpolar liquids, such as mineral oils and silicones, have an advantage.

In switchgear and circuit breakers, oil provides electrical insulation and cooling and assists in interrupting the arc. The arc temperature may reach 9000°F; consequently the effects on insulating oil are quite radical. An oil of low viscosity, high dielectric strength, and good chemical stability is required. Provision is made for sludge, which contains carbon particles, to settle to the bottom of the tank. Halogenated compounds, such as askarels, are avoided because of the corrosive decomposition products.

High-voltage cables and bushings, like capacitors, place very stringent demands on the properties of liquid dielectrics. Long exposures under large electric-field gradients in a three-phase system of oil, paper, and air are responsible for these demands. Obviously the impregnating compound should have high dielectric strength, a low loss factor, and good chemical stability. It is also usually desirable to use a low-dielectric-constant material to reduce the over-all capacitance of cables. Petroleum oils treated with stabilizers are the main dielectric liquids in use. Silicone oils would also be satisfactory.

Many of the failures encountered in cables originate with the formation of localized gas pockets. It is impossible to remove the last traces of air in the impregnating process, and under electrical stress corona discharges produce additional ionization products. The process, which tends to be cumulative, generates gas and a polymerization product, known as "cable wax," until ultimately breakdown occurs.

13-5 Basic Radiation Effects

The various modes of interaction between ionizing radiation and matter are considered in Ch. 2. Chapters 3 and 4 follow the ensuing molecular dissociations and chemical reactions in the detail permitted by the present state of knowledge. Only points of immediate concern in determining the extent of radiation damage in liquid dielectrics are discussed here.

13-5.1 Influence of Type and Rate of Radiation

The problem of comparing radiation effects from light particles (β and γ) and from heavy particles (α, n, and p) has received considerable attention. When these effects are compared on the basis of equal energy absorbed in the dielectric, it is found that equal chemical damage (as measured in terms of hydrogen-gas yield, change in viscosity, or reaction with iodine) results for some materials but not for others.[15,18] Recent work at Harwell[2] has shown that fast neutrons cause greater yields of gas and polymers than gamma rays.

The influence of radiation type on dielectric properties has not yet been fully appraised.

13-5.2 Ionization Products

After the initial process of ionization and excitation, the excited species expends energy, as outlined in Ch. 3, by rupturing bonds to form radicals or stable molecules. In liquids the molecular mobility ensures that reactive species, such as ions and free radicals, will undergo chemical reactions until stable molecules are produced. Consequently there are two types of products to be considered in assaying the radiation effects on dielectrics: (1) transient products, such as ions, electrons, and radicals, and (2) new stable molecules. If the new molecules are sufficiently similar to the original molecules, the dielectric properties of the bulk material will not be permanently impaired. Unfortunately, this situation does not occur in the fluids listed in Tables 13.1 and 13.2. Under irradiation all these materials evolve gas; and under extended exposures the commercial insulating oils form gels and thus indicate that both condensation and polymerization occur.

It is possible to follow some of the effects on a molecular basis by such techniques as electron paramagnetic resonance (EPR) spectroscopy. If the reactions going by a radical process are arrested by irradiating at liquid-nitrogen temperature, the radicals can be trapped and detected by their paramagnetic properties. Current evidence for simple paraffins indicates that a hydrogen atom is removed from the molecule to form a radical.[24] During irradiation hydrogen escapes from the solid. When the sample is warmed, the EPR spectrum disappears as the radicals react to form stable compounds. These observations are in accord with the theory developed in Ch. 3 and suggest that there is a basis for transient radiolysis effects on dielectric properties.

13-5.3 ENERGY CONSIDERATIONS AND G VALUES

The average energy expended in disrupting a molecule or forming a new product depends strongly on the molecular structure and to some extent on the environment, i.e., temperature and phase. Generally the efficiency of the process is described in terms of product yields, or G values.† Typical G values for gamma-ray and electron bombardment of some compounds and oils from Tables 13.1 and 13.2 are given in Table 13.3. On the basis of free-radical production during separate gamma-ray and electron bombardments, the various organic compounds have been arranged in the following descending order of stability: aromatic hydrocarbons, aliphatic hydrocarbons, oxygenated compounds, and halogenated compounds.[17] Hydrogen production does not always give an accurate indication of the overall irradiation effect, particularly in unsaturated compounds that have a strong tendency to polymerize or cross link. Double-bonded compounds, such as cyclohexene, yield only approximately one-quarter the hydrogen found for equivalent saturated compounds. The effect of saturation is also noticeable in the mineral oils where a high degree of refinement removes most of the unsaturated compounds and produces an oil with a higher susceptibility to gas production; e.g., in Table 13.3, compare Midcontinent oil, 55 to 80, and Naphthenic oil, 100 to 180.

Electronegative elements, such as oxygen and the halogens, favor decomposition. Sizable $G_{radical}$ and G_{acid} yields are obtained for the chlorinated benzene and biphenyl compounds. Although compounds with equivalent hydrogen and chlorine content, such as trichlorobenzene and penta-

† G = number of molecules produced per 100 ev of absorbed energy.

Table 13.3 — YIELDS OF IRRADIATION PRODUCTS FROM LIQUID DIELECTRICS

Materials	Radiation	G values				
		H_2 (Refs. 19 and 27)	CH_4 (Refs. 19 and 27)	Radical (Ref.17)	Acid (Ref. 3)	Polymer (Ref. 27)
Electron irradiation:						
n-Hexane	0.17-Mev e⁻	4.1	0.33			
Cyclohexane	0.17-Mev e⁻	4.4	0.09	14.3		1.7
Cyclohexene	0.17-Mev e⁻	1.2	0.019			4.2 to 12.4
Benzene	1.5-Mev e⁻	0.036	0.0012	1.8		0.76
Midcontinent, moderate[a],55[b]	0.17-Mev e⁻	2.2	0.10			
Midcontinent, high[a], 80[b]	0.17-Mev e⁻	2.8	0.09			
Naphthenic, moderate[a],100[b]	0.17-Mev e⁻	0.93	0.04			
Naphthenic, high[a],180[b]	0.17-Mev e⁻	3.5	0.08			
Gamma irradiation:						
Chlorobenzene	γ			17.5		
o-Dichlorobenzene	γ			30		
Transformer oil	Co⁶⁰ γ				1.5	
Castor oil	Co⁶⁰ γ				0.3	
Silicone oil	Co⁶⁰ γ				Very small	
Trichlorobenzene	Co⁶⁰ γ	0			3.2	
Pentachlorobiphenyl	Co⁶⁰ γ	0			5.0	

[a] Degree of refinement.
[b] Viscosity, Saybolt seconds at 100°F.

chlorobiphenyl, yield no hydrogen gas, the production of HCl is appreciable. On the basis of acid production, G_{acid} in Table 13.3, silicone oil and castor oil look impressive. Unfortunately the silicones cross link readily to form a gel.

13-6 Radiation Effects on Dielectric Properties

Radiation-induced reactions affect the dielectric properties at several stages of the over-all process. First, the charge carriers released during ionization can move and contribute directly to the conductivity. Second, the gas generated may start a spiral of electrochemical activity. In a liquid the generation of hydrogen gas is of little consequence if the gas can escape; however, in devices such as impregnated cables and capacitors, the layers of paper provide a place for the gas molecules to collect into bubbles. The high electric fields characteristic of these devices can generate localized corona discharges in the gas pockets; this leads to further decomposition of the liquid which releases more gas, and so on. Third, the reaction products increase in concentration as the irradiation progresses, and thereby the composition and characteristics of the liquid are changed. Initially these products have a negligible effect compared to the transient free electrons and ions, but ultimately the new molecules make their contribution.

13-6.1 TRANSIENT EFFECTS

During irradiation electrons and ions are produced which can move in an electric field; this leads to a radiation-induced current, such as that shown in Fig. 13.4. With pure isooctane in low-intensity radiation fields, the induced conduction was found to be proportional to the radiation intensity.[16] In Fig. 13.4 the sample absorbed less than 1 rad/hr; consequently few new species were formed, and the curve is typical of the transient contribution to conduction. The induced current is shown as a function of the applied electric field. Since the current is still increasing at the maximum field strength, not all the ions produced are reaching the ëlectrodes.

Similar measurements[7] on silicone fluids exposed to Co^{60} gamma rays at dose rates up to 0.5 megarad/hr gave an exponential relation between the resistivity (ρ) and the dose rate (R): $\rho \propto R^{-0.64}$. Variations in the exponent from 1 to 0.64 have been observed. This is not surprising in view of differences in dose rate, material, and test procedure. Exponents covering the same range have been reported for plastics, such as polyethylene.[9] This change in resistivity[7] is reflected in an exponential increase in the dissipation factor from 10^{-4} to 10^{-2} as the silicone fluid was irradiated at rates up to 10^5 rad/hr. The dielectric constant (ϵ') and the dielectric strength are relatively insensitive to the transient radiation effects, and, in the silicone fluids examined, these parameters remained essentially unchanged.[7]

In view of the microscopic processes involved, this behavior of resistivity (ρ), dissipation (tan δ), dielectric constant (ϵ'), and the breakdown strength is reasonable. For example, if it is assumed that an average energy of about 16 ev is expended per silicone molecule ionized,[3] an irradiation rate of 0.5 megarad/hr would yield about 5.4×10^{14} ions/sec or about

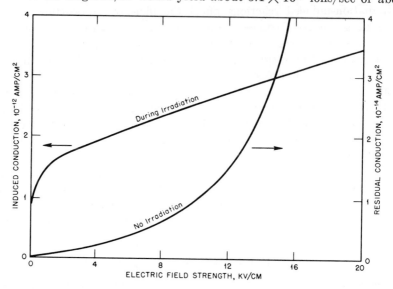

Fig. 13.4 Effect of gamma irradiation (1 rad/hr) on conduction at 32°F in pure isooctane. (From C. S. Pao, *The Physical Review*, Ref. 16.)

one ion for every 10^5 molecules in the 1000-centistoke liquid. These ions and their electron counterparts correspond to about 8.7×10^{-5} coulombs of charge per gram, which is free to move under the influence of the electric field thereby dissipating energy. This charge is large compared to the available current carried in the unirradiated liquid, which has a resistivity of about 10^{14} ohm-cm.

Two factors lead to the small transient radiation effect on the dielectric constant. First, there is little opportunity for space-charge polarization since, in a standard test cell, the ions not neutralized by electron capture in the liquid can move to the electrodes. Second, if a charge asymmetry exists in the ion, the dipole contribution remains small because of the small fraction of molecules involved.

If, as is believed,[28] dielectric puncture involved an electronic process through impact ionization and space-charge formation,[27] the presence of free electrons would assure that breakdown occurs as soon as the necessary electric field exists. However, in the absence of nonuniform space charges, the electrons would not appreciably change the field strength required.

Presumably, as in the case of ultraviolet irradiation of gases, more consistent breakdown values would be obtained under irradiation. An overvoltage would have no opportunity to form because of a scarcity of electrons required to start an avalanche.

There are two apparent situations in which the transient effects become important. First, in high-impedance or electrometer circuits, the small induced current, lowered resistance, or increased dissipation factor can become troublesome. Second, in very high radiation fields, such as in the core of a reactor, the losses become appreciable. Nevertheless, failure generally will develop from the build-up of permanent reaction products in the dielectric.

13-6.2 GAS PRODUCTION

The regenerative action of gas production in a high electric field has been described; but, even in the absence of this field, ionizing radiation can generate sufficient gas to cause mechanical difficulties. In the gassing experiments referred to in Table 13.3, gas production was a linear function of dose under electron bombardment. In terms of volumes at room temperature, 1 cm^3 of oil will liberate approximately 0.2 cm^3 of H_2 at a 10^7-rad dose and 20 cm^3 at a 10^9-rad dose. In an oil-impregnated cable or capacitor, such amounts of gas can cause serious difficulties, both electrically and mechanically. Electrically, the gas can lower the breakdown strength by creating a gas phase of low ionization potential; mechanically, the pressure can rupture the oil container. Capacitors are normally made with thin tank walls, which flex to accommodate thermal expansion and contraction of the sealed-in liquid. When standard condensers and potted transformers were irradiated to destruction, the failure was usually physical from the release of gas rather than electrical.[22] As many failures resulted from case rupture by gas pressure as did from permanent electrical damage. The polyhydric alcohols used in electrolytic capacitors are particularly susceptible to gas production; e.g., G_{H_2} is about 5 for glycerin and ethylene glycol.

13-6.3 SOLID AND LIQUID REACTION PRODUCTS

Some of the earliest investigations of radiation damage in insulating oils were concerned with the formation of cable wax found in oil-filled high-voltage cables. This wax developed in regions associated with local corona discharges, and initially such discharges were used to synthesize the wax. Later the wax was produced by bombarding oil in a vacuum with high-energy electrons.[10] The mechanisms by which molecules can increase in size through polymerization and condensation are considered in Ch. 3, Sect. 3-4. In the cable waxes the ratio of carbon to hydrogen is higher than it is in the original oil. The waxes also show the presence of double

Table 13.4 — EFFECT OF GAMMA IRRADIATION ON DIELECTRIC PROPERTIES[a]

Insulating liquid	Dose, 10^6 rads	Relative dielectric constant (ϵ'/ϵ_o)		Loss factor (ϵ'')	
		Initially	After irradiation	Initially	After irradiation
Transformer oil:					
At 1 kc	41	2.23	8.59	0.006	6.150
At 10 kc	41	2.23	2.84	0.006	1.420
Castor oil:					
At 1 kc	41	4.46	4.59	0.022	0.036
At 10 kc	41	4.47	4.60	0.013	0.023
Silicone oil:					
At 1 kc	23	2.73	2.77	0.008	0.033
At 10 kc	23	2.73	2.74	0.008	0.016
Trichlorobenzene:					
At 1 kc	4	4.11	4.15	0.450	1.722
At 10 kc	4	3.94	3.96	0.047	0.181
Pentachlorobiphenyl:					
At 1 kc	7	5.04	5.10	0.025	0.132
At 10 kc	7	5.00	5.04	0.045	0.121

[a]From T. D. Callinan, *Electrical Engineering*, Ref. 3.

bonds and react readily with oxygen. These results are in line with the evolution of hydrogen during irradiation. Although the wax may have adequate dielectric properties, historically its formation has been associated with cable failure.

In cables and capacitors the combination of wax, trapped gas, and unsaturated molecules leads to a reduced dielectric strength and an increased conductivity and loss. The dielectric constant is usually the least affected of the electrical parameters. Table 13.4 summarizes the effects of gamma radiation on the dielectric properties of five of the liquids considered in Table 13.3. Here, the change in loss and dielectric constant is due to reaction products generated in substantial exposures ranging from about 4 to 41 megarads. The change in dielectric constant is less than 3% for all the liquids, except the transformer oil, which increased by a factor of 3 at 1 kc. Either polar species or ions could be responsible for this increase. In view of the three- to fourfold increase in loss factor for all liquids except castor oil, the presence of ions has been favored.[3] The G values for acid formation listed in Table 13.3 appear to substantiate this conclusion. The exposures were not all the same because the chlorinated compound and the silicone oil failed at intermediate doses; e.g., at 20 megarads the loss factor in pentachlorobiphenyl became too large to measure, and at 28 megarads the silicone oil became a gel.

More-extensive information regarding the permanent changes in silicone fluids has been reported by Currin.[7] Figures 13.5 and 13.6 show appreciable changes in the resistivity and dielectric strength, respectively, in a phenyl methyl silicone that received doses up to 10^9 rads. A dimethyl silicone was found to form a gel before the electrical properties changed significantly. In all cases the principal permanent effect of irradiation on the electrical properties was to increase the losses as measured by the dissipation factor $(\tan \delta)$.

All the materials in Table 13.4 ultimately became viscous and formed gels or solids, although the exact exposures required for solidification depended on the size and stability of the original molecules. An order of magnitude indication of the total gamma-ray or fast-neutron dose that can be tolerated by various dielectrics before failure is given in Fig. 13.1. For comparable molecular sizes the silicone oils are the first to form gels. The gas evolved during the solidification process can become trapped and ultimately generate a foam. Irradiation increases the viscosity of transformer oil and forms a sludge that reduces the free flowing and cooling action of the oil. Frequently the viscosity change limits the tolerance to irradiation before the electrical properties become inadequate.

Chlorinated compounds have a low radiation tolerance because of the reactive HCl liberated and because more gamma and neutron energy is absorbed owing to the chlorine. The HCl reacts with both cellulose insula-

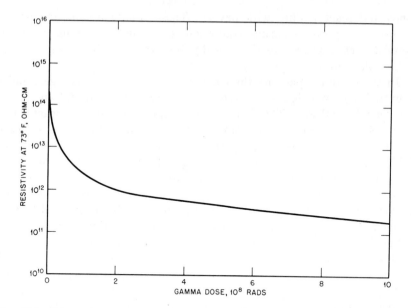

FIG. 13.5 Effect of radiation on the resistivity of phenyl methyl silicone fluid (40 centistokes). (From C. G. Currin, *Transactions of the American Institute of Electrical Engineers,* Ref. 7.)

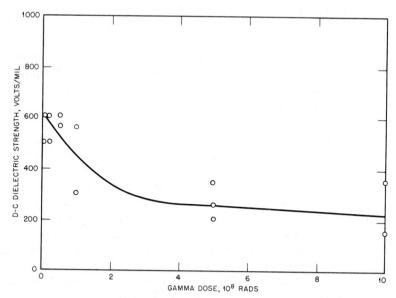

FIG. 13.6 Effect of radiation on dielectric strength of phenyl methyl silicone fluid (40 centistokes); 0.50-in.-diameter spherical electrodes with 0.020-in. cap were used. (From C. G. Currin, *Transactions of the American Institute of Electrical Engineers,* Ref. 7.)

tion and metal parts. Chlorine has an appreciable absorption cross section for thermal neutrons; these compounds, therefore, are particularly susceptible to reactor radiation.

13-7 Engineering Considerations

The problem of matching liquid dielectrics to environments consisting of high electric fields, metal and solid dielectric components, and gases is further complicated by ionizing radiation, which imposes another restriction on the use and life of the liquid. Radiation levels to be encountered cover a wide range. Fast neutrons and gamma rays provide the main problem since alpha and beta particles and positive ions are readily absorbed in very thin layers of shielding. Sources capable of damaging dielectric liquids include nuclear reactors, kilocurie radioactive sources, and some accelerators. Obviously, when possible, dielectric-containing equipment should be located outside any biological shield.

Additives are sometimes mixed with transformer oils and capacitor fluids to reduce oxidation and provide protection against reactive decomposition products. In the case of radiation-induced reactions, these additives may act at various steps in the decomposition process. The ideal protective agent would dissipate the absorbed energy without disrupting either the base or the protective molecules. Molecules that could convert the absorbed energy to fluorescent light or heat without rupture represent a possible application of this type of protection. Stable molecules, such as benzene or other aromatic molecules, serve in this capacity. Mineral oils refined to the proper degree contain some aromatics that provide the protection responsible for the difference noted in Table 13.3 between moderate and highly refined oils. In the case of ionization, a scavenger might be able to trap electrons, dissipate the excess energy, and achieve neutralization without molecular disruption. The free-radical scavenger offers a third type of protection through reaction with radicals to form stable compounds, hopefully with properties equal to those of the base material. Scavengers that are exhausted in the protection process offer only limited protection.

Much of the early experience with scavengers stems from the use of additives in chlorinated capacitor liquids to avoid the deleterious effects of HCl formed in the electrochemical reactions induced by high electric fields. Studies of these reactions have given support to a free-radical mechanism for the chemical breakdown of oil under corona conditions.[1] Free-radical scavengers effectively reduced the damage to the insulating properties of oils under these conditions. Since the reaction products from corona and electron bombardment are similar, free-radical scavengers have been used, with some success, as protective agents with other sources of ionizing radiation. For example, when the trichlorobenzene of Table 13.4 was fortified with 0.3% of various free-radical scavengers (substituted benzophenones), the G_{acid} was reduced by a factor[3] of about 2. Another example of a protective system involving pure compounds (benzene in cyclohexane) is discussed in Ch. 4.

Part of the problem of matching the dielectric liquid to its radiation environment involves tailoring the design to accommodate the liquid. The obvious approach is to avoid all the radiation possible. In reactor installations where weight and cost of shielding are not a major problem, it has been possible to keep the insulating liquids outside the biological shield. Designs with a minimum of shielding, such as those for flight propulsion, may involve high exposures; in this case the components should be designed to accommodate the reaction products, liberated gas, sludge, and wax. Cooling systems should allow for the change in viscosity and the production of sludge during irradiation. Geometries should be arranged to intercept a minimum of radiation. The relative importance of σ, ϵ', ϵ'', and breakdown strength should guide the choice of dielectric liquid in accordance with such characteristics as are displayed in Tables 13.3 and 13.4. Ultimately the highly stable biphenyl and terphenyl compounds might be used in dielectric materials. The effects of radiation on their physical and chemical properties are discussed extensively in Ch. 8. Since permanent changes in electrical properties depend on the new molecules formed under irradiation, the high physical and chemical stability of these polyphenyls under irradiation should be reflected in comparable electrical stability.

Finally, designs utilizing solid insulators may be able to benefit from the higher radiation stability of inorganic componds as indicated in Fig. 13.1.

References

Several of the following were cited in the text as authority for statements made. Others were not quoted but are included because they contain pertinent information. All were consulted in the preparation of this chapter.

1. Basseches, H., and McLean, D. A., Gassing of Liquid Dielectrics Under Electrical Stress, *Ind. Eng. Chem.*, *47*(9): 1782 (September 1955).
2. Burns, W. G., Wild, W., and Williams, T. F., The Effect of Fast Electrons and Fast Neutrons on Polyphenyls at High Temperatures, *Proceedings of the Second International Conference on the Peaceful Uses of Atomic Energy, Geneva, 1958*, Vol. 29, p. 266, United Nations, New York, 1959.
3. Callinan, T. D., Gamma Radiation Effects on Liquid Dielectrics, *Elec. Eng.*, *74*(6): 510 (June 1955).
4. Charlesby, A., Changes in Silicone Polymeric Fluids Due to High-Energy Radiation, *Proc. Roy. Soc.(London)*, *A230*(1180): 120 (June 1955).
5. Clark, F. M., Nonflammable Dielectric Organic Compounds, *Ind. Eng. Chem.*, *29* (4): 698 (April 1937).
6. Collins, C. G., and Calkins, V. P., *Radiation Damage to Elastomers, Plastics, and Organic Liquids*, USAEC Report APEX-261, General Electric Co., Aircraft Nuclear Propulsion Department, 1956.
7. Currin, C. G., Effects of Gamma Radiation at 25°C on Silicone Dielectrics, *Trans. Am. Inst. Elec. Engrs.*, Part I, *78*(44): 297–308 (1959).

8. Dewhurst, H. A., Radiation Chemistry of Organic Compounds. II. *n*-Hexane, *J. Phys. Chem., 62*(1): 15 (January 1958).

9. Fowler, J. F., X-Ray Induced Conductivity in Insulating Materials, *Proc. Roy. Soc.(London), A236*(1207): 464 (September 1956).

10. Gemant, Andreas, *Liquid Dielectrics*, p. 4, John Wiley & Sons, Inc., New York, 1933.

11. Kircher, J. R., *Survey of Irradiation Facilities*, Report REIC 7, Battelle Memorial Institute, May 1950.

12. Klein, P. H., and Mannal, C., Effects of High Energy Gamma Radiation on Dielectric Solids, *Trans. Am. Inst. Elec. Engrs.* Part I, *74:* 723–729 (1955).

13. Lane, J. A., How to Design Reactor Shields for Low Cost, *Nucleonics, 13*(6): 57 (June 1955).

14. Macfadyen, K. A., Some Researches into the Electrical Conduction and Breakdown of Liquid Dielectrics, *Brit. J. Appl. Phys., 6*: 1 (January 1955).

15. McDonell, W. R., and Gordon, S., Decomposition of Methyl Alcohol by Co^{60} Gamma Radiation, *J. Chem. Phys., 23*(1): 208 (January 1955).

16. Pao, C. S., Conduction of Electricity in Highly Insulating Liquids, *Phys. Rev., 64*(3,4): 60 (August 1943).

17. Prevot-Bernas, A., Chapiro, A., Cousin, C., Landler, Y., and Magat, M., The Radiolysis of Some Organic Liquids, *Discussions Faraday Soc.*, No. 12: 98 (1952).

18. Saldick, J., Analytical Evaluation of the Effects of Radiation on Organic Materials, *Conference on Effects of Radiation on Dielectric Materials, Naval Research Laboratory, Washington, D. C., December 14–15, 1954*, Report ACR-2.

19. Schoepfle, C. S., and Connell, L. H., Effect of Cathode Rays on Hydrocarbon Oils and on Paper, *Ind. Eng. Chem., 21*(6): 529 (June 1929).

20. Schoepfle, C. S., and Fellows, C. H., Gaseous Products from Action of Cathode Rays on Hydrocarbons, *Ind. Eng. Chem., 23*(12): 1396 (December 1931).

21. Schuler, R. H., Radiation-Chemical Studies with Cyclotron Beams, *J. Am. Chem. Soc., 77*(2): 507 (January 1955).

22. Shelton, R. D., and Kenney, J. G., Damage Effects of Radiation on Electronic Components, *Nucleonics, 14*(9): 66 (September 1956).

23. Sisman, O., and Wilson, J. C., Engineering Use of Damage Data, *Nucleonics, 14* (9): 58 (September 1956).

24. Smaller, B., and Matheson, M. S., Paramagnetic Species Produced by Gamma Irradiation of Organic Compounds, *J. Chem. Phys., 28*(6): 1169 (June 1958).

25. Smyth, C. P., *Dielectric Behavior and Structure*, p. 52, McGraw-Hill Book Company, Inc., New York, 1955.

26. Sullivan, R. J., and Silvey, F. C., *Dielectric Properties of Terphenyl Mixtures*, USAEC Report NAA-SR-4764, North American Aviation, Inc., May 1, 1960.

27. Tolbert, B. M., and Lemmon, R. M., Radiation Decomposition of Pure Organic Compounds, *Radiation Research, 3*(1): 52 (September 1955).

28. Von Hippel, A. R., *Dielectrics and Waves*, p. 234, John Wiley & Sons, Inc., New York, 1954.

29. Von Hippel, A. R., (Ed.), *Dielectric Materials and Applications*, Technology Press of Massachusetts Institute of Technology in collaboration with John Wiley & Sons, Inc., 1954.

30. White, A. H., and Morgan, S. O., The Dielectric Properties of Chlorinated Diphenyls, *J. Franklin Inst., 216:* 638 (November 1933).

31. Wilson, J. C., Experimental Approaches to Radiation Studies—Radiation Sources and Dosimetry, in *Effects of Radiation on Materials*, pp. 48 and 214, Harwood, J. J., Hausner, H. H., Morse, J. G., and Rauch, W. G., (Eds.), Reinhold Publishing Corp., New York, 1958.

CHAPTER 14

Fuels and Fluid Shield Materials

By James G. Carroll and Robert O. Bolt

14-1 Introduction

Hydrogen-containing substances are very efficient for slowing down fast neutrons; moderation occurs principally by elastic scattering (see Ch. 2, Sect. 2-3.3). Thus most neutron shields contain hydrogen in some form, and methods for calculating neutron attenuation by hydrogen are included in most shielding manuals.[21,32,33] Organic materials generally contain hydrogen and therefore are popular candidates for shielding materials. Hydrocarbons, in particular, are attractive for this use.

Fluid hydrocarbons are of particular interest as neutron shields for mobile reactors, e.g., reactors in nuclear-powered aircraft. Here, the fluid material not only can perform the shielding function but also can be used as fuel for emergency power generation and can provide a heat sink for either the main or the accessory equipment.

The practical advantages of a hydrogenous organic-fluid shield include the following:

1. Reasonably good heat transfer from a compact primary shield or reactor wall.
2. Low vapor pressure (as compared with water) to permit small (low-pressure) containment vessels.
3. High hydrogen content (20% less weight than water for an equal volume per cent of hydrogen).
4. No reaction with metals such as sodium which are often used as primary coolants.
5. Combustibility in conventional burners.

Recognition of these properties prompted support of work with organic fluids. In 1949 Greenfield[22] calculated that mixtures of decarborane, boron, and decosane would effectively shield against the entire neutron spectrum. This shielding ability of numerous organic species of different types was also calculated.[8] No significant radiation-effects work was included.

If the organic shield is to be burned, the effects of radiation on all properties associated with the complicated handling operation and combustion process become of foremost importance. Effects on the less complicated shielding process are of secondary interest. Most of the work (see Refs. 4–6, 28, and 29) pertaining to the effects of radiation on fuels emphasizes property changes; this emphasis is retained in the presentation to follow.

Because over 75% of the information available about fuels is on jet fuels, the discussion will center around these materials. Mention will also be made of gasoline, kerosene, diesel fuel, and other organic fluids where appropriate. Irradiations were conducted under a wide variety of experimental conditions. Most exposures were with gamma rays from spent fuel elements from reactors at Hanford and Idaho. Gamma rays from Co^{60} sources were also used, and some irradiations were with electrons from Van de Graaff generators. In some cases samples were exposed to combined reactor radiation in the Materials Testing Reactor (MTR) and in the Nuclear Aircraft Research Facility (NARF).

14-2 Fuel Properties

Hydrocarbon fuels are blends of low-molecular-weight hydrocarbons. Straight-run distillates and cracked stocks are the basic components; small amounts of inhibitors are sometimes used. Pertinent chemical and physical properties of individual fuels are discussed in ensuing sections. Actual make-up of fuel types varies considerably both with the type of crude oil used and with the process used. Typical compositions of representative fuels are shown in Table 14.1.

Table 14.1 — TYPICAL COMPOSITION OF FUELS

	JP-4	JP-5	Kerosene	Aviation gasoline
Compound type, wt. %				
Paraffins } saturates Naphthenes	84	80	99	89
Olefins	1	1	Trace	1
Aromatics	15	17	1	10
Elements, wt. %				
Sulfur	0.07	0.33	0.02	0.01
Carbon	86	86	85.3	
Hydrogen	13.8	13.3	14.7	14.0
Average molecular weight	120	360	~360	94
Initial boiling point, °F	150	400	350	110
Viscosity at 0 °F, centistokes	< 2.40	< 7.00	~ 5.20	1.00

Throughout this discussion repeated reference will be made to certain jet fuels. These are listed in Table 14.2 together with their crude sources and code names.

Table 14.2 — IDENTITY OF JET FUELS

Type	Number[a]	Code	Description
JP-4		Westex	West Texas crude
		Salake	Salt Lake (Rangely) crude
	RAF-105	Mideast	Middle East crude
	RAF-106	Midcont.	Midcontinent crude
	RAF-107	San Jo	San Joaquin crude
JP-5	RAF-104	LA	Los Angeles Basin crude
	RAF-99	East US	Eastern U.S. crude paraffinic kerosene
	RAF-F-112	Spcl.	Highly refined aromatic-free kerosene from Eastern U.S. crude
RP-1		RP-1	Highly refined California kerosene

[a]Identification of fuels from same refinery run as those under study by Coordinating Research Council (CRC).

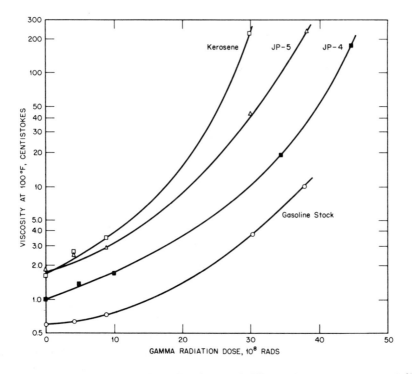

FIG. 14.1 Viscosity change of irradiated fuels. MTR canal gamma source at 65°F; 410 stainless-steel capsules under helium. (From J. G. Carroll, R. O. Bolt, and J. A. Bert, *Aeronautical Engineering Review*, Ref. 8.)

The over-all effect of radiation on hydrocarbon fuels is dehydrogenation and carbon-chain fissure with the subsequent formation of unsaturates, formation of a substance with a lower boiling point than the original material (light ends), and formation of higher boiling substances (polymers). These chemical changes induce varying degrees of change in physical properties. In all fuels radiation produces a tan to brown color, quite unlike the yellow caused by normal aging. Irradiated fuels acquire a characteristic acrid odor.

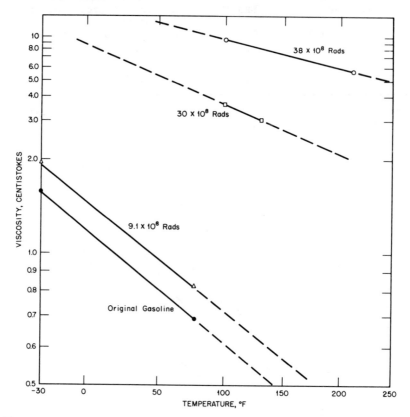

Fig. 14.2 Viscosity–temperature properties of irradiated gasoline. MTR canal gamma source at 65°F; 410 stainless-steel capsules under helium.

For all fuels viscosity increases with increasing radiation dose. This is not significant below about 2.5×10^7 rads and is usually of the order of a few per cent at 10^8 rads. Above 17×10^8 rads, irradiated fuels rapidly get into the lubricating-oil range in viscosity. Figure 14.1 illustrates typical viscosity changes for four fuels.[8] JP-5 fuels generally cannot tolerate doses that the less viscous JP-4 fuels can before reaching the 10-centistoke level that restricts the starting of jet engines. Inherent resistance to radiation-induced thickening was found to be about the same for JP-4 and JP-5 fuels from various crude sources.[23]

Irradiation was found to decrease progressively the rate of change of viscosity with temperature for fuels. This effect, illustrated† in Fig. 14.2, was most noticeable with the materials with the lowest starting viscosity. It is undoubtedly caused by the formation of radiation-induced polymer.

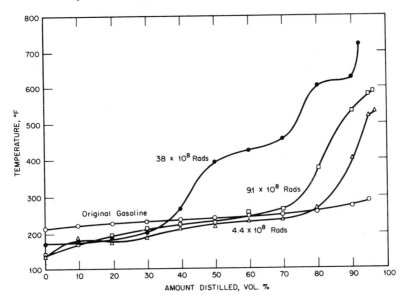

FIG. 14.3 Distillation of irradiated gasoline stock. MTR canal gamma source at 65°F; 410 stainless-steel capsules under helium. (From J. G. Carroll, R. O. Bolt, and J. A. Bert, *Aeronautical Engineering Review*, Ref. 8.)

Volatility, a key property affecting the handling and combustion of fuels, is determined by distillation according to ASTM procedures.[1] As would be expected, the polymer formed by irradiation increases the percentage of higher boiling-point material in all fuels; the increase depends on total dose. Figure 14.3 illustrates this increase for a gasoline stock. The irradiations were made in small capsules; so the gas phase was retained during exposure. Thus the volatile portions were also retained in the fuel and appeared as material having lower boiling points than the original. JP-4 and JP-5 fuels similarly irradiated in inert atmospheres showed comparable increases in high-boiling-point materials.[8] However, they did not show the same degree of formation of volatile ends, as shown in Fig. 14.4 for a dose level of about 7.5×10^8 rads. JP-4 fuels did not change much below the 50% distillation point; however, the JP-5 fuels con-

---

† Hydrocarbons normally form a straight line on a plot[1] such as Fig. 14.2; hence, the extrapolations are not unreasonable.

sistently showed the formation of light ends.[23] No consistent pattern was observed for Reid vapor pressures.[1,20] Some fuels showed a decrease and some showed an increase.

Because of the evolution of hydrogen and subsequent reactions, the density of all fuels increased with irradiation.[24] The more volatile fuels showed the greater increases. For example,[8] at 37×10^8 rads gasoline increased by 12.3%, JP-4 fuels increased by 9.6%, and a stove oil increased by 5.4%. When irradiated in closed containers, some fuels showed an

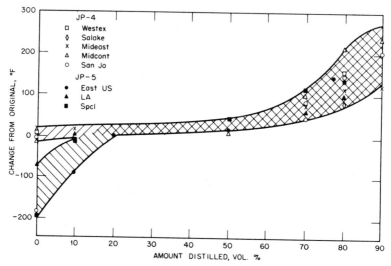

FIG. 14.4 Distillation of irradiated jet fuels. Dose, 6.6 to 7.9×10^8 rads; MTR canal gamma source at 65°F; vented aluminum containers. (From J. T. Guerin, J. G. Carroll, R. O. Bolt, and J. A. Bert, *Aero/Space Engineering*, Ref. 23.)

initial drop in density. This may have resulted from saturation with radiolytic gases. Gas evolution became high above 10^9 rads, as shown in Fig. 14.5. The formation of radiolytic gas and light ends can be objectionable in closed systems because this produces increased pressures.

Refractive index increased slightly with dose. For one fuel (East US) this increase[29] was 0.0015 per 10^8 rads.

Heat of combustion showed[29] no significant change up to about 10^8 rads. There is a slight downward trend for higher doses, approximately 20 cal per 10^8 rads.

Burner tests were not run on irradiated fuels because of the large quantities needed for such tests. The *smoke volatility index*[12] was calculated for several irradiated fuels. This index, which predicts burner performance for jet fuels, showed a slight decrease above 10×10^8 rads for JP-4, kerosene, and gasoline.[8] This decrease indicates poor burning properties and was probably due to the high-boiling-point materials present.

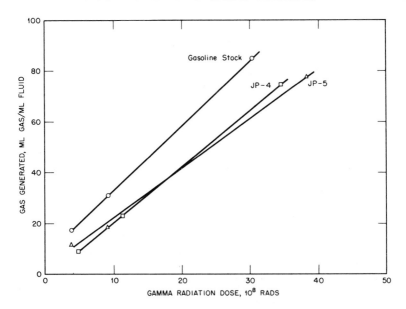

Fig. 14.5 Gassing of fuels during irradiation. MTR canal gamma source at 65°F; 410 stainless-steel capsules under helium. (From J. G. Carroll, R. O. Bolt, and J. A. Bert, *Aeronautical Engineering Review,* Ref. 8.)

Peroxide numbers† increased[29] with dose in the range 10^7 to 10^9 rads. Some fuels showed a rapid change at low doses and then leveled off at higher levels. For others the rate of change increased at higher doses.

Table 14.3 — EFFECT OF GAMMA IRRADIATION[a] ON STEAM-JET GUM

Gamma dose, 10^8 rads	Steam-jet gum (500 °F), mg/100 ml fluid				
	0	0.2	0.7	1.9	8.0
Before thermal-stability tests:					
JP-5 (East U. S.)	0.2	10.8	217	2059	15,828
JP-4 (San Jo)	1.4	26.7	73	714	4,768
After thermal-stability tests at 450°F:					
JP-5 (East U. S.)	2.8	279	345	2444	16,620
JP-4 (San Jo)	2.0	30	141	982	5,756

[a]Hanford spent-fuel-element source at 65 °F, air access, aluminum canisters.

Polymers soluble in a fuel are measured by steam-jet gum values. The gum content increases rapidly with radiation dose. Subsequent heating

† Peroxide numbers indicate the quantity of oxidizable constituents present (see Ref. 1, Method D 1516-58T).

sometimes causes further increases, but the major portion arises from irradiation. This is shown in Table 14.3 for two jet fuels.[29] A few of the
soluble gums were analyzed after the steam-jet gum evaluation. The JP-5
(East US) residue was a comparatively soft gum having an oxygen content of 1.7 wt. %. The JP-4 (San Jo) yielded a brittle gum with an oxygen
content of 3.56 wt. %. The saturated hydrocarbon content of the two fuels
was 99 and 84%, respectively. The observed gums contained only about
$\frac{1}{16}$ to $\frac{1}{12}$ as much oxygen as the natural gums normally deposited from
the fuels. The radiolysis gums had a molecular weight of about 800; values
for the original fuels were 130 to 200. The radiolysis gums apparently result from radiation-induced polymerization.

14-3 Thermal-stability Properties

Tests of these properties were made in the CFR† fuel coker[10] on original and irradiated fuels. A sketch of the device is shown in Fig. 14.6; it
measures the tendency of jet fuels to form deposits on hot surfaces and to
plug filters at high temperatures. The fuel coker simulates the hot portion
of turbojet-engine fuel systems.

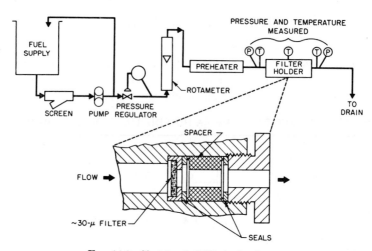

Fig. 14.6 Sketch of CFR fuel coker.

The heated components of the fuel coker are the preheater and the
filter. Test conditions are expressed in three numbers, e.g., 400/500/6. The
first number is the fuel temperature (°F) out of the preheater, the second
is the filter temperature (°F), and the third is the fuel flow rate (pounds
per hour). For each fuel, test conditions were chosen so that the irradiated fuel could be tested under the same conditions as the original fuel.

The results of the coker tests are expressed by two scales developed

† Coordinating Fuel Research (CFR) Panel of the Coordinating Research Council
(CRC).

by the CRC Aviation Fuel Thermal Stability Group.[11] Filter plugging is expressed as "filter merit rating" on a scale from 0 to 99, in which 0 indicates immediate plugging and 99 indicates no plugging after a 5-hr test period. Preheater tube deposits are expressed as "log of deposit function" on a scale from 0 to about 5, where 0 indicates a clean tube and 5 indicates a tube completely coated with black deposit.

14-3.1 TESTS BEFORE AND AFTER IRRADIATION

Filter merit ratings for the five JP-4 fuels listed in Table 14.2 for doses of up to 7.1×10^8 rads are[23] given in Table 14.4. No trend is evident at

Table 14.4—EFFECT OF IRRADIATION[a] ON FILTER PLUGGING OF JP-4 FUELS IN CFR FUEL COKER

Fuel	Aromatics, vol. %	Filter merit rating			
Gamma dose, 10^8 rads		0	0.8	4.2	7.1
Westex[b]	9	60	35	33	74
Salake[b]	11	53	49	79	99
Mideast[c]	12	47	25	87	83
Midcont.[c]	8	42	83	44	83
San Jo[d]	10	27	47	47	99

[a] MTR canal source at 65 °F in vented aluminum canisters.
[b] 400/400/6.
[c] 350/400/6.
[d] 375/400/6.

the lowest dose, but uniform improvement took place at the highest dose. The three JP-5 fuels listed in Table 14.2 also showed consistent improvement at the two highest doses. Ratings[23] of preheater deposits are given in Table 14.5. Here, again, the improvement at high doses is evident; the three JP-5 fuels showed no deposits at the two highest doses.

Table 14.5—EFFECT OF IRRADIATION[a] ON PREHEATER DEPOSITION OF JP-4 FUELS

Fuel	Log of deposit function			
Gamma dose, 10^8 rads	0	0.8	4.2	7.1
Westex[b]	0	2.12	0.82	0
Salake[b]	2.04	1.82	2.00	1.47
Mideast[c]	1.24	2.16	1.94	1.32
Midcont.[c]	0	1.55	0	0.90
San Jo[d]	0	2.50	1.80	0

[a] MTR canal source at 65 °F in vented aluminum canisters.
[b] 400/400/6.
[c] 350/400/6.
[d] 375/400/6.

The minimum in thermal stability at about 2×10^6 rads and the subsequent improvement were confirmed in another test.[26,29] Here, the fuel at 450°F was pumped through a 5-μ pore size stainless-steel filter. The time required to plug the filter was the criterion of stability. Figure 14.7 pre-

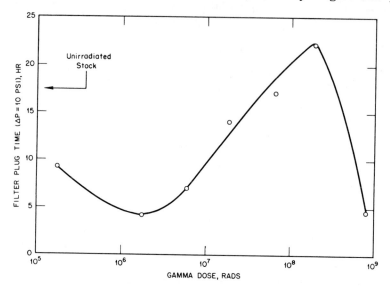

Fig. 14.7 Effect of irradiation on thermal stability of a JP-5 fuel. Fuel through filter at 450°F; irradiation in Hanford fuel-element source at 65°F; air access, aluminum canister.

sents data from this test on a JP-5 fuel. No general pattern existed in the preheater deposits for the fuels in this test work.

Because thermal-stability impairment was most evident at low radiation doses, an RP-1 type kerosene fuel was studied over the 10^4- to 10^8-rad dose range. Samples were irradiated in a circulating loop in a Co^{60} source and statically in the MTR gamma canal source prior to testing. As shown in Fig. 14.8, all irradiated samples had lower filter merit ratings than the base fuel, except for the sample at the highest dose and a rerun at an intermediate dose.

A barrel sample of the RP-1 was also exposed (air present, 100°F) in the NARF to determine the effects of the reactor environment. Tests revealed a reduction in rating, as shown in Fig. 14.8, for this sample, which received the equivalent of about 8×10^6 rads. Tests at other coker conditions consistently showed the thermal stability of the RP-1 fuel to have been degraded by this reactor exposure.[3]

Other jet fuels were also exposed[35] in the NARF. Changes in physical properties, including unsaturation and aromatic content, were consistent with changes associated with about 8×10^6 rads gamma irradiation. Ther-

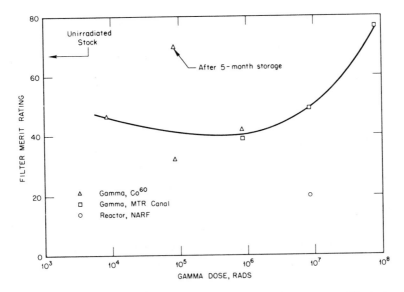

Fig. 14.8 Effect of irradiation on thermal stability of RP-1 fuel. CFR fuel coker 400/500/6; irradiations at 65 to 100° in air. (From J. T. Guerin, J. G. Carroll, R. O. Bolt, and J. A. Bert, *Aero/Space Engineering*, Ref. 23.)

mal stability following reactor exposure was drastically reduced as compared to that from gamma exposures, as shown in Table 14.6; preheater deposition rates were much higher. The paraffinic kerosene (JP-5, East US) was of particular interest because of its good thermal stability after a gamma dose of about 10^8 rads.

Table 14.6 — COMPARATIVE EFFECTS OF GAMMA AND REACTOR
EXPOSURES ON JET-FUEL THERMAL STABILITY
(Plugging of 5-μ filter at 450°F)

Fuel	Exposure[a]	Change in filter plugging time, %
JP-5 (East U. S.)	None W-2 NARF	 -59[b] -96[b]
JP-4 (San Jo)	None W-2 NARF	 -35[c] -65[c]

[a]W-2   = Hanford canal gamma facility at 65°F; vented aluminum canister; ~6 x 10^6 rads.

NARF = Nuclear Aircraft Reactor Facility at 100°F; vented steel drum; 3 to 4 x 10^{14} thermal neutrons/cm² plus 4 to 6 x 10^6 rads gamma. Total ≅ 4 to 6 x 10^6 rads.

[b]Plugging at ΔP = 10 psi.
[c]Plugging at ΔP = 30 psi.

A portion of the difference between gamma and reactor exposures was attributed to slight differences in doses.[35] A portion, however, was also ascribed to an increase in soluble-iron content during reactor exposures. The iron content of East US increased from 0.03 to 0.8 ppm. Such a change would adversely affect thermal stability. Nevertheless, the increased degradation following reactor exposure has not yet been completely explained. Additional work with various fuels exposed in the NARF and in a gamma source to doses of 10^5 to 10^8 rads was inconclusive.[27] It is likely, however, that the "neutron effect" is a combination of several items of which dosage (and dosimetry) and soluble-iron content are but two.

14-3.2 IN-SOURCE TESTS

The questions applied to the use of most materials in the presence of radiation are also applied to the use of fuels: Do static irradiations correctly predict performance in machinery operating in a radiation environment? and is the effect of applying thermal, radiation, and mechanical stresses simultaneously greater than applying them singly? Fainman tested 79 different jet fuels to investigate these questions.[18]

The tests were conducted in a hot cell in which 50,000 curies of Co^{60} provided the gamma flux. A standard CFR fuel coker was operated in the usual way in this environment. Removal of the source permitted check tests in the same equipment in the absence of radiation. Average gamma flux through the coker was about 4×10^5 rads/hr. Thus, for the standard 5-hr test, 2×10^6 rads could be administered to the fluid. Static irradiation supplemented this "dynamic" dose; thus total irradiation reached a significant level. Irradiation in this manner is not unlike the situation in a vehicle in which the fuel serves as a shield and is consumed near the end of the journey.

Most of the tests were in the 10^7- to 10^8-rad dose range. With static irradiations changes in physical properties were very small. Occasionally a brown precipitate was observed. Similar residues were noted during dynamic testing in a radiation environment, although not during coker tests without radiation. Preirradiation altered the thermal stability of the test fuels: some became better; some became worse. Combined static and dynamic irradiation also produced mixed results. Of 34 JP-5 fuels so exposed and tested in the fuel coker, 12 showed better thermal stability than the original fuel, 12 were worse, and 10 showed no significant change.[17] The data are too few to allow conclusions, but they do indicate the complexity of results from this type work.[18]

The necessity of testing under environmental conditions to evaluate fuel performance adequately was emphasized in further dynamic tests.[15] Here, Co^{60} provided a dose rate of about 2×10^6 rads/hr to a CFR fuel coker. About 1×10^4 rads was received by the fuel in passing through the preheater. An approach section permitted higher doses. Drastic increases in filter plugging expressed as "goodness rating"† were reported for fairly low doses. Typical results (coker conditions, 400/500/6) on a JP-5 fuel show an original rating of 900 going to 560 and then to 80 while the fuel received 10^4 and 7×10^5 rads, respectively.

The test was reasonably reproducible when treatment conditions were uniform.[15] The sensitivity to storage time after static irradiations is shown in Table 14.7. The mechanism of "healing" of statically radiolyzed fuel with increased storage time is not clear.

Table 14.7 — DYNAMIC IRRADIATION AS COMPARED TO STATIC IRRADIATION WITH A VARIABLE AGING PERIOD FOR A JP-5 FUEL

Treatment	Goodness rating
No irradiation	850
Static irradiation[a]	
One-week aging	550
Five-hour aging	315
Dynamic irradiation[a]	160

[a]CFR fuel coker; 400/500/6; 7.0×10^5 rads gamma dose.

For fuels, as with lubricants, comparative results from static vs. dynamic testing give few unequivocal answers. This undoubtedly results from the interaction of the various environments involved, such as radiation, oxygen, heat, and shear stresses. In some cases a combination of these accelerates property changes; e.g., radiation in the presence of oxygen accelerates damage. In some cases other combinations retard property changes; e.g., radiation-induced polymer can be destroyed by mechanical shear. Thus the results of dynamic tests are difficult to interpret because they depend upon the relative balance of stresses and on the properties being observed. Static tests are better in this regard, but they do not simulate as closely the eventual application.

14-4 Shielding

The ability of organic substances to attenuate fast neutrons depends upon their hydrogen content. The slowing-down process is by elastic scattering. For neutrons of less than 8 Mev energy, the cross section of hydrogen is considerably larger than that of oxygen or carbon. Thus for candidate neutron-shield materials the hydrogen content and its variations with irradiation must be examined.

The radiolytic gas evolved from the fluid is also of interest. Although

† Goodness rating is another empirical method of rating filter plugging (i.e., pressure drop across filter) on an arbitrary scale. Immediate plugging receives a rating of 0; no pressure drop in 5 hr is rated 900.

the gas is chiefly hydrogen, the loss does not affect hydrogen density appreciably, as will be shown. However, above certain levels ($\sim 10^8$ rads), removal of the gas may be a problem.

For shielding studies hydrogen content has been expressed on a volume basis in atoms per milliliter. The term N_H is defined:

$$N_H = 6.02 \times 10^{23} \ (\rho \times \text{wt. fraction H}), \text{ atoms H/ml organic}$$

N_H varies directly with density (ρ) and thus decreases with increasing temperature. The N_H values of several types of organic fluids are shown in Table 14.8.

Table 14.8—HYDROGEN CONTENT OF SEVERAL FLUIDS AT 68°F

Compound	Empirical formula	Density $\frac{20}{4}$, g/ml	N_H, 10^{22} atoms H/ml
n-Decylamine	$C_{10}H_{23}N$	0.951	8.45
Hydrazine	$(NH_2)_2$	1.004	7.55
n-Dodecane	$C_{12}H_{26}$	0.751	6.95
JP-5 fuel		0.833	6.79
Kerosene		0.803	6.77
Water	H_2O	0.998	6.67
JP-4 fuel		0.793	6.66
Gasoline		0.750	6.61
Ethylene glycol	$C_2H_6O_2$	1.107	6.60
Alkylbenzene 250	$C_{18}H_{30}$	0.867	6.30

14-4.1 JET FUELS

As discussed in Sect. 14-2, the density of jet fuels increases with radiation dose. This coincides with hydrogen evolution; 90% of the radiolytic gas (see Fig. 14.5) is hydrogen. This evolution was found[29] to be linear with gamma dose, but small losses occurred below 10^7 rads. Different rates of hydrogen generation were observed.[29] For example, for 10^8 rads in air:

	Wt. % hydrogen
JP-5 (East US)	0.40
JP-5 (LA)	0.23
JP-5 (Spcl.)	0.87

An interesting comparison[8] with these data is taken from fuels irradiated for 38 to 45×10^8 rads under helium. Here hydrogen evolution was retarded. Loss of hydrogen at 10^8 rads was as follows:

	Wt. % hydrogen
Gasoline	0.04
JP-4	0.02

The radiolytic gas evolved from a shield material might pose a problem of removal. However, it has negligible effect on N_H even in exposures under unpressurized, aerobic conditions, as shown in Table 14.9. Appar-

Table 14.9 — VARIATION OF HYDROGEN DENSITY AT
68 °F WITH IRRADIATION

Fuel	N_H, 10^{22} atoms H/ml fluid			
Gamma dose, 10^8 rads	0	0.8	4.2	7.1
JP-4:				
Westex	6.61	6.67	6.59	6.62
Salake	6.67	6.91	6.53	6.82
Mideast	6.79	6.91	6.79	7.13
Midcont.	6.67	7.12	6.71	6.63
JP-5:				
Spcl.	7.11	7.14	6.89	7.04
LA	6.70	7.02	6.68	6.70

ently the density increase is balanced by the reduction in weight fraction of hydrogen. Similar results[9] were obtained at doses of the order of 50 $\times$ 10^8 rads.

14-4.2 DIESEL FUELS

Samples of a 50-cetane and of a 73-cetane diesel fuel were irradiated with gamma rays.[5] Sea water and distilled water were admixed with some of the samples to determine their effect on radiolysis. As shown in Table 14.10, the sea water increased gas evolution, although the sea water itself gave off a surprising amount of gas.

Table 14.10 — GASSING OF FLUID SHIELDS

	Gamma[a] dose, 10^8 rads	Gassing, ml gas/ml fluid
73-cetane diesel fuel	0.38	0.64
50/50 vol. % 73-cetane fuel + sea water	0.38	1.02
Sea water	0.42	1.03
Alkylbenzene 250	2.2	1.26
Distilled water	2.2	0.10

[a]Irradiated in sealed 1020 steel capsules at about 65 °F in a Co^{60} source.

Changes in molecular weight, density, hydrogen content (N_H), and cetane number were slight ($<5\%$) for the diesel fuels at 0.4×10^8 rads. Sea water consistently increased changes in the organic materials. Corrosion of metals was, of course, accelerated by the sea water.

14-4.3 ALKYL AROMATIC COMPOUNDS

Alkylbenzene 250,[†] Alkylbenzene 350,[‡] and Dowtherm A[§] were exposed[31] in the Low Intensity Test Reactor (LITR). The tests were conducted in a circulating loop in which the energy absorbed was

$$1.0 \times 10^{18} nvt \ (\leqq 0.5 \ \text{Mev}) \equiv 58 \times 10^8 \ \text{rads}$$

The objective of the work was to study engineering properties of the fluids for possible shield–coolant use. The relative stabilities were Dowtherm

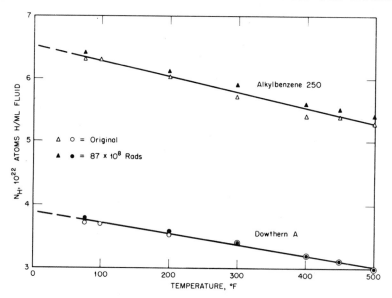

FIG. 14.9 Influence of reactor irradiation on hydrogen content. Exposed in LITR at ~300°F under CO_2.

A > Alkylbenzene 250 > Alkylbenzene 350. Of the three, Alkylbenzene 250 is of most interest as a shield material because of its relatively high N_H and its good radiation stability (still fluid after 87×10^8 rads).

The alkylbenzenes evolved gas copiously during the LITR irradiation. This evolution was approximately linear with dose out to 87×10^8 rads. In

† Oronite Division of California Chemical Co., Alkane '56, monoalkylbenzene (molecular weight ~250).
‡ Oronite Division of California Chemical Co., Aromatics ABH, dialkylbenzene (molecular weight ~350).
§ Dow Chemical Co., ~23% biphenyl in diphenyl ether.

a 300°F irradiation about 1.7 ml of gas per milliliter of fluid was given off for each 10^8 rads. At 500°F this rate doubled. Changes in N_H were negligible for Dowtherm A and for Alkylbenzene 250. The N_H values, of course, varied with temperature, as can be seen in Fig. 14.9. Alkylbenzene 350, with about 7% higher N_H than Alkylbenzene 250, showed about the same pattern of change as the latter. Alkylbenzene 250 was the more radiation stable.

14-4.4 ETHYLENE GLYCOL

This compound, $(CH_2OH)_2$, is of interest as a shield material and as a pump lubricant. Coking tendencies of the material were studied to evaluate it for such applications. In these tests the fluid was splashed for 5 hr onto an aluminum panel maintained at a controlled temperature.

At a 500°F panel temperature, appreciable coking was observed with the original glycol. At 350°F less coke was formed. However, the total deposit weight was two to three times that of the 500°F test because of a crystalline residue not observed at 500°F. Exposures in a nitrogen atmosphere reduced measurably the total deposit and eliminated the crystalline portion. However, samples irradiated for 10^7 rads under nitrogen produced a noncrystalline deposit at 350°F which was twice the weight of that from the original fluid.

A gamma dose of 2.2×10^8 rads under helium at 85°F produced only minor apparent changes in ethylene glycol. Viscosity at 100°F increased 6%; density at 68°F increased 1.1%; and about 10.4 volumes of gas evolved per volume of glycol. The gas was 83% hydrogen, 11.7% methane, 2.2% C_2 and C_3 fragments, and 2.3% carbon oxides. After 3.2×10^8 rads gamma dose at 75°F, viscosity at 100°F increased 11%. Neither tar formation nor corrosive tendencies were observed in any of the irradiations.[7]

14-4.5 ETHYLDECABORANE†

This compound was irradiated[4] with Co^{60} gamma rays under vacuum in a sealed glass vessel. Because of the small quantities available and the

Table 14.11 — GAS EVOLUTION FROM ETHYLDECABORANE

Gamma dose, 10^8 rads	Gas evolved, ml/ml
0.6	6
1.0	8
2.5	11
4.8	19
12.0	44

necessary handling precautions, only limited data were obtained. Gas evo-

† Olin Mathieson Chemical Corp., Sample Z279-1.

lution was considerably greater than for hydrocarbons (see Fig. 14.5), as shown in Table 14.11.

Spectrometric analyses indicated that at least 16% of the original material was decomposed at the highest dose. The following products were qualitatively identified: diethyldecaborane, decaborane, octaborane, ethylpentaborane, pentaborane, propane, ethane, methane, and hydrogen.

14-4.6 HYDRAZINE

This inorganic compound (N_2H_4) and its lower melting organic derivatives, such as unsymmetrical dimethylhydrazine, are outstanding rocket fuels. Hydrazine is also used in very small concentrations as a reducing agent in the water feed for pressurized-water reactors.

In aqueous solutions hydrazine decomposes rapidly (at 10^5 to 10^6 rads) to nitrogen, hydrogen, and ammonia.[34] In the presence of added hydrogen, the yield of ammonia is increased.

The yields of decomposition products from hydrazine solutions were found[14] to be independent of hydrazine content above $0.02M$. Hydrazine disappearance ($G_{-N_2H_4}$) was about equal to ammonia formation (G_{NH_3}); the rate was 5.2 molecules/100 ev absorbed. Nitrogen and hydrogen formation rates were also about equal ($G_{N_2} \cong G_{H_2} \cong 2.5$). There may be significant recombination of the radiolysis products in a closed system to re-form hydrazine. Higher homologs of hydrazine, e.g., $H_2NN(H)N(H)NH_2$, which might be expected to form, have not been reported in the literature and are presumably unstable.

Recent preliminary data[13] indicate that unsymmetrical dimethylhydrazine withstands a modest gamma dose. No decomposition was observed after an air-free irradiation to 10^7 rads.

14-5 Factors Influencing Stability

14-5.1 ROLE OF CONSTITUENTS

Sulfur was reported[29] in one instance to have disappeared from fuels during gamma irradiation in air. For a JP-4 (San Jo), sulfur content was reduced 31% (from 0.082 to 0.057 wt. %) by an exposure of 7.8×10^8 rads. It is possible that radiolytic hydrogen helped to purge the system of sulfur or that oxidation by the air to sulfur dioxide was involved.

The chemistry of radiolytic changes in jet fuels has been studied.[28] Ten fuels received gamma radiation of about 10^8 rads in both air and nitrogen atmospheres. Chemical changes were identified by infrared and ultraviolet spectroscopy and also by mass spectral analysis. As expected, the two most general changes observed were carbonyl formation and olefin formation. Attack on benzene was also generally noted.

Carbonyl compounds were usually formed only when air was present. Contaminants were believed responsible for the appearance of carbonyl compounds after exposures under nitrogen. Increases of 7 to 10% occurred[29] after aerobic irradiation of a JP-4 and a kerosene to 3×10^8 rads. (Even larger increases were measured[8] at doses up to 50×10^8 rads.) In some instances[29] decreases in olefin content at high doses were observed irrespective of exposure atmosphere, presumably because of radiolytic polymerization of the olefins.

Destruction of benzene was reportedly[31] more marked under nitrogen than in air. This suggests that active radicals are formed which react with the benzene in the absence of an efficient radical scavenger such as oxygen. The effect was noted in fuels having a benzene concentration of about 0.25 wt. %. At this low concentration, benzene appeared to act as a sacrificial protector. If benzene were to act as a sponge type protector, a concentration of at least 5% would be needed.

There are reports[8] of aromatic constituents being formed in the irradiation of jet fuels. Such data are probably in error because of the inadequacy of the analytical methods used. No aromatics formed[29] in a kerosene or in a JP-4 after gamma irradiation for 2.4×10^8 rads. This confirmed observations[8] on six different fuels after gamma irradiation of 44×10^8 rads under helium.

14-5.2 COMPONENTS

A JP-4 fuel (San Jo) was separated[29] by chromatographic adsorption into saturated and aromatic components. The saturated portion was composed mostly of one-ring naphthenes, almost entirely cyclopentane derivatives. The fuel was also separated by distillation into four fractions. The whole fuel and these components were then tested for thermal stability at 450°F before and after 10^8 rads gamma dose. Results are summarized as follows:

1. The unirradiated saturate fraction was three times as stable as the whole fuel. After 10^8 rads this fraction was about as thermally stable as the irradiated whole fuel. Thus the degrading effect of irradiation was much greater with the saturates.

2. Ten per cent of the aromatic fraction was added to a stable fuel; the thermal stability of the fuel dropped fourfold. This confirmed earlier studies that aromatics generally decrease the stability of jet fuels in the absence of radiation.

3. The lower boiling and the higher boiling fractions from the fuel each showed threefold greater thermal stability (filter plugging) than the whole fuel before irradiation. After 10^8 rads the fractions were comparable to the whole fuel in stability.

14-5.3 MODEL COMPOUNDS

Simple model compounds were studied[29] to elucidate radiation effects on the complex jet fuel mixture. Cyclohexane was irradiated with gamma rays under both aerobic and anaerobic conditions for about 7×10^8 rads. This compound is typical of the naphthene rings found in jet fuels. About 3.3 wt. % of the material was altered by irradiation. Bicyclohexyl was the major product of radiolysis. Methylcyclopentane and small amounts of the polymers of cyclohexadiene were also identified. The latter polymers were highly prone to oxidation in air on handling. The amount of cyclohexane reacting appeared to be independent of irradiation atmosphere. Yields, however, varied; for example, larger quantities of methylcyclopentane were formed under anaerobic conditions.

Decalin was also irradiated in air for nominal doses of 8×10^7 and 8×10^8 rads. There were only minor changes at the lower dose, but significant changes in physical properties occurred at the higher dose. At the higher level the *cis*-decalin content decreased by 30%, and the *trans*-isomer decreased by 11%. For the higher dose about 6% olefins was present and a considerable amount ($\sim$26 wt. %) of polymer having molecular weights as high as 2100 was present. Thermal stability was reduced fourfold by the 8×10^7 rad exposure. Thus the thermal-stability damage to the decalin was more pronounced than it was to the jet fuels. However, the damage compares closely to the effect on the saturate portion of the San Jo JP-4.

Additional gamma radiolysis of decalin under nitrogen confirmed the preferential attack on the *cis*-isomer. In fact, at 8×10^7 rads, the *trans*-isomer increased by some 16 wt. % while the *cis* form *decreased* 13%. The *trans* form is the more stable configuration energetically. Although not uncommon for unsaturates, this effect on *cis–trans* isomers is reportedly unique for saturates. The results suggest a way of minimizing radiation damage by the use of tailor-made fuels. Numerous substituted five- and six-membered ring systems are available which exist in both *cis* and *trans* forms. Conceivably a portion of ionizing energy could be dissipated in isomerization.[29]

14-5.4 RADIATION PROTECTORS

Several aromatic compounds at concentrations ranging from 2.5 to 20 wt. % were used[29] as additives in jet fuels. These protectors included benzene, naphthalene, and 8-hydroxyquinoline. The base stocks were three typical JP-4 and JP-5 fuels (San Jo, East US, LA). The mixtures were irradiated in both air and helium for about 9×10^7 rads gamma dose. The concentration of the protector was determined by infrared analysis.

In most cases, under both aerobic and anaerobic conditions, the added aromatics were altered. Benzene was the most reactive of the protectors. In 20 wt. % solutions, about one quarter of the additive was destroyed. Naphthalene reacted to a much smaller extent and the behavior of 8-hydroxyquinoline was extremely variable. If pure benzene were irradiated under similar conditions, about 1% would be destroyed. Thus it seems that benzene protects as a radical scavenger in this particular system. Some olefins were observed even when 20 wt. % benzene was used as a protector. Infrared analysis indicated that the benzene "consumed" appeared as additional alkylbenzenes in the reaction products.

14-6 Principles

1. The neutron-shielding ability of hydrogenous fluids, as measured by the number of hydrogen atoms per milliliter, does not change appreciably with irradiation up to the order of 50×10^8 rads.

2. The most important effect of radiation on jet fuels is a degrading of thermal stability as measured by filter-plugging tendency at high temperatures. This property is a complex function of dose. Between 10^5 and 10^7 rads, thermal stability is impaired for most fuels. At 10^8 rads some fuels show no change; others are degraded. Above 5×10^8 rads, thermal stability appears to be improved.

3. It appears that neutrons are more damaging to jet fuel thermal stability than gamma rays. However, this is not clear cut and needs further clarification.

4. Physical and chemical properties of jet fuels are not materially changed by doses below about 10^7 rads. Changes in viscosity, gum content, and volatility are appreciable at 10^8 rads but are not great enough to hinder handling or combustion. Significant changes in properties occur at 10^9 rads.

5. Dehydrogenation, olefin formation, and polymerization are the major chemical reactions induced by ionizing radiations in jet fuels.

6. Aromatics are not produced during the radiolysis of jet fuels; significant amounts of olefins are produced by dehydrogenation of paraffins and naphthenes.

References

Several of the following were cited in the text as authority for statements made. Others were not quoted but are included because they contain pertinent information. All were consulted in the preparation of this chapter.

1. American Society for Testing Materials, *1959 Supplement to Book of ASTM Standards. Part 7: Petroleum Products, Lubricants, Tank Measurement, Engine Tests,* ASTM, Philadelphia, Pa., 1959.
2. Bolt, R. O., *Effects of Nuclear Radiation on Lubricants and Other Organic Fluids,* paper presented at the Twenty-ninth International Congress of Industrial Chemistry, Paris, France, November 1956.

3. Bolt, R. O., and Carroll, J. G., *Effects of Radiation on Aircraft Lubricants and Fuels*, Report WADC-TR-56-646, Part II, April 1958.

4. Bolt, R. O., and Carroll, J. G., Report WADC-TR-56-646, December 1956. (Classified)

5. Bolt, R. O., and Carroll, J. G., *The Stability of Certain Organic Fluid Shield Materials to Gamma Radiation*, USAEC Report TID-5136, February 1953.

6. Bolt, R. O., Carroll, J. G., *et al.*, *Survey of Possible Fluid Hydrogenous Shield Materials*, Report NEPA-1381, April 1950. (Classified)

7. Bolt, R. O., and Carroll, J. G., California Research Corporation, unpublished data, 1955.

8. Carroll, J. G., Bolt, R. O., and Bert, J. A., A Survey of the Radiation Stability of Hydrocarbon Fuels, *Aeronaut. Eng. Rev.*, *17*(3): 61 (March 1958).

9. Carroll, J. G., Bolt, R. O., and Bert, J. A., *A Survey of the Radiation Stability of Jet Fuels*, USAEC Report TID-5366, June 1956.

10. Coordinating Research Council, *Instructions for Operation and Maintenance of CFR Fuel Coker*, CRC Manual No. 3, CRC, New York, March 1959.

11. Coordinating Research Council, *Report of the Panel on Data Analysis, CRC-AFD Fuel Thermal Stability Group*, CRC, New York, Jan. 1956.

12. Department of Defense, *Fuel, Aircraft Turbine, and Jet Engine Grades JP-3, JP-4, JP-5*, U. S. Military Specification MIL-F-5624C, May 1955.

13. Deutsch, D. E., Aerojet-General Nucleonics, San Ramon, California, personal communication, October 1958.

14. Dewhurst, H. A., and Burton, M., Radiolysis of Aqueous Solution of Hydrazine, *J. Am. Chem. Soc.*, *77*(22): 5781 (November 1955).

15. Droegemueller, E. A., and Clark, J. M., Dynamic Gamma Radiation Effects on Hydrocarbon Fluids Under Thermal Oxidative and Mechanical Stress, in *Proceedings of the Second Semiannual 125A Radiation Effects Symposium, October 22–23, 1957*, Vol. IV, Battelle Memorial Institute.

16. Fainman, M. Z., The Behavior of Fuels and Lubricants in Dynamic Test Equipment Operating in the Presence of Gamma Radiation in *Third Semiannual Radiation Effects Symposium, October 28–30, 1958*, Vol. 5, Lockheed Nuclear Products.

17. Fainman, M. Z., Krasnow, M. E., Kaufman, E. D., Reynolds, O. P., Thistlethwaite, R. L., and Wolford, O. C., *The Behavior of Fuels and Lubricants in Dynamic Test Equipment Operating in the Presence of Gamma Radiation*, Report WADC-TR-58-264, March 1958.

18. Fainman, M. Z., Reynolds, O. P., Wolford, O. C., and Kaufman, E. D., *The Behavior of Fuels and Lubricants in Dynamic Test Equipment Operating in the Presence of Gamma Radiation*, Third Progress Report, Cook Electric Company July 1958.

19. Fraces, A. P., Nuclear Aircraft Shielding, *Aeronaut. Eng. Rev.*, *15*(9): 39 (September 1956).

20. General Services Administration, *Lubricants, Liquid Fuels, and Related Products Method of Testing*, U. S. Federal Test Method No. 791, December 1955.

21. Goldstein, H., *The Attenuation of Gamma Rays and Neutrons in Reactor Shields*, Superintendent of Documents, U. S. Government Printing Office, Washington, D. C., May 1957.

22. Greenfield, M. A., *Calculations on Mixtures of Neutron Shielding Materials*, USAEC Report NAA-SR-24, January 1949.

23. Guerin, J. T., Carroll, J. G., Bolt, R. O., and Bert, J. A., *Nuclear Radiation and the Thermal Stability of Jet Fuels*, *Aero/Space Eng.*, *18*(1): 27 (January 1959).

24. Hillenbrand, L. J., *The Effect of Nuclear Radiation on Hydrocarbon Fuels*,

Battelle Memorial Institute, REIC Technical Memorandum No. 11, November 1958 (AD-207702).

25. Krasnow, M. E., Reynolds, O. P., and Wolford, O. C., *The Behavior of Fuels and Lubricants in Dynamic Test Equipment Operating in the Presence of Gamma Radiation,* Report WADC-TR-58-264, Part II, March 1959.

26. Lusebrink, T. R., Minor, H. B., Nixon, A. C., and Thorpe, R. E., Nuclear Irradiation of Jet Fuels: Effect of Dose on Thermal Stability and Other Properties, in *Proceedings of the Second Semiannual 125A Radiation Effects Symposium, October 22–23, 1957,* Vol. IV, Battelle Memorial Institute.

27. Nixon, A. C., and Lusebrink, T. R., *Research on the Evaluation of Neutron and Gamma Irradiation Effects of Six Hydrocarbon Fuels,* Report WADC-TR-59-108, April 1959.

28. Nixon, A. C., and Thorpe, R. E., *Stability of Jet Turbine Fuels, Effect of Nuclear Radiation,* Report WADC-TR-53-63, Part V, April 1957.

29. Nixon, A. C., Thorpe, R. E., Minor, H. B., and Lusebrink, T. R., *Research on Determination of the Stability of Jet Engine Fuels,* Report WADC-TR-53-63, Part VI, January 1958.

30. Nixon, A. C., Thorpe, R: E., and Minor, H. B., *Effects of Nuclear Radiation on Jet Fuels, Am. Chem. Soc., Abstracts of Papers, 133d Meeting, Apr. 13–18, 1958,* p. 3p, Abstract 7.

31. Pomeroy, G. W., and Calkins, V. P., *Irradiation Testing of Organic Liquids,* USAEC Report APEX 411, August 1955.

32. Price, B. T., Horton, C. C., and Spinney, K. T., *Radiation Shielding,* Pergamon Press, New York, 1957.

33. Rockwell, T. C., *Reactor Shielding Design Manual,* D. Van Nostrand Co., Inc., Princeton, N. J., 1956.

34. Rockwell, T. C., and Cohen, P., Pressurized Water Reactor Chemistry in *Proceedings of the First International Conference on the Peaceful Uses of Atomic Energy,* Vol. 9, p. 423, United Nations, New York, 1956.

35. Thorpe, R. E., and Nixon, A. C., Jet Fuel, in *Results of System Panels Test No. 2,* p. 59, Report NARF-58-1T (Addendum 5), Convair, September 1958.

CHAPTER 15

Coal, Wood, and Explosives

By Irving A. Breger, James G. Carroll, and Robert O. Bolt

15-1 Coal†

15-1.1 Introduction

Geologists, chemists, combustion engineers, and fuel technologists have recently become interested in the effects of nuclear radiation on coal. Such radiation has been considered as a potential substitute for time in geochemical reactions and as a source of energy in chemical reactions involving coal. These factors have spurred a considerable effort in this field, some results of which have been reported only in preliminary or abstract form or orally. A brief summary of the research is given in this section. The chapter as a whole includes not only a review of the known effects of nuclear radiation on coal as they may apply in problems of coal combustion but also suggestions regarding other applications of irradiated coal.

In 1956 initial results were reported[4] on the effects of reactor radiation on humic acid isolated from peat and on lignite, subbituminous coal, cannel coal, and Boghead coal. Breger[2] exposed these substances for periods up to 30 days in the Brookhaven Research Reactor (BGRR) and then drew analogies from the irradiation of polymers.[6] Although a dose of 4.6×10^9 rads (see Sect. 15-1.3.2) failed to produce extensive changes in the composition of the irradiated substances, continued investigation was indicated.

As described more fully in Sect. 15-1.3, a lignite, a subbituminous coal, and high, medium, and low volatile bituminous coals were irradiated to 1.3×10^{10} rads in the BGRR. Measurements showed a considerable increase in free-radical content[9] with a decrease in volatility of the starting material. These coals also became more difficult to grind after irradiation. Infrared spectra suggested that polymerization might have occurred.

In addition to these exposures to mixed radiation, a number of coals have also been exposed to gamma radiation only. In one study the compositions and properties of high, medium, and low volatile bituminous coals did not change appreciably on exposure to 10^7 rads.[10] Exposure of high volatile bituminous coals to 1.5 to 20×10^6 rads was reported[12] to lead to

† This section was written by Irving A. Breger.

509

"splitting" of the coals with considerable decrease in particle size. Recent work[16] at the Bureau of Mines, however, has failed to disclose any such reduction in particle size following the irradiation of coal with gamma rays.

Lignite, bituminous coals, and coke, either in aqueous or carbon tetrachloride suspension, were exposed to 10^6 to 10^8 rads of gamma radiation. The objective was to solubilize and recover the germanium.[11] After 10^8 rads about 50% of the germanium was transferred from the coal to the aqueous medium, and 100% of the germanium in the lignite was transferred to the carbon tetrachloride. In a similar study coal suspended in carbon tetrachloride took up about 4 wt. % of chlorine during irradiation.

Coals have also been exposed to alpha particles. Preliminary studies indicated dehydrogenation to be the major radiochemical effect.[2] This work has since been extended and is reported in more detail in Sect. 15-1.2. Stach[15] observed changes in bituminous coal caused by alpha particles from enclosed radioactive zircons. These effects took the form of bright halos, which were interpreted from petrographic evidence to show that the coal had been radiochemically converted from high volatile rank to medium volatile or anthracitic rank. Although reflectance of the irradiated coal is high, the increased reflectance was found to be the result of increase in density rather than increase in aromatic content.[7] This view was supported by X-ray diffraction patterns.

15-1.2 EFFECTS OF ALPHA PARTICLES

In studies of uranium-bearing coals, any radiochemical reactions that occur are assumed to be caused by alpha particles. These particles carry approximately 75% of the energy released during the decay of uranium and its daughter products. The effects of alpha particles on coal are of particular interest because induced chemical reactions caused by alphas can be compared to reactions caused by neutrons or by gamma rays.

Many of the exploitable uranium deposits of the United States occur in Triassic and Jurassic sediments of the Colorado Plateau. Tree trunks, branches, and woody fragments were buried in these sediments and were subsequently converted[13] into lignite, subbituminous, or high volatile bituminous coal. Geological evidence indicates that uranium was introduced into the sediments isochronously about 60 to 100 million years after their deposition.[17,18] At that time varying percentages of the element became dispersed nearly homogeneously throughout many of the coalified logs and woody fragments. As a result these substances were irradiated for many millions of years by alpha particles from uranium and its daughter products. The availability of unusually large quantities (up to 2 lb) of these samples permitted a detailed study of the effects of alpha particles on coalified wood. Individual coalified logs that were studied had uranium contents ranging from 0.001 to 16.5 wt. %. Correlation of the composition of the samples with uranium content revealed a number of trends that could be explained only as radiochemical effects.

As shown in Fig. 15.1, the hydrogen content of the coal samples is essentially independent of the uranium values until the latter reach 0.3 wt. %. This independence between 0.001 and 0.3 wt. % uranium probably represents the inability of the analytical technique to detect small radiochemical decreases of hydrogen. The data of Fig. 15.1 are plotted on a

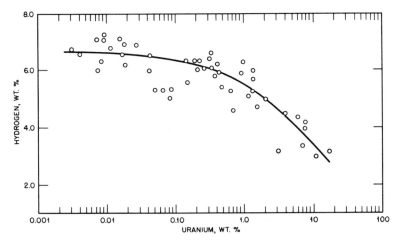

FIG. 15.1 Relation of hydrogen content to uranium content in coalified logs.

semilog scale for convenience; if the data are replotted on a linear scale, a relation can be developed up to uranium values of 5 wt. % in which hydrogen decreases by 1% for every increase of 1% in uranium content. Beyond this value relatively less hydrogen is lost, this fact indicating that (1) self-absorption of alpha particles has occurred in the irradiation, (2) hydrogen in different and more stable structures is more difficult to remove, or (3) with decreases in hydrogen content, less hydrogen becomes available for dehydrogenation.

The dependence of heat values for the moisture- and ash-free coal on uranium content has also been noted. Samples with less than 0.3 wt. % uranium have heating values of approximately 15,100 Btu; these values drop with increasing uranium content until the corresponding value for a sample with 6.7% uranium is about 13,000 Btu.

The volatile content of the coalified logs decreases in a general trend with increase in uranium, an indication of polymerization. Although the analytical values show some scatter, volatile content drops from about 65 to 30% as uranium rises from 0.001 to 10 wt. %.

Dehydrogenation is a major radiochemical reaction for the coals irradiated by alpha particles. X-ray, density, and reflectivity studies were made of a number of coals having approximately 80 wt. % carbon and percentages of hydrogen varying with uranium content.[7] Results show that radiochemical dehydrogenation led to the formation of tetrahedral bonding rather than the trigonal bonding representative of unirradiated coals.

15-1.3 Reactor Irradiations

Samples of lignite, subbituminous, high volatile bituminous, medium volatile bituminous, and low volatile bituminous coals were chosen for this work. In addition, humic acid isolated from a Wisconsin peat was used.

15-1.3.1 *Experimental Details*

Spectroscopic analyses showed that none of the samples contained ash constituents that would become appreciably radioactive and thereby create a handling problem after irradiation; sulfur contents were also less than 1 wt. % of the original coals. For each irradiation the samples were individually wrapped in aluminum foil, and a set of six was placed in an aluminum can 8 in. long and 2 in. in diameter. Because initial experiments showed the evolution of gas to be very small, no precautions against bursting were taken; i.e., the cans were merely sealed under vacuum.

Conditions of exposure in the BGRR were chosen so that temperatures could be maintained below 122°F. Sets of samples were irradiated for periods of about 10, 30, 60, 90, and 120 days; doses ranged from 0.2 to 1.33×10^{10} rads. Following removal from the reactor, the samples were set aside for several weeks to permit the induced activity of the aluminum containers to decay. The cans were then opened in an atmosphere of helium, and the samples were stored under helium pending analysis. Preliminary carbon and hydrogen analyses of irradiated samples were carried out under carefully controlled conditions to prevent exposure of the samples to air. Duplicate determinations performed under routine conditions, however, showed that oxidation of samples did not occur during the analytical process.

Increased irradiation doses were investigated next. Samples (5 to 14 g) of humic acid and lignite were irradiated in the Materials Testing Reactor (MTR) in Idaho. Exposures of 1, 10, or 16 days were chosen so that data from the longest BGRR runs could be compared with data from the shortest MTR runs. The lignite used was the same as that previously studied; the humic acid, however, was isolated from peat from the Cedar Creek bog in Minnesota. The MTR exposures were carried out in stainless-steel containers equipped with rupture disks through which gas liberated during the irradiations could be extracted for analysis.[14]

Following completion of the MTR exposures, the samples were stored for several months to permit induced radioactivity to drop to a point where the containers could be handled and opened safely. Gas was collected for mass spectrometric analysis, and the appearance of each irradiated sample was noted.

15-1.3.2 *Results*

Irradiation of medium volatile or low volatile bituminous coal in the BGRR at doses up to 1.33×10^{10} rads† led to a decrease of only about 2 wt. % in carbon content. Inasmuch as the medium volatile coal contained 89.3% carbon and the low volatile coal contained 90.5% carbon prior to exposure, only slight change in carbon content following irradiation could be expected. Such changes as did occur, however, were linear and showed a decrease of approximately 1.6% carbon for each 10^{10} rads. Such a decrease of carbon content of irradiated products is possible through elimination of methane from the coal.

Of the other samples irradiated in the BGRR, the high volatile coal underwent a linear decrease in carbon content with exposure similar to that demonstrated by medium and low volatile coals. Up to 1.33×10^{10} rads, the decrease in carbon content was 3 wt. % carbon for each 10^{10} rads.

Samples of humic acid irradiated in the BGRR showed a linear increase in carbon content with exposure (6.1 wt. % carbon for each 10^{10} rads) up to total exposure of 1.05×10^{10} rads, as shown in Fig. 15.2. Hydrogen, on the other hand, went through a maximum at about 0.5×10^{10} rads and then decreased slightly. Because coal is composed primarily of carbon, hydrogen, and oxygen, increases in carbon and hydrogen can only be effected by a differential loss of oxygen as water or as carbon dioxide. The decrease in hydrogen content of irradiated humic acid as irradiation proceeds might be explained by dehydrogenation.

These same trends are evident in Fig. 15.3, where data for irradiations of humic acid in the MTR are summarized. The similarity of the carbon and hydrogen curves at low irradiations are striking (Figs. 15.2 and 15.3) since the studies were carried out in two different reactors with different samples of humic acid. Between exposures of 1.34 and 49.7×10^{10} rads, the rate of change in carbon and hydrogen content decreases.

Mass spectrometric analyses of gas evolved during MTR irradiations of humic acid confirmed the relative importance of decarboxylation and dehydrogenation reactions at different stages of irradiation. The first gas evolved consisted of approximately 10 vol. % hydrogen and 90 vol. %

---

† Rads are calculated from Fig. 1.2 with the following assumptions: (a) coal corresponds to a hydrocarbon in its absorption of reactor radiation, (b) coal contains 5 wt. % hydrogen, and (c) the BGRR exposures were carried out in holes N-7 and N-8, for which Fig. 1.2 is assumed to be valid (the MTR work was in hole VH-3 as in Fig. 1.2). Based on these assumptions, the conversion factors obtained from Fig. 1.2 are

$$\text{BGRR: } 5.8 \text{ rads/}10^{10} \text{ slow neutrons/cm}^2$$
$$\text{MTR: } 7.9 \text{ rads/}10^{10} \text{ slow neutrons/cm}^2$$

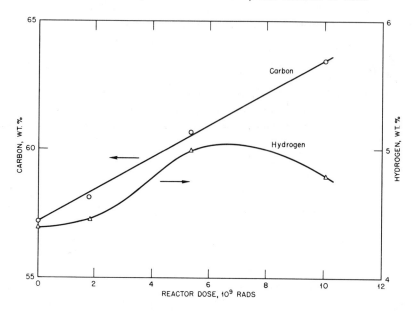

FIG. 15.2 Changes in composition of humic acid following irradiation in the BGRR.

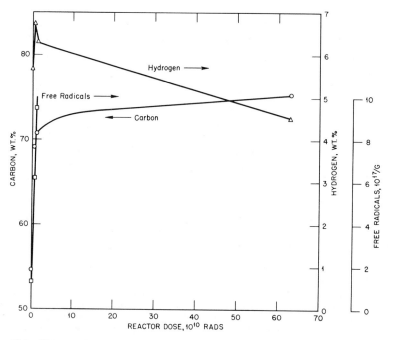

FIG. 15.3 Changes in composition and free-radical content of humic acid following irradiation in the MTR.

carbon dioxide; as irradiation progressed, the composition changed to 83% hydrogen and only 17% carbon dioxide. Total gas evolved amounted to approximately 25 to 35 ml/g of humic acid irradiated.

The humic acid irradiated in the MTR became brittle and swelled on prolonged exposure. The sample irradiated at the highest dose swelled to such a degree that it filled the entire capsule becoming hard and brittle during the process. Such behavior occurs during the formation of coke from coal.

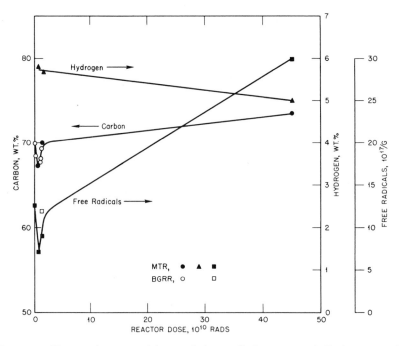

FIG. 15.4 Changes in composition and free-radical content of lignite exposed to reactor radiation.

Electron paramagnetic resonance measurements were made on the unirradiated and on two samples of irradiated humic acid. The values[8,9] given in Fig. 15.3 show an almost linear increase in free-radical content of the humic acid with irradiation up to a dose of 1.5×10^{10} rads. This linear relationship closely parallels the increase in carbon content of the irradiated humic acid over this range of exposures.

This parallelism was also shown in the irradiation of a lignite (Fig. 15.4). Exposures were conducted in both the BGRR and the MTR. Up to 2×10^{10} rads, there is excellent concordance of data for experiments in the two reactors.

When the lignite was subjected to exposures up to 0.5×10^{10} rads, the carbon content of the exposed sample dropped; between 0.5×10^{10} and about 1.5×10^{10} rads, the carbon content rose. The drop can be explained by demethanation of the lignite; the rise, by decarboxylation (loss of carbon dioxide) and dehydrogenation. After these reactions are complete (at about 1.5×10^{10} rads), the carbon content of the irradiated product increases only slightly upon continued exposure. Gas analyses have shown elimination of hydrogen to rise and elimination of carbon dioxide to decrease between exposures of about 1.5×10^{10} and 45×10^{10} rads in accord with the mechanisms suggested. Although only three determinations of hydrogen in the irradiated samples are shown in Fig. 15.4, the values point toward a linear decrease in hydrogen with increasing exposure.

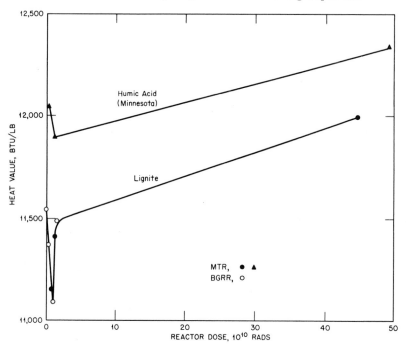

FIG. 15.5 Changes in heat value of lignite and humic acid on exposure to reactor radiation.

As in the case of humic acid, the free-radical concentrations of the lignite seem to be related to the carbon content of the irradiated products; increase or decrease in carbon is closely paralleled by increase or decrease in free radicals.

Figure 15.5 shows that the heat value of the irradiated lignite also parallels the carbon curve of Fig. 15.4. The drop in heat values for irradiations up to 0.5×10^{10} rads can also be explained by elimination of methane from the coal since the irradiated product has a higher oxygen content.

Reversal of the trend between 0.5×10^{10} and about 1.5×10^{10} rads also corresponds to the conclusion already noted; i.e., carbon dioxide is being eliminated from the coal. In this case the higher heat values correspond to products having lower oxygen contents. The increase in heat values on prolonged exposure must indicate that decarboxylation is still taking place but on a much smaller scale.

Only three points are shown for the heat value of irradiated humic acid in Fig. 15.5, and it is not possible to arrive at any conclusions regarding the mechanisms of degradation. On the other hand, the rise in the heat value beyond 1.4×10^{10} rads suggests that oxygen is being lost from the humic acid, probably as carbon dioxide. This conclusion is in agreement with the interpretation of Fig. 15.3 and with the analysis of the gas produced during several irradiations.

15-1.4 POTENTIAL APPLICATIONS OF IRRADIATED COAL

A major consequence of the irradiation of coal by either alpha particles or reactor radiation is dehydrogenation. In the case of alpha-particle irradiation, dehydrogenation is thought to result in the cross linking of coal molecules to form products of decreased solubility;[5] reactor-irradiated coals are similarly polymerized, as indicated by infrared spectra and increased hardness.[9] It has been suggested that polymerized coals might yield harder cokes for metallurgical purposes.

The decarboxylation of coal during relatively early stages of reactor irradiation should lead to a product more readily dispersed in diesel fuel and, therefore, to a product of value as an oil–coal suspension for use in diesel engines. As noted by McBrian,[12] a 10% coal-in-oil mixture, using irradiated coal, could result in the use of 4,000,000 lb of coal per month by the Denver and Rio Grande Railroad Company with an approximate 10% savings in fuel cost. It is particularly fortunate that extreme irradiations do not appear to be necessary; changes in the coal beyond exposures of about 2×10^{10} rads are relatively small.

Some work has been carried out on the effect of gamma radiation on the gasification of coal.[1] This work offers some promise of success, especially if the reactor radiation replaces gamma radiation since increases in free-radical concentrations accompany reactor irradiations.[9] Such increase should be directly related to enhanced reactivity of the coal. Similarly the reaction of coal with a medium in which it is suspended during irradiation offers hope of bringing about regulated free-radical reactions at low temperature to produce chemically altered coal. This work may lead to intermediates useful for the determination of the chemical structure of coal or for the utilization of coal in the production of chemicals.[3]

There is an inescapable conclusion that coal is extremely resistant to degradation by radiation. After early demethanation and decarboxylation, continued exposures lead primarily to dehydrogenation and presumed cross linking of molecules. These effects reflect the initial loss of sensitive side chains to form a residue of primarily aromatic structures, which, from much other work, are known to be relatively insensitive to degradation. As an example, biphenyl has been studied in much detail for use as a coolant in reactors (see Ch. 8). With the information already available on the effects of radiation on coal and with general background knowledge on the effects of radiation on various types of organic substances, it becomes possible to predict the results of future studies with a reasonable degree of accuracy.

15-2 Wood Products†

15-2.1 INTRODUCTION

The literature on the radiolysis of wood products deals almost entirely with chemical rather than physical effects. Much work has involved cellulose because it is the main building block in wood; lignin has also received special attention. Considerable interest has been shown in the radiation-induced depolymerization of cellulose to make it water soluble. Practical applications of such a process include converting sawdust to cattle feed. The effects of radiation on the structural properties of wood have received little attention even though there has been some interest in the use of wood as a reactor shield.

Wood is 50 to 60 wt. % cellulose, a carbohydrate made up of 6500 to 9000 glucose units:

The structure is remarkably uniform regardless of the source of the cellulose. These chains are easily hydrolyzed, as in the digestive process, and are reduced to the ultimate unit of *D*-glucose. The smallest part of the

† This section was written by James G. Carroll and Robert O. Bolt.

macromolecule having the characteristics of cellulose comprises two glucose units, the cellobiose unit. Most of the mechanical properties of wood are derived from its cellulose content.

About 25% of wood is lignin, a complex aromatic material; the remaining solids are water-soluble carbohydrates, gums, and resins. These raw materials in wood are organized into a familiar cell and ring structure.

The important properties of wood include elasticity, swelling, shrinkage, and strength.[1] Moisture content, grain angle, specific gravity, grain deviation, and decay influence these properties. Moisture content is particularly critical, and tables of properties for wood always specify this property. Some idea if its importance can be noted from Table 15.1.

Table 15.1—EFFECT OF MOISTURE IN SITKA SPRUCE[19]

	Green	Air dry
Moisture content, wt. %	42	12
Weight, lb/cu ft	33	28
Fiber stress at proportional limit, psi:		
Static bending	3,300	6,700
Impact bending	8,400	11,400
Compression parallel to grain	2,240	4,780
Compression perpendicular to grain	340	710
Hardness (end), lb	430	760
Radial cleavage strength, lb/in.	130	180

Temperature exerts a negligible effect on properties except as it affects moisture content. Temperatures much above 200°F, of course, induce irreversible effects.

15-2.2 PHYSICAL BEHAVIOR

15-2.2.1 *Wood*

In early exploratory studies samples of several types of wood were exposed[28] in the Canadian NRX. For doses of about 2.5×10^9 rads,† maple, fir, and pine blocks lost about 65% of their compression strength. In other work at Oak Ridge,[6,7] interest was shown in wood as a possible physiological shield material. Irradiations were conducted to determine the amount of gas evolved from samples of pine and paper. Results are shown in Table 15.2 compared with paraffin and cellulose powder. The identity of gas constituents from certain products is shown in Table 15.3.

† Original data in slow neutrons/cm² assumed relationship: 1 rad $\cong 1.2 \times 10^9$ slow neutrons/cm².

Table 15.2 — GASSING OF IRRADIATED MATERIALS[7]

Dose,[a] 10^6 rads	10^{-6} moles gas/g				
	Solid paraffin[b]	Pine[b]	Dry pine[b]	Brown paper[c]	Cellulose powder[c]
3.8	76	76	76	18	16
6.2	128	123	120	27	24
9.1	183	154	146	32	30
11.0	218	168	156	36	34
12.7	250	180	167	40	38
14.8		194	177	48	44

[a]Original data in Mev; 10^{15} Mev/g $\cong 1.02 \times 10^6$ rads.
[b]Deuterons, 0.5 μa at 6.9×10^6 volts.
[c]Electrons, 0.5 μa at 2×10^6 volts.

Table 15.3 — MAJOR CONSTITUENTS OF RADIOLYTIC GAS[6]

	Dose,[a] 10^6 rads	Gas composition, %			
		H_2O	CO_2	H_2	CO
Dry pine[b]	12.6	5	7	63	22
Dry pine[c]	31.2	5	50	20	17
Oak[b]	12.6	4	14	52	21
Masonite[b,d]	14.6	18	10	59	10
Paraffin[c]	14.6	0	15	84	1

[a]Original data in Mev; 10^{15} Mev/g $\cong 1.02 \times 10^6$ rads.
[b]Electrons, 0.5 μa at 2×10^6 volts.
[c]Deuterons, 0.5 μa at 6.9×10^6 volts.
[d]Pressed-wood product; trademark of Masonite Corp.

The following observations came from this work:
1. Drying had no effect on the gas yield from pine.
2. Oak decreased slightly in volume with irradiation.
3. Wood charred slightly during deuteron irradiation.
4. There was no indication that gas was trapped in the solid material.
A wooden table made of ⅝-in. plywood was reported[4] to have collapsed after a year in a gamma source. The highest dose received was about 11.6×10^8 rads. Following exposure to this dose, the wood was dry and crumbly giving the appearance of having "dry rot." A similar experience was reported[21] with a plywood rack used to hold samples during gamma irradiations. After about 10^8 to 5×10^8 rads, the plywood could be crumbled with the fingers.

15-2.2.2 *Paper*

The instability of paper to ionizing radiation has long been known.[25] In 1929 Schoepfle irradiated insulating paper for about 2×10^7 rads in a vacuum. Water, hydrogen, carbon dioxide, carbon monoxide, methane, and acetylene were evolved. The irradiated paper was brittle and powdered readily. Tests showed that the cellulose had degraded.

There are over 300 commercial types of papers used in the packaging industry. In the food-sterilization program, some papers were irradiated in the studies of packaged food.[27] After 10^7 rads a 35-lb (per 1000 sq ft) kraft paper coated with 18 lb (per 1000 sq ft) of polyethylene deteriorated moderately. Tensile strength decreased about 20%, internal tearing resistance decreased about 10%, and the sealing strength (peel) decreased about 25%. From the packaging standpoint this loss is not serious because heavier paper can be used; and, in general, food-sterilization levels are well below 10^7 rads.

15-2.2.3 Cork

Cork is used chiefly in seals and gasket materials and may find its way into systems and components that are exposed to radiation. The compression flexibility and tensile strength of cork strips were tested[8] after gamma exposures of up to 10^8 rads in air. There was a slight (4%) increase in tensile strength; flexibility was not impaired. Compression and recovery from compression were reduced only about 5%.

Cork is quite stable to radiation. Ordinary stopper corks exposed to gamma radiation of about 5×10^8 rads showed no discoloration or increased brittleness.[28] Samples exposed in the NRX[29] showed only slight darkening after a dosage of 6×10^9 rads.

15-2.3 CHEMICAL BEHAVIOR

15-2.3.1 Wood Constituents

Irradiation causes profound changes in cellulose.[2,24] These include depolymerization, reduction in crystallinity, and decomposition (see Ch. 11,

Table 15.4—DECOMPOSITION OF CELLULOSE[34]

Electron dose,[a] 10^7 rads	Decomposition, %			
	0.9	4.4	8.7	44
Cotton linters	2	12	14	44
Wood pulp	5	10	17	
Wood	3		9	
Glucose	2		14	

[a]Samples sealed in polyethylene, air access.

Sect. 11-2). At about 10^5 rads changes can be detected; large changes occur above 10^6 rads, and at 5×10^8 rads cellulose is converted to water-soluble material. At 10^8 rads about 10^{20} single depolymerizations occur per gram, and 5×10^{20} glucose units per gram are destroyed. Cotton linters† and a purified wood pulp depolymerize at about the same rate. Initial values of about 1000 glucose units were reduced to 600, 180, and 35 by respective doses[24] (approximate) of 10^6, 10^7, and 10^8 rads. The extent of decomposition is shown in Table 15.4.

Charlesby[5] developed a relationship for this decomposition. Radiation reduces molecular weight; this, in turn, decreases intrinsic viscosity.‡ The relationship showed a straight line for a plot of the logarithm of intrinsic viscosity vs. radiation dose. The observed data of Saeman et al.[24] agreed well with the calculation. For example, a 16% decomposition is calculated for the data at 8.7×10^7 rads in Table 15.4.

Glegg and Kertesz[11] exposed cellulose to gamma rays to understand better the softening of the tissue of fruits and vegetables. Cotton and wood cellulose of different moisture contents received up to 2×10^6 rads. Degradation was significant even at this low level. Moisture content in the range of 0.26 to 5.6 wt. % did not significantly affect the rate of radiation-induced degradation. The intrinsic viscosity of the wood and the cotton cellulose decreased by 44 and 49%, respectively, at the highest dosage shown in Fig. 15.6.

A progressive decrease in intrinsic viscosity was also noted after radiation ceased.[11] In 35 days this effect was from 43 to 54% of the total decrease. Thus the aftereffect was about as great as the primary radiation effect. Further work[10] indicated that the aftereffect occurred only in the presence of oxygen and at low moisture contents.

Dextran (the 1,6-polymer of α-D-glucose) is similar to cellulose and has an initial molecular weight of about 6.5×10^5. This polysaccharide is used medically as a blood plasma extender after its molecular weight is reduced to about 50,000. This is done commercially by acid hydrolysis in a low-yield reaction. Ricketts and Rowe[23] found that dextran powder decreased in intrinsic viscosity to 36% of the original after 3×10^5 rads. For the same dose a 1% solution decreased to 60% of the original value. Extensive degradation in dextran was found[22] after 10^8 rads; i.e., molecular weight had decreased from 6.5×10^5 to 2.9×10^4.

The lignin component of wood was observed[16] to be comparatively unaffected after 3×10^8 rads. The data suggest that the lignin protects wood and prevents hydrolysis or digestion in the presence of radiation. Red-

---

† The short fibrous material adhering to cotton seed after the ginning operation.

‡ Intrinsic viscosity [η], the limiting value ror the solute as its concentration approaches zero, is defined as

$$[\eta] \equiv \lim_{C \to 0} \frac{(\eta_s - \eta_0)}{\eta_0 C}$$

in deciliters per gram, where η_0 is the viscosity of the solvent, η_s is the viscosity of the solution, and C is the concentration in grams per deciliter.

wood has been irradiated to study further this effect.[26] Redwood has a high aromatic content in the form of both lignin and tannin extractives. Exposures of up to 18×10^6 rads were conducted on both natural samples of redwood chips and also on samples from which lignin had been removed by chlorite extraction. Intrinsic viscosities were then measured,

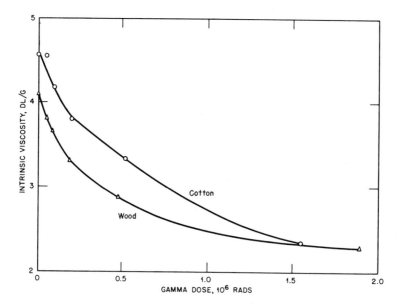

FIG. 15.6 Viscosity of irradiated cellulose in cupriethylenediamine solution.

and the degree of polymerization was calculated. The lignin-free samples decreased in glucose units from 1377 to 405 and 254, whereas the lignin-containing samples decreased to only 548 and 350. Thus the lignin and other natural aromatic extractives exerted a mild protective effect on the redwood.

15-2.3.2 Hygroscopicity

Wood is highly hygroscopic; i.e., it absorbs and retains water. The equilibrium moisture content depends upon humidity and temperature; for example, dry wood will adsorb about one third of its own weight of water from a saturated atmosphere. Paton and Hearmon[20] irradiated disks of Sitka spruce with gamma rays. Dose levels of 10^6, 10^7, and 10^8 rads were used. There was no change in appearance after irradiation at the highest doses. The moisture absorption curves for exposures of 0 and 10^8 rads are shown in Fig. 15.7. There is a small reduction in equilibrium moisture content at all relative humidities. The reduction for the lower doses was not significant.

Small blocks of Ponderosa pine sapwood were irradiated[15] with gamma rays for doses up to about 10^7 rads. Samples of various moisture content from oven dry to saturation were exposed, and the hygroscopicity was expressed as equilibrium moisture content at 77°F and 76% relative

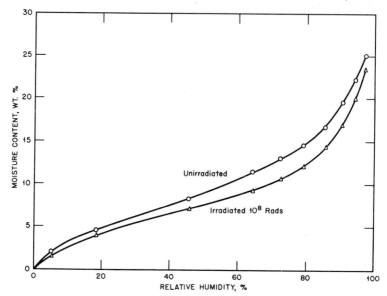

Fɪɢ. 15.7   Moisture content of irradiated Sitka spruce. (One-millimeter-thick samples exposed to Co^{60} at 100°F, air access.) (From J. M. Paton and R. F. S. Hearmon, *Nature,* Ref. 20; courtesy of H. M. Stationery Office, London.)

humidity; a small but significant reduction occurred at 10^4 and 10^6 rads followed by a slight but significant increase at 10^7 rads. A small reduction in the tangential swelling properties resulted also. From the standpoint of application, these small changes are of little significance.

15-2.3.3 *Decay*

The decay susceptibility of irradiated Ponderosa pine was studied[15] by using a test fungus. Irradiated and control blocks were brought to 50 wt. % moisture content and placed near the test fungus in decay chambers. These were held at 81°F and 80% relative humidity for four to nine weeks. Decay was measured in terms of weight loss of a dried sample after the incubation. Gamma radiation doses below 10^7 rads induced small but statistically significant increases in the decay susceptibility. The irradiated wood, however, did not show a markedly greater decay hazard.

The use of gamma radiation has been suggested[3] for the destruction of insects that attack wood. About 6×10^4 rads was shown necessary to kill mature eggs of typical beetles. Thus doses needed for controlling wood-boring insects in practice would have no significant effect on the susceptibility of wood to decay.

15-2.3.4 *Digestibility*

Irradiated basswood shows a structure so altered that some of the insoluble carbohydrates become available to bacteria.[16] The production of volatile acids from the incubation of irradiated wood samples with fresh rumen bacteria was used to measure digestibility. Little increase in digestibility by irradiation up to about 6×10^6 rads was noted. Between 6×10^6 and 6×10^8 rads, increased irradiation gave increased fermentability. At 10^8 rads the digestibility by the rumen contents was comparable to that of hay. Above this level radiolysis products apparently cannot be used by the rumen bacteria; both cellulose and lignin components of the wood are too degraded.

Cotton linters are reported[24] to become water soluble after 10^8 rads. The maximum over-all sugar yield by dilute acid hydrolysis increased about two and one-half fold for cotton linters, wood pulp, and wood after this dose.

This and other work[17] point to the practical conversion of Douglas fir sawdust to cattle feed by means of irradiation. Ruminants can digest certain forms of cellulose or its degradation products. In the case of wood, some pretreatment is necessary to make the polysaccharides available. The pretreatment must hydrolyze the glucosidic linkages in the cellulose. It is also necessary to break any lignin-to-cellulose bonds. Irradiation to 3×10^8 rads resulted in the destruction of about one third of the carbohydrates in the Douglas fir sawdust. About 16 wt. % of the original carbohydrate material was found utilizable by the bacteria after irradiation. Only 1 to 3% of carbohydrates in unirradiated sawdust was utilizable. Russian workers[9] report a similar interest in this aspect of wood irradiation.

15-3 Explosives and Solid Propellants†

15-3.1 INTRODUCTION

The materials to be discussed here are of two main types: high explosives and low explosives. High explosives detonate with high rates of reaction and produce high pressures. There are usually two subdivisions: (a) the primary explosives, which detonate by simple ignition, i.e., spark, impact, or flame; and (b) the secondary explosives, which require an auxiliary igniter, i.e., detonator, arming fuse, or blasting cap. Low explosives burn rapidly and develop relatively low pressures. Propellants are of this type. Certain properties of these explosive types are shown in Table 15.5.

† This section was written by James G. Carroll and Robert O. Bolt.

Table 15.5 — CHARACTERISTICS OF EXPLOSIVES[4]

	Low	High
Complete gasification, sec	Milli	Micro
Velocity of flame, miles/sec	1/3 to 1	1 to 6
Pressure of explosion, 10^4 psi	<5	5 to 400
Use	Propellant	Demolition

Some common explosives are listed in Table 15.6. Inorganic types are included for completeness.

All materials listed in Table 15.6 decompose readily. They are sensitive to friction, thermal shock, and impact. Temperature is probably the most important environmental condition, and excessively high temperatures will cause explosions. For reasonable storage periods humidity does not affect these materials. Even under ideal temperature and humidity conditions, however, explosives and propellants lose power with prolonged storage.

Table 15.6—COMMON EXPLOSIVES[4]

High Explosives

Primary:

Mercury fulminate
Lead azide
Lead styphnate
DDNP (diazodinitrophenol)

Secondary

TNT (trinitrotoluene)
Tetryl [(trinitrophenyl)methylnitramine]
RDX (cyclotrimethylenetrinitramine)
PETN (pentaerythritol tetranitrate)

Low Explosives or Solid Propellants

Nitrocellulose
Nitroglycerin

Many compounds such as organic nitrates are used both as high explosives and as propellants. For some uses explosives are compounded to various recipes. For example, Composition B is a binary explosive of TNT and RDX having very high brisance.† Similarly ballistite, one of the oldest double-base propellants, is based on nitrocellulose and nitroglycerin. M-15 propellant consists of nitrocellulose, nitroglycerine, nitroguanidine, and other ingredients. Materials such as charcoal, ammonium nitrate, metal nitrates, sulfur, and perchlorates are often included in recipes to influence reactions.

† Shattering power; brisance is related to demolition pressure.

The most significant study of radiation effects on explosives was carried out by Sisman and Warren at Oak Ridge National Laboratory. The original interim progress reports were combined into a single report.[16] Short reviews[3,11,12] of these are also available. Explosives, including propellants and primers, were exposed to gamma radiation from Au^{198}. Gas evolution was the chief criterion of damage. Some brisance tests and impact sensitivity tests were also made. The work presented in this chapter is based chiefly on the report by Rosenwasser.[16] Supplemental information on the exposure of JPN propellant[13,18] and nitrocellulose[14] to gamma radiation is also cited.

The decomposition of the explosives during irradiation was generally determined by the following tests:

1. Gas evolution was measured continuously and accurately by capillary manometers.

2. Sensitivity to impact was measured by two methods, the Bureau of Mines machine and the Picatinny Arsenal machine. In each test a standard weight falls a given distance and strikes a pin that causes detonation of the sample. (In both tests the criterion is the height from which the falling weight causes an explosion.)

3. Measurements of brisance were made with the standard sand test. This method consists of detonating the explosive in a bed of sand and reporting the weight of sand crushed.

15-3.2 IRRADIATION STUDIES

15-3.2.1 *High Explosives*

Radiation effects on simple nitrogen compounds have been studied. In general, materials such as lead azide[1,8] and sodium azide[9] undergo changes in color[15] and structure between 10^4 and 10^7 rads. None (with the exception of nitrogen iodide) exploded under irradiation,[1,2,8] although time for thermal decomposition following irradiation was shortened.[8] Other studies showed methyl azide[6] and nitrates[5,10] to be unstable to low-level radiation.

Under irradiation,[16] lead azide ($Pb(N_3)_2$) evolved 4.4 to 5.6 ml of gas (S.T.P.) per gram after 47×10^6 rads (Fig. 15.8). After exposure practically pure nitrogen continued to evolve but at a reduced rate. For this dose at $72°F$, no observable differences resulted in sensitivity of the azide to impact. In the sand test the weight of crushed sand was 18.7 and 20.5 g, respectively, for irradiated and unirradiated material.

Irradiations were also carried out at three different temperatures: $-40°F$, $72°F$ (ambient), and $160°F$. After an exposure of 26×10^6 rads, the gas formation at ambient temperature was 1.35 times that at $-40°F$. At $160°F$ gas formation was 3 times that at $-40°F$. These values were adjusted for gassing at $160°F$ in the absence of radiation.

An unexpected phenomenon was observed with lead azide and with other explosives that exhibit postirradiation gas formation. When samples being irradiated at 160°F were removed from the gamma source and cooled to ambient temperatures, no postirradiation gassing occurred. However, when other samples were maintained at 160°F after being irradiated, postirradiation gas formation did occur. In all cases more gas was evolved than could have resulted from thermal effects alone.

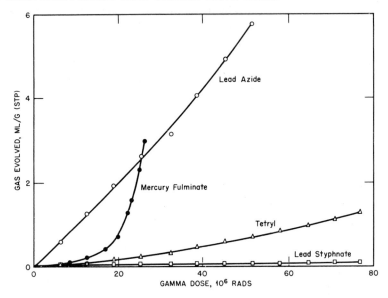

Fig. 15.8   Gas evolution from explosives during irradiation. (Au[198] source, 72°F, air access.)

The rate of gas formation from mercury fulminate $[Hg(CN{=}C)_2]$ was comparatively rapid [2.97 ml/g after 26×10^6 rads (see Fig. 15.8)] and increased with the time of exposure. Gas formation following irradiation was also noted and may be an indication of further deterioration after irradiation. Chemical analysis showed the offgas to consist of 71 vol. % CO_2 and 19% N_2. Tests for NO, NO_2, and CO were negative. The irradiated solid was found to be only 65.5 wt. % mercury fulminate; its original purity was 97.5%.

The sensitivity to impact of the irradiated fulminate approximated that of the original. However, the irradiated sample failed to explode when ignited by a black-powder fuse. No sand was crushed in the sand test when the irradiated fulminate was tested alone. When initiated with lead azide, the exposed fulminate crushed about one half the sand that is normal for this explosive. Thus the gamma exposure effectively nullified the initiating ability of mercury fulminate.

Lead styphnate

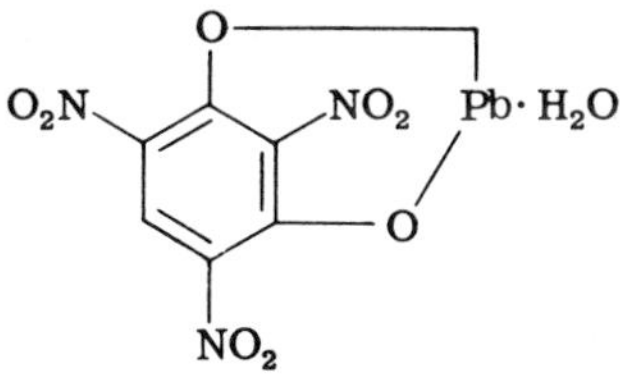

produced, when irradiated, the smallest volumes of gas of any of the explosives tested. About 0.12 ml/g was formed during exposure to 76×10^6 rads, as shown in Fig. 15.8. The sensitivity to impact and the brisance of lead styphnate were essentially unaltered by this irradiation at 72°F.

Irradiation of DDNP

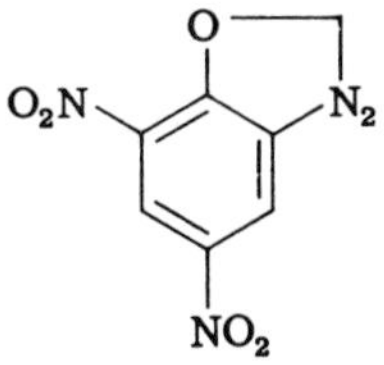

(anhydride) at ambient temperature produced gas quantities similar to those from lead azide. Increasing amounts of gas were given off for incremental dosages. After 40×10^6 rads, a total of 7.2 ml/g was produced. Impact sensitivity was not impaired, but the ability to crush sand was reduced. The irradiation was considered sufficient to render this explosive unreliable for use as an initiator.

TNT

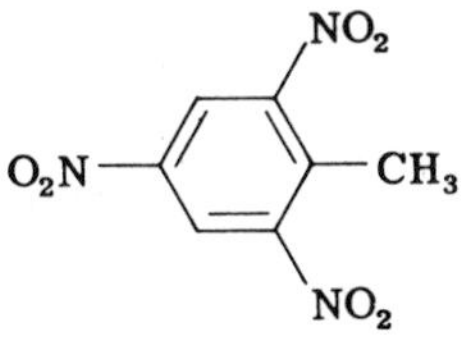

is comparatively stable to gamma radiation. After 54×10^6 rads, gas evolution was about 0.14 ml/g. Impact sensitivity by the two methods was about the same before and after irradiation. Sand-test values were also similar. At 72°F gas formation was 1.75 times that at −40°F. At 160°F evolution increased to 7.5 times that at −40°F.

As shown in Fig. 15.8, after 76×10^6 rads at 72°F, 1.4 ml of gas per gram was evolved by tetryl

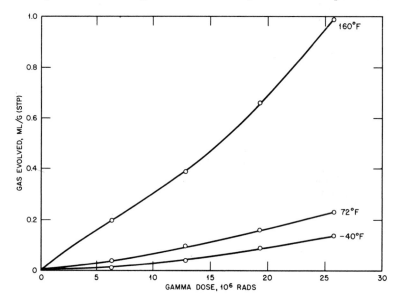

Nevertheless, this material showed a "resistance" considerably greater than that shown by RDX, lead azide, mercury fulminate, and nitroglycerin. During this irradiation, sufficient soluble impurity was formed to lower the melting point by 2°F. The irradiated material, however, was not impaired as to its impact sensitivity or its ability to crush sand.

After 26×10^6 rads, tetryl evolved four times as much gas at 160°F as at 72°F, as shown in Fig. 15.9. For the equivalent time period without

FIG. 15.9 Influence of temperature on radiation-induced gassing of tetryl. (Au[198] source, air access.)

radiation at 160°F, tetryl evolved 0.06 ml/g.

After 40×10^6 rads, RDX

produced 1.8 ml/g. Irradiation was discontinued, but an additional 2.5 ml/g evolved during the next 40 days. The colorless gas was a mixture of N_2, CO_2, and a trace of hydrogen. Tests for ammonia, nitrogen oxides, oxygen, and CO were negative. Gas evolution from RDX tended to increase with increasing irradiation. Color and melting point of RDX were unchanged by exposure. Sensitivity to impact was increased slightly, whereas sand-test values were unchanged after the 40×10^6 rads exposure.

During 38×10^6 rads gamma irradiation at 72°F, 2.7 ml of gas per gram was formed by PETN [$C(CH_2ONO_2)_4$]. This is much lower than that from nitroglycerin. PETN, based on gassing, is more resistant to radiation damage than are lead azide, mercury fulminate, and DDNP but much less resistant than TNT or tetryl. The gas-evolution curve for PETN trends sharply upward after about 10^7 rads. Further evidence of damage was shown by a 7°F depression of the melting point.

Several binary explosives were irradiated. In most cases the volume of gas formed corresponded closely to the gassing characteristics of the major gas-producing component. Typical results are shown in Table 15.7.

Table 15.7 — RADIATION-INDUCED[a] GASSING OF BINARY EXPLOSIVES

Material, wt. %	Gas evolved at 26×10^6 rads, ml/g (S. T. P.)
Tetrytol (65% tetryl, 35% TNT)	0.32
Baratol [67% $Ba(NO_3)_2$, 33% TNT]	0.09
Composition B (60% RDX, 40% TNT)	0.83
Tritonal (20% Al, 80% TNT)	0.09
Pentolite (50% PETN, 50% TNT)	0.24

[a]Au^{198} source, 70°F, air access.

Two types of detonators were investigated. In the M-26 primer the explosive mixture is PA-100, which is composed of 53 wt. % potassium chlorate, 17% ammonium sulfide, 25% lead styphnate, and 5% lead azide. The M-129A2 detonator employs 105 mg of the PA-100 primer mixture as its upper charge; an intermediate charge of 250 mg of lead azide is in contact with 142 mg of the tetryl booster.

The M-26 primer functioned normally under stab-action testing after 13, 27, and 54×10^6 rads at 72°F; but 2% failed to explode after 80×10^6 rads. (In stab-action testing a firing pin impinges on the test primer or detonator. Stab action was provided by a ball falling through a prescribed distance and striking the firing pin.) In general, sensitivity of the primers was increased by irradiation; i.e., detonation occurred by a ball dropped from a lower height. The M-19A2 detonators also increased in sensitivity after irradiation. Reliability, however, decreased, as shown in Fig. 15.10. Malfunctioning occurred because lead azide failed to initiate the tetryl.

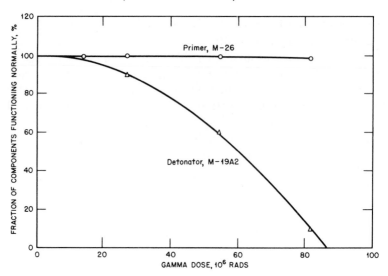

FIG. 15.10   Effect of irradiation on the reliability of primers and detonators. (Au[198] source, 72°F, air access.)

15-3.2.2 *Low Explosives and Propellants*

Pure nitroglycerin $[CH_2(ONO_2)CH(ONO_2)CH_2(ONO_2)]$ decomposed under gamma radiation at 72°F and produced 11.5 ml of gas per gram after 50×10^6 rads. The decomposition gases corroded mercury, an action that was not observed with the other explosives tested. The irradiated residue was very viscous and evolved fumes of nitrogen dioxide; after standing for 50 days, it practically solidified. Because of this severe deterioration, no further test work was conducted.

Dried uncolloided nitrocellulose $[(C_6H_{10-y}O_5)_n(NO_2)_y]$ was irradiated[14] with gamma rays up to about 10^7 rads. The nitrogen content decreased only about 1 wt. %. However, intrinsic viscosity (determined in solutions of acetone) was reduced to one third of its initial value. This instability is typical of the cellulosic polymer and is attributed to bond breakage.[14]

The M-15 propellant consists of 54.7 wt. % nitroguanidine, 20% nitrocellulose, 19% nitroglycerin, 6% ethyl centralite,† and 0.3% cryolite.‡ A granular sample produced 3.35 ml of gas per gram at 54×10^6 rads. Nitroglycerin was probably the major source of this gas.

The double-base propellant ballistite is composed of 69.25 wt. % nitrocellulose, 30.50% nitroglycerin, and 0.25% diphenylamine. A graphite-flake powder (1918 vintage) was exposed to radioactive gold. After 34×10^6

† Symmetrical diethyldiphenylurea.
‡ Na_3AlF_6.

rads at 72°F, gassing was about 2.80 ml/g of sample. The rate of gas evolution for ballistite is compared with that of M-15 in Fig. 15.11. Nitroglycerin is included for reference.

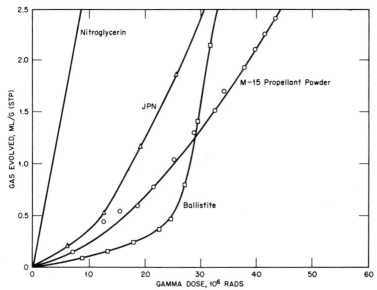

FIG. 15.11   Radiation-induced gas evolution from propellants. (Au[198] source, 72°F, air access.)

Strips of JPN propellant (see Table 15.8) were subjected to gamma radiation.[13] Exposures were at 68°F for total doses of up to 4.6×10^6 rads. The viscosity of the nitrocellulose, the available centralite, and the stability of the propellant were observed. The highest dose sample was approximately comparable in stability to a similar propellant after storage at 176°F for 20 days without radiation.

Table 15.8—COMPOSITION OF JPN PROPELLANT[a,18]

Constituent	Wt. %
Nitrocellulose	51.40 ± 1.0
Nitroglycerin	42.90 ± 0.5
Diethyl phthalate	3.23 ± 0.25
Potassium sulphate	1.25 ± 0.15
Ethyl centralite (carbamite)	1.00 ± 0.20
Carbon black	0.20 ± 0.03
Condellila wax	0.02 ± 0.01
	100.00

[a]Usually delivered as sheets 0.060 to 0.090 in. thick.

The only significant change detectable by chemical analysis was in the available centralite. After the highest dose only a trace of the ethyl centralite remained; 4-nitrocentralite was present in 0.72 wt. % concentration. A loss of only 0.1% nitrogen from the nitrocellulose would completely convert centralite to this derivative. The odor of nitrogen oxides was quite evident in the irradiated propellant. Stability tests indicated some breakdown in the irradiated samples.

After 4.6×10^6 rads, tensile strength decreased by 7 to 8%, and elongation decreased 17 to 22%. Various burning tests indicated no apparent differences from the original due to radiation damage. Intrinsic viscosity decreased by about 30%.

15-3.3 CONCLUSIONS

Kaufman[12] reviewed the Oak Ridge work and observed that a few nonrigid generalizations are permissible:

1. The materials can be ordered relative to decomposition, but a variation in kinetics exists. Kaufman calculated:

Material	Activation energy, kcal/mole	Temp. coeff. of gas evolution, ml/g/°C (S.T.P.)
Lead styphnate	1.8	8.55×10^{-5}
TNT	2.8	1.46×10^{-4}
Tetryl	6.5	5.18×10^{-4}
Lead azide	7.5	$5.8 \ \times 10^{-2}$

2. Large gas evolution is not entirely related to a decrease in explosiveness. For example, DDNP and mercury fulminate gassed excessively and showed reduced ability to crush sand after irradiation; RDX and lead azide also evolved much gas but did not show impairment of sand values.

3. The lower limit at which decomposition could be detected was about 10^6 rads.

References

Several of the following were cited in the text as authority for statements made. Others were not quoted but are included because they contain pertinent information. All were consulted in the preparation of this chapter.

Coal

1. Anon., "Hot" Coal Breeds Heating Gas, *Chem. Eng. News,* *36*(1): **51** (January 1958).
2. Breger, I. A., Studies of Fossil Plant Debris Associated with Uranium on the Colorado Plateau, *Proceedings of the Third Conference on the Origin and Constitution of Coal,* Crystal Cliffs, Nova Scotia, June 1956, in press; see also *Bull. Geol. Soc. Am., 67* (12, Pt. 2): 1675 (December 1956).
3. Breger, I. A., U. S. Geological Survey, Washington, D. C., unpublished work, 1959.
4. Breger, I. A., and Brittin, E. B., *Effects of Radiation on Coal,* preprint, National Colloid Symposium, Madison, Wis., June 1956, 9 pp.

5. Breger, I. A., and Deul, M., Association of Uranium with Carbonaceous Materials, with Special Reference to Temple Mountain Region, *U. S. Geol. Survey Profess. Papers, No. 320,* p. 139, 1959.

6. Charlesby, A., and Ross, M., The Effect of Cross-linking on the Density and Melting of Polythene, *Proc. Roy. Soc. (London), A217*(1128): 122 (March 1953).

7. Ergun, S., Donaldson, W. F., and Breger, I. A., Some Physical and Chemical Properties of Vitrains Associated with Uranium, *Fuel, 39*(1): 71 (January 1960).

8. Friedel, R. A., U. S. Bureau of Mines, Pittsburgh, Pa., personal communication, February 1960.

9. Friedel, R. A., and Breger, I. A., Free-Radical Concentrations and Other Properties of Pile-Irradiated Coals, *Science, 130*(3391): 1762 (December 1959).

10. Hoover, G. E., Chesapeake and Ohio Railway Co., Huntington, W. Va., personal communication, August 1955.

11. Losev, B. I., Troianskaia, M. A., and Bylyna, E. A., The Effects of γ-Radiation on Coal in an Aqueous Medium and in a Carbon Tetrachloride Medium, *Doklady Akad. Nauk SSSR, 120*(2): 355 (May 1958).

12. McBrian, R., Nuclear Irradiation of Coal for use with Diesel Fuel, *Mining Congr. J., 44*(8): 82 (August 1958).

13. Scott, R. A., U. S. Geological Survey, Washington, D. C., personal communication, 1957.

14. Shiells, N. P., Bolt, R. O., and Carroll, J. G., Safe Containers Hold Organics for Irradiation, *Nucleonics, 14*(8): 54 (August 1956).

15. Stach, E., Radioactive Coalification, *Brennstoff-Chem., 39*(21/22): 329 (November 1958).

16. Stewart, R. F., U. S. Bureau of Mines, Morgantown, W. Va., personal communication, October 1960.

17. Stieff, L. R., Stern, T. W., and Milkey, R. G., A Preliminary Determination of the Age of Some Uranium Ores of the Colorado Plateau by the Lead–Uranium Method, *U. S. Geol. Survey Circ., No. 271,* 1953.

18. Wood, H. B., Relations of the Origins of Host Rocks to Uranium Deposits and Ore Production in Western United States, *U. S. Geol. Survey Profess. Papers, No. 300,* p. 533, 1956.

Wood Products

1. American Society for Testing Materials, *1960 Supplement to Book of ASTM Standards, Part 6, Wood, Paper, Shipping Containers, Adhesives, Cellulose, Leather, and Casein,* ASTM, Philadelphia, October 1960.

2. Anon., Cathode Irradiation Causes Profound Changes in Cellulose, *Chem. Eng. News, 30*(15): 1515 (April 1952).

3. Bletchly, J. D., and Fisher, R. C., Use of Gamma Radiation for the Destruction of Wood-Boring Insects, *Nature, 179*(4561): 670 (March 1957).

4. Brownell, L. E., *et al., Utilization of Gross Fission Products,* p. 241, USAEC Report No. COO-198, University of Michigan, March 1954.

5. Charlesby, A., The Degradation of Cellulose by Ionizing Radiation, *J. Polymer Sci., 15*(79): 263 (January 1955).

6. Day, R. A., and Scott, R. B., *Metallurgical Laboratory Chemical Research Report to July 15, 1943,* USAEC Report CC-784, University of Chicago.

7. Day, R. A., and Scott, R. B., *Metallurgical Laboratory Chemical Research Report to May 15, 1943,* USAEC Report CC-648, University of Chicago.

8. De Zeih. C. J.. Effects of Nuclear Radiation on Cork, Leather, and Elastomers, in

Third Semiannual Radiation Effects Symposium, October 28–30, 1958, Vol. 5, paper No. 62, Lockheed Nuclear Products.

9. Freydin, A. S., Malinsky, Y. N., and Karpow, V. L., The Effect of Ionizing Radiation on the Chemical Stability of Wood, *Gidroliz. i. Lesokhim. Prom., 12*(4): 4 (May 1959); abstracted in Scientific Information Report PB-131891T-29, Sept. 4, 1959.
10. Glegg, R. E., The Influence of Oxygen and Water on the Aftereffect in Cellulose Degradation by Gamma Rays, *Radiation Research, 6*(4): 469 (April 1957).
11. Glegg, R. E., and Kertesz, A. I., Effect of Gamma Radiation on Cellulose, *J. Polymer Sci., 26*(114): 289 (December 1957).
12. Hausner, H. H., *Modern Materials,* Vol. 1, Academic Press Inc., New York, 1958.
13. Haworth, W. N., *Constitution of Sugars,* p. 90, Edward Arnold Publishers, Ltd., London, 1929.
14. Kempe, L. L., Graikoski, J. T., and Brownell, L. E., Gamma Ray Sterilization of Food Packaging Materials, *Food Eng., 25*(11): 55 (1953).
15. Kenaga, D. L., and Cowling, E. B., Effect of Gamma Radiation on Ponderosa Pine: Hygroscopicity, Swelling, and Decay Susceptibility, *Forest Prods. J., 9*(3): 112 (March 1959).
16. Lawton, E. J., Bellamy, W. D., Hungate, M. E., Bryant, M. P., and Hall, E., Some Effects of High Velocity Electrons on Wood, *Science, 113*(2936): 380 (April 1951).
17. Mater, J., Chemical Effects of High Energy Irradiation of Wood, *Forest Prods. J., 7*(6): 208 (June 1957).
18. Mark, H., Radiation Chemistry and Wood, *Composite Wood (India), 14*(1, 2): 1 (May 1957).
19. Meredith, R., *Mechanical Properties of Wood and Paper,* Interscience Publishers, Inc., New York, 1953.
20. Paton, J. M., and Hearmon, R. F. S., Effect of Exposure to Gamma Rays on the Hygroscopicity of Sitka Spruce Wood, *Nature, 180*(4587): 651 (September 1957).
21. Pestaner, J. A., U. S. Naval Radiological Defense Laboratory, personal communication, October 1959.
22. Price, F. P., Bellamy, W. D., and Lawton, E. J., Effect of High Velocity Electrons on Dry Dextran, *J. Phys. Chem., 58*(10): 821 (October 1954).
23. Ricketts, C. R., and Rowe, C. E., The Effect of Gamma Rays Upon Dextran, *Chem. & Ind. (London), 32*(7): 189 (February 1954).
24. Saeman, J. F., Millett, M. A., and Lawton, E. J., Effect of High Energy Cathode Rays on Cellulose, *Ind. Eng. Chem., 44*(12): 2848 (December 1952).
25. Schoepfle, C. S., and Connell, L. H., Effect of Cathode Rays on Hydrocarbon Oils and Paper, *Ind. Eng. Chem., 21*(6): 529 (June 1929).
26. Smith, D. M., and Mixer, R. Y., The Effects of Lignin on the Degradation of Wood by Gamma Irradiation, *Radiation Research, 11*(6): 776 (December 1959).
27. U. S. Army Quartermaster Corps, *Radiation Preservation of Food,* Report PB 151493, pp. 284 and 306, Aug. 1, 1957.
28. West, W. W., and Carroll, J. G., California Research Corporation, unpublished data, 1957.
29. Yoshida, N., and Horsman, J. C., *Summary of Engineering Materials Irradiated in NRX Reactor,* Canadian Report NEI-4, February 1951.

Explosives and Solid Propellants

1. Bowden, F. P., The Initiation of Explosions by Neutrons, α-Particles, and Fission Products, *Proc. Roy. Soc. (London), A246*(1245): 216 (July 1958).

2. Bowden, F. P., and Singh, K., Size Effects in the Initiation and Growth of Explosions, *Nature*, *172*(4374): 378 (August 1953).
3. Convair Division, General Dynamics Corp., *Radiation Effects—Methods and Data*, Report NARF-58-43T, Convair, pp. 359–368, October 1958.
4. Cook, M. A., *The Science of High Explosives*, pp. 1–17, Reinhold Publishing Corp., New York, 1958.
5. Cunningham, J., and Heal, H. G., The Decomposition of Solid Nitrates by X-Rays, *Trans. Faraday Soc.*, *54*, Part 9(249): 1355 (September 1958).
6. Franklin, J. L., Dabeler, V. H., Reese, R. M., and Krauss, M., Ionization and Dissociation of Hydrazoic Acid and Methyl Azide by Electron Impact, *J. Am. Chem. Soc.*, *80*(2): 298 (January 1958).
7. Frost, F. E., *Effects of Nuclear Radiation on Explosives and Solid Propellants—A Bibliography*, USAEC Report UCRL-5322, University of California, August 1958.
8. Groocock, J. M., The Effect of High Energy X-Rays and Pile Radiation on the Thermal Decomposition and Thermal Explosion of α-Lead Azide, *Proc. Roy. Soc. (London)*, *A246*(1245): 225 (July 1958).
9. Heal, H. G., The Decomposition of Crystalline Sodium Azide by X-Rays, *Can. J. Chem.*, *31*(12): 1153 (December 1953).
10. Johnson, E. R., Radiation-Induced Decomposition of Lead Nitrate, *J. Am. Chem. Soc.*, *80*(17): 4460 (September 1958).
11. Kaufman, J. V. R., The Effects of Nuclear Radiation on Explosives, *Proc. Roy. Soc. (London)*, *A246*(1245): 219 (July 1958).
12. Kaufman, J. V. R., The Effect of Nuclear Radiation on Explosives (unclassified), in *Proceedings Second Semiannual 125A Radiation Effects Symposium, October 1957*, Vol. II, Battelle Memorial Institute. (Classified).
13. Owyang, A., and Rosenwasser, H., *The Effects of Gamma Radiation on JPN Propellants*, U. S. Navy Powder Factory Report No. 122, July 1956.
14. Rosenwasser, H., and Whitman, C. L., *Effects of Gamma Radiation on Nitrocellulose*, U. S. Navy Powder Factory Report No. 128, January 1959.
15. Rosenwasser, H., Dreyfus, R. W., and Levy, P., Radiation-Induced Coloring of Sodium Azide, *J. Chem. Phys.*, *24*(2): 184 (February 1956).
16. Rosenwasser, H., *Effects of Gamma Radiation on Explosives*, USAEC Report ORNL-1720, Oak Ridge National Laboratory, December 1955.
17. Thomas, J. G. N., and Tompkins, F. C., On the Decomposition of Metal Azides, *J. Chem. Phys.*, *20*(4): 662 (April 1952).
18. U. S. Navy, *Propellant, Double-Base, Type N-2 (JPN)*, Military Specification No. MIL-P-18617 (Nord), June 30, 1955.

CHAPTER 16

Potential Benefits

By James G. Carroll and Robert O. Bolt

16-1 Introduction

Most materials of construction are designed so that they are initially in an optimum state for their intended use. Thus most changes from this state, such as those caused by radiolysis, are undesirable and are degrading. There are, however, some instances in which radiation induces a beneficial effect; i.e., a certain property of a material is actually upgraded by irradiation. Such instances are cited throughout the preceding chapters. A discussion of beneficial effects immediately becomes involved in chemical processing and in economics; both subjects are beyond the scope of this book. Here, the use of radiation to produce a useful or upgraded product will be highlighted, a minimum of processing detail cited, and a few comments on economics given.

There is much speculation that radiation will eventually attain in connection with organic materials the status of a processing agent along with temperature, pressure, and catalysts. Since about 1954, research has generated a continuing flow of patents and a moderate amount of technical-journal literature on this subject. However, few processes using radiation to produce useful products have reached the prototype stage; most of these have been proprietary developments about which companies are understandably reluctant to divulge details. Very few products made by irradiation have actually come to market. Nevertheless, laboratory research continues to unveil interesting radiation-induced reactions and to promise that there are few technical barriers to the use of ionizing radiation as a processing tool.

16-2 Types of Reactions

Ideally, and from an economic viewpoint, a little radiation should go a long way in radiation processing. Thus all reactions with high G values, or yields, are of potential interest. Any organic reaction that proceeds by a free-radical mechanism should be initiated by ionizing radiation. Particularly attractive are chain reactions in which the goal is a product of high molecular weight. Outside the realm of synthesis, there are applications of interest in the sterilization of food and medical sutures. Examples of radiation-induced reactions of potential interest in these and other domains include the following:

1. Reactions in which radiation produces a novel product of high economic value, e.g., grafting of styrene to polyethylene film to form permionic membranes and certain other graft copolymerizations.[13,59,65]
2. Reactions in which heat is released to accelerate further reaction, e.g., synthesis[5] of ethylene glycol.
3. Highly specific reactions in which there are few by-products, e.g., sulfoxidation[11] of paraffinic hydrocarbons.

16-3 Radiation Sources

From a practical viewpoint the use of radiation must take into account the following items:

1. Uniform penetration of the target material.
2. High absorption in the target material.
3. Minimum induced radioactivity.
4. Reliable reaction control, operation, and safety.
5. Reasonable installation, maintenance, and supply situations.
6. Reasonable shielding provisions.

Ionizing radiation is available from a variety of sources, as shown in Table 16.1.

Particle accelerators produce helium ions, electrons, protons, and deuterons; an electron beam is most used in processing. The radiation

Table 16.1 — **PRINCIPLE SOURCES OF IONIZING RADIATION**

	Approximate power, kw
Particle accelerators	2 to 50
Radionuclides	2 to 30
Fission products (spent fuel or gross products)	2 to 30
Reactors	200 to 1000 and above

beam can be focused to deliver uniform radiation at a constant level. It also can be turned off, leaves no residual radiation, and requires relatively little shielding. Machines are available commercially from several sources.[82]

Nuclides are materials made radioactive by exposure to neutrons. They give off secondary radiations, usually gammas or betas. Perhaps the best known nuclide is Co^{60}. This material emits two gamma rays (1.33 and 1.17 Mev) and has a half life of 5.3 years. Irradiators[60] of this type can be prefabricated to any shape and size, limited only by the geometry of the reactor facility in which they are to be exposed to neutrons.

Spent reactor fuel elements have been widely used as experimental gamma irradiators after long exposure at high specific reactor power. The elements are arrayed around the objects to be exposed. Only about 25% of the radiation can be usefully absorbed because geometry can seldom be optimized. Owing to their high intensity, such sources are most often used under about 20 ft of water for shielding purposes. Shipping problems usually limit the use of spent elements to locations near the reactor in which the elements were exposed.

Gross fission products[15] remain after the chemical separation of uranium and plutonium from spent fuel. They have attracted much interest as radiation sources. Because large quantities of fission products are produced and their disposal is a problem,[4] their utilization is very desirable. Little commercial interest has existed in gross product sources because they have low specific activity and they decay relatively rapidly (this rapid decay necessitates their periodic replacement). The gross products can, of course, be dehydrated and separated to almost any desired degree. Particular interest has been shown in the separation of Cs^{137} (33-year half life and a 0.66-Mev gamma ray) and Sr^{90} (20-year half life and a 2.18-Mev beta ray).

Irradiation in *nuclear reactors* is the most direct way of using radiation for industrial processing (see Refs. 6, 14, 28, 70, 74). However, this application on a large scale, as in the reactor core, is still in the distant future. The thought here is to use the feed as a coolant and in some cases as a moderator. In this way about 4 to 8% of the thermal power would be absorbed in a liquid hydrocarbon. This represents a 30 to 60% utilization of the fast-neutron and gamma radiant energy potentially available[55] in the core. As seen in Table 16.2, the kinetic energy of the fission fragments

Table 16.2 — FISSION ENERGY

	Mev	%
Fission fragments, kinetic energy	162	83
Neutrons, fission energy	6	3.1
Gamma rays, fission energy	6	3.1
Neutrinos	11	5.7
Fission products, delayed energy	10	5.1
	195	100.0

constitutes the main source of fission energy. In most conventional reactors the energy from the short-range fission fragments is largely absorbed in the uranium fuel and is dissipated as heat. However, this principal source of fission energy can be made available in a "chemonuclear" reactor. The uranium fuel and the chemical reactants must be in intimate molecular contact to maximize energy transfer to the reactants. Although liquid solutions promote good contact, the concept is most attractive for gas-phase product irradiations. Here, the vapor-phase reactants would be mixed with finely divided fuel of 0.5 to 10 μ (hence the term "dust reactor"). Decontamination of the end product, i.e., removal of radioactive particles, would be a serious but not insurmountable technical complication. Chemonuclear reactors have been proposed: (1) to synthesize hydrazine from ammonia,[26] (2) to produce nitric acid by the radiolytic oxidation of nitrogen,[5,46] and (3) to make ethylene glycol by the dimerization of methanol.[5]

Treatment of reaction mixtures in a reactor core is now in the early stages of feasibility studies, both technical and economic. This means of irradiation would probably represent the ultimate low in radiation costs. Great interest and much speculation have been shown in a dual-purpose reactor[6,30,66] in which the primary function would be the production of power and the secondary function would be to process organic chemicals or petroleum products. A schematic diagram of such a reactor is shown in Fig. 16.1.

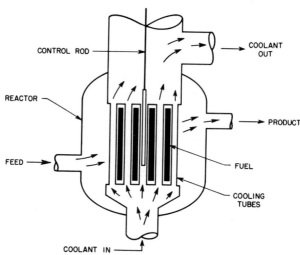

Fig. 16.1 Dual-purpose nuclear reactor for irradiation processing and power production. (From F. T. Barr, H. J. Ogorzally, and T. A. Reiter, *Petroleum Engineer*, Ref. 6.)

A modification of the dual-purpose reactor involves an in-pile loop containing a material that would become a gamma emitter upon radioactivation, for example, indium sulfate.[14,30,60] As illustrated in Fig. 16.2, the external part of the loop could then be used as the gamma irradiator.

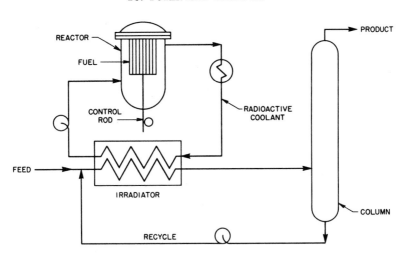

FIG. 16.2 Gamma irradiator produced by nuclear reactor. (From M. R. Dushabek, *Petroleum Refiner*, Ref. 30.)

16-4 Hydrocarbons

In Ch. 14, Sect. 14-2, a gamma dose of 38×10^8 rads was reported to raise the viscosity of a gasoline into the lubricating-oil range. The viscosity index of the irradiated material was higher than that of any commonly used single-phase lubricant. Such an enhancement of viscosity–temperature characteristics is of interest because much conventional refining of lubricant stocks is for this purpose. Improvement in viscosity index with reactor irradiation has also been observed[32,35] with n-paraffins (cetane through eicosene) in the presence of metal oxides (silica, alumina, platina). Five to fifty per cent of the feed stock was converted to high-molecular-weight polymer. The radiation-formed polymer was more stable than conventional polyesters in ultrasonic shear tests.

Cracking of hydrocarbons by irradiation is of great potential interest to the petroleum industry. Hydrocarbons can be cracked with reactor radiation below 700°F in the presence of acid-centered catalysts.[56,57] With a 400 to 1150°F boiling distillate and radiation inputs equivalent to 0.3 to 3000 Btu/lb, conversions of at least 10% were obtained and yields of C_5 were surprisingly good.

When deuterium was mixed with hydrocarbon gases undergoing radiolytic cracking, protons and neutrons were made from the action of gamma rays on deuterium. A conversion of 1 to 10% was claimed[81] for energy inputs of 10^3 to 10^8 rads. Hydrocarbon conversion was hastened by the addition of B^{10} or Li^6 in systems exposed to neutrons. The additives were used in amounts such that greater than 10% of the total absorbed energy came from the solute. As an example, a cycle oil alone was completely unconverted after 10 days in the Brookhaven Research Reactor. With 0.1% B^{10} present all the feed stock was converted either to gas or to polymer.[50]

It has been stated[38] that irradiation of petroleum oils can be carried out to obtain the following effects: (1) contaminant removal, e.g., desulfurization, (2) isomerization, (3) dehydrogenation, (4) cracking, (5) alkylation, (6) aromatization, and (7) polymerization. These involve the major processes in petroleum refining, a broad subject beyond the scope of this book. Although the general reactions cited are promoted by irradiation, control of specific reactions is still to be achieved, and optimum yields of desired products is far from defined. Much work with selected charge stocks, catalysts, and temperature conditions remains to be conducted.

16-5 Plastics

Because unsaturated materials are readily altered (high yields) by irradiation, the production of polymers by this means has received much attention. Of most interest is the cross linking of polyethylene. This product has unique properties compared with those of the chemically produced polymer. Fundamental research on polyethylene exceeds that on all other plastics combined, and a great deal of development work is still under way.

Polyethylene actually undergoes a series of radiation-induced changes.[19] At low doses ($<10^7$ rads) cross linking causes an increase in melting point and tensile strength. This facilitates precasting to stable molded shapes. Increased doses produce a rubbery material,[72] and above 5×10^8 rads a glasslike substance of no practical interest results. Properties of polyethylene depend upon crystallinity, which irradiation effectively destroys. Crystallinity is also destroyed by heating to 185 to 230°F. This amorphous material can be irradiated to yield a product of good physical stability and improved resistance to oxidation.[40,52,53]

The only radiation-produced products that thus far have become articles of commerce are made from polyethylene.[73] These include Irrathene and Vulkene by General Electric, electrical and insulating tape by Tube Investments, and polyethylene-coated wire by W. R. Grace. The first shrinkable polyethylene, Cryovac L, has also been produced by W. R. Grace.[69] A low-density polyethylene film, 1 mm thick, is irradiated in an electron beam to make the material. Its tensile strength is increased fivefold, and it has low tear resistance. Initially one million pounds per year production was scheduled for this material, and it is competitive with other packaging films.

Although polyethylene dominates the radiation plastics field, interesting work is reported on other polymers and polymerizations including curing of films,[22] applying protective coatings, and reducing molecular weight of polypropylene[33] and polybutylene.[34] Gamma doses of about 5×10^4 to

5×10^7 rads were effective in producing these physical changes. All relate to the use of radiation to control the molecular weight of polymers to a relatively narrow desired range. Such work will be of commercial interest as a unique product or process develops or a cheaper product emerges.

Typical yields of radiation-induced polymers are 10% per 10^6 rads for the most susceptible materials, e.g., poly(vinyl chloride). As shown in Table 16.3, there is little incentive to polymerize styrene by irradiation

Table 16.3 — EFFECT OF RADIATION DOSE ON CERTAIN PLASTICS

| Polymer | Dose required for effect, 10^6 rads | | | |
	Polymerization of monomer	Grafting	Cross linking	Degradation
Polyethylene	5-7	1-3	5-25	80-150
Polystyrene	10-1000	1-3	100+	4000
Poly(vinyl chloride)	0.2-5	0.02-0.05	0.1-0.5	1-100

since the process would be uneconomical and time consuming because of the large amount of radiation required. Besides, styrene polymerizes readily by heat alone without catalysts. Vinyl chloride polymerizes so rapidly that it is technically and economically feasible at the present time to substitute radiation for the presently used peroxide catalysts.[13]

16-6 Elastomers

The radiation-induced vulcanization, or cross linking, of rubbers has received considerable attention. Those polymers which cross link can be cured by gamma irradiation with 10 to 40×10^6 rads. In many cases the mechanical properties are as good as, or better than, those of rubbers cured by chemical methods to an equivalent molecular weight between cross links. Fillers, additives, and temperature affect the degree of cure.

As noted in Ch. 7, Sect. 7-6.2, basic work has led to the radiation vulcanization of two aircraft tires made from a GR-S tread and a natural-rubber carcass with no other agents. A dose of 4×10^7 rads in nitrogen produced a vulcanizate[83] with good abrasion resistance, heat aging, and uniformity of tread. A multipurpose reactor for the vulcanization of tires has been proposed.[16]

16-7 Graft Copolymers

One of the most exciting applications of radiation is the production of graft copolymers, as discussed in Ch. 6, Sect. 6-5, and Ch. 7, Sect. 7-5. Boyer[13] lists six radiolytic methods by which grafts can be made to a homopolymer backbone. In practical applications these methods compete with each other and with chemical methods, ultraviolet techniques, and mechanical milling.

Mesrobian[65] reports on a copolymer formed by a styrene graft to polyethylene film. The resulting films can be directly sulfonated to cation membranes or can be treated for anion exchange. Notable properties of such a membrane include low area resistance, high permeaselectivity (selective diffusion), and high tensile strength. Many attempts have been made to prepare ion-exchange membranes from mechanical mixtures of the two monomers. Membranes of this sort have important uses in the removal of salts from water.

Another practical type surface graft is that of a vinyl monomer to a radiation-sensitive polymer such as poly(vinyl chloride), cellulose, and poly(methyl methacrylate). Similarly the surface graft of styrene to Teflon yields a product that shows no reduction of tensile strength and shows increased adhesion and good ink retention.

The criteria for choosing between irradiation techniques and chemical processing are numerous, complex, and inevitably involve costs as well as technical considerations. There appears to be a strong future for graft copolymers, and radiation will certainly play a part in this. Manley[59] concludes that (1) most conventional plastics can be made by irradiation, usually with improved properties; (2) radiation can be used to modify plastics, again with improved properties; (3) radiation can produce new plastics and combinations of plastics with unique properties which cannot be produced by other methods; and (4) the cost of radiation is expected to fall sharply.

McFedries[64] adds a point concerning the largely unknown industrial technology of employing radiation versus the standard industrial technology of chemical catalysts. He observes that any technical problem will be solvable once research demonstrates that radiation is the preferred tool. He concludes that atomic radiation will play an important role in the area of polymerization, vulcanization, and the graft copolymerization of plastics.

16-8 Chemicals

Gamma rays initiate sulfoxidation of saturated hydrocarbons by a chain reaction in which sulfonic acids are produced in surprisingly good yields. G values from C_6 through C_9 hydrocarbons range from 3000 to 6000. Typical conversions[11] to sulfonic acids are as follows:

n-Hexane, %	44.9
n-Octane, %	65.4
Cyclohexane, %	57.1

A wide variety of hydrocarbons can be sulfonated, but normal paraffins from C_6 to C_{16} are preferred. Oxygen and SO_2 are introduced into the organic liquid in the presence of radiation. Thus the reaction is readily adaptable to a continuous process. Compared to conventional -processes, the radiation process proceeds at lower temperatures and pressures and with better process control.[37] The sulfonic acids so produced hold some promise as a new class of detergents.[9,10,11,39]

The halogenation of aromatics is influenced by radiation, and high yields of useful products are observed in many systems. Of particular interest in this country and abroad is the chlorination of benzene to form benzene hexachloride, because the gamma isomer of this is an important insecticide. The material is made commercially by ultraviolet-light irradiation, which yields 15% of the gamma isomer. The gamma-ray-induced reaction gives G values greater than 10^5. Some calculations show that gamma radiation is significantly more effective than ultraviolet light. The gamma isomer appears in about the same concentration in both radiation mixtures. Preliminary cost estimates[55] indicate that the product could be produced commercially by gamma radiation competitively with the ultraviolet-light process.[51]

Inorganic catalysts are widely used in the chemical and petroleum industries to enhance desired yields and to promote specificity of reactions. Only a few attempts have been made to study the effects of radiation on catalysts; almost no experiments have been reported with catalysts to influence radiochemical reactions. Gamma irradiation of metal oxides has been shown to double or triple yields in specific oxidation and reduction reactions.[43] The activity of iron oxide in converting CO and H_2 to hydrocarbons increased[41] by 40% after 10^6 rads. Neutron irradiation of pure SiO_2 (silica gel, which is normally catalytically inert) for 7.5×10^8 rads increased[87] its catalytic activity for the isomerization of the double bond in 1-hexene.

Taylor[85] reports that the catalytic activity of alumina increased sevenfold after 10^5 rads of reactor irradiation at $-100°F$ in vacuum. The enhancement disappeared when the capsule stood from two to four days at room temperature but could be restored by further irradiation. Of 49 samples irradiated, 38 showed a significant increase in activity. These few data apply to a specific system, and no generalizations can be made. However, the use of chemical catalysts for promoting radiochemical reactions appears to be a very fruitful area for investigation.

Harteck[47] studied the fixation of nitrogen by irradiating air under a range of pressures for doses up to 2×10^{11} rads. Above 10 atm and about 400°F, he obtained a 10% yield of nitrogen dioxide and nitrous oxide. This yield is in the range of commercial usefulness. On the basis of these results, the experiment was scaled up to conceptual design for an attractive commercial process.[46] Interest has also been shown in a commercialization of this process for the production of fertilizers.[42]

A conceptual design was announced for the production of ethylene glycol in 65% yield by the dimerization of methanol vapor in a dust type reactor.[5] This irradiation process was discussed in Sect. 16-3. The design is based on 10 years of laboratory work indicating that the ethylene glycol so produced would be competitive with that from conventional processes. In addition, there would be credits for the formaldehyde and the heat produced.

There is a proposal to manufacture the rocket fuel hydrazine (N_2H_4) in a dust type reactor according to the following reaction:

$$4NH_3 \xrightarrow[\text{fragments}]{\text{fission}} N_2H_4 + N_2 + 4H_2$$

In a 17.5 Mw(t) plant,[26] 1-μ UO_2 fuel would be suspended in a slurry of 99 wt. % anhydrous liquid ammonia and 1% hydrazine. Reaction conditions would include 100°F in, 160°F out, and 750 psia. Although the nitrogen and hydrogen would be undesirable by-products, the gamma- or neutron-induced formation or decomposition of N_2H_4 would be insignificant compared to its concurrent production from fission-fragment energy. Hydrazine from this new method has been estimated, with an experimentally determined $G_{N_2H_4}$ of 2, to cost less than 25% of that of material made by conventional means.

16-9 Conclusions

Ionizing radiation produces various effects of potential benefit in organic technology. Many existing products can be made or can have their properties improved by the use of radiation. In addition, there are a few instances of the preparation of unique products with radiation. Thus from a technical viewpoint ionizing radiation offers promise of becoming an industrial process tool. This status is years away, however, simply because radiation has not yet demonstrated sufficient advantage over established methods for achieving similar results.

Applied radiation as a tool might be likened to catalysis in the chemical and petroleum fields in the 1920's. Catalysis now holds a very prominent place in these two industries. Considerably more work remains to be done in the laboratory with radiation to develop specific products and processes from present interesting general reactions. The scale-up of these developments to the prototype stage must follow before radiation can be elevated from a curiosity to an industrial tool. The radiation processing of tomorrow has its roots in the radiation chemistry of today.

Applied radiation very definitely has a future. Whereas today radiation competes with conventional agents such as pressure, temperature, and catalysts, it will eventually supplement them as processing agents to produce new and useful materials. Developments will probably trail those of the power-reactor program, which is just now entering the advanced prototype stage. This experience is essential to develop the background in radiation safety, economics, technology, plant replacement, and so forth. Without this background the technical promise cannot reach practical realization.

References

Several of the following were cited in the text as authority for statements made. Others were not quoted but are included because they contain pertinent information. All were consulted in the preparation of this chapter.

1. Agius, P. J., and Evans, E. B., *Polymerization Process,* British Patent 802,082, Oct. 1, 1958.
2. Anon., Japan Pushes Process Radiation, *Chem. Eng. News, 39*(45): 54 (November 1961).
3. Anon., Radiation Boosts Reactivity of Cellulosics, *Chem. Eng. News, 38*(45): 52 (November 1960).
4. Anon., Atomic Wastes Pose Big Problem, *Chem. Eng. News, 37*(6): 23 (February 1959).
5. Anon., Fission Energy May Make Chemicals, *Chem. Eng. News, 37*(51): 42 (December 1959).
6. Barr, F. T., Ogorzaly, H. J., and Reiter, T. A., Nuclear Radiation in Chemical Processing, *Petrol. Engr., 30*(12): C-48 (November 1958).
7. Baxter, E. F., Jr., and Black, J. F., *The Effect of Radiation on Petroleum and Its Products,* USAEC Report ESSO-MA-1, Esso Research and Engineering Co., August 1959.
8. Bishop, J. E., Radiation Chemistry, *Wall Street Journal,* p. 1, May 5, 1960.
9. Black, J. F., *Radio-Sulfochlorination of Paraffins,* U. S. Patent 2,974,094, Mar. 7, 1961.
10. Black, J. F., and Baxter, E. F., Jr., Detergents by Nuclear Process, *Soap Chem. Specialties, 34*(10): 43 (October 1958).
11. Black, J. F., and Baxter, E. F., Jr., Radiation Induced Sulfoxidation of Hydrocarbons, in *Proceedings of the Second International Conference on the Peaceful Uses of Atomic Energy, Geneva, 1958,* Vol. 29, p. 162, United Nations, New York, 1959.
12. Black, R. M., and Charlesby, A., The Oxidation of Irradiated Polyethylene. I. Radiooxidation, *Intern. J. Appl. Radiation and Isotopes, 7*(2): 126 (December 1959).
13. Boyer, R. F., Polymerization with Radiation. I. General Considerations, *SPE Journal, 14*(9): 47 (September 1958).
14. Bray, D. T., and Leyse, C. F., Food-Irradiation Reactor, *Nucleonics, 15*(7): 76 (July 1957).
15. Brownell, L. E., Martin, J. J., Vincent, E. T., *et al., Utilization of Gross Fission Products,* USAEC Report COO-198, University of Michigan (March 1954).
16. Brownell, L. E., Purohit, S. N., Weech, M., Balzhiser, R. E., and Lobo, A. H., *Considerations of the Use of a Multiple-Purpose Reactor in a Rubber Tire Plant,* USAEC Report AECU-3390, University of Michigan, August 1956.

17. Caffrey, J. M., *Catalytic Conversion of Organic Compounds Using Penetrating Radiation*, U. S. Patent 3,002,910, Oct. 3, 1961.
18. Calfee, J. D., and Erbaugh, L. E., *Production of Polyethylene*, U. S. Patent 2,887,445, May 19, 1959.
19. Charlesby, A., *Atomic Radiation and Polymers*, Vol. 1, Pergamon Press, Inc., New York, 1960.
20. Charlesby, A., Beneficial Effects of Radiation on Polymers, *Nucleonics*, *14*(9): 82 (September 1956).
21. Charlesby, A., and Davison, W. H. T., Temperature Effects in the Irradiation of Polymers, *Chem. & Ind. (London)* (8): 232 (February 1957).
22. Charlesby, A., Greenwood, T. T., and Wycherley, V., *Improvements Relating to the Curing of Plastics*, British Patent 828,717, Feb. 24, 1960.
23. Cook, L. G., What is the Future of Radiation Chemistry in Industrial Processing, *Gen. Elec. Rev.*, *61*(5): 33 (September 1958).
24. Cox, R. A., and Swallow, A. J., The Chlorination and Bromination of Hydrocarbons Under Influence of High Energy Radiation and Other Initiating Agents, Part III, *J. Chem. Soc., 1958:* 3727 (1958).
25. Cox, R. A., and Swallow, A. J., Ionizing Radiation as a Catalyst for Chlorination and Bromination, *Chem. & Ind. (London)* (43): 1277 (November 1956).
26. Cusack, J. H., Miller, R. J., and Yockey, H. P., *Nuclear Hydrazine Program*, USAF-ASD Technical Report 61-7-840, July 1961.
27. d'Emus, H. M., Bray, B. G., *et al.*, Synthesis of Butadiene-Styrene Elastomers and of Polysulfones by Gamma Radiation, *Ind. Eng. Chem.*, *49*(11): 1891 (November 1957).
28. Diethorn, W. S., Scholl, P., and Calkins, G. D., Direct Utilization of Fission Energy for Radiation Processing, in *Nuclear Engineering, Part VI, Chemical Engineering Progress* Symposium Series Vol. 55, No. 22, p. 119, American Institute of Chemical Engineers, New York, 1959.
29. Duffey, D., Poly(vinyl Methyl Ether) Elastomers by High Energy Radiation, *Ind. Eng. Chem.*, *50*(9): 1267 (September 1958).
30. Dushabek, M. R., Nuclear Reactors Seen as Process Tool, *Petrol. Refiner, 36*(9): 243 (September 1957).
31. Eaton, S. E., Radiation Seeks Commercial Use, *Nucleonics, 18*(2): 105 (February 1960).
32. Esso Research, *Improved Lubricants*, British Patent 823,099, Nov. 4, 1959.
33. Esso Research, *Irradiation of Polymeric Materials*, British Patent 819,147, Aug. 26, 1959.
34. Esso Research, *Irradiaiton of Polymeric Compounds*, British Patent 818,919, Aug. 26, 1959.
35. Esso Research, *Irradiation of Hydrocarbons*, British Patent 814,562, June 10, 1959.
36. Esso Research, *Curing Films of Butadiene-Styrene Copolymers*, British Patent 811,903, Apr. 15, 1959.
37. Esso Research, *Preparation of Sulfonates*, British Patent 810,574, Mar. 18, 1959.
38. Esso Research, *Reactions Involving Irradiation*, British Patent 802,552, Oct. 8, 1958.
39. Esso Research, *Loop Type Gamma Radiation Facility*, British Patent 886,089, Jan. 3, 1962.
40. General Electric Company, *Polyethylene of Improved Stability*, British Patent 818,963, Aug. 26, 1959.
41. Gileson, E. J., Clarke, R. W., Dorling, T. A., and Pope, D., The Effect of Ionizing

Radiations on Solid Catalysts, in *Proceedings of the Second International Conference on the Peaceful Uses of Atomic Energy, Geneva, 1958,* Vol. 29, p. 312, United Nations, New York, 1959.

42. Graham, R. K., and Gluckman, M. S., *Preparation of Graft Copolymers,* U. S. Patent 2,926,126, Feb. 23, 1960.

43. Haissinsky, M. M., and Duflo, M., Heterogeneous Catalysis in Radiation Chemistry, in *Proceedings of the Second International Conference on the Peaceful Uses of Atomic Energy, Geneva, 1958,* Vol. 29, p. 47, United Nations, New York, 1959.

44. Hardwick, T. J., and Nejak, R. P., Radiation in the Petroleum Industry, *Chem. Eng. Progr.,* 54(2): 72 February 1958).

45. Harmer, D. E., *The Reaction of Chlorine with Aromatic Compounds Under Intense Gamma Irradiation,* USAEC Report AECU-3077, University of Michigan, May 1955.

46. Harteck, P., and Dondes, S., Producing Chemicals with Reactor Radiations, *Nucleonics,* 14(7): 22 (July 1956).

47. Harteck, P., and Dondes, P., Radiation Chemistry of Gases, in *Proceedings of the Second International Conference on the Peaceful Uses of Atomic Energy, Geneva, 1958,* Vol. 29, p. 415, United Nations, New York, 1959.

48. Heath, C. E., and Lucchesi, P. J., *Radioalkylation of Normal Paraffins,* U. S. Patent 2,978,397, Apr. 4, 1961.

49. Henley, E. J., and Chandler, H. W., Radiation Processing, *Ind. Eng. Chem.,* 51 (11): 1395 (November 1959).

50. Houston, R. W., Tarmy, B. L., and Long, R. B., *Radiochemical Reactions,* U. S. Patent 2,904,484, Sept. 15, 1959.

51. Kung, F. E., *Manufacture of Benzene Hexachloride,* U. S. Patent 2,911,342, Nov. 3, 1959.

52. Lawton, E. J., *Irradiated Polyethylene,* U. S. Patent 2,906,679, Sept. 29, 1959.

53. Lawton, E. J., and Bueche, A. M., *Process of Irradiating Polyethylene at Elevated Temperatures,* U. S. Patent 2,906,678, Sept. 29, 1959.

54. Lemiazka, T., and Shewmaker, J., *High Unsaturation Irradiated Butyl Rubbers,* U. S. Patent 2,982,706, May 2, 1961.

55. Little, Arthur D., Inc., *Radiation: A Tool for Industry,* USAEC Report ALI 52, January 1959.

56. Long, R. B., *Conversion of Hydrocarbons in the Presence of Neutron Radiation and a Cracking Catalyst,* U. S. Patent 2,905,607, Sept. 22, 1959.

57. Long, R. B., Hibshman, J. H., Longwell, J. P., and Houston, R. W., *Conversion of Hydrocarbons in the Presence of Neutron Radiation and a Hydrogenation Catalyst,* U. S. Patent 2,905,606, Sept. 22, 1959.

58. Maddock, A. G., Applied Irradiation, *Nuclear Power,* 5(45): 105 (January 1960).

59. Manley, T. R., The Irradiation of Plastics, *Research (London),* 12(2): 42 (February 1959).

60. Manowitz, B., Kuhl, O., Richman, D., and Galanter, L., Development of High Power Irradiation, in *Proceedings of the Second International Conference on the Peaceful Uses of Atomic Energy, Geneva, 1958,* Vol. 29, p. 447, United Nations, New York, 1959.

61. Martin, J. J., Where We Stand in Radiation Processing, *Chem. Eng. Progr.,* 54 (2): 66 (February 1958).

62. Martin, J. J., and Anderson, L. C., *The Effect of Radiation on Chemical Reactions,* USAEC Report AECU-3615, University of Michigan, August 1957.

63. Mathes, K. N., and Morgan, H. I., *Irradiated Polyethylene and Products Therefrom,* U. S. Patent 2,929,744, Mar. 22, 1960.

64. McFedries, R., Polymerization with Radiation. Part II: Technological Considerations, *SPE Journal, 41*(10): 33 (October 1958).

65. Mesrobian, R. B., Modification of Polymers by Ionizing Radiation: Vulcanization and Graft Copolymer Formation, in *Proceedings of the Second International Conference on the Peaceful Uses of Atomic Energy, Geneva, 1958,* Vol. 29, p. 196, United Nations, New York, 1959.

66. Mims, L. S., Chemonuclear Reactor for In-pile Process Irradiation, *in Proceedings of the Large Radiation Sources in Industry Conference, Warsaw, Sept. 8–12, 1959,* Vol. 2, p. 357–361, International Atomic Energy Commission, Vienna, 1960.

67. Noddings, C. R., Miller, W. E., and Engelder, T. C., *Treatment of Catalysts Materials with High Energy Radiations,* U. S. Patent 2,905,608, Sept. 22, 1959.

68. Ogorzaly, H. J., Radiation Processing, *Oil Gas J., 55*(12): 213 (March 1957).

69. O'Toole, T., W. R. Grace Says It Is Using Radiation to Make Clear Strong Polyethylene Film, *Wall Street Journal,* p. 4, Mar. 16, 1960.

70. Perazich, G., *Productive Uses of Nuclear Energy—Nuclear Process Heat in Industry,* Report TL-9146, p. 6, National Planning Association, Washington, D. C., October 1958.

71. Pinner, S. H., Irradiation of Polymerization Products, *Repts. Progr. Appl. Chem., 43*:463–467 (1958).

72. Rady, A. A., Dynamical Properties of the New 'Rubber-Like' Irradiated Polyethylene, *J. Applied Polymer Sci., 1*(2): 129 (March–April 1959).

73. Reinsmith, G., Nuclear Radiation Effects on Materials, *ASTM Bull. No. 232* (September 1958).

74. Ritzman, R. W., Use of a Nuclear Reactor as a Process Heat Source, in *Nuclear Engineering, Part V, Chemical Engineering Progress Symposium Series,* Vol. 55, No. 22, p. 19, American Institute of Chemical Engineers, New York, 1959.

75. Roberts, R., Radiation Initiated Graft Polymerization, *Rubber & Plastics Age, 40*(2): 145 (February 1959).

76. Ruskin, S. L., *Treatment of Petroleum and Petroleum Products by Irradiation,* British Patent 881,492, Nov. 1, 1961.

77. Ruskin, S. L., *Promotion of Chemical Reactions,* U. S. Patent 2,934,481, Apr. 26, 1960.

78. Sarantites, A. D., *Producing Polymerized Materials by Irradiation,* U. S. Patent 3,008,886, Nov. 14, 1961.

79. Schmitz, J. V., and Lawton, E. J., *Polymerization with High Energy Electrons,* U. S. Patent 2,921,006, Jan. 12, 1960.

80. Schneider, A., *Sulfochlorination of Hydrocarbons Induced by Gamma Radiation,* USAEC Report ANL-5863, Argonne National Laboratory, June 1958.

81. Schutze, H. G., and Suttle, A. D., *Conversion of Organic Compounds by Radiation,* U. S. Patent 2,914,452, Nov. 24, 1959.

82. Stockman, C. H., and Bauman, R. G., Machines Give Cheaper Radiation, *Chem. Eng. News., 35*(31): 16 (August 1957).

83. Stockman, C. H., Harmon, D. J., and Neff, H. F., Radiation Makes Better, Longer Lasting Tires, *Nucleonics, 15*(11): 94 (November 1957).

84. Tarrice, R. R., and Towle, L. H., *Ionizing Radiation,* Stanford Research Institute Report No. 29, December 1959.

85. Taylor, E. H., and Kohn, H. W., An Enhancement of Catalytic Activity by Gamma Radiation, *J. Am. Chem. Soc., 79*(1): 252 (January 1957).

86. Union Carbide Corporation, *Improvement in the Preparation of Graft Copolymers,* British Patent 823,460, Nov. 11, 1959.

87. Weisz, P. B., and Swegler, E. W., Catalytic Activity Induced by Neutron Irradiation of Inert Silica, *J. Chem. Phys., 23*(9): 1567 (September 1955).

Author Index

Numbers in parenthesis are reference numbers and are inserted to assist in locating a reference when the author's name is not cited at the point of reference in the text. Numbers in italic indicate the page on which the complete reference is listed.

A

Ablitt, J. F., *341*

Abraham, R. J., 152(1, 2), *177*, 211(1), *240*

Achhammer, B. G., *459*

Adair, R. K., *32*

Adams, G. E., 93(1), 96(1), 97(1, 2), 101 (2), 104(2), 107(2), 110(2), 111(2), *118*

Adams, H. E., 257(47), 260(47), *287*

Adams, J. S., 340(125 see footnote), *348*

Adicoff, A., 84(14), *119*

Adler, G., 84(8), *118*

Aggarwall, S. L., 188(2), *240*

Agius, P. J., *549*

Aiken, W., 146(3), *177*

Aitken, I. D., 224(3), 225(4), 226(3), 235 (3), *240*

Albrecht, T. W., *402*

Alexander, P., 59(1), *60*, 127(5), 160(5), 161(6), 163(7), 171(6, 8, 9), 172(9), *177*, 188(6), 195(6), 205(5), 207(5, 6), 208(5, 6), 209, 210(6), *240*, 252(1), 270 (2), *285*

Alfrey, T., Jr., 133(10), 137(10), 138(10), 140(10), 141(10), 144(10), 145(10), 146(3, 10), *177*

Alger, R. L., *242*

Allen, A. O., 13(41), 24(39), 31(46), *34*, 37(38), *62*, 71(38, 115), 76(38, 115), *120, 124*

Amemiya, A., *240*

Ander, P., 84(95), *123*

Anderson, L. C., 79(85), 80(85), 83(85), *122, 551*

Anderson, W. F., *346*

Anderson, W. K., 298, *342*

Andrew, A., 350(3), *402*

Arlook, R. S., 226(8), *240*, 409(2), 411, 415(2), 417, 420, *423*

Armstrong, J. W., 395(49), 396(49), *404*

Arnim, *see* von Arnim, E.

Arnold, J. S., 409(3), *423*

Aron, W. A., 7(2), 16(2), *32*

Arthur, J. C., Jr., 431(2), 432, 433(2, 5), 434(5), 436, *444*

Arvia, A. J., 148(49), *179*, 191(27), 193 (27), *241*

Asanovich, G., 330(10), *342, 345*

Ashkin, J., 11(4), 30(4), *32*

Atchison, G. J., 175(11), *177*, 226(9), *240*

Auerbach, I., 257(31), *286*

Ausloos, P., 101(3), 102(3), 103(3), 105(3, 4), 107(4), *118*

B

Back, R. A., 64(5), 71(5), 72(5), 76(5), *118*

Bakh, N. A., 59(2), *60*, 189(10), *240*

Ballantine, D. S., 84(6, 8, 95), *118, 123*

Balivit, J. S., 127(72), 152(71), 160(73), 161(79), 171(70), 175(73), *180*, 184(44), 185(44), 189(50), 192(44), 193(44), 194 (44), 195(44), 203(49), 214(44), *242*, *444*, 458(17), *459*

Balzhiser, R. E., 545(16), *549*

Bardwell, D. C., 72(88), *122*

Barker, A., 79(7), *118*

Barker, K. R., *342*

Barker, R., 114(106), *123*

Barnum, E. R., 352(63, 65), 359(59, 65), 360(63, 65), 379(59, 60), 380(65), 387 (63, 64), 396(65), *404, 405*

Barr, F. T., 541(6), 542, *549*

Barr, N. F., 83(70), *121*

Barry, E. G., *405*

Barzan, M. L., 257(47), 260(47), *287*

Basseches, H., 481(1), *482*

Bauman, R. G., 163(12), 172(13), *177*, 249 (5), 255(5), 256(5), 265(6), 268(5, 6), 277, *285*, 540(82), *552*

Subject Index

A

APAMS, 368
APEMS, 368–369
Arnel fibers, 425
Aromatic compounds, as radiation-damage inhibitors, in fuels, 504
  in lubricants, 364
  temperature thresholds, 301
Aromatic hydrocarbons, radiolysis of, 85–90
Aromatic rings, condensed, pyrolysis of, 293
  protective effect in polymers, 162–163
Askarels as dielectrics, 469, 471
Asphalts as basin liners, 456
ASTM methods in rubber technology, 251–252

B

Ballistite, gas evolution in radiolysis, 532–533
Basswood, digestibility following irradiation, 525
Bast fibers, 425
Benzene, protective effect in polymers, 163
  radiolysis of, 86
  in radiolyzed polyphenyls, 335
Benzene hexachloride from benzene, 547
Benzyl alcohol, radiolysis of, 94
Biphenyl, critical heat flux for burnout, 300
  physical-property changes in radiolysis, 320
  pyrolysis of, at 920°F, 293–296
    at 1000°F, 291–293
    in loop, 298
  radiolysis of, 89
    composition of gas from, 335
    at high temperature, 302
    in loop tests, 314
    polymer formation vs. temperature in, 324
Bis(phenoxyphenoxy)benzene, 388–391
Bis(phenoxyphenyl) ether, 388–391
Bituminous coals, 512–513
Boghead coal, 509
Boiling-water reactor, radiation rates in lubrication area, 350
Bragg, energy-loss curve, 16
  rule of energy loss, 9
Breit-Wigner theory, 20

Bremsstrahlung, production of, 11
  with X rays, 25
Brisance, of explosives, 529
  definition, 526
  of mercury fulminate, 528
Bromides, organic, radiolysis of, 111–116
n-Butylbenzene, radiolysis of, 303

C

Cable wax, 472, 477
Cannel coal, radiolysis of, 509
Capacitors, dielectric fluids in, 471
Carboxylic (fatty) acids, effect of additives on, 111
  as oiliness agents, 374
  radiolysis of, 107–111
Casein resin, 230
Catalysts, inorganic, effect of radiation on, 547
Cellobiose unit, 519
Cellophane film, irradiation and mechanical properties of, 455
Cellulose, decomposition of, 521–523
  intrinsic viscosity of, 522
  structure of, 518
Cellulose esters (in textiles), 425
Cellulose polymers, 165–166
Cellulose powder, gassing of in radiolysis, 520
Cellulose-derived plastics, 217–219
Cellulosic fibers (in textiles), degree of polymerization, 434
  formula, 425
  oxidation of, 433
  property changes on radiolysis, 431
  scission in, 432
Cellulosic films, 454
Centralite in JPN propellant, 533
CFR fuel coker, 492
Charge-exchange reaction, 40
Chlorides, organic, radiolysis of, 111–116
Circuit breakers, dielectric fluids in, 471
Cis-polyisoprene, crystallinity in, 134
Cleavage of polymers (*see* Scission)
Coal, exposure to alpha rays, 510–512
  applications of irradiated, 517–518
  gassing in irradiation of, 513, 517
  hydrogen content of, 513
  reaction mechanism, 516
  reactor exposures of, 512–517
Coatings, protective, 447